Majesty's Rancho

ZANE GREY

Majesty's Rancho

WALTER J. BLACK, INC.

ROSLYN, NEW YORK

MAJESTY'S RANCHO

Printed in the United States of America

By arrangement with HARPER & BROTHERS

Majesty's Rancho

Chapter One

LANCE SIDWAY pulled himself up from the stone steps of the Natural History Museum. He laughed ruefully as he realized that this was his third visit to the institution. As on his two previous excursions, he had wandered round and round the inside halls examining the mounted specimens of wild animals. He loved four-footed creatures, and though a pang beset him to see these lifeless counterfeits of what had once been the free beasts of the wild, he yet experienced a sense of escape and peace that he had not felt since he left his Oregon range home for Hollywood.

There was, he knew now, a future in the motion picture studios for his great horse "Umpqua," and perhaps one for himself as well. But he shied at becoming an actor and hated to double for the handsome cowboy Apollos of the screen; and to hang around the studios merely as the owner of a wonderful horse, letting the spirited animal earn his living for him, did not fit his idea of a career. As a matter of fact, he had never desired a future in Hollywood under such circumstances and the immediate necessity for earning money was over. Nance, his sister, was perfectly well again after her operation and would soon be married. So in demand, indeed, had Umpqua been that Lance found himself with at least enough cash in hand to last him until he could find a job more to his liking.

He found himself leaning toward a horseback ride through southern California, across Arizona, perhaps into New Mexico. To be sure the cattle business was practically ruined, but the desert ranges and purple uplands of Arizona, or the silver grassed valleys of New Mexico, about which he had read so much, would be vastly wilder and infinitely freer than the old pastures he had ridden, and surely there would be some kind of a job for a husky chap who was fond of animals.

There was a singular zest in the thought of new adventure in a harder country than he had known. But the truth was, Hollywood did not let go its grip so easily. And why? Lance knew that he had no ambition to beat the movie game. Still he admitted the fascination of the gay bright whirl of the picture world. Reducing this down to the lure of feminine charm seemed another step in the right direction. Lance dubiously admitted to himself that he was afraid he had more than the ordinary male's weakness for the fair sex. But hell! he thought in self-defense, just think of Hollywood's thousands of extras, and more thousands of girls unable to find even jobs as extras, many of them exceptionally beautiful, all of them pretty! Here was a case where it was hard to break away. And he ruefully recalled the three girls to whose attraction he had succumbed—Coretta—and Virginia—and lastly Maurine. Only last night Maurine had faced him, a little pale, with dark eyes steady. "Lance, you've been swell to me," she had said. "I could lie to you, but I won't. At last I've got a break. You know what that means. I must make the grade. . . . Sure I love you. String along with me, darling, and when I'm a star. . . ."

That was Hollywood, but it was not Lance Sidway. Looked at now, in this serious moment, it seemed a deciding factor. "It'd happen again," muttered Lance, sadly. "And I might fall worse. It's coming to me. . . . I'm through!"

And he arose with springy step to gaze at the hazy Sierra Madres beyond which barrier there was an unsettled land. He strolled through a long terrace of roses, sensitive to their color and fragrance. They were beautiful, but he liked wild flowers best. Meanwhile he was revolving in mind the problem of riding Umpqua out of California. The horse was fat and needed work. He would not care much for the asphalt roads; perhaps, however, from Palm Springs south Lance could keep mostly to soft ground. Once in condition again, Umpqua was good for fifty miles a day without turning a hair.

Lance emerged from the Museum park, and presently, strolling along, he found himself on the edge of the University campus. Students of both sexes were in evidence, some chatting in groups, others moving along with books under their arms. These bare-headed boys and girls in their colorful sweaters, young and full of the joy of life, aroused memory and regret in Lance. After high school he had attended college in Corvallis for nearly a year, and outside of freshman miseries, which now seemed sweet, he had done well in his studies and better in athletics. But financial trouble had intervened and Nance's illness . . . both of which had sent him to Hollywood. This college atmosphere was something that he liked. If only his father had not died, to leave Nance and him orphans! Lance cast off the sadness. His sister was well —happy—and he had the greatest horse in the West and a new adventure in that West before him. Pretty lucky, Lance thought he should be telling himself! Reaching a cross street Lance halted to absorb more of the flash of color on the campus. He sauntered up the cross street toward some shade trees. On that side there were more students. He heard bantering voices and gay high-pitched laughter.

The shrill sound of a siren disrupted his attention, as well as that of the students. Wheeling, Lance saw a bright topless roadster turning the corner from the main street. Its driver was a bare-headed girl with hair bright as spun gold. At the moment she withdrew her extended left arm. Behind her raced the car with the loud horn. It caught up with her. One of the two occupants, surely policemen, yelled for her to stop. The young woman took her time about it, and passing Lance, finally halted at the first shade trees where half a dozen students had congregated. Lance had not far to go to reach them and he strolled along, curious, expectant, and a little angry at the gruff yell of the officer. Lance was in time to hear:

"Why didn't you stop?"

"I have stopped," replied the girl, coolly.

Lance joined the group of students who had advanced to the curb. From all points on the campus others were coming, some on the run. Then Lance saw the girl at close range. Many a time in the studios and on the locations had he sustained a shock of masculine transport, but he had never seen a motion picture star who in his opinion could hold a candle to this girl.

"Majesty, what do these cops want?" queried a tall young fellow, stepping out.

"I'm not sure, Rollie," she replied, with a laugh. "But I think they want to chase me off the streets."

"What's the idea, officer?"

"If it's any of your business, freshie, she was speedin'," returned the other, a burly man, red-faced and thin-lipped, alighting from the police car. "*I* know her an' *she* knows me."

"Yeah?" queried the student, insolently.

"Yeah! She was makin' forty-five on the turn an' she didn't even hold out her hand."

"Say, ossifer, *we* saw this lady turn and she wasn't making twenty," interposed another student.

"Lay off us kids, can't you?" asked another, plaintively.

"Aren't there enough drunk drivers to keep you busy?"

"Looks a little steamed up himself."

Good-natured cat calls and boos sounded from back of the circle of students, crowding closer and denser. They sensed events. Lance gathered that the officers did not fail to grasp something inimical to their own well-being at the moment.

"Give the girl a ticket, Brady, and let's get going," advised the one at the wheel.

A storm of protest went up from the foremost line of students. Rollie, who evidently had some distinction on the campus, yelled for them to shut up.

"Beat it, you flat-feet!" he called, sharply. "You hang around here and run us fellows ragged. But lay off the girls. Get that? We won't stand for it."

"You shut up or I'll run you in," said Brady angrily, as he began writing the summons.

"Madge, is it coming to you?" Rollie asked.

"Not this time, Rollie, I swear," she replied. "I did run away from him some days ago. But today I wasn't making twenty."

"You tell that to the Judge," said Brady, coldly. "An' you're interferin' with an officer of the law."

"Law, hooey! Only when there's nothing in it for you. Get the hell out of here!"

The crowd of students surged over the sidewalk and pulled the officer from the running board of the car. He made the mistake of raising his fist, and striking himself free he shouted to his companion: "Send a riot call!" At that juncture a motorcycle policeman roared up to make a fringe of students in the street hop out of his way. Brady hoarsely repeated his order to him, and with his comrade, both swinging their arms, cleared a space.

Lance had been shoved off the pavement by the pushing of the students, all of them roused now and full of devilment. Rollie appeared to be the only one who took the affair seriously. The girl, Madge, acted as if she were enjoying the proceedings. But her violet eyes were ablaze. Rollie leaped on the running board and leaned close to speak low to her. Then Brady turning with red visage and bristling front jerked Rollie down.

"Young woman, get away from that wheel," he ordered, opening the door. "I'll take you for a little ride."

"Like hell you will," she rejoined, her voice as ringing as a bell. And she snapped the door shut.

Brady's attention veered to a charging crowd of students who pushed the officers' car down the street, while another gang, yelling like Indians, rushed the truck of a fruit and vegetable vender who had happened along. They halted him, and in gold and red streams they spilled the mounds of oranges and tomatoes into the street. Another moment saw the air full of colored missiles. Their target was the offending car of the law. A smashing of windows and clinking of glass mingled with the derisive yells of the assailants. Then the driver, who had attempted in no gentle manner to drive the students from crowding Brady, turned to roar at the slingers. A huge soft tomato struck him squarely in the face. That elicited a howl of fiendish glee from the armed force in the street. A hail of oranges and tomatoes not only halted his belligerent rush but blinded him, swamped him, knocked him flat. At the moment, then, a blare of sirens announced the arrival of reinforcements.

Lance hung by the girl's car while the students, numbering hundreds by now, rushed pell-mell into the street, whooping like a lot of Indians. What was left of the vender's ample supply of oranges and tomatoes disappeared from his truck as if by magic to take swift form of a colorful barrage right at the charging policemen. For a while they were held back, but as the supply of ammunition began to diminish, they forged forward, eventually to drive the students out of the street upon the campus. But it was not an onslaught such as Brady and his man had attempted. The students were having a wonderful time, but the officers, plainly disgusted and angered though they were, did not resort to violence. Against three hundred crazy students they could do nothing save harangue them off the street.

Lance, keenly enjoying the whole performance, was suddenly startled by a cry from the girl in the car. And as he wheeled he leaped off the curb. Brady had opened the car door.

"Move over, Blondie," he ordered, a rude hand on her shoulder.

"You dirty bum! Don't you dare paw me!"

It appeared to Lance that the officer's action exceeded his authority. Even if it had not, the girl's poignant outburst and the flash of her magnificent eyes would have been enough for Lance.

"I'm drivin' you to the station," declared Brady, shoving at her.

"You are not!" she cried, starting the engine. "Get off or I'll spread you along the street. . . . I'll drive to . . ."

Lance snatched the policeman's hand off the car and as he turned in surprise Lance hit him a not-too-gentle blow on his rather protruding abdomen. A gasping expulsion of breath followed the sodden drumlike sound. Brady began to sag. Lance reached up with powerful hand, pulled him off the running board, and then with a vicious swing of fist at the convulsed visage he laid the officer neatly in the street. In action as swift, Lance vaulted into the car.

"Step on it!" he yelled. And almost before the words passed his lips the little car shot ahead. Lance's knees came up hard under the dash. A shrill blast from the horn sent several students leaping for their lives. Then the car ate up the open street, to whirl at the corner, and speed on, describing swift half-circles in the traffic. Lance's hat went flying, and as the car grazed a trolley his hair stood up stiff. Though scared as he had never been, Lance's heart strangled a cowboy yell in his throat and his blood beat thick in his ears and he was possessed by a wild elation. The car whirled off the thoroughfare into a quiet street, on which the houses blurred in Lance's sight. Another turn, then block after block on a traffic-congested street, then a break in the speed—and at last a parking place!

"Whew!" exploded Lance, catching his breath. "We'd have shaken them—if they had chased us."

"Swell, wasn't it?" rejoined the girl, with an amazing coolness. And she uttered a low laugh.

"I'll tell the world. Say, but you can drive," burst out Lance, turning to look at her. With steady beautiful hands, and shapely coral-tinted finger tips she was taking a gold monogrammed cigarette case from her purse.

"Thanks. Have a cigarette?"

"Don't mind."

"Did I scare you?"

"Yes—but it was a great ride."

"Well, we got the best of those cops anyway, and now we're just two fugitives from justice."

All this time Lance was gazing at the girl, conscious of a mounting exhilaration. To find pleasure in the beauty of women had been the only debt he owed Hollywood. But this visual experience seemed a magnifying of all former sensations.

"Oh, your hand!" she exclaimed, in sudden solicitude.

Then Lance became aware that he was opening and shutting his right hand, the knuckles of which were bruised. It was a big brown member, matching his brawny wrist.

"Bunged my fist—a little," he said, awkwardly. "Nothing much."

"No?—I wonder what that cop thought. I'll never forget his face. I was looking at it when you socked him. Did that tickle me?"

"Then I'm glad," returned Lance, beaming at her.

"You see he was sore at me. He's caught me before. Last time I made eyes at him, you know, and let him think. . . . I had a date and was late. Next time he spotted me I ran away from him. Today he must have been laying for me."

"So that was it? Big fathead! You'll get hauled up for this. I'm sorry. But I had to slug him. . . . I was looking at you when he . . ."

"Don't be sorry. You made me your friend for life. Rollie was mad, but he wouldn't have done that. . . . You're not a college man?"

"No. I went one year at Corvallis. Then . . . but that wouldn't interest you. I—I'd better be going."

"Don't go yet," she replied, detaining him with a hand on his sleeve. "Indeed I am interested. You're not going to walk out on me after such a romantic adventure. Are you?"

"Why, Miss Madge—I—you . . . of course, that's up to the lady."

"It always should be, even if it isn't. Tell me about yourself. I'll bet you're from Hollywood. You have that cut."

"Yeah? You don't mean movie actor?" inquired Lance, quickly.

"No? Too bad! You're handsome enough to be one. My sorority sisters will be jealous. I'll have you out to the house to meet them."

"That'd be swell. But I'm afraid it's not possible. Thank you."

"You're not married?"

"I should say not."

"Nor in love. I know how that malady affects them," she replied, flippantly. "You'll come, won't you?"

"You're very kind. I—I have to say no."

"Well, of all things. A turn-down from a cavalier who fought for me! . . . It doesn't happen, at least never yet. . . . They always say: 'How about a date?' . . . What're you doing out in Hollywood?"

"I own a horse. He's been in pictures, not I. Oh, I've had to ride him a few times, doubling for these actors. I hated that. It's almost as tough on me as letting them ride him."

"A wonderful horse. How thrilling! I love horses."

"As much as cars?"

"More. We have a ranch and some Arabians. . . . What's his name?"

"Umpqua."

"Umpqua? Must be Indian?"

"Yes, it is. Means swift."

"Then he can run?"

"Run!—See here, little lady, Umpqua is as swift as the wind."

"I'll bet I've a horse that can beat him."

Lance laughed. Here apparently was a real western girl. It did not detract from the dazzling glamour of her.

"Is he pretty—beautiful—grand, or what?" she continued.

"All of them. Umpqua has Arabian blood," replied Lance,

warming to her interest. That seemed to put him on her level. "He is big and rangy. Mottled black with white feet and nose. Bright soft eyes. Spirited but gentle. And this Hollywood game hasn't done him any good. That's why I'm going to quit it and leave this place. Ump is too fine, too sweet a horse for Hollywood."

"You love him, don't you?" she said, softly, as if she understood.

"I'll say I do. Why, he saved Nance's life. . . . Nance is my sister. Umpqua was given to me when he was a colt. He's cowboy bred. On the Oregon range near Bend. And no horse ever had ten years' better breeding. . . . Well, Nance and I were left alone. We lost the ranch. I had to quit college. She fell ill. It was necessary to have special treatment for her—operations and all—to save her life. So to earn the money I brought Umpqua to Hollywood where I had been assured of a job. And did he make good? I'm telling you."

The girl's eyes were bright with interest.

"Splendid. And your sister—Nance?"

"Just fine now. She's going to be married soon."

"Swell! . . . Oh, wouldn't I love to see Umpqua? But I wouldn't dare. I'd want to buy him. I always try to buy everything I like. And you'd hate me. That wouldn't do at all. . . . Cowboy, are you leaving town? Wouldn't you like . . . couldn't we meet again?"

"Why—I—I . . . hope to see you again," stammered Lance.

"We have a lot in common. Horses and ranches—and things," she went on, consulting her wrist watch. "Let's see. If I don't get pinched and haled into court, I can cut psych. Say two-thirty, here, tomorrow. Will that be convenient?"

"Okay by me," replied Lance, and opened the door to step out.

"Thank you for all you did. Good-by till tomorrow. And be careful. Don't forget you punched a cop. They'll be looking for you if they can remember what you look like. I won't forget."

Lance stood there rooted to the spot, watching the bright car and golden head flash out of sight. Then expecting to come down to earth with a dull thud, he found himself in the clouds. He soared while he hunted for a westbound trolley and the long ride out seemed only a few moments. Riding a block past his street augured further of his mental aberration. He strode on, out of the main zone of buildings, into the hills, and up the canyon where he had lodgings with a man who rented him a little pasture and stall for his horse. Lance went into the alfalfa-odorous barn. Umpqua nickered at him. "My God, Ump!" said Lance, as he put his arm over the noble arched neck and laid his cheek against the glossy mane. "I've fallen like a ton of bricks. Hardest ever!—No, old pard, not a movie extra or even a star. But a college girl. Another blonde, Ump! Only this one has them all backed off the lot. . . . So that's what was wrong with me when I sat dumb in her car?"

Contact with Umpqua brought Lance down to reality and to the fact that he was leaving Hollywood. Against his sober judgment he would keep the date with the girl, which would be a last sentimental gesture before he rode out toward the open ranges and to the life he was meant for.

Lance packed and tagged his outfit, walked down town to an express office, and checked it to be sent for later. Then he cashed his last check from the studio. It was still only mid-afternoon. On the boulevard he dropped into a movie theater and sat through two pictures, no details of which he could have even faintly remembered afterward. Then he went to a restaurant for his supper. Even his usually keen appetite did not return to break his abstraction. Thereafter he strolled up the boulevard, knowing it would be the last time. There was a première at the Chinese, heralded aloft by great searchlight beams, streaking up and sweeping across the heavens. Hollywood's main thoroughfare blazed with colored lights. Cars hummed to and fro, halted for the signals, rolled on again. Lance stood on the corner of Vine Street, absorbing the flash, the glitter, the roar, the vivid life of the strange city. There was a little sadness mixed with his varied feelings and he could not quite analyze the cause. He did not really want this life. Then a shining black limousine sped noiselessly by. Lance caught a fleeting limpse of a lovely fair girl, radiant in white, lying languorously back against the black-clad shoulder of her companion. That was Hollywood. How many times Lance had seen the same sight, always with a vague envy!

He let that glimpse be the last to intrigue him, and striding back to his room, he went to bed. There, wide-awake, he lay in the dark, remembering, wondering, feeling more clearly than at any time since his adventure.

A vivid and entrancing picture of the girl appeared etched against the blackness. Her face floated there, exquisitely fair. It was oval, crowned by shining golden hair, which waved back from her broad low brow. Slender arched eyebrows marked large intent eyes, wide apart, dark, the color of violets and singularly expressive with a light of friendliness, of frank interest. The whole face had a flash, of which fixed and changeless beauty was only a part.

Feature by feature the girl's face appeared to Lance with a clearness which astonished him.

Lance shut his eyes to blot out this memory picture. But it made no difference. She was there, in his mind, on his heart. Never in all his life had he yearned for anything so dearly as to kiss those red lips. That dragged him rudely out of his trance. It would be wise not to see the girl again. With a pang he abandoned the idea. Majesty. . . . Madge, that student Rollie had called her. The first name suited her. Who was she? Where was that ranch with the Arabian horses? Somewhere in California, no doubt. That girl had class. Yet there was nothing the least snobbish about her. Too lovely, too kind and sweet to be a flirt! No need. She was rich, of course, Lance thought, remembering her clothes and her car! He remembered, too, the jeweled monogram on her cigarette case, but could recall only the letter M. And Lance rolled over to go to sleep. Aw! What the hell? He was always mooning over some pretty dame, especially a blonde, and here he had what was coming to him. Forget it, cowboy, and hit the trail.

All the same he dreamed of her and upon awakening in the morning, he began to waver in his resolution. Why be a sap? She had been grateful. He would want to know how she fared with the police and the college authorities. She would keep the date and wait for him. Lance, in the broad light of day, while he made his final preparations to leave, thought better of his resolve not to meet her. Treat a swell girl like that—stand her up on a promised date—a girl who loved horses—it just was not in him. And all the rest of the morning, at lunch, and when he took the bus downtown, he was conscious of a tingling expectance, a heat in his veins, a glamour over everything.

It amazed Lance extremely that he could not immediately find the parking place where he was to meet the girl. He had been so balmy, he thought, that he had scarcely known whether he was walking or riding. It was a good thing that he had come downtown so early. After wandering around, up one street and down another, at last he found the vacant lot which had been utilized to park cars. He was still a quarter of an hour ahead of time. An attendant, observing Lance loitering around, told him he could sit in one of the cars if he were waiting for someone. Lance promptly availed himself of this permission; in fact he took a back seat in a car standing against a building. Lance did not believe she would come at all; if she did he wanted to see her before she spied him. The buoyancy usual with Lance at a rendezvous seemed to be wanting here. This was a tremendous occasion.

He could see a large blue-handed clock in a tower some distance away, and watching this, as the half hour neared, he gave way more and more to inexplicable feelings. If she came, that would be proof she liked him, and maybe. . . . Why not postpone his departure for Arizona? A few days or even weeks would not make any particular difference. If she wanted to see him, take him to the house to meet her friends, perhaps go out to see Umpqua—how could he ever resist that? He had always been a fool over girls. With this one he would be serious and assuredly she had only a passing fancy or interest in him. Or she might have been one of these beautiful dames who had to have a new flame every day. Maybe he had better just wait to have a farewell look at her, and not let her know he was there. But suppose she really had been struck with him! That was possible. It had happened once. In this case there would never again be any peace away from the glad light of those violet eyes.

"Gosh! I was a dumbbell for coming," he muttered, kicking himself. "She's late now. . . . She won't come—and am I glad?"

Nevertheless he lingered there, sliding down in the seat, watching with hawk eyes the passing cars, slowly succumbing to a pang in his breast. At a quarter to three he gave up hope.

Then a bright tan roadster flashed into sight. It slowed and turned in. The driver was a girl in blue. But her blue hat did not hide a gleam of gold. She had come! Lance's heart gave a leap and his blood gushed through his veins.

Then a seven-passenger car, shiny black in hue, flashed into sight, slowed and stopped outside the turn. From it leaped a slender young man, noticeably well-dressed. He waved the car on with sharp gesture and came hurrying, his piercing gaze on the blonde girl.

Lance saw her sweep a quick glance all around the parking place. She was looking for him, and the disappointment she expressed was so sweet and moving to Lance that it would have drawn him out of his hiding place but for the mien of the newcomer.

She had halted at an angle from Lance's position, perhaps a dozen steps distant, and scarcely had she dismissed the polite attendant when the other man caught up to lean over the side of her car. He did not remove his soft gray hat. He had a remarkably handsome visage, pale, chiseled as if from marble, a square chin and ruthless mouth, and light gray eyes sharp as daggers. He reminded Lance of someone he knew.

"On the lam, eh, Madge? You certainly gave that driver of mine a run," he said, with an air of cool effrontery.

"Hello, Bee. What do you mean—on the lam?" she replied.

"Trying to run away from me again."

"No. I was in a hurry to keep a date. I'm too late. He's come and gone. Damn old Fuzzy-Top! It was his fault."

"Was your date with Fuzzy-Top?"

"No. You don't seem to understand my college talk any better than I do your gangster expressions. Fuzzy is one of my profs."

Gangster! Lance sustained a sudden shock. So that was it. This young man bore a remarkable resemblance to the picture star, Robert Morris, in his racketeer roles. What could the girl possibly have to do with a gangster? Plenty, thought Lance, considering that she had the imperious look of one who had an insatiable thirst for adventure.

"Madge, I haven't said nothing yet," replied the fellow, with a laugh. "Saying it with flowers is not my way. How about cocktails? Take me for a ride."

"Bee, I told you I had a date," she protested. "With a perfectly swell fellow. I'm crazy about him."

"Yeah? He doesn't seem so crazy about you. Dish the date and let's go places." With that the cool gentleman walked around the front of her car, and opening the door he slipped in and slammed it shut.

"You've got a nerve," she retorted.

"Didn't you tell me that was what you liked about me?"

"I suspect I did. You were something new, Bee."

"Thanks. You're a new twist on me. All women are flirts. But I went for you in a big way. And you went out with me, didn't you?"

"Yes. A couple of times. If you recall I met you at the Grove one afternoon for tea. We danced. And one other time at the Biltmore, where we quarreled because you were pretty raw."

"Cooled on me, eh?"

"Not exactly. You still pack a thrill. But you're a little too—too . . ."

"Madge, no broad ever made a sucker of Bee Uhl yet," he rejoined, with a crisp ring in his voice.

"Mr. Uhl, you're quite beyond me," said the girl, with a smile that disarmed her aloofness. "I'm afraid you're going to make me regret my—well, shall we call it playful indiscretion? I never took you for a gentleman, but I thought you a good sport. If I'm not mistaken the favors of our little flirtation were yours. . . . Where can I drop you?"

"Say, Beauty, you hate yourself, don't you? Well, I can take it. But the Honey Bee is not through buzzing around yet. . . . Let me off corner Seventh."

In another moment they were gone, leaving Lance in a queer state of mind. He hardly knew what to think, or why he had not made his presence known. Presently his romance burst like a pricked bubble. But his relief did not equal his regret. He would not be seeing Madge again. If her apparently friendly contact with a gangster had caused her to fall somewhat in his hasty estimation, that did not seem to make any difference. Almost he sympathized with Honey Bee Uhl. That was a cognomen. Lance wondered what it signified. Then his sympathy veered to the spirited girl. He seemed to grasp that it would be impossible for her to have any fun, at least with men, to follow any natural bent of conquest or coquetry, to play around and look for what and whom she wanted from life, without leaving havoc in her wake. A girl as beautiful as she was, radiant with such an intense and fatal charm, would have to go into a nunnery, or else expect a fall of Troy around her. No doubt she desired that very thing. Lance congratulated himself on his great good fortune in avoiding the meeting, yet when it was too late he wanted it otherwise.

In less than two hours Lance was riding Umpqua along the hilly backroads of Hollywood. He was on his way and saw the last of the town from a bridle path high upon a foothill. He knew every bit of soft road under the slope of the mountains and avoided the asphalt wherever possible. At nine o'clock, some twenty miles out of the city, he called it a day and sought lodgings for himself and Umpqua.

Up at dawn he made San Bernardino by nightfall and the next day Banning. This entrance to the desert pass he welcomed as an event. From there on he could keep his horse almost altogether off the paved roads. That night Lance was so tired he went to sleep when his head touched the pillow. On the following morning he headed down San Gorgonio Pass toward the great gray valley of the southernmost California desert.

He knew that arid country, having been to Palm Springs and Indio with motion-picture companies. Still, sight of the rolling wasteland with its knolls of mesquite and flats of greasewood, and the irregular barren mountains zigzagging the horizon, afforded him keen pleasure. How different this country from the golden pastures and black hills and swift streams of Oregon! Lance could not have conceived a greater contrast. And by noonday the June heat of the desert was intense. Sweat oozed out of his every pore and Umpqua was wet. But this heat was what both horse and rider needed. They were heavy from underwork and overeating. By midafternoon Lance reached a little station on the railroad above Indio, where he halted for the night. He slept on a spread of hay under a cottonwood tree; and when the red sun peeped over the Chocolate Mountains next morning Lance felt that the comfort and the lure of Hollywood had been left far behind.

From that point he began a leisurely journey down the long sun-baked desert. Mecca, the Salton Sea, Niland were each marked by hitching up another hole in Umpqua's cinch. But the great horse, once off the automobile roads and loosened up by the heat, soon showed his sound bottom and his love of the open. He knew they were headed for new ranges. Lance struck the five mile stretch of sand dunes at sunrise, and he marveled at the smooth mounds with their knifelike crests, the scalloped vales between the dunes, the opal hues changing and playing across the sands. Umpqua did not like this region where his hoofs sank to his fetlocks. The flinty levels beyond, black and red with polished gravel, the sparse tufts of greasewood and cactus, the volcanic peaks, and finally the dusky arrowwood-bordered road to the Colorado River—these kept Umpqua on his easy ground-covering gait. Lance's first sight of the red river justified what he had anticipated—a sullen swirling muddy flood, inimicable to horse and rider. And Yuma at night struck Lance favorably, with its wide main street and bright lights, its giant Indians and stealthily stepping Mexicans. He was across the river and this was Arizona.

That fact roused Lance at dawn. On his way again he appeared to have Arizona burst upon him in a blaze of brilliant sunlight that flooded vast wastes of barren soil and meager patches of grass, and ranges of ragged mountains asleep in the sunrise, and dim mesas and escarpments in the distance, and ghosts of purple domes hauntingly vague. Lance was a man of the open, but the great distances, the vastness, the endless reach of wasteland allured while it repelled him. He rode on, and dust, heat, wind were his portion. Ranches, service stations, hamlets stretched lonesomely across the desert. He had lost track of days and miles beyond Yuma by the time he reached Florence. Tombstone with its preserved buildings of a hard frontier past, Bisbee with its great mines and bustle, Douglas, an enterprising and progressive town marked Lance's long ride across southern Arizona. Lance meant to strike off the main highway and railroad somewhere beyond Douglas into the ever-increasing rugged grandeur and beautiful valleys of this Arizona land. But his money, which he had thought would hold out for a much longer period, had dwindled to almost nothing, and it was now necessary that he stop and look for work. A rest would do Umpqua good. Lance found a Mexican who owned a small pasture outside of town and here he left the horse. In a pinch he could pawn his watch or gun, but he would have a try at finding work before resorting to that.

Lance accosted men in service stations and stores without any success. What he wanted to encounter was a cowboy. But this type appeared remarkably scarce. One man, evidently a cattleman, laughed gruffly at Lance: "Wal, son, thet kind of two-laiged critter has been aboot washed up on this range."

"You don't say. What by?" queried Lance, blankly.

"I reckon by hard times. North of heah a ways there's some cattle left. But down heah the only successful business is bootlegging."

That discouraged Lance, and he strolled around, slowly succumbing to the need of pawning his watch. Walking in high-heeled cowboy boots was not exactly a joy. It was noon and Lance was hot. Presently he heard voices near at hand, and turning discovered that he had halted close to a big black car, from which issued sharp voices. A second glance at that car struck him singularly. How like the black car that had followed the girl Madge to the parking place where he had chosen to avoid meeting her! With a pang he realized he had not thought of her for days. He was in another world. But this car! . . . Shiny black, without a gleam of metal anywhere, a fine high-priced machine, it certainly resembled. . . .

"Hey, buddy, come here," called a voice that shot through Lance. A young man, with pale face and eyes like gimlets, was leaning out of the front seat opposite the driver. Lance recognized him immediately. The young man Madge had designated as a gangster and who had called himself Honey Bee Uhl.

Chapter Two

Lance advanced slowly, hiding an intense curiosity. Somehow he wanted to find out all he could about this fellow.

"Hello, yourself," he replied.

"You look sort of on the loose."

"Well, I look just what I am," Lance replied.

"No offense. We're loafing here for a guy, and I just wanted to be friendly. Care for a drink?"

"Not till I have a feed."

"Broke?"

"Flat as a pancake. And I can't find a job in this slow burg."

"Say, buddy, there's plenty jobs for the right guys. Can you drive a truck?"

"Mister, I could drive two trucks," retorted Lance, boastfully.

"Yeah? Well, how'd you like to grab a century?"

"Uhuh! Sounds good to me. I'd pull almost any kind of a job for that much dough. Only I'd want to be sure I was going to get it," laughed Lance.

"Exactly. It's okay. Now who are you and what have you been doing?"

"You never heard of me, mister," said Lance, evasively. "But I'll say I've been beating it from L.A."

"Dicks after you?"

Lance laughed grimly and looked blankly silent, and averted his face somewhat from the piercing scrutiny bent upon him.

"Come clean with me, buddy, if you want your luck to change. What you been doing in L.A.?"

"Are you asking me, mister?"

"Yes, I am. It's not for you to ask *me* questions," replied Uhl, with impatient sharpness. "Take it or leave it."

"Aw, what the hell? I'm hungry. . . . I beat it out of Portland ahead of Latzy Cork," hazarded Lance, remembering the name of a shady underworld character who had recently been eluding the police on the coast.

"That racket, eh?" flashed Uhl, snapping his fingers. And with his eyes like gray fire he turned in the seat to his companions. Lance took advantage of this moment to make certain that he would recognize the driver of the car, and the three hard-faced individuals in the back seat, if he ever saw them again. At the side of the one farthest toward the road Lance espied the muzzle of a machine gun. "Cork may have been spotting me. What do you think, Dipper?"

"Not a chance, Bee. He's been in Frisco and north for two months," replied the one addressed.

"We don't know that," said Uhl, doubtfully, and turning again he pulled out a roll of bills, the wrapper of which bore the denomination one hundred. "Here's your dough, buddy. . . . You're on the spot. But the only risk you run is if you double-cross me."

"If I undertake the job, I'll be straight," interposed Lance.

"That's how you strike me. . . . See the big canvas-covered truck across there, back of the service station? Well, she's your bus. You're to take her to Tucson. She's empty, but you drive slow, as if she was loaded heavy. See? You'll be held up sooner or later, probably after dark outside of Tucson. That'll be okay. You're dumb. You just drove the truck over and you don't know me. See?"

"I don't know whether I see or not," rejoined Lance, dubiously. "Who'll hold me up—and why?"

"Say, you won't need to fake being dumb. All you got to do is stop when you're held up. See? You don't know nothing."

"Does that truck belong to you?"

"Yes."

"Rumrunner?"

"I told you it was empty," snapped Uhl. "Is it a go?"

"You bet," declared Lance, taking the proffered money. "What'll I do when I get to Tucson?"

"You'll be on the main highway. Stop at the first service station on the edge of town. Right-hand side."

"Then what?"

"If I don't meet you someone else will."

"Suppose these holdup gents take the truck away from me?"

"That won't be your loss."

"Boss," interposed the sallow-faced Dipper, "this husky bird is packin' a rod."

"Say, are you telling me? I hope he turns cowboy with it on those dopes. . . . Buddy, if you turn this trick there'll be more."

"This one doesn't strike me so hot," declared Lance, tersely. "But one at a time. I'm on my way."

As Lance strode off, carefully pocketing the money he heard Uhl say: "Dip, if he comes through we'll take him on."

"No gamble, Boss. That fellow will do. . . ."

Lance passed on out of earshot. At the station he said to the operator: "That truck ready?" Upon being informed that "she's all set," Lance climbed into the driver's seat and took a look. The machine was a fine make. As he moved out of the station yard he observed that the big black car had gone. Lance did not look to see what had become of it. A block away he turned into the highway and got through Douglas without a stop. Once beyond the town he opened up to twenty-five miles an hour and faced the north with a grim realization that he was in for an adventure he never would have hazarded but for a blonde college girl named Madge who had intrigued him.

"Queer setup," soliloquized Lance, now giving rein to his conjectures. "I hit the bull's-eye with that crack about Latzy Cork. . . . Racket? Wonder which racket? Cork was suspected of most everything up north. . . . Anyhow I got away with it. . . . And this Bee Uhl. He's a crook all right. From Chi. . . . I get it. Chicago, of course. He doesn't seem to care who knows it. And this big truck must have to do with bootlegging. Over the border, maybe. Or up from some harbor on the

Gulf. . . . Nothing to me. It gets my goat, though, what this slick bozo had to do with that girl.

Lance reflected presently that he ought to have that circumstance mastered. Madge's own words testified to that. She had flirted with Uhl, obviously for the thrill of it. She certainly knew he was a gangster. Perhaps that was the secret. A girl like her must be besieged by admirers, importuned and bored until she was tired of them. Still Uhl was handsome, and perhaps his hard and insolent way might have appealed to the girl. Assuredly that had been the inception of the affair. Lance felt glad to convince himself that she had realized her mistake, and in a thoroughbred but kindly way had made it clear to Uhl.

"But what in the hell did *she* want to fall for a guy like that?" bit out Lance, jealously. "Oh, be yourself, Lance!" Just because this Majesty, the student Rollie had called her, happened to be the loveliest and most fascinating girl Lance had ever met, was no reason for him to think her on the plane of the angels.

Lance did not need to bring back the vision of her. That was limned on his memory. No use faking it, he thought—he had fallen in love with her at first sight. That was all right. But he wished the thought and beauty and charm of her would not stick so tenaciously. He could not banish her and again came the regret that he had not stood right out like a man to meet her that day. He could at least have spared her the encounter with Uhl.

All at once Lance had a disturbing thought. Uhl, gangster, racketeer, bootlegger, might have another slant to his crookedness. He might be a kidnaper. That seemed reasonable enough, and the idea grew on Lance. The girl must belong to a rich California family. Her style, her patrician air, her talk of a ranch full of Arabian horses, surely these attested wealth. And that might explain Bee Uhl's interest in her. With the near approach of repeal of prohibition these bootleggers must work up other rackets. Already there had been a nationwide activity in kidnaping.

"Goofy or not, I take it as a hunch," muttered Lance, with finality. "Believe me, I'll get a line on that slicker with his roll of centuries, if I can." And in the stress of the moment Lance thought that if he did verify such suspicion of the gangster, it would not be beyond him to go back to Los Angeles tc warn the girl. Then the realization of his sudden tumult of delight made him look aghast at himself. "Quit your romancing, kid," he said. "This is hard pay. And I'm on a job I should have passed up."

But nothing he thought or reasoned out changed the essential sentiment and presagement of the situation. The way accidents and circumstances fell across his path and what came of them had taught him to believe any strange and far-reaching adventure could befall him.

Cars and trucks going and coming passed Lance now and then, the southbound traffic being the heavier. Lance did not see the big black automobile belonging to Uhl. Once he looked back down a league-long stretch, half expecting to discover the car following. But he did not.

Driving a truck did not permit of close attention to the desert scenery, which had been his pleasure while riding Umpqua. However, that labor and his concentration on the peculiar circumstances leading to this ride, certainly made the time fly. Almost before he knew it, he was climbing the tortuous grade through Bisbee, keeping keen lookout for the holdup he had been told to expect. About midafternoon he went through picturesque Tombstone on the outskirts of which he halted for gasoline. This necessitated his breaking the hundred dollar bill Uhl had given him. The service-station man, a westerner of middle age, glanced from the bill to Lance with keen blue eyes. "Seen bills like this before—an' also that truck you're drivin'. How aboot yore company?"

"Don't savvy," returned Lance, gruffly. "What you mean by company?"

"Wal, usually thar's two or three trucks like this one strung along. Reckon you're new to . . ."

"To what, mister?" interrupted Lance.

"Wal, I ain't sayin'," responded the operator, in cool evasion.

"Yeah? Well, as a matter of fact, I'm damn new at this job."

That little wordy byplay roused Lance anew to the possibilities that might be thickening ahead of him. Thereafter he kept keen as a whip, increasing his speed a little. It was almost dark when he passed Mescal, a desert hamlet, and he did not halt to appease thirst or hunger. He wanted to get this job over. The desert night was soft and balmy, cooling as the radiation of the day's heat passed away. Jackrabbits and coyotes leaped across the road, gray in the flash of his lamps. The headlights of cars grew from pin points in the blackness to yellow orbs, rushing at him and passing by, to leave the distant road dark again. The dry odor of dust and desert growths clogged his nostrils. Under favorable circumstances Lance would have liked closer acquaintance with that desert. The spectral arms of cactus and the dense thickets of mesquite accentuated the lonesomeness.

Some miles beyond Vail there appeared to come a brightening to the north. Soon Lance made that out to be the lights of Tucson, miles away still, but clear in the rarefied atmosphere. Lance rolling along at forty miles or more an hour, began to feel an edge for the expected holdup. Every time he caught the gleam of headlights behind he prepared for the order to halt. But so many cars passed him the next hour and so bright grew the illuminated horizon that he began to believe he might reach the first service station on the right without being stopped.

Presently a car came up behind and held its place for a couple of miles. Lance anticipated that this was the one, and he forced himself to be ready. He slowed down to thirty, then to twenty. The car kept behind him, somewhat to the left. At length it slipped up alongside Lance. "Hey, you driver. Halt!"

rang out a hoarse voice. Lance shut off, and applying the brakes, screeched to a stop.

"Stick 'em up!" came from the car. A flashlight blinded Lance.

"Okay!" he yelled, complying with the order.

Two men leaped out and a door clicked. The car moved on ahead to come to a standstill in front of the truck. Lance's door was jerked open. Light flooded his cab. Over an extended gun he caught indistinct sight of two faces, the foremost of which was masked. Lance heard footsteps running back behind his truck and the clank of bolts.

"Bud, j'ever see this one before?" queried the bandit with the gun.

"Nope. Another new one," came the laconic answer.

"Who are you?" followed the demand.

"Arizona cowpuncher," replied Lance. "Broke. Agreed to drive this truck."

"Who hired you?"

"I don't know. Five men in a black car at Douglas."

From behind clanked the hinge and there was a slap of canvas. "Empty, by God!" cried a hoarse voice, in anger. Footsteps preceded the appearance of two more men, one of whom Lance managed to distinguish despite the blinding flashlight. "Henny, we're tricked. He's made suckers out of us again. This truck is empty."

"Ah, hell no!"

"Aw, hell yes! It's a cattle car. As late as yesterday, when we picked them cars up, this one was full of steers. The other one had the . . ."

"Shut up!" yapped the leader, pounding his gun on the door. "Hey, driver, how many trucks like this have you lamped lately?"

"Off and on I've seen a good many," rejoined Lance, glibly. "Three in a row day before yesterday."

"Goin' which way?"

"North. out of Douglas."

"Ah ha! I *told* you, Henny," yelled the enraged bandit. "An' they'll all come back full of steers. He's took to buyin' steers. What you think of that? In the cattle bizness. A blind. Ha! Ha! An' it made a sucker out of you."

"Driver, is there a short cut to El Paso without goin' through Douglas?" queried the leader, sharply.

"Yes, at Benson," replied Lance, readily. "Poor road, but passable."

The leader snapped off his flashlight. "Beat it, cowboy, wherever you're goin'. An' tell your boss we're onto his racket."

"Henny, if there's a short cut, no matter how bad, we might head off that car," rasped the man Bud. He had a bitter raucous voice that Lance would remember. The four bandits ran to pile into their car. "Turn an' step on it!" ordered the leader. In another moment their car was roaring east on the highway, and Lance had a clear road ahead. Relieved, and more interested than ever, he threw in his clutch and sped on toward Tucson. Lance saw that he had been used merely to throw this gang off the track. The cattle slant to the business seemed a trick that would take more than one carload of bandits to beat.

The run from that lonely stretch of road to the service station designated was accomplished in short order, Lance driving at a fast clip. The truck appeared to ooze along as smoothly as a limousine. Hardly had Lance come to a halt in the station yard when two men in dark garb, slouch hats pulled down, hurried out to meet him. Lance was ready for them, and opening the door he stepped out with a long whew of relief.

"Hello. Am I glad to see you? Take her away," he said, vociferously.

"Dey stick you up?" queried one, tensely, while the other leaped into the seat.

"You bet. About five miles out. You should have heard Bud and Henny cuss to find her empty. I gave them a bum steer."

"Yeah? An' how bum?"

"They asked me if there was a short cut to El Paso and I

told them yes, at Benson. I heard it was some road. They'll get lost."

"Thet'll go hot with the boss. How much'd you dole out for gas? He forgot thet, an' told me to square it."

Lance named the sum, which was handed to him in a five dollar note and no change wanted.

"Blick, have we got all night?" demanded the man in the driver's seat. "Cut it."

"Keep your shirt on. Honey Bee gave me an order, didn't he? . . . Driver, yer come through clean. I'm to tell you thet if you're hangin' round Douglas next run, you can get another job."

"Swell. I'll hang around, if it's not too long. When's the next run?"

"I don't know. Mebbe in a month—mebbe longer."

When they had gone Lance went into the service station, aware that his arrival and the short conference had been observed.

"How far to a hash joint? I'm sure starved," he began, genially.

"Stranger hereabouts?" the man returned, with a keen look. "Plenty grub places up the street."

"Thanks. Yes, I'm a stranger. And I don't mind telling you I drove that truck because I was broke. I was held up out here and scared stiff."

"You don't say. Well, that's not strange considerin' the company. You got off lucky."

"Yeah? What was I up against?"

"Couldn't say."

"Did you ever see that truck before?"

"Yep, an' some more like it. They been comin' and goin' every six weeks or so."

"Cattle business must be good when steers get hauled in trucks," commented Lance; then waiting a moment for an answer, which did not come, he strode up the street. In the middle of the second block he found a café, where he obtained his supper. At the next corner there was a hotel. Inquiry brought the information that he could take a bus early next morning for Douglas. Then he went to bed. Events of the day had been thought-provoking, but they did not keep him awake.

On the bus the following morning, however, he had nothing to do but think. It took Lance practically all that long ride to reason out the futility of any further interest in Uhl. Lance did not want to drive any more questionable trucks. Aside from an interesting experience, this meeting with Uhl had no warrant to absorb him. It was the singular connection with the college girl that kept him wondering and conjecturing, and thinking that he should warn her somehow. But he did not even know her last name. And to go back to Los Angeles on such a fanciful assumption seemed absurd. Nevertheless his conscience bothered him. That passed, however, leaving Lance with only the increasing pang of regret. When at Douglas he went out to see Umpqua, and quite provokingly he conceived a picture of Madge on his beautiful horse, he almost gave way to rage at his sentimentality. All the same, thought of the girl persisted, and Lance finally reconciled himself to being haunted.

Riding northeast from Douglas the Arizona desert land magnified its proportions of color and wildness and rugged grandeur to such a degree that Lance was loath to travel on and turn his back to ranges that dwarfed those he had ridden in Oregon. What a grand country he was entering! Ahead of him were mountains, peaked and lofty, purple in the distance, growing black and gray as league after league he neared them. Lance took his time stopping to ask questions, but the several little hamlets along the way failed to yield much information. He spent one night at Chiricahua, which town appeared to be in the center of a vast green and gray range surrounded by mountains. He had begun to see cattle in considerable numbers, though not one hundredth as many as the country might have supported. He rode on and on over a rolling and lovely valley.

Darkness overtook Lance. He had inquired at Apache about towns farther north. He had been told they were few and far between. It looked as though his preoccupation with the solitude and beauty of this upland valley was going to make him spend a night in the open. He did not mind that. The day had been hot and the night still remained warm. However, three hours after sunset he sighted lights ahead and soon entered a place called Bolton. Unlike most of the other towns, this one appeared to be comparatively new and located on both highway and railroad. There was a wide main street with bright lights and many parked cars, stores and cafés, a hotel and an inn, a bank and motion-picture theater. Lance rode on through to the outer zone of garages and autocamps. Umpqua, staunch as he was, had begun to tire. Lance was pleased to see several horses tethered beyond a garage off the main street, and next a livery stable. The garage, evidently, also provided the facilities of a service station and was quite modest compared to showy places Lance had passed.

"Howdy, cowboy," drawled a pleasant voice. "Git down an' come in."

"Hello, yourself," replied Lance, greeting a sturdy bow-legged young man who had appeared from somewhere. There was enough light to make out a lean tanned face from which shone narrow slits of eyes, keen and friendly.

"My Gawd!—Where'd you steal thet hawse?" queried this individual.

"Are you kidding me or is that the way horsemen are greeted here?" asked Lance.

"Shore kiddin', cowboy. We got some grand hawses in this country an' thet's why I got fresh. But on the level where *did* you find him?"

"Oregon bred. He was given us when he was a colt. And I raised him."

"You from Oregon?" went on the other, walking around the horse in a way that betrayed a love of horseflesh. It was an open sesame to Lance's friendliness.

"Yes, rode him all the way."

"Don't tell. I'll be dog-goned. . . . Wal, lookin' him over I ain't so surprised. All hawse, cowboy, an' I'd trade you my garage for him."

"Sounds cowboy," laughed Lance.

"Shore I was—I *am* a cowboy. Been ridin' Arizona ranges all my life. But these hard times I had to make a livin' for my mother an' me."

"Gee, that's bad news. I came to Arizona to find a job with some cattle outfit."

"Wal, you're jest outa luck. Cowboys air scarce these days. As scarce as jobs. Plenty of cattle all through heah. An' the outfits thinned down to two or three riders. My job for three years before this bust-up hit us was with Gene Stewart. Finest rancher in these parts. Used to run eighty thousand haid. But of late years Gene has lost out. An' as I couldn't ride no more for nothin' I had to take this place. Pays fair, but I just hate it."

"Don't blame you. . . . How about me bedding down Umpqua in this livery stable?"

"*Umpqua?* What a name! Where'n hell did you git thet?"

"It's Indian. Name of a river in Oregon. Means swift."

"Swell handle at thet. Shore, this stable is okay. I'll go in with you. . . . What'd you say your name was? Mine's Ren Starr."

"I didn't say yet. It's Lance Sidway."

"Air you gonna hang about heah a spell?"

"Yes, if I can find work."

The livery stable man turned out to be an old fellow with an unmistakable cattle range air about him. He was almost as enthusiastic over Umpqua as Starr had been. For the first time in a long while Lance began to feel at home with his kind.

"Ump, old boy, this barn smells good, doesn't it?" said Lance, and giving his pet a parting smack he went out with Starr. "Where can I eat and sleep?"

"Several places, but outside the hotel, you'll like Mrs.

Goodman's café. Nice woman, dotes on cowboys, an' runs a swell little chuck house."

"Won't you come with me? I'd like to talk."

"Wal, shore. I've had my supper. But I can always eat. An' it's closin' time for my place anyway."

Presently Lance was ushered into a clean fragrant little shop, with more of a homey than a café look, and introduced to a portly woman of kind and genial aspect. Evidently she had a warm spot in her heart for cowboys.

"Wal, Oregon, I'd shore like to see you stop heah," said Starr, eagerly. Manifestly he had taken to Lance as Lance had to him.

"All the way up from Apache I've liked the range more and more."

"Hell, this ain't nothin'. You ought to see thet range down along the west slope of the Peloncillo Mountains. Swell deer an' antelope huntin'. Bear an' cougar up high. Trout fishin', oh boy! Grass an' sage ranges."

"Sounds more than swell. Is that where your Gene Stewart runs cattle?"

"Used to, when he had ten outfits. But now he's only got about a thousand haid left, not countin' yearlin's an' calves. He jest lets them graze around his ranch, with a couple of Mexican kids ridin' for him."

"How far away is his ranch?"

"I reckon about thirty by trail. The road runs round an' up an' down. Cars register forty-two miles. No road work this spring makes tough goin', an' I don't mean mebbe."

"Wonder what chance I'd have getting on with him? Wages no object for a while. I want to ride open country, and have a square meal often, with pasture for Umpqua. You see he was raised to fare for himself. Alfalfa and grain would spoil him."

"My idee of trainin' a hawse right. . . . I'll tell you, Sidway, there's a pretty shore chance for you out with Gene. He needs riders most damn bad. I'll give you a note to him in the mawnin'. Thet'll cinch it, if you really want a job for nothin' 'cept board. He'll be glad. Only you gotta approach him sorta careful. . . . Sensitive fellow, Gene is, but the salt of this range. For two bits I'll sell out an' go with you."

"That'd be swell. Why don't you?"

"It'd be all right with Mom. She wants to get out of this hot country for a while. But I'm makin' money an' I reckon I ought to save plenty before hittin' the trail again."

"All right, Ren. Thanks for the hunch. I'll go. Maybe we can see each other sometimes. I'd like that."

"Me too. Shore we can. Gene would give you a Sunday off now an' then. I'd run out after you."

"What kind of ranch does Stewart own?"

"Gee whiz! I reckoned every puncher in the West had heahed of it. Close to the border. Used to belong to a Mexican named Don Carlos. He was shot long before I come to this part or Arizona. I was hardly borned then. But I've heahed the story. Durin' the Mexican Revolution around twenty-five years ago Don Carlos had thet ranch. It was a Spanish grant. An' he was sellin' contraband along the border. Gene Stewart was a tough cowboy them days. Great with the rope an' hawse—a daid shot—an' nerve, say! they didn't come no cooler than thet *hombre.* Wal, he joined up with the revolutionists. They called him *El Capitan.* After Madero was assassinated Gene come back heah. About thet time a rich girl from Noo Yoork come along. She bought Don Carlos' Ranch. Stillwell, the foreman then, corralled the hardest bunch of cowboys thet ever rode a range. But nobody could boss them until he put Gene on the job. They run Don Carlos an' his band off the range. An' they made thet ranch the finest in the West. It's as beautiful as ever, but turrible run down these last two years . . . Wal, Gene married his boss, the rich girl from the East, an' was thet a romance!"

"Darned interesting, Ren. I'm going to like Stewart."

"You shore will, an' if you turn out as good as you look—excuse me bein' personal—Gene is goin' to cotton to you. He was grand to me. An' I just love him as if he was my dad. He always stops in to see me, hopin' I'll come back. But he never says so. He was in town today, worried plain about somethin' He said it was only cause he was losin' a few cattle."

"Cattle thieves?" exclaimed Lance, quickly.

"Rustlers over heah, Sid."

"No!"

"Shore. There's still some rustlin' all over. Nothin' heah like it used to be. But you see a dozen haid to Gene now means more'n a thousand, years ago. He was sore because he couldn't find out how the cattle was stole. An' old Nels, the last of thet great outfit of cowboys, couldn't find out either."

"Too old-fashioned, maybe."

"Dog-gone, Sid. I had thet very idee."

"Say, Starr," spoke up Lance, as if with an inspiration. "Not so many days ago I drove a big truck from Douglas to Tucson. It was empty but it had been full of steers."

Lance related briefly the circumstances that made it necessary for him to earn some money, but he did not go into detail about the men he had met on that adventure.

"Wal, I'm a son-of-a-gun! . . . What kind of a truck?"

"A big one, fine make, and canvas-covered. I took the license number and the name of the owner. Which I suspect is not the name of the right owner."

"Sidway, you're sayin' things," rejoined Starr, growing cool after his excitement. "I've seen three or four trucks like thet one pass heah every month or so. One went through north four days ago."

"Did you pay any particular attention to it?"

"No. Only saw it an' was sore as usual 'cause the driver got gas from one of the other stations. You see them fellers never have bought a gallon of gas from me. Thet's okay, shore. My place is as you saw it."

"Starr, they passed you up because you were a cowboy."

"You don't say! Thet's an idee. A hot one."

"Something I heard on my drive gives me a hunch now that

these truck men bought cattle as a blind. Perhaps of late they *steal* cattle. All kinds of business pretty punk these days."

"Pard, you are a whiz," ejaculated Starr, intensely. "Rackin' my haid I figger thet I haven't seen them trucks go through heah *southbound* since last fall. They do go through, shore. I been told thet. But late in the night."

"We got something to work on."

"I should smile. I'll grow curious as hell. Sid, this heah is goin' to be most damn interestin' to Gene. You tell him pronto. All about them trucks."

"You bet. And, Starr, if I get in with Stewart I'll send you the receipt and money to send for my baggage in Los Angeles."

"Glad to fetch it out. . . . Wal, I reckon you ought to hit the hay. Your eyes look tired. Come on an' I'll take you to the hotel. Most as reasonable as autocamps, an' good."

On the way across the street Starr said: "There's shore a lot to tell you about Stewart, his ranch an' all. But I cain't think of everythin' all to oncet. . . . You'll find Mrs. Stewart jest swell. Still handsome an' the nicest woman! I most forgot their daughter. No wonder, 'cause I haven't seen her for nearly four years. She was only a kid then. But could she cock her eye at a man? Had all the cowboys dotty. *Me!* I reckoned I had the inside track 'cause she let me kiss her oncet. But I was wrong, Sid. Thet girl was a hells-rattler, but straight as a string. Jest full of fem. . . . Wal, Gene told me today thet she was comin' home. He was plumb excited over thet. Worships the girl! An' mebbe he was worryin' about her too. . . . Sid, if I remember thet girl she will keep you awake nights."

"Not much," declared Lance with a laugh. "Boy, I've been in Hollywood for a spell, hobnobbing with the prettiest and slickest girls in the world."

"Hollywood? My Gawd, what'll you spring on me next? Sid, you are goin' to relieve the tedium of my days. . . . Did you fall for any of them stars?"

"Ren, I fell with a dull thud for three. And not stars, either. Just extras prettier than the stars. Harder every fall! And I can't imagine *me* falling for a ranch girl. No offense, boy. My sister is a ranch girl and she's my pride. *But* you can get what I mean, if you go to the flickers."

"You mean movies? I go every show an' sometimes twice."

"Then you know how safe I'll be on an Arizona ranch."

"Safe out heah, *if* she doesn't come home, which I don't believe she will? Pard, I wouldn't gamble on thet. . . . Wal, heah's your hotel. I'll be sayin' *adios* till mawnin'. I'm shore glad we met, Lance."

"So am I, Ren. It's just swell. See you early tomorrow. Don't forget to write that note to Stewart. Good night."

Lance went to bed glowingly excited and satisfied with the day's happenings, and its promise. Particularly was he pleased at finding the ex-cowboy, Starr. Lance thought he would be a fellow to tie to. Luck had attended this adventuring into a new and far country.

After an early breakfast next morning Lance made his first Arizona purchases, which consisted of a new riding outfit, and a much needed shaving kit and several other articles. His discarded things he tied in his old coat, so that he could carry the bundle conveniently on his saddle. When he presented himself at Starr's garage, that worthy stared in comical surprise.

"Mawnin' Sid," he drawled. "What you been about? All dolled up. My Gawd! I hadn't no idee you was such a handsome galoot. On thet hawse you'll knock 'em cold. Say! I've a hunch you've either seen or heahed about Gene Stewart's daughter."

"Nope, I haven't. But I needed some clean duds and a shave," explained Lance. "Couldn't ask for a job looking like a tramp."

"I ain't so shore, Sid," returned Starr, doubtfully. "Gene likes 'em tough. Why, with thet red scarf an' all you look like Buck Jones."

"Ren, I bought the least gaudy outfit that storekeeper had," protested Lance. "If you think I should change back to . . ."

"Aw, I was half kiddin'. You look okay. In fact you look grand. But no cowpuncher can fool Gene Stewart. He'll see right through you, Sid. An' I'll bet my shop he'll take to you same as I did."

"Well, then, what the hell . . ."

"Thet's it. What the hell will come off if you run plumb into Gene's daughter? She's on her way home. Gene told my mother so yesterday."

"Ren, you certainly harp on that subject. Is the heart of Miss Stewart all you're concerned with?" queried Lance, facetiously.

"Hell no! I'm jest concerned about what'll happen to you, if she sees you. An' in this new outfit you shore stand out from the landscape."

"Like all the Arizona cowboys, aren't you?" went on Lance. "Oh, I knew a lot of them in Hollywood. Swell fellows, but simply nuts on jokes and tricks and girls! . . . Next to that they liked to gamble. I'll bet you five bucks *I* don't even see your Arizona cowgirl queen. . . . Man, I've lived in Hollywood for over a year."

"So you told me before," replied Starr, dryly. "Thet bet's on. Heah's your note to Gene Stewart. I shore hope you turn out half as good as my recommendation."

"Thanks, Ren. I hope I make good. Now tell me how to find this wonderful ranch."

"Go out the highway, south, of course. Take the first road—it's a dirt road—turnin' left. Stick on thet for about five miles, till you come to a bridge over a crick. Lots of green willows. Anyway, it's the first bridge you come to, so you cain't miss it. There's a trail thet follers the crick, on the right-hand side. Hit thet trail, pard, an' good luck to you."

"How'll I know the ranch when I come to it?"

"Hell! it's the only ranch out there. The house, old Spanish style, sets on a knoll among trees. Walls used to be white. But you can see it from the divide, ten miles away."

In very short order Lance was out of Bolton on a road that

seemed to climb and lose itself in gray obscurity. Umpqua, scenting something out there, the sage and the open, perhaps, settled down to his fast ground-gaining trot. Lance saw on his right where the highway, a shining ribbon, followed the railroad and line of telegraph poles off to the southwest across the desert. On his left, beyond the green willows bordering the brook, an occasional humble ranch, or adobe Mexican house, gave life to a range gradually growing wilder as he proceeded. Ahead of him on the horizon mountain ranges stood up, some bold, others dim. Lance's quick eye caught sight of romping jack rabbits and sneaking coyotes, and the white rumps of deer-like animals he concluded were antelope.

Eventually the trail left the brook. Dwarf cedar trees and a line of pale purple marked the zone of sage. Lance was familiar with Oregon and California sage, but neither had the luxuriance and fragrance of this Arizona brand, Umpqua manifestly liked the smell of it. There seemed to be a tang and a zest in this clear air. The sun became hot on Lance's back; heat veils arose like smoke from the ground; the peaks that had been sharp against the blue appeared to dim in haze. Down to the right, toward the road Lance could still see, herds of cattle dotted the gray. The trail, however, headed more to the left, toward rising land, and rugged bits of outcropping rocks red in color, and back clumps of cedars.

By noonday Lance calculated that he had covered at least twenty miles, two thirds of the distance to Stewart's ranch; and soon he had surmounted the divide Starr had mentioned. The scene was so splendid that Lance halted to gaze and gaze spellbound. He saw a moving dust line from a car creeping across this vast gray-purple bowl under him which must be the southern end of Bernardino Valley. Rocky areas and clumps of cedars and darker patches of trees relieved the monotony of that range, sweeping away and upward to the mountains that must be the Peloncillos. Then Lance's keen eyes sighted the forested knoll and the old Spanish mansion built by Don Carlos. Ten miles away still, it appeared to stand out with a magnificence that Starr had hinted of. A lake, blue as a gem, shone in the sun, and its circle of green let out a branch that wound down across the gray, to make a wide bend around the rocky ridge Lance had surmounted. This, of course, was the stream he had encountered below. It was a big country. How vast this country must be when here lay only a mountain-walled valley! Heading down the trail Lance thought gravely, yet somehow with exaltation, that he was won forever. He would find or make a home there, and felt that he owed Ren Starr infinite gratitude.

By midafternoon Lance rode into a pretty little Mexican village at the foot of the knoll. Columns of blue smoke arose slowly. The half-naked children, the burros and dogs, the natives in colored raiment watching idly from the low porches, all appeared to have a leisurely air. Lance ventured a question to one group. An exceedingly pretty Mexican girl, whose big dark eyes shone bright and roguishly upon Lance replied to him: "*Buenos dias, señor.*"

"No savvy. Can't you talk United States?" asked Lance, mildly, smiling at the girl.

"Yes, cowboy, Mr. Stewart is home."

"Thank you, *señorita.* I think I'm going to like it here."

Her dusky eyes snapped with mischief, and quick as their flash she retorted: "It didn't take you long, *señor.*"

Riding away up the gentle slope Lance cogitated that remark of the Mexican lass's. "Say! what did she mean? Can't make out, but sure she was kidding me. Some little peach! Okay by me, *señorita.* I'll be seeing you."

Lance had not proceeded beyond where the road turned up the wooded knoll when a boy overtook him to inform him that *Señor* Stewart was at the corrals, toward which he pointed. Lance threw him a quarter, and kept to the right along the base of the knoll, to come at length into view of log barns and sheds and corrals, a long mossy-roofed bunkhouse, old and weathered, picturesquely falling to decay. A piercing whistle from an unseen horse brought a snort from Umpqua. Lance rode down a lane of tumble-down poles, to turn into a kind of court, at the immediate right of which stood a blacksmith shop; in front of this were several Mexican riders, and a thoroughbred black horse so glossy and well-groomed that he did not appear to belong there. Then a tall white man stepped out from behind the horse. He had a superb build, a dark intent face, deeply lined, piercing dark eyes, and there was white hair over his temples. Lance did not need to be told that this was Gene Stewart. As Lance rode up he caught first a relaxing of this stern face into a smile that warmed it attractively, and then a keen interest in both rider and horse.

"Howdy, cowboy," the rancher greeted Lance, in pleasant deep voice. "You got the jump on them."

"Who . . . what?" stammered Lance. "Are you Gene Stewart?"

"Yes, I'm Stewart. And who're you?"

"Lance Sidway. I want a job."

"Fine. . . . May I ask if you have been recommended by my daughter?"

"No—indeed, sir," replied Lance, recalling Starr's talk, and suddenly filled with dismay. "I don't know your daughter."

"That's quite possible. But might not her return home today have something to do with your asking for a job?" asked Stewart, with a twinkle in his piercing eyes.

"It might, judging from the Arizona cowboys I've met," rejoined Lance, recovering coolness at the fun evidently enjoyed at his expense. "But in my case it hasn't."

"Indeed? Well, in your case then I'll listen."

"Here's my letter of introduction," went on Lance, producing it.

Stewart opened and read it, suddenly to beam upon Lance. "Pard of Starr's, eh? You sure can't be all Ren says. But if you're anyways near as good . . ."

"Excuse me, Stewart," interposed Lance, hurriedly. "I'm not sailing under false colors. Starr doesn't know me any better than you do. Met him only last night! We liked each other right off. He told me you might take me on. Offered a letter of introduction."

"I see. That's like Ren. Get down and come in."

Lance stepped out of the saddle to drop the bridle. Stewart spoke to one of the admiring native lads: "Pedro, water him and rub the dust off him. . . . Cowboy, you've a grand horse. I can't see a fault in him. Any rancher in the West would give you a job to get a chance to buy him or steal him."

"Umpqua is swell," replied Lance, as the rancher led him to a seat on the porch of what appeared to be a store.

"Nels, come out," called Stewart, into the wide-open door of the old building. Receiving no answer he said plaintively: "Nels must be out back with my daughter, looking at her horses. Cowboy, you'll have hell keeping that horse."

"Oh, I see," laughed Lance, thrilled at the intimation that the rancher might take him on. "Any girl who loves horses would want Umpqua, naturally. But she'll have to take me with him."

"Old-time cowboy spirit! I was that way, once. . . . Where you from?"

Lance briefly told of his home in Oregon, his experience on the ranges there, modestly enumerating his abilities and skipping the Hollywood experience.

"Did you ever hear of this range and my ranch?"

"Only from Starr. It'd be a great place to work. Please give me a trial, Stewart."

"I'd sure like to," returned the rancher, kindly but gravely. "Once I had the best and wildest outfit on the border. But times have changed. . . . Starr says in his note that wages are no object."

"I'll be glad to work for my board."

"Are you rich?"

"Lord, no! I have a few dollars in my pocket. And Umpqua. Yes, I should have said I am rich."

"Sidway, I couldn't let you work for nothing."

"But sir, if it's money don't let that keep you from hiring me," importuned Lance.

"Tell me straight. I'll like you the better if you confess you want this job on account of Madge."

"Madge!—Who's she? Oh, of course, your daughter. . . . Mr. Stewart, on my honor I swear I never heard of her until Starr raved about her last night."

"But that might have been enough. You're cowboy brand, all over."

"It wasn't enough. It wasn't anything. Women are not in my troubles."

"Don't perjure yourself. Girls are always cowboys' troubles. . . . I'll take you on, Sidway, and pay you a few dollars a month till the cattle business looks up."

"Thank you. I'll sure do my best for you."

"Did Ren mention he might come back to me?"

"Yes, he did. He wants to. I'll bet he'll come, soon as he saves a little more money."

"I hate to ask him. But with you hard-riding youngsters to help me and Danny, and my *vaqueros* we might save the herd. You see, Sidway, there's been some queer rustling. . . ."

Stewart was interrupted by a sweet high-pitched voice that came from round the corner of the porch, down the lane.

"*Nels!* . . . For Pete's sake look at this black horse! . . . Oh, what a beauty!—Oh! Oh!"

Clinking spurs attested to the slow steps of a rider.

"Well, lass, I never set eyes on thet hawse before," drawled a quaint voice. "You'll shore hate me when I say he's got yore nags beat to a frazzle."

"Nonsense!—But he *is*. . . . Nels, I want him. I'll have him if it costs ten thousand. . . . Dad! *Dad!*"

Stewart whispered: "Step around and tell her here's one horse she can't buy. It'll be fun."

"Certainly, sir," replied Lance, dubiously. It was his first order from his boss. Besides he seemed curiously struck by the situation or that sweet voice. As he moved to the corner he heard pattering footsteps. Then a vision flashed into sight to plump squarely into his arms.

"Oh!" she screamed, and staggering, would have fallen had she not caught Lance with swift hand. A girl—bareheaded—golden hair flying—lovely flushed face, strangely familiar—violet eyes widening, darkening! "Who on earth? . . . *You!* . . . Of all the miracles! If it isn't my hero!"

Lance recognized her. His girl of the campus adventure and the mad ride through the streets of Los Angeles. As she enveloped him, with gay trill, and her red lips came up nearer to meet his in a cool sweet kiss, his breast seemed to cave in.

Chapter Three

IT WAS along about sunset when Gene Stewart drove into the courtyard of his ranch. The drive out from Bolton, despite the old car, had seemed short, and for once he had failed to enjoy the magnificent range that he had loved so well for over thirty years. That day the many familiar spots, memorable of the wild past, failed to start the old dreams. Even the adobe ruins of the Mexican village where Madeline had importuned him to abandon his bad habits and come to work for her, failed for once to remind him of the turning point, the blessed uplift of his life. Trouble indeed gloomed Gene Stewart's eyes when he could not see the sage flat where, bitter and hopeless, he had pulled Madeline off her horse, and knowing that she was secretly his wife, that though she did not dream of it, she was his, and he was leaving her forever, to ride out on his old hard-shooting, hard-drinking trail to get himself killed, he had kissed her with the mocking passion of renunciation. When Gene, passing the place, did not remember that, though it had been over twenty years ago, he was indeed sore distraught with worries.

Nels, the old Texan who was the last of his great riders of that earlier and wilder day, sat on the porch of the store, smoking and waiting. Gene seemed to see that white head, and the narrow eagle eyes, the lean lined face, with a rare and shocking sense of their age. Nels must be close to seventy now. And all the West showed its life and havoc under that mild mask of tranquillity.

"Wal, you're late, Gene, an' come draggin' along like you was on a bogged hawse," remarked Nels.

"Yes, old-timer," replied Gene, wearily, as he sat down on the porch, a folded newspaper in his hand.

"What's on yore chest?"

"Things have gone from bad to worse, Nels."

"Heahed from Majesty?" queried the old cowman, eagerly.

"Letter and telegram to me. More for Madeline. . . . Madge is on her way home. For good!"

"You don't say?—Aw! Then nothin' can be bad," replied Nels, settling back with an air of beautiful relief.

"Bad news from Madge, Nels. But let that go for the moment. There are lesser evils. Lawson has gone into bankruptcy. No hope of the money he owes me. I had banked on that. My creditors are pressing. Money must be raised."

"Any better market for cattle?"

"Gone down to thirty dollars on the hoof."

"Boss, I reckon I'd sell."

"All the herd?" queried Gene, in surprise. Nels would be the last cattleman to sacrifice all his stock. There was not in Arizona a keener judge of matters pertaining to cattle.

"Every horn an' hide, Gene."

"But that is an unheard of thing for a rancher to do," protested Stewart.

"Shore. How aboot these times? Onheard of, ain't they? Never in my life have I seen the like. Lookin' far ahaid, Gene, I'll predict thet the day of the big cattleman is over."

"Unthinkable!" ejaculated Stewart. The idea somehow hurt him. "What warrant have you for such a prediction?"

"Government interference, sure as shootin'. Then the range land grows less an' less every year. Last an' wust, we already have Argentine meat comin' heah to the U. S., cheaper than we can raise it. Gene, we're in for bum years. I've got a hunch."

"I always respected your hunches, Nels," replied Stewart, testily. "But this seems preposterous."

"Gene, jest how bad in debt air you?"

"I haven't the nerve to figure it up," replied Stewart, evasively.

"Wal, if you sold oot at thirty you could pay up, an' then tide over ontil good times come again. If we live thet long!"

"I might consider selling half my stock," rejoined Stewart, thoughtfully.

"You're the boss. An' you asked my opinion. I forgot to tell you thet Danny Mains rode up today. He ain't makin' oot with his cattle raisin'. Been losin' too many steers. An' Danny is afeared thet the Mexicans air doin' the stealin'."

"But how could a few Mexicans, even if they were crooked, get rid of cattle without leaving any sign?"

"I don't know, Gene. But there's shore somethin' doin'. All of Bonita's relatives cain't be good. Some of them won't be good until they're daid. Danny's got a fine wife in Bonita, an' shore a dandy girl in their daughter, young Bonita. But thet's aboot all. And he's scared of her relatives. Asked me plumb oot what to do?"

"And what'd you say, Nels?"

"Wal, I told him to sell. An' when he bucked on thet I advised him to throw in with you. Then if you hired a couple of good cow hands we could beat this game. At least the stealin' end. Thet's the profit-eatin' cussed part of it."

"Not a bad suggestion, Nels. But what'd we pay hired cow hands with?"

"Aw, shucks, Gene! It cain't be thet bad with you," complained Nels, plaintively.

"I'm sorry, old-timer. But it *is*. I hate to face Madeline. And especially with this." Stewart unrolled the newspaper he had twisted in his hands and spread one over the old cowman's knees. Nels took out his glasses, and adjusting them he read slowly:

COLLEGE CAMPUS RIOT

CO-ED EXPELLED FOR INCITING RIOT
BETWEEN STUDENTS AND POLICE

"Wal, I'll be . . . !" he ejaculated, jerking up his fine white head. Gene had seen those blue eyes flash fire many a time, though hardly ever like this. Nels divined the truth and his affections were attacked.

"*Majesty?*"

"Yes, I'm damn sorry to say. But read what it says, Nels."

"Aw!"

Gene watched that fine lined face as Nels laboriously read the half column in the newspaper. He had seen Nels face death many times and deal it often, with never a gray shade creep over his features nor a convulsive quiver, such as were visible now for a fleeting instant. And he remembered that it was Nels who loved Madge as well as her own father, it was Nels who had long years ago named the imperious child Majesty, who had put her upon a horse and taught her to ride. Nels folded up the newspaper and handed it back.

"Gene, I'd give somethin' to throw a gun on the cuss who wrote thet."

"Nonsense, Nels. Are you crazy? This is 1932."

"Why hell yes! And there's more shootin' in the U. S. now than when we come first to this range, thirty years ago for you an' more for me. . . . He's a damn liar, Gene."

"Who? The writer of this article?"

"Yes. I don't believe a word of thet dirty part. Aboot her bein' wild, rich, an' as hard a drinker as she was a speed demon. Gene, don't you believe thet an' fer Gawd's sake, don't tell Madeline."

"I'm sort of sunk, Nels. Kind of a last blow. I don't know what to think. Madge's letter admits it. Honest, right out! And her telegrams say she's on the way home to stay."

"Gosh! Thet's the best news I've heahed fer a long time."

"It is good news, Nels. It hurts, though. Looks kind of like disgrace is responsible."

"Aw no, Gene. Why, Majesty loves this range, this house where she was born. It's home."

"I don't know my own girl," sighed Stewart. "Remember, Nels, I haven't laid eyes upon Madge for over three years.

You know I was in Mexico the last time she came home. And the summer before that she went to Europe."

"Wal, I have. An' I'm gamblin' on her, Gene. Wild as a young filly, shore she was. But good as gold an' as true as steel. When she was heah last I had some jars, you bet. I had to figger oot thet times had changed since you an' me ran after girls. We've stayed right in one spot, Gene, an' this old world has moved on."

"Right. I'll bet you we have it coming to us. Madge said in her letter she was having a crowd of college friends come to visit her."

"Fine. She did thet last time an' I never had such fun."

"Nels, you're a hopeless old fool. Madge will have you eating out of her hand. But I'm her father!"

"Shore. An' I'm gonna have fun oot of you, Gene."

Gene slowly walked up the winding green-bordered path toward the ranch house. He had not told Nels all his worries. As a matter of fact he was both overjoyed at the prospect of Madge's return and greatly dismayed. A crowd of college friends!

Mockingbirds and quail and robins and magpies were rustling and chattering in the thick pines. The last rays of the setting sun burned gold on the flowering vines and the open weathered walls and arches of the old Spanish mansion. The fragrance of roses mingled with that of pine, and the soft sage wind from off the range. Gene felt the fact that the grounds, the great adobe structure, were more beautiful than ever. But the evidence of decay struck Gene most forcibly this evening. The trellises were falling down; the planking of the porches had rotted through in places, the weathering of plaster showed the adobe bricks.

Passing through the high archway at the rear of the house, Gene entered the patio. It appeared a dusky jungle of dark verdure, running water, drowsy twittering of sleepy birds, and odorous fragrance. A savory smell wafted from the kitchen where he heard the servants talking in their low voices. When

Gene crossed the wide porch to enter Madeline's sitting room, the newspapers to which Nels had objected did not show among the large quantity of mail. Madeline had heard his step on the porch and had come to meet him. Love for this patrician woman who as a girl had forsaken the East to make his country and his life hers, and pride in her well-preserved beauty and charm, seemed to be strong and moving emotions at the moment when these disclosures about their only child had to be made. Would Madge be another Madeline? There was gray visible in Madeline's hair and lines had begun to show in the handsome face. But the light in her lustrous eyes appeared as soft and glad as in her youth.

"Gene!" she exclaimed, kissing him. "A whole day late! . . . You look tired—worried."

"Howdy, Madeline," replied Gene, laying the bundles and packets of mail on the table. "Yes, I'm tired—and worried. Bad news, Wife. It never rains but it pours. Lawson failed, Madeline. Gone into bankruptcy. No hope of money. I'll have to sell some stock. Nels advises selling all my herd. . . . That's nothing though. I've got a big surprise for you. Madge is coming home."

"Madge! Coming home? Why? What has she done now, Gene?" rejoined Madeline, quietly.

"Got herself expelled from college," Gene blurted out, knowing that he should have broken the news more gently, but incapable of the guile necessary to spare his wife's feelings.

"Oh, no! Not on the eve of her graduation? June eleventh."

"Yes. It's tough, but maybe not so bad as it seems. Here's her letter and telegrams to me. Read them before you open yours."

Gene went into his office, which adjoined the sitting room, turned on the lights, and laid all his unopened mail, and some business papers upon his table. Then he repaired to his room to wash and change for the evening meal. He took plenty of time about this, his thoughts under the dominance of gloom. Presently Madeline called him to supper, and he found her in the dining room. If he had expected her to be cast down he was agreeably surprised.

"I ought to be hungry," he said. "Most forgot to eat in town." And he asked Madeline questions pertaining to the ranch during his absence. Nothing had happened. The drowsy languorous summer had come and the tranquil tenor of the lonely range land had not been broken. When Gene had finished a hearty meal he suggested that they go into the sitting room and get it over.

"Dear, it will never be over until you change your habit of mind," she replied, sweetly. "You always look upon the dark side."

"Madeline, this time of trouble has brought back the Gene Stewart of other and darker days."

"It should not. You have made me perfectly happy for more than twenty years. Loss of money, for you and me, is nothing."

"Madeline, I could take my losses without. . . . But it's yours that distress me. All your life you have had luxury. You were born to it. This last year and more you've been using your money to pad Madge's bank account. She keeps overdrawing her income and you keep from telling her that her income isn't one with what it was. Now through me and that spendthrift girl of ours you must suffer. When the depression hit us you should have told Madge the truth. How much her income had fallen off. Instead of that you never told her—made up the difference yourself. And she spends hundreds like a drunken cowboy does dollars. That is what hurts me."

"Gene, I expected the shrinking of capital and income would be only temporary. I still believe, as my lawyer in New York assures me, that we will recover. Madge's capital is intact and eventually her income will grow normal. That was a wise provision of Aunt Helen's. Madge can't spend the capital. And it doesn't make so great a difference that her income has dwindled. But now we should tell her—if we have the courage!"

"We!" expostulated Gene, startled. "Not much. Why, I don't know Madge since she grew up. When she was seventeen—

before she left for college I was scared to death of her. You'll have to tell her."

"That'll be hard. I'm afraid myself of these years she has lived away from us. If I had it to do over I'd not have sent her away to college."

"Well, let's forget the financial side of it for the present. You read her letters and telegrams?"

"Yes. Madge asked me to reserve judgment until I had heard her side. Evidently she became involved in some kind of a college row, for which she was not reponsible, but which resulted in her expulsion. She regretted greatly that she could not graduate."

"Was that all? No regret for the—the disgrace?"

"She never mentioned disgrace. I don't believe that has occurred to her."

"Same old Majesty, eh? She couldn't do any wrong," returned Gene, and there was a tinge of bitterness in his tone. "What else?"

"She said she had invited her college friends to come out here for the summer—for the *summer*, mind you. That will be after graduation. It worries me more than the fact of her being expelled."

"That's easy. Tell Madge she can't have her friends this summer."

"Could you tell her that?"

"Sure I could," replied Gene, grimly.

"Very well. That will be a relief. For the rest she wired from L. A. she was leaving. And last evening from Yuma. Gene, don't excite yourself over probabilities. The fact seems that at that rate she may get here tomorrow."

"Madeline, it—it'll be so wonderful to see her again that I almost don't care what she's done," replied Gene with emotion.

"Gene, she's our problem. She's a composite of you and me."

"Madeline, not much of me?" implored Gene.

"A very good deal of you, her father."

"Suppose she inherited some of that wild blood of mine?" ejaculated Gene, aghast.

"If it hadn't been for that, there might have never been any Madge, darling."

"Lord!—I always said Madge had your beauty, your sweetness, your intelligence. But if she's got my old devil in her, too—come out in these modern days of freedom for women—what, Maddie, what on earth can we do?"

"I don't know, Gene. Love her, trust her. Make her love her home. Let us agree on that right here, Gene."

"I promise, Madeline. But I'm scared."

"So am I. But not the way you are. I'm scared of a crowd of young college people, just freed from cramping restrictions, let loose upon us here."

"Madeline, do you remember your young crowd—that you had come out here from New York just after you bought this place?"

"Indeed, I do," replied his wife, musingly, her eyes shadowed. "My brother Alfred—his romance with Flo—my sister Helen—my best friend Edith Wynne. Oh, they seem so far away—so long ago. But Alfred has been coming back to us for ten years. . . . Gene, did you ever guess that Helen was in love with you—then, when you were *El Capitan*?"

"Helen!—Why, Maddie, you're crazy," protested Gene.

"No. It's the truth. I never told you. Helen never married, you know. And she left her fortune to Madge—which after all has been such a problem—*is* so yet. . . . Gene, if Madge's friends are like her, we would have a more exciting summer than that one twenty-three years ago."

"I haven't the slightest doubt of that," growled Gene.

"If we only had an *El Capitan* to tame Madge!"

"Maddie, we don't want a wild *hombre* like he was."

"Perhaps no other kind could ever win Madge. . . . My husband, why do you always disparage yourself so bitterly?"

"I've failed as a rancher. After raising a herd of eighty thousand head."

"But that was not your fault. Who could foresee what would

happen to the cattle business? Anyway I was referring to your status as the cowboy who came—and conquered. . . . Gene, my memories are beautiful, always, eternally all-satisfying. Even to this day I can dream of that awful ride down into Mexico to save you from being shot—and revel in the sight of you striding out, as you supposed, to your execution. To meet instead—*me*—your wife, who you had no idea knew your secret!"

"Well, I find it sweet too, Madeline. The past would be enough for me. But there is you—our home—and now Madge to think of."

"Gene, it will all come out right."

"Sure it will, dear. I'm an old croaker. Wish I could be like Nels. . . . You'll want to read your mail. And I've a lot of papers to look over."

Gene left his wife, conscious of a sense of guilt and remorse. He had not told her all. The deal with Lawson had been made to raise money to pay a mortgage he had secretly placed upon the ranch. Gene had meant to confess this, but could not bring himself to it. Nels had sensed that something was wrong, though the keen old friend had not dreamed that it was so bad. It was insupportable for Gene to think of Madeline and Madge losing this beautiful ranch.

Outside he walked the old familiar path under the cotton woods that had been planted there before Don Carlos built the house. The sultry heat of day was wafting away; a fragrant incense of flowers and pine needles filled the air; the irrigation ditch in its stone-walled vine-covered confines murmured on musically like a brook.

There was strength and help in this environment, and in the solitude that hung over it. But there was no comfort in Gene's confession that he had not been equipped to cope with these modern days of bewildering changes and upsets in business. Nels was a far better cattleman than he. For fifteen years there had been too much money to spend, and he had spent instead of saving it. Then out of a clear sky, like a thunderbolt, had come the collapse of eastern securities, and the bank that had held the rest of Madeline's fortune. She did not know how poor they really were. Sober reasoning assured Gene that Madge could and probably would save the ranch. Nevertheless telling her of the straits he had brought about seemed absurdly beyond him. Gene made up his mind to sell two thirds of his stock, pay his pressing debts and the interest on the mortgage, then plan and plot somehow to save the situation.

With a mighty effort he threw off the depression, and went back into the house, to deceive Madeline with an apparent return of his old cool unconquerable spirit, and presently to bed.

In the morning there had come a change. Whether or not the anticipated home-coming of Madge had wrought the magic or a vivid realization of the sweetness of life on this glorious June morning, so rich in song of birds and blaze of purple range and golden sun, Gene did not know. A good sleep and then the light of day always worked wonders.

Gene found Danny Mains with Nels, having a cup of coffee in the old cowboy's bachelor quarters which had been his home for twenty-five years. Danny had been one of Gene's wild outfit in those long-past prosperous days. His bow legs, his sturdy build had not altered. But Danny's homely visage betrayed the havoc of the years.

"Howdy, Boss," he greeted Gene, gladly. Danny had not worked for Gene for a whole decade and more, but he always addressed him in the cowboy vernacular of rider to his employer. "I was comin' up. Nels an' me hev been talkin' over my throwin' in with you. I like the idee, Boss. Are you goin' to sell some stock?"

"Good morning, you two old *hombres*," replied Gene, cheerfully. "Yes, I'm selling two thirds of my cattle. What's your angle on that, Danny?"

"Like it, Boss. If the price is goin' up, as Nels figgers, why by the time we can round up an' drive to the railroad it ought to reach thirty-five dollars a haid."

"Shore it will," drawled Nels, as he sipped his coffee. "Danny figgers he has aboot seven hundred haid, probably more. An' he aims to sell half of them."

"Boss, with a lot fewer cattle we can keep count better an' mebbe stop this queer rustlin'."

"Who's doing it?" demanded Gene, angrily.

"I'm damned if I know. I'm shore afeared, though, thet some of my wife's lazy kin are mixed up in it some way."

"Ahuh. So Nels said. That ought to be easy to correct."

"Yes? How'n hell can I hang her relatives?"

"Danny, we don't need to hang them. Just stop them."

"An' you knowin' greasers for thirty years! . . . Gene, we're growin' dotty in our old age."

"Let's pull out of it, Danny."

"I'll drink on thet."

"Nels, I can see you've got it all figured out for us. Spring it pronto."

"Mighty simple to me," rejoined Nels, thoughtfully. "Hire a couple of rattlin' good cowboys. An' with you an' Danny an' the *vaqueros* heah you can do the job in a week."

"Hire two good cowboys, eh? Where? How? What with?" queried Gene, spreading wide his hands.

"Sech ain't to be had, Boss," declared Danny, hopelessly.

"Wal, I've an idee," went on Nels. "Gene, you an' Danny open the store while I clean up heah."

Gene took the key with its buckskin string attached, and accompanied by Danny went out by the long-deserted bunkhouse, across the green toward the store. He could hear the whistling of Madge's horses beyond the corrals.

"Danny, I'd closed up this store long ago but for Nels," said Gene.

"Aw, Boss, you can't do thet. Why, it'd kill the old feller. An' the store ain't runnin' at a loss, is it? All the Mexicans deal with Nels."

"Yes, and they owe him plenty. He must restock. And I just can't go deeper in debt."

"Hell no! We'll do somethin', Boss. I'm afraid we're down in the mouth. As if I didn't hev enough to pester me without thet girl of mine!"

"Bonita?" queried Gene, quickly, with a chord of sympathy.

"Yes, Bonita. Boss, I'm damn ashamed to confess it, but I'm afeared she's a no-good little hussy. After all your wife has done for Bonita—educatin' her—makin' a lady out of her—why, she's jest cussed."

"Danny, what do you mean?"

"Bonita has the *vaqueros* nutty. But she doesn't give a damn for one of them. She's white an' she runs with the white. Ren Starr, you know, was turrible stuck on Bonita. But her flirtin', mebbe wuss, I don't know, queered her with him. She goes to town every chanct thet comes along. She drinks an' Lord knows what. I ought to beat the hell out of her. But I jest can't. I love thet kid like I loved her mother, Bonita, long ago. You remember, Gene, 'cause you saved Bonita for me."

"Yes, I remember, Danny, old pard. It's tough sledding now for us old boys, who can't figure the present and this younger generation. . . . I've a daughter of my own, Danny. An' she's due home today or tomorrow."

"Majesty comin'? Aw, thet's grand! Why, Boss, she'll put the life in us. I'm sure glad, Boss. This time you gotta make her stay home."

"Make her?—Danny, didn't you just admit you couldn't do anything with Bonita?"

"Sure. But what the hell has thet got to do with Madge?".

"I suspect these girls are precisely the same."

"Lord help us, Boss!"

Gene unlocked the rickety door of the old supply store and threw it open. The shelves were almost bare. Some print goods, gaudy in color, and glass jars of pink and yellow candy, and gewgaws for children, and a spare supply of tobacco and cigarettes were about all the stock left for Nels. In the wintertime he sat beside the old stove, to smoke his pipe, and feed billets of wood to the fire; and to talk about the past when, at rare intervals, somebody dropped in.

"Always makes me think we're living in the past," said Gene, coming out to join Danny.

"Aw, Boss, don't talk as if it was all over," returned Danny. "We got a future."

At that juncture Nels appeared behind them, his free clinking stride belying his white locks. As he was about to step up on the porch he halted, his keen blue gaze fixed beyond the village, far down on the range.

"Look!"

Gene sighted a streak of yellow dust tailing out behind a motorcar. His heart swelled up in his throat to check his utterance.

"Car. Comin' hell bent fer election!—Boss, doesn't thet remind you of Link Stevens when he used to drive Madeline's white car across thet sage flat?"

"Yes. I've never forgotten Link. A great cowboy who could no longer ride! He loved to drive and scare us all stiff. But, Danny, it's a cinch Link would turn over in his grave if he could see *that* car coming."

"I should smile. Makin' seventy miles an hour. On thet road. My Gawd, some fellers have nerve! He's young an' don't give a damn fer his life!"

"Wonder who it can be?" queried Gene, under his breath. "Important telegrams, I'll bet. Hope it's not bad news. Nels, have you a field glass handy?"

"Don't need none, Gene. Thet's Majesty!" rang out Nels.

"*Madge!* . . . Say, can you see? Or is it one of your hunches?"

"Both. . . . Look at thet car streak along! Gene, it shore ought to make you feel as young as it does me."

"Young! Man alive, it makes me a doddering old man," replied Gene, thickly, and he sat down to relieve shaky legs.

Somehow he knew that reckless driver was Madge and he wondered why he had not grasped the fact at once. At the same instant he had a resurgence of pride in the girl's spirit and ability. She could drive—she could ride a horse like an Indian—she could do anything.

"Nels, what color is the car?" asked Gene, whose eyes had grown dim.

"Color of a coyote, I reckon. Gene, she had two cars heah last time, both of them black, if I recollect. . . . Dog-gone, but it does my pore heart good to see Madge eatin' up the miles like thet."

"Nels, you always were an inhuman monster, a bloody gunman," declared Gene. "How do you suppose it makes *me* feel to see my only child risking her life that way?"

"Boss," interposed Danny, impressively. "You an' me hev a common cause. Nels has no feelin's. I reckon we oughta git drunk."

"You said it, Danny."

"Say, you fellers air blessed among men," put in Nels. "Both got purty daughters an' you rave aboot yore troubles! I wisht to Gawd they was both mine."

"Boss! Did you see her take thet wash? Must hev forgotten it."

"I'm looking, boys, but I can't see very well."

Nels had walked to the end of the porch. Gene could make out only the streaking dust-comet, blurred in his sight. Yet that appeared to grow magically closer.

"Gene, she's off the wust of the road. Be heah in a few shakes of a lamb's tail. . . . It's a low open car—shiny—with a long front—a nose like them staghounds Madeline used to have."

Presently car and rising dust disappeared under the slope.

"Heah thet drone? All the same airplane," shouted Danny.

Gene heard and thought that his ears had never drunk in such sweet music. Madge—his kid—his little girl—his second Madeline—come home for good! He heard Danny babbling in his old cowboy manner, and then Nels let out a: "Kiyi!" The drone gave place to hum and then a mellow roar. Then like a flash a tan car shot into sight, passed the village, to turn left at the fork of the road, and speed out of sight up the knoll into the green foliage.

"Shore, I oughta reckoned on thet," said Nels to himself.

"Boss, I'll be waitin' home when you come down," added Danny. "Welcome Majesty home fer me."

"Nels, I think I'll go up."

"Wal, I should smile. . . . Tell her my heart ain't as strong as it used to be," drawled Nels, with a hand on his breast.

That jest in earnestness troubled Gene Stewart as he made his way up the knoll. The years were flying by. This homecoming of his daughter seemed to mark an epoch in his life and Nels', too. The old cowboy had no kin; he did not remember his age and he could not have worshiped Madge more if she had been his own. Gene fought a disloyal and disturbing thought about Madge. If she turned out to be wild and flighty, undutiful! . . . But he conquered the incipient fear. As a child she had been warmhearted, loving, imperious and willful as her mother had been. Gene expected to find Madge bewildering, and he walked slowly up the shady path, seeking to prepare himself for he knew not what. His steps, however, led him inevitably up to the house, through the great arch into the patio and on toward the east wing. Before he stepped into the flagstone corridor he heard a strange voice, swift and high-pitched, sweet and happy. That would be Madge. She was with her mother in the living room. Gene took some long strides to reach the wide doorway. He saw Madeline in her big armchair with the girl on her lap.

". . . Mom, darling, I am wild with joy to be home. I have forgotten nothing. I am drunk with the sage. I am. . . ."

And then Gene stepped into the room. They heard his step. The girl raised a lovely face, flushed and radiant, with great violet eyes that were wet and dim. Gene knew her, yet he did not know her. This Madge had golden hair.

"*Dad!*" she cried, poignantly.

"Yes—if you are—Madge," he replied, a little huskily.

She sprang up, taller than he remembered her, and not so slim, to rush at him arms spread. She threw them around his neck, and swinging free of the floor she hugged him tight. "My handsome Dad! My *El Capitan*! . . . Oh, how—good to see—you!" And with kisses and incoherent words she at last let down her feet, to lean upon him breathlessly. As Gene gazed down, his breast congested and his utterance clogged, he saw that her long dark lashes lay upon her cheeks, and tears were streaming from under her lids.

"Madge, is—is it really you?"

"Yes, Dad—your bad chicken come home to roost." And she opened eyes that were like her mother's, only a deeper, darker blue, exquisite in their soft and misty lights. "Darling! You've changed somehow. Lines I don't remember. . . . And this white over your temples!—Mom, what has grieved our *El Capitan*?"

"Dearest, the years leave their marks," replied Madeline, her voice not quite steady.

"I think he's handsomer. Can you find me a lover like him?"

"Lord forbid, Madge!" laughed Gene. "Now stand away and let me look at you."

She revolved for his inspection, like the models in fashion shows, and from the crown of her golden head to her suede shoes she appeared to be the ultimate in grace and beauty, in vivid and intense pulsing life. Then her eyes, wide upon him, brought back the child and the girl to prove this lovely young woman his own Madge. It was a profound and moving moment for Gene.

"Madge, my girl. It is you, yet not you. I recognize your eyes, your look, your smile. All else is strange—especially *this*." And he caressed a waving tress of her golden hair.

"Mom said almost the same," rejoined Madge, with a laugh. "Both of you have forgotten your darling."

"Not much," said Gene.

"Madge, once your hair was chestnut, like mine before it darkened," added her mother.

"Well, honey bunches, we will waive that question. But really I am disappointed. I was sure you'd fall for me hard."

"Daughter, if you are one hundredth as good as you are lovely, I shall be the happiest father in all the West."

"Dubious, but eminently satisfactory." Then with striking suddenness she changed from gay to grave. "Let's get it over, my darling Mom and Dad." It struck Gene that she addressed both of them but looked at him with eyes no man on earth could have doubted. "You had my letters and wires. I hope you did not see the L.A. papers. . . . I was expelled from college, in disgrace. It was hateful—the publicity. I'm sorry I couldn't graduate, for your sakes. For mine, I don't care in the least. I learned all they gave me and yelped for more. I was secretary of the student body and I'm a Phi Beta."

"What does that mean, Madge?" asked Gene.

"Why Dad!—To belong to the Phi Beta is one of the highest honors any woman can attain in college."

"Dearest," murmured Madeline, "that makes me happy indeed."

"Madge, what did they expel you for?" queried Gene, stern despite his emotion.

"Dad, I was indirectly to blame for a riot between the students and the police."

"Indirectly? Does that mean innocently?"

"It certainly does."

"Okay. Tell us what came off."

"I like to drive fast and I didn't pay overmuch attention to laws and rules," rejoined Madge, frankly. "I never had time to poke along slowly. Several times I received tickets for speeding. Once after that I was in a rush and the officer who caught me happened to be the same one. Well, he was a sap, swelled on himself, and by making eyes at him and telling him he wouldn't pinch his little co-ed, or some such rot, I kept him from taking me to court; he said, 'I'll be seeing you, sweetie,' and the next time he saw me he was fresh. I cut him dead, of course. One afternoon I was driving up to college and saw him coming up alongside. That time I was not exceeding the speed limit. Nor did I forget to put out my hand at the corner, but he accused me of that. He followed, calling for me to stop, which I did presently along the side street halfway down the campus. It happened in between classes, and there were students everywhere. Some of my friends were right there when I stopped. They heard my argument with this policeman. And did they take my side? Students came running from everywhere. Then I noticed a young fellow in the front line, and at first took him for a student. There were two policemen in this car and a motorcycle cop came up. Both officers got out, and the mean one stepped on the running board of my car—told me to move over—that he was taking me for a ride. Then the students rushed a vegetable truck, and loading up with tomatoes and oranges they just swamped that police car. The motorcycle cop called out the reserves, and the dirty bum of a policeman who had been to blame for this—he actually laid his hands on me—to push me out of my seat. Then this young fellow I mentioned, socked him in the stomach—a terrific wham! The officer began to fold up. Did I get a kick out of that? Then my champion laid him out in the street and leaping into my car told me to step on it. We left the mob of reserves and students having a swell fight. When I got out of the crowd I *did* step on it. We escaped. . . . That's all, Dad, except the board of directors expelled me and the officers forgot to come and arrest me."

"It doesn't strike me as so terrible," replied Gene, with a reassuring smile. It was certain Madge had no idea she had done the least wrong. "What do you think, Madeline?"

"Madge was rather thoughtless and indiscreet."

"What became of the young man?" queried Gene. "I'd like to shake hands with him."

"So would I," flashed Madge, her eyes lighting up. "I drove him downtown, to a parking place where we chatted. He was the handsomest fellow. Shy. He had no line at all. Oh, I liked him. Made a date with him to meet me right there the next day. But he didn't come, the idiot! Instead, oh, never mind—that was all of that."

"If you don't feel badly over it, why should we?" asked Madeline, happily.

"Then we'll forget it. I think you are both darling. I'm going to make up for my long absence by loving you to death."

"Madge, we can stand some loving," returned Gene, fervently. "Are you really going to stay home now?"

"Dad! Don't look so wistful. Oh, how I have neglected you both! But you wanted me educated. You've had your way. I am, and how!"

Neither Madeline nor Gene could resist a laugh.

"You will stay home with us—at least once in a while?" asked her mother.

"Forever, darling. I'll have my friends come to see me. I wired you to expect a crowd after graduation. What a place this ranch is to entertain city tenderfeet! I'll have the time of my life."

"Madge, the ranch—is run down," said Gene, hesitatingly. "Hardly fit now for your friends."

"But, Dad, it's so western, so Spanish. I adore the atmosphere of years and leisure. Before I left L.A., I bought three truckloads of stuff. Everything under the sun. Mom, I hope you like my modernistic taste. I'll refurnish my rooms, and all those in the west wing. Oh, it'll be swell."

"Only three truckloads!" ejaculated Gene, with a smile at Madeline. He had to laugh. His daughter was amazing, electrifying. He felt shot through and through with new life. The flush on Madeline's lovely face was pleasant to behold. "What about your baggage?"

"My car outside is full. And I expressed ten trunks and a lot of bags. They will be at Bolton today. The other stuff comes by freight. I do hope soon. We have only two weeks to get ready for my crowd. . . . Dad, will you carry in my truck? I brought you both presents galore, when I can unpack. Mom, are my rooms ready?"

"They are clean, my dear, and exactly as you left them."

Gene went out in front, conscious of varied emotions. A good deal of the happiness that possessed him was the pent-up delight Madeline had betrayed.

"Gosh! No wonder this car could travel!" ejaculated Gene, sizing up the magnificent machine, new, glittering, apparently all engine. The back seat was packed full of bags and parcels. And there were three beautiful coats, one of them fur. All about the car and its contents reminded Gene of Madeline Hammond when she had first arrived at El Cajon, which was now Bolton. Like mother, like daughter! Still could Madge ever adjust herself to the changed times? She had a fortune but she could not squander her principal. Aunt Helen, wise in her vision, had seen to that. But Madge's income now could not support her present extravagance. Gene thought of these things and many more, in the fifteen trips he made with Madge's baggage. On the last she and her mother met him in Madge's sitting room.

"Mom! Why should you apologize for my rooms?" Madge was saying. "They are just swell. I wouldn't change them. Of course the furnishings are rather dingy and old. But I anticipated that. . . . I'll paint these walls."

"You'll what?" asked Gene, incredulously.

"I'll paint them. I bought the paint and brushes."

"You learned that in college?"

"I certainly did. See here, Dad Stewart, you give me a job I *can't* do?"

"You're on, Madge. . . . I'd like, though, that you'd run down to see Nels."

"Nels and my horses! Oh, am I happy? . . . Where's my purse? I don't want Nels to see me such a sight," she babbled. Finding the purse she sat down to open it and take out something shiny on a chain. From this she extracted a powder puff, with which she powdered her nose. This act was performed deftly and while she talked to her mother. But when she took out a small metal tube and began to paint her lips with it,

Gene observed that she was careful and quiet. Her lips took on a hue still more scarlet. Madge, bouncing up, encountered her father's nonplused gaze, and she burst into mirth.

"Why do you do that?" he asked, curiously.

"You old range rider! Why do you suppose?"

"I've no idea, unless you imagine it makes you prettier. Nothing artificial could do that."

"Dad, don't you fool yourself. I just could. I'll make up really for you some day. It's an art. . . . I suppose, to answer you, that the custom grew popular through motion pictures. The most beautiful stars are those who have the artistry, or do their making up under experts. . . . Mom, would it interest you to know that I had an offer to go into the movies?"

"Yes, of course. But it wouldn't surprise me."

"There was one studio hot after me. It turned out that I had met some official or director at some function, or the Grove, I forget which. He talked me deaf, and phoned the house until I told him where to get off. I was interested, of course. Any girl in the world is keen about the movies. I'd like to have taken a fly at it. But—I decided it would cost more than I'd pay."

"Cost? Why, I read about the big salaries the companies pay their stars."

"Oh, Dad!—Mom, isn't he a darling old dumbbell? . . . I'll be back right away to unpack." She ran out, her high heels clicking.

Gene stood there, smiling quizzically at Madeline. Presently he heard the slam of a car door and the burst of engine.

"Dumbbell? I suppose I am. Por Nels and I are in for hell."

"Gene, I'm tremendously relieved. Whatever college and city may have done to her these four years she is wholesome and sweet. And oh! so lovely!"

"I liked the way she looked when I spoke of Nels. . . . Maddie, I think, if she's got a heart, we can stand anything."

"Be assured then, Gene, and relieved as I am. She is warm-hearted. She loves us. She loves—this home."

"Why, Madeline! You're crying. . . . At that I feel sort of—weak myself. Our little girl come home—grown up—a woman! I never saw a princess, but she's one. I'm so proud of her I could burst. . . . Wife, I forgot to ask you. Don't you think we ought to patch up the telephone system to town? The wires are down in places. And there are other things." Whereupon Gene went over with her the talk he had had with Nels and Danny Mains. After that he proceeded to the room Madeline and he used as an office, and there he read neglected mail, carefully studied books, and figures that always were Greek to him, and wrote some important letters. Madge's coming had seemed to fire his energy, to make a break in the old *mañana* habit of mind he had fallen into, and to stimulate his determination to see this climax of hard times through. To Gene's surprise he was called to lunch before he had any idea the morning had passed.

Madge met him as he entered the living room, and he halted in sheer amazement. She looked like a slim boy.

"Madge, what kind of a riding outfit is that?" Evidently his reaction to her appearance gave her delight.

"Dad, I have on slacks. Don't you like them?"

"Daughter, I'm afraid I'll like anything you wear," he replied, putting his arm around her.

"Against your better judgment, yes?"

They entered the dining room, which appeared brighter than for many years. The sunshine sifted through the foliage over the open window. There were roses and Indian paintbrushes and sage in the vases. Madeline had celebrated the occasion by gracing the table with white linen and some of her old silver and china.

"Swell to be home!" exclaimed Madge.

"Disappointed in—anything?" asked Gene, haltingly.

"Not a thing. The ranch had gone to hell when I was home last. But I didn't mind the tumble-down corrals and sheds. Fits the range. But the big barn must have a new roof. . . . Dad, it gave me a shock to see Nels. I think he has failed a little. But he is the same old darling. I was so overjoyed to see him that I forgot my horses. Fancy that? Then the luncheon bell rang. I had scarcely time to change. This afternoon I'll get into riding togs, just to please Nels. What do you think he said, Dad? . . . 'Wal, Majesty, the only things aboot this heah ranch thet ain't gone daid is yore hawses. Me an' yore *vaqueros* hev seen to thet.' . . . Oh, I love to hear the old Texan talk."

"Yes, your horses are okay, Madge," replied Gene. "I hope Nels didn't talk too much."

"He couldn't keep anything from me. . . . Dad, I've known for a couple of years that your financial situation was not so hot. Mom told me when I was home last. And of course I've read about the depression going from bad to worse. Just how bad is it for you?"

Madge's direct query and the gaze that added more to it were not easy to meet.

"Pretty tough, Madge—but I'd rather not confess just what a poor businessman your dad is."

"Gene, it is not your management of the ranch," interposed Madeline. "You made it pay expenses until the bottom dropped out of everything."

"Madeline, that's darn good of you," protested Gene. "But it's not so. We had too much money and too many cattle. For ten years we ran behind, a little more every year. Then came the crash. . . ."

Gene hesitated, spreading wide his hands, looking from wife to daughter. Nels was not the only one who would find it difficult to lie to Madge Stewart.

"I get it," she said, soberly, dropping those penetrating eyes. "I've always understood Majesty's Rancho was mine. You know, just in a vain and playful way, perhaps. How about that, Dad—seriously?"

"Of course this ranch is yours—or will be someday, which is just the same. And a white elephant—my daughter."

"Not for little Madge. What do you suppose I went to college for? What did I study economics for? . . . Dad—Mom, I tell you I'm home for good. I'm crazy about my home. It has been swell to have unlimited money. Let me play around this summer—entertain my friends—then I'll hop to the job."

Chapter Four

IN THE afternoon Gene rode out on the range toward Bolton with one of his half-Mexican riders, Manuel Mains, son of Danny, the only one of Danny's four youngsters that Gene thought was worth much. Bonita, the eldest, was distractingly pretty, to be sure, but that seemed to be a bad thing for the girl.

Gene wanted to find out how many telephone poles were down on the short cut of the line across the valley and over the ridge. From that point on in to Bolton, both the survey of the line and the necessary repair work could be done by truck. Manuel and he met some horses later, and the sum of their report was an agreeable surprise to Gene. Less than a dozen poles were down and there was only one break in the wire. Several days' labor, after the new poles had been snaked down from the foothills, would put the telephone in working order again, which Gene saw was important in view of Madge's return and the activity presaged for the summer. Then it would be very necessary to go over the road and make that safe for automobilists. The problem of help occupied his mind. That, added to his other difficulties seemed an insurmountable fact, yet somehow, Madge's presence counteracted it, and made that afternoon sojourn in the colorful and fragrant sage as pleasant as it was serious. Riding back he thought that he could not succumb to gloom and hopelessness.

Manuel turned off at the village to get his supper. Bonita, whose sharp eyes always saw everybody and everything, waved a red scarf at Gene, as if he had been a cowboy with whom to flirt. Gene waved back at her. Despite her deviltry, she was lovable. "Gosh! there'll be young fellows in Madge's crowd," suddenly exclaimed Gene. "What Bonita will do to them! But I'll gamble on her."

It was almost sunset when Gene turned his horse over to Jose. He saw Madge's golden head blazing from the top of the pasture fence. Nels' white locks appeared brighter by contrast. They were watching Madge's horses, which no doubt had been turned loose. Gene, about to join them, was deflected by the sight of a strange rider coming down the lane. Instead Gene proceeded to the square where one of the *vaqueros* and some Mexican boys surrounded a black horse in front of the blacksmith shop. Gene ascertained that the horse was lame. He examined the leg, which proved not to be badly sprained, and upon rising he saw that the strange rider had arrived. Gene's first glance at the handsome young man in his flashy cowboy attire occasioned him some amusement. A forerunner of the range contingent that inevitably would throng there to see Madge!

The rider got down, and introduced himself, saying bluntly that he wanted a job. Gene looked him over, favorably impressed. He seemed under twenty-five, tall and lithe, powerful of limb and shoulder, and he had a strong open countenance and fine hazel eyes, medium dark and very penetrating. His black horse would have been an asset for any cowboy.

Gene read a letter of recommendation from Ren Starr, and it was not many moments till he liked Lance Sidway's looks, his words, and had given him a job on the ranch.

Meanwhile one of the lads had taken the black horse down the lane for a drink. Gene anticipated results from that procedure and he was tinglingly prepared for Madge's ecstatic squeal. That girl had cowboy blood in her. Then Gene, with malice aforethought, sent the unwilling Sidway in Madge's direction. They met, so precipitously that Madge ran into Sidway and almost fell out of his arms. Astounded, plainly stunned for an instant, Madge's vivid face suddenly flashed radiance. Recognition and rapture were evident in her speaking eyes.

"*You!* . . . Oh, if it isn't my hero!" she cried in intense excitement. "Of all the surprises I *ever* had! You darling!" And with swift action that matched her voice, she lifted her gauntleted hands to Sidway's shoulders and rose on her tiptoes to kiss him warmly. Evidently she had aimed at his lips, but she missed them, leaving half of a red bow to the side.

Gene, utterly astonished as he was at his daughter's impetuous action, yet did not fail to catch the reaction in the boy. When she ran into his arms he gave a violent start and uttered a gasp. Then at her words of surprise and delight, followed by that impulsive kiss, his face turned a dusky scarlet. It receded as she drew back until he was pale.

"My God! . . . You? . . . Not *you!*"

"Yes—me!" she replied, sweetly.

"You can't be—be Stewart's daughter?" he implored. "You can't be Madge—not Majesty Stewart!"

"I am. And you know that, you clever devil," she returned, in positive admiration. "You put one over, didn't you—meeting me *here*? No crowded noisy parking place for you, Mr. Oregon. You wanted to keep that date here, at my home, on the Arizona range. Romantic—individual—beautiful! I figured you perfectly, my campus champion. I knew you weren't ordinary. And almost I can forgive you for not keeping that date."

"I—I did keep it," he gulped.

"You did?" she echoed, her violet eyes wide and dark. "Then you didn't disgrace me by being the first fellow ever to break a date with Madge Stewart?"

"I came—Miss—Miss Stewart," replied Sidway, still overcome. "I was there—long before you came. In a car. . . . I saw you drive in. Then that—that fellow followed you. . . ."

"You saw him—heard us?"

"Yes, I was quite close."

"Why didn't you jump out and let him see you were my date? He would have acted true to type—and you could have socked him, too. I'm afraid you lost a golden opportunity."

"I'm sorry, Miss Stewart," he said, in awkward though sincere regret. "But I was—sort of paralyzed. I never got over it until after you drove away with him."

"Then I do forgive you. What is your name?"

"Lance Sidway."

She touched his arm and turned him toward Gene, who had leaned against a post, taking it all in. Gene had no idea how he looked, but he felt highly amused at this clever ruse of Sidway's.

"Dad, isn't it just darling?" said Madge. "This is my hero—the young man whom I told you and Mom about—who rescued me at the campus riot. . . . Lance Sidway—my father, Gene Stewart."

"Madge, we haven't been introduced, but we've met," replied Gene, genially, and he eyed Lance as if he had been taken in a bit.

"Of course. How silly of me! He just rode in and you . . ."

"I gave him a job," interposed Gene.

"What? . . . To ride for you!—He is a fast worker. . . . Lance Sidway, I don't know just what to make of you."

"That goes for me, too," replied Gene, with a smile which softened the doubt.

"Mr. Stewart, I am on the spot," burst out Sidway. "I told you I'd never met your daughter—never heard of her till I met Starr. How could I guess she was that one? . . . I did meet her—as she told you. . . . I'm innocent of . . ."

"Sidway, don't take it so hard," went on Gene, kindly. "I was young once. It didn't turn out just as you planned. But I'd have liked you better if you'd told me . . ."

"I did not lie to you," declared the cowboy, with such vehemence that Gene began to feel sorry for him. Then Madge claimed Sidway's attention.

"I get you, Mr. Lance Sidway. But I've been kidded by experts," she said, with laughing eyes. She was pleased with his subterfuge.

"Yeah? You get what?" he demanded bluntly, and it appeared that his awkwardness was vanishing.

"What is so obvious."

"Miss Stewart, it may look obvious that I knew who you were—that I deliberately rode out here because of you. But it is not true."

"Oh, so you are ashamed to be caught?" she taunted. "You're a pretty smooth actor, cowboy, but you can't fool little Madge."

"You may be pretty smart but you're wrong this time," he retorted, and there was plainly resentment in his tone.

"Let's skip it," she returned, without the archness. And at that moment Nels, and the lad leading Sidway's horse, came around the corner.

"Nels, shake hands with Lance Sidway," interposed Gene, glad to relieve the growing strain between the young couple. "He hails from Oregon. And I've just given him a job."

"Howdy," drawled Nels, and shook hands with the flustered lad. Gene was of the opinion that Sidway had no conception how he was being looked over by the keenest eyes in Arizona. Gene's conclusion was that the cowboy showed up favorably in a most trying situation. When Madge saw the black horse again, her swift reversal of mood eased the situation. Like a true range rider she walked around the black, all eyes, placing a careful yet confident hand on him, and never saying a word until she had made a second circuit.

"Nels!" she importuned, as if wanting him to refute her judgment.

"Wal, I'm shore sorry, lass," drawled Nels. "He's a grand hawse. He's got Cedar beat all holler."

"Traitor!" she flashed, her eyes blazing purple fire at Nels. "You're teasing me. Nels darling, you don't mean that?"

"Wal, mebbe I'm exaggeratin' some. But see heah, Majesty. Even if you been away from the range so long, you know a great hawse when you see him."

"I'm afraid I do. . . . Mr. Sidway, will you *please* let me get on him?" Her query to the cowboy was tinged with slight sarcasm, yet her desire was deeply sincere.

"Of course—if you wish. . . . The stirrups will be long."

Madge swung gracefully up into the saddle and Nels beat the cowboy to her side. Presently the stirrups were laced up to fit Madge and she walked Umpqua across the green square, trotted him up the lane a few hundred yards, paced him a little and loped him back. What a picture the black horse and the golden-haired girl made! Turning away from the sight himself, Gene saw it in Nels' worshipful eyes, and then he caught a gleam of the eternal cowboy in Sidway's.

Madge sat the saddle as if reluctant to get off, while she patted the arched glossy neck. She was flushed of face. Her eyes were soft, glowing. At that moment Gene experienced the old fullness of love for her in his heart. She was Madeline's daughter, but she was western. Presently she sat up in the saddle, the glamorous spell vanished, and she faced the three men coolly. Gene imagined he could read her mind.

"His trot does not equal Cedar's, but his pace and lope beat that of any horse I ever rode."

"Wal, lass, thet's strong praise from you," declared Nels. "Justified, I reckon."

"Madge, never go back on your own horses," warned Gene.

"I don't, Dad. But I must be just. . . . Mr. Sidway, do *you* know how fine Umpqua is?"

"Me!" ejaculated the cowboy, amazed. "Nobody can tell me anything about him."

"I'll bet I can."

"Go to it."

"What'll you bet?"

"Aw, the truth is I haven't anything. Of course I wouldn't bet Umpqua."

"No? Oh, you're a cowboy. You might some day," she returned, subtly. "Umpqua reminds me of something I read—that an Arab chieftain said. I didn't have to commit it to memory. It just stuck in my mind . . . 'If in the course of your life you alight upon a horse of noble origin, with large lively eyes wide apart, and black broad nostrils close together, whose neck, shoulders and haunches are long, his forehead, loins and limbs broad, his back and hip-bones and pasterns short, all covered with soft skin, fine hair, and his lungs wide and powerful, and his feet good, with heels high off the ground—hasten to buy or trade or steal that horse—secure him, and always afterward bless Allah for your good fortune!' "

"Wal, if thet doesn't beat me," said Nels, in rapt admiration.

"Madge, you've the high sign on us. But it was good," added Gene.

"You win," chimed in Sidway, reluctantly smiling.

"It seems superfluous to ask—can he run—is he fast?" asked Madge, tensely.

"He can beat your Cedar or any other nag you own."

"That remains to be seen, cowboy," returned Madge, darkly.

"What's more," went on Sidway, "he's the best cowboy horse ever bred in Oregon."

"Now yore talkin'," said Nels. "An Arab is no good to us riders, onless he's a cow-hawse."

"Nels, Umpqua can run over rocks as if they were level ground."

"I seen that from his hoofs."

Madge slipped slowly out of the saddle, facing Sidway: "No need to ask how you love Umpqua," she said, with a softness rounding the turn of her words. "You won't take it amiss if I—almost insult you?"

Sidway stared at her, and then with something of a gallant gesture he repudiated any possibility of her doing that.

"What value do you place on Umpqua?" she launched, suddenly keen, vibrant.

"Value! . . . None, Miss Stewart."

"Every horse has a value. Tell me."

"Diamonds, rubies, gold!"

"Swell! I like you the better for that. . . . Do you know that you could sell him for five thousand dollars?"

"Humph. A movie star offered me that," returned the cowboy, contemptuously.

"Yeah? . . . I'll give you six thousand for Umpqua."

"No."

"Seven thousand."

"No."

"Eight thousand."

"No!"

"Ten thousand!"

Sidway's flushed face turned pale, either with anger or some other emotion.

"Miss Stewart, don't you know that money can't buy everything?" he queried, with dignity. "Umpqua is all I own in the world. He has saved my life twice. I love him. We raised him from a colt, and all of us loved him."

"I know I'm rotten," she cried, as if forced. "But no matter. I love him, too."

"That's well. I'm glad you do. But—you can't buy him."

"I always have what I want," she flashed, imperiously.

"You probably have had."

"But be reasonable." Madge stamped her booted foot until her spur jingled sharply. Tears of vexation and disappointment burned out of her big eyes and they glowed and dilated like mystic balls. "You admit you're broke. I offer you a small fortune. You can get a start here on the range. Dad and Nels will help you. I will. You can still go on loving Umpqua. You may ride him—sometimes. You can make me happy. Please, Mr. Lance Sidway."

The cowboy gazed at her, listened to her eloquent appeal as if fascinated by something beside and beyond her offer.

"Really, Miss Stewart," he said, finally. "You may be Gene Stewart's daughter, born on this wonderful range, but you don't know cowboys."

Madge betrayed that she could not gainsay that, and it seemed a struggle went on in her between realization and selfishness. The latter evidently conquered. Anger at herself for being so little or at him for frustrating her desire burned out that momentary softness.

"You won't sell him?" she queried.

"I told you—no."

"Mr. Sidway, I can't have you riding around here on a finer horse than—a horse that I want."

"That'll be just too bad," returned the cowboy, in a tone which brought a hue to her cheeks that matched the carmine on her lips.

"You appear to be rather dense. Do I have to tell you I will not have you on this ranch?"

"You don't have to tell me anything, lady. Your father hired me and he'll have to fire me."

She looked at Gene with great luminous eyes. "Dad!"

"Madge, you're unreasonable," replied Gene, coolly, smiling upon her. "I need riders badly. Sidway has offered to ride for me at a wage I am ashamed to take advantage of. I couldn't discharge him just because he refuses to sell you his horse. Could I, Nels?"

Nels showed plainly that he was between the devil and the deep sea. Madge had been his especial joy and treasure all her life, as Gene well knew, and he had always spoiled her. Gene enjoyed his old cowman's extreme discomfiture, but knew he would extract himself somehow.

"Majesty, I shore know how you feel aboot this hawse," he began, in his slow drawl. "But, lass, you're bound to respect Sidway for his feelin's. I reckon you wouldn't be playin' the game if you fired him. Shore I never heahed of you bein' unfair. You used to give hawses to cowboys. An' I reckon, if yore happiness actooly depends on ownin' Umpqua, wal, in the nature of things on the range, you know, he'll jest naturally drift yore way."

The persuasive cool voice of the old cattleman, the significant content of his last words, spread oil upon the troubled waters.

"Very well, Mr. Sidway, you stay," said Madge, loftily. "I'm sorry if I was unfair. But I will have that horse."

The dark passionate glance she bent upon Sidway had infinite and unknown possibilities.

"Thank you, Miss Stewart. But I do not want to remain under false pretenses. You will not have Umpqua."

"I accept your challenge. If you don't show yellow and ride off—we'll see." Then she smiled upon him without malice or resentment, and wheeled to start up the path.

"Hey, Madge, you're forgetting your car," called Gene. "What'll we do with it?"

She turned to call back in a sweet high-pitched voice: "Mr. Lance Sidway can use it to bed down his darling Umpqua." Then she was gone into the foliage.

"Whoopee," sighed Gene, and Nels came back with: "Dog-gone, old pard! Seems like old times when you fust came to Majesty's Rancho, before thet lass was borned."

Sidway had been lengthening his stirrups with swift hands. Presently he turned with pale face and hazel eyes shadowed.

"I'll be on my way. Thank you, Gene Stewart," he said.

"Hold on, Sidway. You wouldn't let my daughter's taunt. . . ."

"No, it's not that, altogether. I know you didn't believe me—that I didn't come here on—on Miss Stewart's account. And under the circumstances I don't want to stay."

"No, I didn't believe you," rejoined Gene, seriously, searching the troubled face.

"See heah, cowboy," interposed Nels, descending from the porch with clinking slow steps. "Don't ride off hot-haided. Air you on the level? You didn't know this was Majesty's Rancho an' thet the lass you done a favor for in Los Angeles was Madge?"

"Nels, I did not," replied Sidway, forcibly.

After a keen scrutiny of Sidway's face the old cowman turned to Gene: "Boss, he's tellin' the truth. Don't let him go."

"Hanged if I don't believe it myself."

"Stewart, I swear that I am on the level. I didn't know. It was just an infernal coincidence," rejoined Sidway huskily.

"Okay then. Let's shake on it. . . . Maybe your infernal

coincidence will turn out well for me and this ranch problem. I've a hunch it will."

Sidway appeared too poignantly affected to voice his manifest relief and gladness. Gene's conviction was that the young man felt too strongly for the mere misunderstanding. There was more behind it. Gene liked this cowboy, and that Nels did also added a good deal of satisfaction.

"What'd you say yore fust name was?" drawled Nels.

"Lance. It's screwy, I know. Bad as Umpqua."

"Not so orful bad. . . . Gene, yore supper bell has rung. I'll look after Lance. He can hev supper with me, an' the bunk room next to mine. . . . Whar'll I hev Jose put his hawse?"

"Not in the pasture tonight. Better in the barn. . . . Say, wouldn't it be funny if we could bed him down in Madge's car?"

"Not so damn funny in the mawnin'."

Dusk was settling under the pines when Gene mounted the slope to the house. A ruddy glow faded over the peaks in the west. Coyotes were wailing somewhere low down. Plodding up the low ascent, Gene was revolving in mind the events of the day. He had to side with the cowboy against Madge. She was willful and spoiled. That came out when she could not have her own way. He recalled the tone of her voice, her imperious look, her temper; and he shook his head sadly. But what could have been expected of the girl, their only daughter, adored and petted, born with a gold spoon in her mouth, and left a million when she was fifteen? But Gene reflected that despite these faults she seemed to be irresistible. If only one or more of his own besetting sins did not crop up in her! The cowboy Lance was in love with her—there was no doubt about that, even if he had not found it out yet. Gene, remembering that Madge had always had what she wanted, was heartily glad that Sidway had been strong enough to brook her will. He had good stuff in him, that lad. Gene's yearning for a son, long buried, had a rebirth. If Lance Sidway turned out as fine as he promised he would come somewhere near the ideal Gene had dreamed of.

By the time Gene had washed and changed, the second supper bell rang. He found Madeline and Madge waiting. The girl wore white, some clinging soft stuff that made Gene catch his breath. He thought of what little chance he had or Sidway or Nels, or any man, to resist this lovely and bewildering creature. Not a trace of the recent mood showed on her face.

". . . and he wouldn't part with Umpqua, the sap!" she was saying to her mother. And as Gene entered she extended a hand to him with a radiant smile. "Dad, I'm telling Mom about my hero and his wonderful horse. What a liar he is! He found out who I am and where I lived. I can't get what possessed him to deny that. He needn't. It was a clever stunt. Intrigued me. After I fell so hard for him that day he rescued me! . . . Well, I fell for his horse a thousand times harder. Oh, Mom, what a beautiful horse! Has it all over Cedar and Range and Bellefontaine—all of them. I wanted Umpqua so badly that I could have murdered the cowboy. . . . At first I had a kick out of it. Never occurred to me that I couldn't buy the black. But it turned out that I couldn't. Then I lost my temper. I'm afraid I reverted to feline type with claws out. Did Mr. Sidway jar me? I'm constrained to admit that he did. Made me feel selfish, mean, rotten. Which I was. But I'd do worse to get that horse. And all the time I was so mad I had a sneaking respect for Lance, though I hated him. He's just swell, Mom. Don't you agree, Dad?"

"Rather cottoned to him myself," replied Gene to this long monologue.

"So did Nels, the traitor," she retorted.

"I am indeed interested to meet this paragon among cowboys. And see his Umpqua," said Madeline, with a smile. "Madge, in the succeeding days of trial I might be of service to you. I've had some experiences!" Madeline threw a laughing glance at her husband.

"Mom darling!" expostulated Madge. "Falling for Mr. Sidway doesn't mean a thing in the world. I've done that nineteen times this last semester. . . . But will I give that big boy a ride? It'll be a kick. And I'll have that horse if—if . . ."

"Well, if what, my girl?" taunted Gene.

"If I have to *marry* him."

Madeline neither reproved her nor showed surprise, but she remarked that cowboys must have vastly more than horses to be eligible for marriage.

"But I could divorce him next day," Madge flashed bewilderingly.

Next morning Gene was out early enough to catch Nels and Sidway at a sunrise breakfast.

"Wal, look who's heah," drawled the old cowman. "Mawnin', Gene. You ain't got oot this early fer years."

"Neither have you, old-timer," returned Gene, jocularly. "Shall we put it down to our lately acquired cowboy, Mr. Sidway?"

"You shore can. The son-of-a-gun kept me up till eleven o'clock tellin' stories, an' then, by thunder, he rustled me oot before sunup."

Manifestly Nels and the newcomer had gotten along famously. Sidway appeared fresh and eager, and having donned his old outfit, he looked a lithe and striking rider.

"Don't call me Mr. Stewart," Gene replied to his greeting. "I'm Gene, or Boss, or Stewart."

"Okay, Boss. I sure appreciate falling in with you. And I'm asking if I may have the day on my own."

"On your own? What do you mean?" inquired Gene, puzzled.

"If you give me the day, I'm pretty sure I can tell you where your cattle have been rustled lately."

"Gene, he made some such crack as thet to me," drawled Nels. "Jest young hot blood. But I don't know."

"Sidway, are you hinting that you can find out what Nels and I and Danny Mains couldn't?"

"No, I'm not hinting. I'm telling you," replied the cowboy, with an engaging smile.

"You don't lack nerve," returned Gene, shortly.

"Boss, I don't mean to be fresh. I just think you men have been hunting for rustlers in an old-fashioned way."

"Old-fashioned?" echoed Gene, while Nels ha-ha'd vociferously.

"Listen, young man, rustling is rustling. Cattle don't fly. They have to be driven. On their hoofs. And hoofs leave tracks."

"Only so far. I'll bet you tracked yours as far as a macadamized road, and no farther."

"Yes, that's true. Or I should say, Jose and Manuel tracked them."

"Then what?"

"Wal," interposed Nels, "Them two riders split an' rode east and west fer twenty-odd miles, an' never found the place where them hoof tracks left thet highway."

"Swell!" ejaculated Sidway, clapping his hands. "That's exactly what I wanted to be sure of. Saves me the trouble."

"Of what?"

"Bothering with tracks *on* the highway. They never left the highway short of Douglas or Tucson."

"Listen, son," returned Nels, his drawl more pronounced than ever, and very patient. "Shore you're talkin' to a couple of old cowmen, oot of date, an' I reckon pretty dumb, as you youngsters say. Will you talk a language we know? These heah modern days air hell on speed, shore, but cattle cain't be drove on a cement road fer hundreds of miles."

"Sure they can. It's a cinch. Your cattle *were* so driven."

"Dog-gone!" complained Nels, turning to Gene. "An' I was kinda takin' to this lad."

"Nels, he's got something on us," declared Gene. "See here, Lance, just how were my cattle driven along the highway?"

"Simple as a, b, c.—In trucks."

"*Trucks!*" burst out Gene, incredulously.

Nels swore, and dropped one of his galvanized utensils on the floor. "Gene, it's shore simple. But we'd never guess such two-bit rustlin' of twenty or forty-odd haid would be done thet way."

"Well, I'll be damned. Sidway, how'd you find that out?" added Gene.

"I've seen inside one of these cattle trucks. Fact is I drove one of them," explained the young man.

"Yes? Wal, I reckon you'll be tellin' us next you're one of these newfangled rustlers," drawled Nels, dryly.

"I might have been without knowing, if the truck had been loaded. . . . On the way over here to Arizona I went broke at Douglas. Hung around for any kind of a job. Well, it came along, and it was to drive a big canvas-covered truck to Tucson. I was paid a hundred bucks, and told to expect to be held up somewhere along the road. I was held up all right a little ways out of Tucson, by a gang who expected just what I'd figured out—that the truck was full of booze. But it wasn't—and were they burned up? These highjackers corroborated my suspicions. . . . All right now. To come short with it, by figuring, and asking questions I found out that a string of trucks go through Douglas east about once in six weeks. Presumably they go east loaded with bootleg liquor and come back west loaded with bought or stolen cattle. My hunch is that this gang used to buy cattle for a blind to their real operations, but finally turned to rustling. Just easy money! . . . On the other hand it may be that only one of the trucks is loaded with booze, and possibly it may come west, along with the cattle. We can safely gamble, however, on this—that your cattle have been stolen in this manner."

"Wal, what air we comin' to?" ejaculated Nels, scratching his white head. "Gene, shore we can look forward to be robbed by airplanes next."

"Fake rustling, likely," added Gene. "What'd the money for a few cattle mean to these bootleggers?"

"Nothing to the big shots," rejoined Sidway. "I've had a hunch that maybe the drivers of these trucks are grabbing a little money on their own hook. What I want to find out now is *who* drives the cattle to the highway. That'd have to be done on horses. . . . Boss, give me some idea where these last cattle tracks were made. I'll ride out and see if I can pick up some horse tracks. If I do I'll measure them, make sure I'll know them again, and then ride all over this darned range."

"Fork your horse and hit— No, let Umpqua rest. Tell Jose to saddle Range for you."

"I'm on my way," replied the cowboy, and he strode out of Nels' bunkhouse. Presently he passed off the porch carrying his saddle and accessories.

Nels went on wiping his utensils. Presently Gene said: "What do you know about that?"

"Gene, that feller proves how much old-time cowboys like us want to figger on new angles. Since the war, you know, we've jest been goin' back. Smart, this boy Sidway. If we only had Ren oot here now!"

"Yes. We know Ren Starr," replied Gene, ponderingly.

"Gene, did you ever know me to be fooled aboot a cowboy?"

"You mean his being straight? . . . I can't remember one, Nels."

"Wal, if this Oregon lad can ride an' shoot, he'll be a Gawd-send to you."

After that encomium from the old cattleman Gene felt himself convinced. He talked a while longer with Nels, went to the store with him, and presently set about an inspection tour of the barns and sheds and corrals, the reservoir, the lake, the irrigation ditches, the fences, and all pertaining to the ranch. He had divined that Madge would be coming to him presently and he wanted to be well posted. This survey was a melancholy task. He saw now why for years he had neglected it. In some degree verdure around the water hid the rack and ruin of the wooden structures. Those built of adobe were also damaged. And in fact repairs were badly needed everywhere.

Upon returning to the store Gene found Madge there with Nels. She wore overalls, high-top boots and spurs, and a blue sweater with a red scarf. The mere sight of her flushed and disheveled, and clad as she was, chased away Gene's gloom.

"Mawnin', Dad," she drawled. "I caught Nels drinking red likker."

"She did, at thet," admitted Nels, ruefully. An' I'm darned if she didn't ask me for some."

That was a touchy point with Gene, which he passed by. "How'd you find your horses?" he asked.

"Cedar wild as a March hare. Bellefontaine as sweet as ever. Range was gone, and I learned from Jose that our new cow hand took him," returned Madge, and the dangerous tone of the last words were not lost upon Gene. He hastened to explain that he had told Sidway to saddle Range.

"Oh. . . . What's the matter with your own horses?"

"Sold most of my saddle stock. Your horses are fat and lazy, Madge. They need to be worked out."

"Indeed they do. That was okay, Dad. I thought Mr. Sidway, seeing he is so fresh, might have taken Range on his own. . . . Dad, his horse Umpqua came right to me. Oh, I was tickled pink. He likes me. I'll have no trouble winning him from his owner. And will I do it?"

"Madge, that'd be a dirty trick."

"So it would be. But I'm crazy about the horse—and Nels said I couldn't do it. Added fuel to the flame! . . . Besides," she pouted, "Nels has fallen for that cowboy in a most unaccountable way."

"So have I, Madge."

"*Et tu, Brute,*" she returned, reproachfully.

"I can account for it in more ways than one. Let me tell

you just one. . . . First thing this morning he told Nels and me how we had been losing stock so mysteriously."

"How?" she queried, suddenly intent. Gene liked that instant response.

"Driven away in trucks. That was a new one on us. It floored Nels. Sidway . . ." Here Gene briefly told her about the cowboy's experience on the trip over, and how swiftly he had put two and two together. "He's gone off down the valley to get a line on horse tracks."

"I told you he was a regular guy," declared Madge, enthusiastically.

"Yes, you did. But it turned out—you don't like him," said Gene, casually.

"Unfortunately, it did. You saw me kiss him. I was just delighted. If it had not been for him I'd have had to go to court. . . . But my feelings don't matter. If Sidway doesn't start something round here he may be a big help to you and Nels. Between the two of us, we will put this ranch on its feet."

"Wal now, lass. What you mean—start somethin'?" interposed Nels, greatly interested.

"Nels, you old spoofer. You know what I mean."

"He's already started somethin' with thet hawse."

"I'll say. But I meant particularly what invariably happens to fresh cowboys when I'm here."

"Ahuh. An' thet poor devil will hev to go draggin' himself off withoot his hawse—an' his heart."

"Nels! You're the same old darling!" she cried, gleefully as she left them. Presently she turned a happy face over her shoulder. "Dad, it's swell to be home!"

"Oh! that's good, Madge. It's sure swell to have you."

Madge looked in at the open shed where they had parked her car, then crossed the court and disappeared up the path. Gene observed that Nels' eyes had never left her while she was in sight.

"Gosh! . . . Nels, I wouldn't be in that poor devil's boots for a lot."

"Wal, you jest bet I would," averred Nels. "If I know cowboys, this Sidway feller will give Majesty a run for her money."

"Humph! He doesn't strike me as the fortune-huntin' breed."

"All cowboys air fortune hunters. You was, Gene. An' if I remember you, old *El Capitan*, this Oregon boy has you tied fer all 'cept drinkin' hard an' shootin' hard. I reckon no *hombre* ever beat you at thet."

"Nels, you're a sharp old rascal. I've relied upon you for years. But let's not get sold on this stranger so pronto."

"Wal, I'm sold now—same as Majesty is. Reckon it'd be a good idee for you to keep yore haid."

"Madge sold on Sidway?" ejaculated Gene.

"Shore. Only she has no idee atall aboot it yet."

"You romantic old geezer! . . . It'd just suit you now—if Madge would take to a man of our kind, wouldn't it? . . . Well, to be honest, I'd like it, too. But I think that's only a dream. Madge will marry some city man, tire of us and our simple life here on the open range—and go for the fleshpots of Egypt."

"Natural for her Dad to hev sich pessimistic ideas. But ump-umm!"

"Why natural?" demanded Gene.

" 'Cause you reckon she has inherited a lot of yore no-good blood."

"Right again, old-timer. I am afraid."

"Thet lass will turn oot like her mother. But I ain't sayin', Gene, thet we won't hev hell with her before she turns oot."

During the afternoon Gene persuaded Madge to drive him up the old road toward the foothills, where was located the big spring that fed the lake and provided irrigation for the ranch. As the road was rough they did not get back until toward the end of the afternoon. Passing through the little Mexican village, the inhabitants of which had once depended solely upon the ranch, Gene said to Madge: "Thanks, daughter. You're almost as good a driver as you are a horseman. I'll stop off at Danny Mains' and walk home from there."

"Oh—oh!" said Madge, presently. "Look who's here."

Then Gene espied Sidway, on foot, leaning on the gate talking to Bonita Mains. Range, bridle down, stood near by. There was no more denying the cowboy's demeanor than Bonita's delight. The dusky-eyed maiden radiated charm and coquetry. That Sidway was not in the least embarrassed by their arrival somehow gave Gene a tingle of expectancy and satisfaction. The car stopped. Gene stepped out.

"I'll wait, Dad," said Madge, lightly. "No need to walk home when you can ride. . . . Bonita!—*Buenas tardes.* How are you?"

"*Buenas tardes,* Miss Stewart," returned Bonita, shy and flushed. "I am so happy to see you. Welcome home to Majesty's Rancho!"

"Thanks, Bonita. I'm glad to see you. Introduce me to your boy friend. . . . Oh, it's Mr. Sidway. I thought I knew that horse. How'd you like him?"

"Not so much. He's cranky, contrary. Spoiled by girls, I expect," replied Sidway, coolly.

"That's fine. I'd rather you didn't ride him."

Gene spoke up: "Bonita, please call your father." And as the girl flashed toward the house, Gene turned with interest to Madge and the cowboy. She was quietly lighting a cigarette. But Gene had never seen her eyes as magnificent as now. Sidway, however, had stepped away from the gate to bend eagle eyes down upon the sage.

"Boss, look at that car," he said quickly. "Hitting only the high spots!"

Gene espied a speeding black car appearing to run away from a long trail of dust.

"He's sure coming," agreed Gene, puzzled. Drivers did not race on that rough road for nothing.

"Hope it's my mail," spoke up Madge. "I left orders for it to be sent out."

At that juncture Danny Mains came out, his homely weatherbeaten face wrinkled in a huge smile. Gene called his attention to the car. Mains took one look and then said: "Darn fool'll break his neck, ridin' like thet."

Then he greeted Madge and the cowboy. Bonita, bright-eyed and self-conscious, came out to join her father and gaze down the slope.

"Ren Starr!" she cried.

Gene was quick to detect a note of fear stronger than the surprise in her exclamation. Sidway must have caught it too, for he turned a narrowed gaze upon the girl. Then the group watched the racing car until it passed out of sight under the slope. Bonita, with troubled face, left them to enter the house. Gene, attending to Danny's speculation about Starr still had an ear for a byplay between Sidway and Madge.

"Awful pretty girl—this Bonita," the cowboy was saying.

"Swell kid. On the make, too. But am I telling you?" retorted Madge.

"You appear to be. I didn't get that about her."

"And you such a fast worker— Well!"

"I—I like your horse," went on Lance, evidently no match for her at repartee. Her voice had a cutting edge.

"But you said Range was cranky."

"Sure. Can't a fellow like cranky horses—and girls, too, for that matter?"

"I don't know anything about such fellows."

"Yeah? I'll bet what you don't know wouldn't fill a book. . . . When is your college crowd coming?"

"Oh, you are interested? My sorority sisters, I suppose?"

"No. . . . Just the crowd. When? The time?"

"That can hardly concern you, Mr. Sidway. But they arrive on the twentieth."

"Thank you. I wanted to know because I'd like to help your father a little. Then I'll beat it."

"Oh!—I get you. Dad thought you had taken to him and the ranch."

"I had. You see, I just left Hollywood. I was fed up on a lot of glamour gals and pretty boys. And I'm leery of a college outfit."

"Indeed. Mine would not embarrass you, Mr. Sidway. Certainly my girl friends do not aspire to collect cowboys."

"Yeah! Too slow, I suppose. Prefer gangsters, eh?"

"*What?* . . . You insulting . . ."

"You can't kid me, Miss Majesty Stewart. . . . Listen, let me tell you something while I've a chance. Your dad is swell. A grand guy. And if you were a credit to him you'd not have this crowd of yours out here now."

"Oh!—And—why?" gasped Madge, as if stifled.

"Because he's in trouble—deep—without your fast crowd to make it worse."

At that moment the humming car sped over the brow of the slope to draw swiftly up to the waiting group. The driver was Ren Starr. As he stopped, Gene espied the tip of a rifle barrel sticking above the door, and in the back seat a pile of duffel, topped with a saddle and bedroll.

"Howdy, folks," he said, laconically. "Heah we all air."

"Wal, Ren, you look like bizness," returned Danny Mains, soberly.

"Glad to see you, Starr," added Gene.

"Boss, you got another new cowboy. Right heah an' now. . . . Ah, Miss Majesty, I shore am glad to see you back home. Hope it's fer good. . . . An' heah's my new pard, Lance Sidway."

"Darn glad to see you, Starr," rejoined Sidway, eager and puzzled.

"Gather around, Gene an' Danny. You'll get an earful," announced the newcomer, and as the three leaned over his car he whispered, directly to Sidway: "Pard, yore trucks rolled in no more'n a couple of hours ago. Stopped at the big garage acrost the street. I got most damn curious. An' when the six drivers mosied into the lunchroom I went round aboot to peep into the trucks. *Empty!* . . . Graves, the new hired hand at the garage, was pilin' up, gas, oil, water, air. And he give it away thet the trucks was stayin' over, mebbe all night. Like hell they will! Pard, these air yore canvas-covered cattle-rustlin' trucks. Them drivers air timed fer tonight. Gene, they're gonna make one of them two-bit raids on yore cattle. An' I'll tell the world they're gonna get a helluva jar."

Gene swore under his breath, and feeling a handclasp on his arm, he turned to see Madge, pale, with dilating eyes of purple fire, close behind him.

"Wal, you gasoline hound!" declared Danny Mains. "Back on the job."

"Starr, you've more hunch than that. Spill it," said Sidway.

"Shore. I seen a rider—stranger—who'd been hangin' aboot all day—go into thet lunchroom. He was the go-between. An then I beat it fer heah."

Chapter Five

MADGE's unexpected encounter with Uhl at the parking place, where she had failed to find Sidway, made her abruptly conscious of the fact that her indiscreet affair with the gangster had lost its interest for her. She admitted this to herself while concealing her annoyance from Uhl. Her impulses were quick and she gave in to them daringly, up to a certain point. But she was just as keen to divine when a new one had superseded the old. She did not even have to see Uhl to realize that the man she expected to meet had effaced the fascination of the strange, cold-eyed and masterful gangster. Looking at Uhl, listening to him, Madge felt relief that this was so. She regretted her short flirtation with him. And presently it occurred to her that the thing to do was to get him away, drop him somewhere, and then come back.

"Jump in, Honey Bee," she said, brightly. "I'm too late for my date here and must rush back to campus. Where can I drop you?"

"But, baby, you can't flag me that way," retorted Uhl, getting in beside her. "I know where there's a speak close. Let's have a drink—and a chin."

"Indeed, I'm sorry, but I simply haven't the time. I can't even run you downtown. I'll have to drop you at the first streetcar corner."

"Me ride on streetcars? That's a kick. . . . What's the dope on this newspaper stuff about you this morning?"

"Damn tough break! I wasn't to blame for that campus riot. But I'll tell you. . . . Say, Thursday. Give me a ring, and I'll meet you," said Madge, and she slowed up and halted on a corner.

Uhl left the car ungraciously, plainly against his will. That steely something about him which had appealed to Madge did not affect her again.

"Yeah? I've called you twice and nothing doing. That doesn't go with me, sweetheart. I don't wait on no girl."

"Perhaps you've found me a new species, as I you," returned Madge. "Sorry. Bye. I'll be seeing you."

"She'd better be," Madge heard, and then she had flashed across the intersection. The dumb cluck! Whatever had possessed her to let him sit down beside her that day at André's? Madge reflected she was not so much to blame as Dixie Cune. But before she had circled several blocks to get back to the parking place she had forgotten Uhl. Then, half an hour late, she drove to the rendezvous, and did an unprecedented thing —she waited half an hour longer for this Oregon boy who loved his sister and his horse Umpqua. Not until Madge thought of how long she had waited, how much she wanted to see him again, did she realize that her weakness for new faces, new adventures, had in this instance established an extraordinary parallel. How nice he was! How different! And evidently he had not felt that way about her. Madge suffered a new sensation akin to pique, and that melted into disappointment. Here was one fellow who would not call her up to make a date. He did not even know her name. Why had she not told him and the phone number of the house? Nevertheless on the way back to campus her injured feelings were assuaged by an inexplicable premonition that she would meet him again.

Fraternity Row appeared to be more than usually crowded with cars. All the houses had several parked out in front. Madge pulled into the driveway and ran into the living room. All her senior sorority sisters, except Maramee, were there, with two boys from the Tau Phi house. The circle did not, as was its wont, let out a whoop as she entered. They all looked pretty glum and their greetings were forced. Madge now prepared for the worst.

"That sharp-voiced boy friend of yours just called up, Madge. Uhl's the name. Has he a string on you?"

"I was foolish enough to let him think so," rejoined Madge. "You all look like death's-heads. What's the worst? I can take it?"

"Majesty, I just came from campus," replied Rollie Stevens. "They've called a meeting for tomorrow morning. Looks like curtains for you."

"I met the Dean just now," said Pequita Nelson, reluctantly. "She is afraid—because you already were on probation."

"Madge, if you hadn't pulled so many stunts this semester!" exclaimed her roommate and her closest friend, Allie Leland. "They'll hate to expel you—at this late date—graduation right at hand—and you an honor student. But ever since you were elected in your junior year you've ——"

"Don't heap it on, Allie. . . . I've been a damn fool. But I had a lot of fun. For myself I wouldn't care—much—only it'll reflect on the house. And if Dad and Mom see the papers —Oh, that'll hurt. . . . After all, I didn't egg on the students to throw that party."

"I can vouch for that, Majesty," admitted Rollie gloomily. "I did. I collected some of the boys and we went to the President. He was swell. But . . ."

"Rollie, that was darling of you. I'm obliged. If it were up to him I'd come through. Mad Everett, however, has it in for me. . . . How about a bull session this time tomorrow? About my ranch party. . . . Rollie, be sure my boy friends come."

"Humph! In that case we'll have to hold your session in the chapel. You couldn't park them here."

"Rollie Stevens, I said my boy friends," retorted Madge.

"Am I one—or just a messenger boy?"

"You're number one, when you're nice."

"It was never obvious to me, Majesty. . . . Then I'm to page Barg—Dawson—Nate—Brand?—Here my judgment, not my imagination, halts shrinkingly."

"You left out Snake!" protested Madge.

"That muscle man?—Majesty!"

"Yeah? I get you. But I like him. I wonder if I have a horse that can hold him up."

"It'd take an elephant," chimed in Allie.

"But, Majesty," importuned Pequita, eloquently. "Will footballer and cowboy mix?"

"We've got to have something beside drinks and dances," averred Madge, and then she thought of her champion. "If I had only had a chance to ask *him*!"

Rollie threw up his hands and departed, and presently Madge and her roommate were upstairs on the third floor, in their light colorful room.

"Who's him?" asked Allie.

"Him!—Why the wonderful fellow who slugged the cop and saved me from being pinched."

"Hadn't heard of him. Madge, you can dig up more romance and more trouble than any girl on campus."

"Rather a doubtful distinction, Allie, darling. If they expel me I'll have to think about myself at long last."

"They won't. Why, they'd be afraid the senior class would walk out on them!"

Dinner that night was not the usual merry gathering. Madge seemed the only cheerful girl in the house. She felt a thickening atmosphere of disaster. Her friends knew, perhaps, what she could only anticipate, and they were stricken. Soon after supper Madge phoned to break an engagement and went to her room and presently to bed. When Allie came in and crept into Madge's bed and into her arms to weep unrestrainedly —then Madge made certain of the worst. She did not sleep well until late. At breakfast she missed the girls. Summoned to the office on campus she went with her chin up and her face tranquil, but inwardly she felt a little sick. She had an interview with the Vice-President, and it was short. The directors of the college had expelled her. They had to take into account the fact of her former derelictions and that she had been on probation. To overlook this last escapade would be establishing a precedent that would have a very bad effect. Madge accepted the decree gracefully, without a word of self-defense, and left the embarrassed official to go out, and cross the campus for the last time.

For her own sake Madge did not care particularly. She was tired of college, and traditions, such as graduating and receiving a degree, had never held any significance for her. She felt she had absorbed everything that this university could give her that would ever have any meaning in her life. When she crossed the row she did not look back at the campus, and knew that she never would again.

Nevertheless, up in her room alone Madge shed some bitter hot tears. She had loved that room, and to realize its intimacies, its joys and sorrows, its plans and stunts, were over forever struck her with her first deep grief. But in an hour Madge, to all appearances, was her old self again, and had turned her facile mind upon the problem ahead of her.

There was trouble out in her Arizona home. Long ago she had sensed that. And it was high time she returned there to take up the burden, whatever it was, for her beloved parents. Madge knew she was going home to stay. A trip now and then to the coast, and perhaps an occasional one East, would suffice her. Before she had come to college the lonely range, the stately Spanish ranch house, the horses, and her lovely soft-spoken, stately mother, and her stalwart father, had filled her life with action and excitement and love. Now that she was a woman, they would be all the more to her. And somewhere there was a man like her Dad . . . but she dismissed that disturbing thought.

Allie came in at the lunch hour to disrupt Madge's concentration on a long-considered task, that of making a list of things to select and order for the ranch. Once given up to that occupation, Madge found it absorbing. "Honey," she begged of Allie, "fetch me up some food. Anything."

A long while seemed to have elapsed when at four o'clock

Madge tripped downstairs, in a new and striking gown, to meet the bull session. Rollie had them all there, even to the hulking Snake Elwell, whose rosy cherub-like visage for once wore an intelligent expression. As Madge stood in the wide door the faces of her friends flashed expectantly and tragically at her.

"Friends, Romans, Countrymen—don't look like that!" she cried, gayly. "It's over. And I can take it! . . . I've asked you all here to talk over my cherished dream—to have you out to the ranch. Do I need to sell the idea to any one of you?"

"*No!*" came the concerted reply.

"Okay then. Here's the dirt. I want you to arrive on the twentieth or as near that date as possible. There are eleven of us. Allie will come in my little car, Nate driving; unless darling, you'd prefer Brand?"

"Ow! Ow!" squealed Nate. "That is a hot one. Majesty, damn your honest tongue!"

"I'll match you for that honor," spoke up Brand.

"You're on—if you got a nickel to toss."

When that dire contingency was settled in Nate's favor Madge went on, consulting her notes.

"The rest of you can come in two cars, that is, by expressing most of your baggage. Jot this down . . . Bolton, Arizona. And ship your baggage three days ahead, so it will be there. . . . Rollie's big car for one. Dawson has one. And Snake, whose big bus is it I've seen you in—with a redheaded girl?"

"Madge, it belongs to Bu—and I can't get it unless I bring her along," said Elwell, awkwardly.

"Ha! Ha! Snake's on the spot," shouted Rollie.

"Well, he can't wiggle like a snake through this field," declared Madge, laughing. "Bu who?"

"Aw, never mind."

"Madge, it's Beulah Allen," declared one of the boys, sotto voce.

"That number!" ejaculated Rollie, aghast. "Swell kid, Majesty—but I'm afraid she would disrupt the sweet tenor of our Tau Phi constancy."

"You telling me?" retorted Madge. "I know Beulah. Snake, it's up to you. Do you want her, for herself and not for her car?"

"Go into a huddle, Snake," taunted someone.

"Madge, do you like Bu?" countered the athlete, earnestness stronger than his confusion.

"Certainly I like her, or I wouldn't consider her. But, Snake, if you're crazy about her. . . . Cowboys and *vaqueros* are even more susceptible than students."

"I'll take a chance, and Madge, you're a peach," declared Elwell, in red relief.

"That's that," said Madge, when the roar subsided, and she checked her list. "You can fight among yourselves who's going to ride with whom."

"Madge, sweetest, get down to it—Clothes!—What'll we need to wear?" burst out Maramee Joyce.

"Your ruling passion, Maramee, for once will be foiled. . . . We're on a ranch you know—grand place to wear out all your old clothes. Mostly outdoor stuff, both heavy and light; your riding togs and don't forget a bathing suit. In fact, girls, I want you—if you have to come without a stitch to your backs," declared Madge, warmly.

"Suits us swell!" yelled the boys. "And Majesty—" added Rollie, "we're tired of pink teas and cakes, you know."

"I'm sending over cases and cases," replied Madge, radiantly. And when the row had subsided she continued: "I can supply anything in the world but happy hearts. You must bring them.

"I've been hours on end making up lists. It'll take two full days to shop. Oh, some job! And then I'm off. No more dates. The sooner I go the better, dear friends. . . . That's my say—for my—last bull session!"

She fled in a silence that hurt.

Early and late for three days Madge shopped in the Los

Angeles stores. At night she packed, with Allie to help, and sometimes Pequita or Selma. What a relief when the expressman took her trunks away! At length all her tasks were done, even to the packing of bags in her car. Next morning when she awoke the sun was flashing on the vine-covered walls of the chapel. With Allie in her pajamas, Madge tiptoed down the stairs, passed the closed doors of her sisters, and hurried to the garage. Her last load of baggage was stowed away.

"Don't make me—cry—" she whispered, huskily, to the weeping mute Allie. "I've got to drive some. . . . Tell them all—good-by . . . darling—I'll—be—seeing . . ."

Madge drove out with blurred eyes that did not clear until she rounded the corner and turned her back to the campus forever. An early rising student halloed, but she did not look. The constriction in her throat eased as she threaded into the traffic. It was over—college and all that went with it. Madge did not deceive herself. All these lovely contacts would sever and fade away in the conflicting tides of new and wider life.

Not to press down on the accelerator seemed harder to resist than ever. In one of the suburban towns Madge stopped for breakfast and to send telegrams home. To her sorority sisters she wired: "All's well. I'll be seeing you." Soon then she faced the long orange-grove—and vineyard-bordered road, and here she drove the powerful car up to sixty along the straight stretches. Madge loved to drive, to speed, to feel the impact of wind, to see the narrow thread of road flash under her, and the blurred greens pass by. By ten o'clock she was in Banning, where she halted for fuel. The service man paid Madge and her car an admiring gaze.

A hot furnacelike breath waved into Madge's face up from the long Gorgonio Pass, as she left Banning. Once, however, under way again, the pressing air felt cool to her. At Indio she had a bite to eat and a malted milk, then leaving her car at a service station she crossed out of the copper sun to the shade of cottonwoods. These green full-foliaged trees, like the pines, were reminiscent of her ranch, and the ranges of the

West. Palms and orange trees belonged to California, somehow removed from Arizona. A sultry breeze blew off the desert, tinged with an acrid dust, that felt gritty to her moist hands. Gloves were almost intolerable, and the skin of her lips and cheeks felt drying up. Nevertheless she welcomed this dry heat. Soon she would be across the desert, up on the sage ranges of Arizona, where the air was different. The sun could shine down hot, but in the shade the air felt cool. Then in her beloved home state there was never that copper sky or the blurred distance which she saw now. San Jacinto stood up shrouded in heat; smoky veils curled up from the gray weed-spotted desert; the ragged line of the barren ranges stretched south to fade in the distance; the pale expanse of the Salton Sea gleamed in the hollow of the valley, its salty shore line ghastly and weird.

Madge walked a few minutes under the cottonwoods, despite the discomfort. The next two hundred miles and more would be the most trying of this drive. To traverse a long stretch of flat country below sea level was far from a joy ride in June. Madge, rested from nervous strain, went back to her car to resume her journey. From Indio to El Centro Madge reveled in speed and the rare delight of catapulting through space. Beyond El Centro, where she halted for a little while, sunset caught her in the dunes, those exquisitely graceful curves and mounds and scallops of sand, beginning to color with opal tints, and shadow darkly away from the sun. This five-mile stretch was the only one on the journey that she longed to acquire for Arizona. Through that stately region Madge drove at a snail's pace, and rediscovered her love of color and symmetry and solitude. She felt like a Navajo at sunset, part of the nature she watched.

When dusk mantled the black lava point of Pilot Knob, and dim purple Picacho, Madge sighted the lights of Yuma and soon the broad Colorado, chafing in sullen flood away into the darkness of a bend toward the south.

In a few more minutes she crossed the bridge into Arizona,

and drove to the Alcatraz, a new hotel where she had stayed coming and going on her visit home the preceding summer. Her head and eyes ached, and her body was stiff from the long drive. And hungry and thirsty as she was she enjoyed the luxury of a bath and change before going downstairs. Apparently there were only a few guests at the hotel. After finishing a light dinner Madge went out to walk up and down the street and send some telegrams. The night was sultry and warm, with no air stirring, but she required exercise more than comfort. She walked to a corner and back. Mexicans with sloe-black eyes passed her, and a group of the lofty statured Yuma Indians who wrapped their long hair in a coil on top of their heads and set a cake of mud upon it. The glaring twin lights of cars loomed and passed by. Madge did not succumb to an impulse to walk down to the main street. Yuma was fascinating at any hour, especially after nightfall.

A long black car had drawn up to the curb before the hotel. Madge, as she passed it, heard a low exclamation, then quick footsteps. A slim hand with fingers like steel clutched her arm.

"Gold-top, what you doing here?" called a sharp voice, cold as ice. Madge knew to whom it belonged before she turned to see Uhl, bareheaded under the electric light, his eyes glittering from his pale face.

"Oh!—hello—this is a surprise," replied Madge, haltingly, as her wits leaped to meet the situation.

"You alone?"

"Yes. On my way home," she said, slowly, fighting a confusion of thought. She did not like his look nor the hard clutch on her arm.

"Home! Say, what kind of a twist are you? Told me you lived in Santa Barbara."

"Did I? Will you be good enough to let go my arm? You hurt."

"Come for a ride," he returned, in a voice that brooked no opposition to his will and he almost dragged her toward the big black car.

"No, thanks," rejoined Madge, as, supple and strong, with one wrench she freed herself. "I'm tired. Drove all day. See you tomorrow."

"Like hell you will! Same as phone calls. I'm seeing you right now. Get that, baby!" He was neither angry nor insolent. His face had the clear cold chiseling of a diamond. Madge was not afraid of him, but she realized that she should be. She wavered between turning her back upon him and asking him into the hotel. The important thing was to get in off the street, and acting upon that she said: "I won't talk here. Come in for a moment."

Uhl hung close to her, hand at her elbow, and did not speak while they went through the lobby. He steered Madge into a back room with subdued lights, where several couples sat at tables, drinking. Here Uhl led her to a seat at a corner table and ordered cocktails from the attendant.

"What kind of a deal are you giving me, sister?" he began, forcefully, as he leaned toward her across the table. All about him was cold, suspicious, repellent.

"Deal?" she queried, playing for time.

"You knew I fell for you. I told you. And you met me, danced and drank with me. Then when I get stuck deep you try to pull this 'I'll be seeing you' gag. That doesn't go. See?"

"Mr. Uhl, I seem to see that you have misunderstood me."

"Yeah? Nothing doing, eh?"

"If you wish to put it that way."

He controlled what must have been a murderous fire, judging from the instant lowering of his blazing eyes and the quiver of his slim hands. Strangely, this reaction of his again restored a certain fascination he had exerted over Madge, she felt that it was almost an attraction of repugnance. She had had too much adulation, too many at her feet. There was in her, unconsciously, a primitive longing.

"Baby, I've gone nuts over some dames," began Uhl deliberately, apparently having suppressed his violent feelings. "But none ever held a copper to you. I'm horribly in love with you, sweetheart."

"Oh, I'm sorry you've allowed it to go so far," murmured Madge. "Any girl would be flattered and. . . . But, you see, I'm engaged."

"Yeah? What's that to me?"

"I can't imagine, I'm sure. But I know a girl can't accept serious attentions from one man when she's engaged to another."

"The hell dames can't. They do. They all do . . . Aw, Beauty, don't be such a plaster. I'm crazy about you. . . . If you're alone here tonight let me. . . ."

Madge felt his slim hand slide upon her knee under the table. His eyes, gray as molten metal had a hypnotic power. For a moment she felt paralyzed. Then her rigidity broke to a start, to a stinging heat, to an insupportable sensation. That tearing thing seemed to actuate Madge more than Uhl's outrage. In a fury she kicked out with all her might. And her onslaught sent the man sprawling over his chair. Madge almost overturned the table as she leaped up. Wheeling she fled from the room, and never stopped until she backed up against her locked door.

"Serves you damn—right!" she panted, passionately. "Playing with a heel like him! . . . Are you ever—going to think?"

Madge hardly had time to think then. Hurried steps in the hall preceded a knock on the door. Another knock, louder, followed, and the handle of the door was tried.

"Madge!"

"Who is it?" she called.

"Bee. Let me in. I want to square myself."

"I'll take your word for it—from that side."

"I was out of my head. I'll come clean. You're not like other dames."

"Thanks, Mr. Uhl. You discovered that rather late. But I take the blame for your mistake."

"Will you let me in?"

"No. I'm going to bed."

"That wouldn't make any difference to me. I want to talk to you."

"Well, I don't want to listen. . . . But I'll see you in the morning. At breakfast. Eight o'clock," she replied, thinking that might be a way to get rid of him.

"Okay, baby. But don't string me again."

Uhl's voice had an ominous ring that jarred unpleasantly upon Madge's ruffled nerves. Uhl was dangerous. Recalling his bragging, the roll of bills he exhibited, his extraordinary intimation of some kind of power, which Madge now analyzed as underworld, she realized that she might be in actual peril and by no means should she encounter him again. She determined to be a hundred miles and more beyond Yuma by eight o'clock next morning. Following that decision her first impulse was to telephone the desk to leave a call for five o'clock, but she thought better of it. She always awakened early, provided she went to bed early. This she did at once, and eventually fell asleep.

The roaring of a motor truck awakened Madge. She hardly seemed to have done more than close her eyes. Ruddy light on the desert ridges attested to sunrise. Her wrist watch said ten minutes to five. By five o'clock she was at the desk downstairs, paying her bill. She told the night clerk, in case anyone asked, that she had received a telegram which recalled her to Los Angeles. In another ten minutes she was speeding east on the Arizona highway.

The morning was fresh and cool. A line of fire rimmed the ranges. No cars, no curves on the empty black road ahead gave full rein to her desire and her need to drive fast. Sixty miles an hour had been her conservative limit, except a few times on short favorable stretches. Here Madge had the course and the incentive to increase her speed to seventy and more. The motor droned like a homing bee. It ate up the miles. At eighty miles on the indicator Madge tasted the last complete and full elation of the speedster. The telegraph poles were almost as fence posts.

Madge never looked back once. She drove under the urge that Uhl was pursuing her and that she could run away from him. At Gila Bend where the highway forked she slowed down and took the right branch, then opened up again. Mohawk, Aztec, Sentinel—the stations that she knew well were overtaken and passed by. At Casa Grande, while the car was being refueled and gone over, she had breakfast and lunch in one. From there Madge again faced the waving colored desert, with its black buttes and red ranges, ever growing rougher. But she took little account of it or of the hours. She was bent on a record drive. Tucson for once was not interesting, only as a service station; and the quaint Tombstone and bustling Bisbee only obstacles on the road. Late that day, which had flashed by like the hamlets, Madge drove into Douglas with the most perfect satisfaction for a driving mania she had ever experienced.

She stopped at an automobile camp, had her dinner at a lunch counter, and by eight o'clock she was in bed, her eyelids heavy. Her last thought was of what she would do on the morrow to the hundred-odd miles between Douglas and Majesty's Rancho.

Next morning she was on the way by six o'clock, after having breakfasted. She would have made the run to Bolton in an hour but for the fact that she was held back by a detour, and some heavily laden, slow-moving canvas-covered trucks that simply stuck to the middle of the road. They annoyed her so that she thought that she would not soon forget them, nor one of the drivers, a swarthy visaged fellow who glared at her when at last with incessant honking she forced him over.

At Bolton Madge tarried long enough to leave orders with the stationmaster about her baggage and freight due to arrive. Then she refueled again, and drove on, beginning to feel strangely happy—with the journey almost ended, with turmoil behind her, and rest and home almost gained.

But when she struck off the highway beyond the culvert, up the old rancho road, which proved to be annoyingly full of lumps and gutters and rocks, she passed from an amused impatience to a burst of temper. She endured the jolting and the messing of her baggage and packages for some miles, then she had to drive slowly. What an atrocious road! And she with a crowd of guests due in less than two weeks! How would three truckloads of purchases ever safely negotiate that trail for steers and cowboys? Did her father have that same old loafing bunch of *vaqueros*? She would hire a gang of Mexicans to make a decent road out of it pronto. It took Madge three quarters of an hour to drive from the culvert to the summit of the slope—approximately fifteen miles.

Madge, surmounting the slope, abruptly to face the vast purple valley, with its arresting black knoll topped by the gray mansion which was her home, and the grand uplifting range beyond, stopped the car to gaze as one in transport. How astoundingly familiar! She had only to see to realize that all these blue distances and splendid landmarks were veritably a part of herself. But absence and life too full for memory had come between them, and her thought and her love, now suddenly leaping to vivid and poignant life again. The morning was still fresh; shadows still lingered under the ridges; every wash and rock shone white; the waves of sage rolled on and on, in an endless sea, dotted with cattle; the league-long slope up to the knoll had a beautiful sweep; and there peeping out of the black pines, lonely and superb, stood the mansion of the old Dons. As a fitting background the mountains loomed impressively, white-slided and black-canyoned, upflung in rock battlements to the blue sky.

"Oh, darling, darling home!" cried Madge, in rapture and reproach. "I have been faithless. But I have come back. For good! Forever, to you—to my home—to the love and life I shall find here!"

The moment of exaltation was difficult for Madge, inasmuch as she had a vague realization that she was not big enough, not good enough for this noble country, nor for the devoted mother and father who awaited her coming. But she had a clear conception that if she were true to the emotion this magnificent scene had aroused in her heart, she would grow far toward being worthy of it. That thought persisted helpfully, too strong even for her misgivings.

She drove on. The descent into the valley afforded swifter travel. She had left rocks and ruts behind. Soon she was down to a level, on a white road, six inches deep in dust; and here she cut loose again with a shriek of joy, to shoot ahead of the yellow clouds that puffed up from the wheels. The wash in the center was sand and she hit that at a fifty-mile clip, to veer and leap and plunge, the wheel lurching under her strong grip, and roar safely across to another strip of dust. Beyond that the long slope of yellow road was like a country lane, with its two narrow wheel strips, its weedy center, its hard ground. Madge hummed up that, out of the grass and sage, into the pines, and on up the shaded brown-matted aisle to the green oval before the stately mansion.

And on the porch, telescope in hand, her eyes deeply dark with joy stood her mother. Madge pressed the brake so forcibly that the great car, answering with a grinding scream on gravel, stopped so suddenly that she and the bags had a violent jerk. Madge threw off gloves, goggles, hat all in one swift action, and leaping out she ran up the steps into her mother's arms.

They were inside, in the living room, and Madge, wiping her eyes was saying: "Fancy *me* being such a baby! But somehow it's different this time. Coming home! . . . Let me look at you, Mom darling. . . . Oh, the same lovely patrician mother!—But, darling, you *have* some gray in this beautiful hair—and a few lines I never saw before. But you're more perfect than ever!"

"Madge! How you rave!" exclaimed her mother, her voice low. "But it's worth a great deal to have you home—and hear you talk like that. . . . I hope it's not all—let me say, remorse."

"*Mom!* . . . Come, let's not stand all day. My legs are weak. . . . I'll sit on the arm of your chair. . . . There," and Madge slipped her arm around her mother and drew the handsome head to her shoulder. "I'm the little girl who has courage to confess—but who would rather not face her mother's loving eyes. . . . Let me get it over, darling. . . . You had my letters—my telegrams?"

"Yes, child."

"Well?"

"I understand, Madge. You need not tell me anything. I went to college once. And all these years you've been away—these hard and changing years—I've tried to keep abreast of the times, even if it was only through newspapers and magazines and books. Most of all, your letters have told me. I know what has gone on, what has come to pass, even if I have trouble grasping it."

"Mom, I knew you'd say that," replied Madge, earnestly. "But I doubt, Mother darling, that with all your intelligence and wisdom you could realize what has actually happened to us, to my generation. Somehow I can't get it. Yet they call me brainy, Mom. You'll get some firsthand information soon. My crowd of sorority sisters and student friends will be here to spend the summer. They are normal, as young people go today. They are all radical. But I'll let you judge them for yourself. . . . My self, Mom, this contrite daughter returned to you, is an enigma to herself. . . . I hate restraint. I won't be told what I should or should not do. I have no idea what I want, except that I want something terribly. I read trash where once I read poetry, history, fiction. I've read Freud and he's all wet. My favorite authors at present are Cabell and the best detective writers, wide apart as the poles. Most grown-ups give me a pain in the neck. But you don't, Mom! I am scared of Dad, though as a girl I worshiped him. He was my hero, my *El Capitan*, as he was yours. But will he get me—my crowd? . . . In my freshman year I went a little haywire—drinking, dancing, petting, smoking—*all*, Mom, except

I didn't go the limit. I tell you that, a little ashamed, as if I were an old-fashioned virgin. But college girls, except some who are fools, work out of that worst mess in their upperclassman years. Still the pace is swift, Mom, in education, achievement, in a social way, in the modern thing. . . . For young people that modern thing seems to be to break all the laws—speed laws, booze laws! There is no such thing as modesty, as I remember you taught it to me. Pagans, I fear! I haven't opened a Bible since my religion course during my sophomore year. Lastly, Mom, don't think that *all* co-eds fall under this category. There are loads and loads of girls besides. Only my crowd, and the other sorority crowds—they get by the college courses somehow, though a few like me gain class honors and high scholarships—only for these the aim and end of existence are cocktails, dances, clothes, cars and men. . . . There, Mom, darling, that's all. Will I dare tell Dad—and will he understand?"

"My dear," replied her mother, quietly, after a moment fraught with suspense for Madge, "I don't think you should tell your father—all that. . . . And there—his step in the patio!"

Her father entered, sending Madge's blood rushing back to her heart, still the stalking giant with the piercing eyes she remembered, yet somehow indefinably changed. Was it the white over his temples—the hollow cheeks and lean jaw? Then followed the greeting, the embrace, which made Madge mistress of that errant and incredible weakness, leaving only the resurgence of her girlish love for her ideal of all men. During the disposal of her luggage in her rooms, so thrillingly the same, and the luncheon afterward, Madge babbled on and on, listening but little, far removed from the honest girl she had been to her mother. She divined that she thirsted for something from her father—something she knew she had, beautifully and everlastingly, from her mother. But here was a Westerner, one of the old school, that daredevil *El Capitan* of the Revolution, the cowboy who had killed men! He had worshiped her mother, but would his love for his little girl survive all that the years and changes had made her?

After luncheon Madge leisurely unpacked her numerous bags and suitcases, stopping dreamily at intervals, or finding some excuse to go to her mother. During all this while the desire to see Nels and her horses grew stronger, until at length it was too demanding to resist. It need not have been anything to resist, if she had been able to put aside the strong desire to change to riding garb, and vault upon Cedar once more. Nels surely would not have liked her in these new English riding breeches, so tight and leggy, and that first day home she could not don overalls and boots. Wherefore at length she went down the old back road, now an overgrown trail, to gray ruin of ranch buildings and corrals.

Nels was her second father. He had taught her to ride, to shoot, to rope—all the tricks of the range. He had told her the terrible stories about her famous father, and that lovely and appalling romance of her mother and all about ranch and cowboy life, even before she was old enough to understand.

Meeting Nels proved to mean more, to be a deeper experience, than even her memories had anticipated. The change in him was not indefinable. Madge felt the warm blood recede from her cheeks. The years had told on Nels.

Not until she sat with him on the top bar of the corral fence to see her horses did the zest and stir of home-coming return. What a glossy, long-maned, plume-tailed, racy and thoroughbred troop of horses! Cedar, gray as the cedars for which he was named, pranced before her, soft-eyed, whinnying, high-stepping and sensitive, knowing her yet not sure. And Range, the long rangy sorrel, red as fire in the rays of the setting sun; and Bellefontaine, that dainty proud little mare, sure of Madge, poking her nose up for sugar; and Blackboy, like shining coal in his well-groomed hide, and Sultan, the roan, and Dervish and Arab, twin whites, as perfect as the movie horses, but not so tame. and Leatherstocking, a range cow horse, loved despite his plebeian blood, and Pinto, a mustang—all her own, and the corral full of shaggy jealous horses and colts, snorting and kicking—all of them brought home to Madge the stinging truth of her return.

But it was when she walked up the lane with Nels to encounter a Mexican lad leading a black horse that Madge's emotion flooded to a bursting pitch. A strange horse, a grand horse, dusty and lame, bearing a cowboy's accouterments, in one inconceivable flash, added a bitter drop to the sweet cup which she had just tasted. Screeching to Nels, importuning the lad, this got Madge nowhere. Full tilt then she ran around the corner of the store, straight into the arms of a clanking cowboy, gorgeously arrayed—a strangely familiar cowboy whose face went white and then a dusky red.

As if by magic Madge confronted her campus champion, and under this last straw her burdened feelings burst in glad amaze and gay delight, to a welcome she did not consider and a kiss she could not recall.

Could she have paid him a more flattering compliment for his cleverness in contriving to be there at her own home? In the following exchange of words, in this cowboy's well-simulated protest and confusion, Madge experienced a reaction which inwardly she divined was something more, something deeply and inexplicably glad. And that, at his denial, submerged this sweet self. What was the matter with the fool? To be sure there stood her dad, his piercing eyes hard to meet, and his slight amused smile disconcerting. But even so, Madge argued to her ruffled vanity, her welcome, her kiss should have inspired him to confront half a dozen fathers and confess his duplicity.

It was the horse Umpqua that saved the embarrassing situation for the moment, and which precipitated a really serious one. Madge left them, furious with the cowboy. She spied upon the group below from the covert of pines, curious even in her anger to see what Sidway would do. There was no doubt about the sincerity of his purpose, when he went to his horse. He meant to ride away. And would have done so but for her father and Nels. "Can't he take it, the big handsome stiff?" muttered Madge, in her angry surprise. "What'd he beat me here for *if* not to make a hit with me? It did! . . . And—I was hit before. . . . Oh, the dumbbell! To spoil it all! . . . Now I'll have to jolly him along and play with him to get that horse—when I really liked him . . . how much? . . . Am I burned up?"

By the time Madge had told the story, with reservations as to her own uncertain feelings, to her mother, her resentment had gone into eclipse. She could not bear ill will. And she had developed a merciless truth about herself.

"What is young Sidway like?" asked her mother, presently.

"Oh, swell!"

"That is rather an ambiguous term these days."

"Mom, I'd hate to spoil a pleasant surprise for you. Also I'd like to get your reaction to Sidway before I tell you mine. *I* may be—I must have been all wet, if you get what I mean."

"I don't, my dearest," replied her mother, with a bewildered smile. "But I'm sure you like him."

"Not on your life!—I did, yes. . . . The dirty look he gave me—what he said! . . . Such things just aren't done to *me*."

Madge leisurely changed for dinner, and after catching herself approving of the white image in the long mirror, she had the grace to be ponderingly amused at that part of her thought which conceived a possibility of Sidway seeing her thus. No telling where that Hollywood extra might bob up! She arrived late in the dining room, yet in time to hear her father say: "He'd have gone, too, Madeline, if Nels and I hadn't believed him when he swore he didn't come here on account of Madge."

"Well, Dad Stewart!" declared Madge, in mock solemnity. "So that cowboy put it over?"

"Daughter! You look like your mother—the first time I ever saw her in white!"

"Oh, thank you, Dad! Then I must look just stunning."

"You do. . . . Madge, young Sidway didn't put it over. He told the truth. Nels believed him. So did I. He hadn't the remotest idea that my daughter, the girl Ren Starr told him about, was you—the girl he'd actually met and befriended."

"Dad, he's a liar. I wouldn't believe that on a bet," declared Madge.

"I'll bet you find it out and you'll be sorry."

"Preposterous! So he put up a big bluff to you and Nels? . . . Dad, that cowboy is right up to date. He knows his stuff. . . . What I can't get is why he was ashamed of his clever stunt?"

"Madge, it's conceivable that he seemed ashamed because of his innocence when all of you believed in his deceit," observed her mother.

"Oh, my adorable parents! What you must learn about us! Mr. Sidway's ears must be burning. Let's forget him."

Nevertheless, despite her suggestion, Madge had no slight difficulty in conforming to it. She succeeded presently by launching into an account of what she wanted done to the road, and the patio and the long-deserted rooms in the west wing, and about more servants from the Mexican village—all in the interest of her guests who were to arrive on the twentieth. She was indeed not disappointed in her anticipation that both of her parents seemed heartily interested in her summer party, with no wish but to contribute in every way to its success. If they appeared a little bewildered several times during the discussion, and at a loss for words, Madge put that down to her elaborate and extravagant plans.

They stayed up late, at least for them, and when Madge bade them good night, she went to her rooms thinking how perfectly splendid they were, and that she was happy, and the most fortunate girl in the world.

Next morning she satisfied a craving that had long beset her —that of getting into the saddle again. To find Range gone gave quick rise to her temper, which strangely did not greatly fall when her father explained that the cowboy had merely obeyed orders. She had resolutely to keep her eyes off Umpqua or she would have yielded to riding him again, which pride bade her forego.

That afternoon Madge found great enjoyment in driving her father high up the old road, to an elevation that permitted their gazing down upon the ranch and the house, and the flowing sage flats with their speckled knots of cattle. While her father puttered around the boxed-in spring and repaired the outlet, Madge sat at ease, lulled by the heights and the depths of this wide-spreading land.

"No wonder the lake and reservoir went almost dry," said her father, when he came back to the car. "Two thirds of the water leaking away."

"Oh, I forgot to look at the lake. Will it be full again by the time my friends arrive? We'll want to go in bathing. Dad, is there any sand near enough to haul?"

"Sand. The wash down below is all sand. Fine and white, too."

"Swell! I'll want a nice sandy beach for us to lie around on in the sun."

"That's an easy one, Madge."

The end of a perfect day just had to have a drawback. When Madge caught sight of Lance Sidway leaning over the gate, apparently deeply interested in Bonita Mains, she fell victim to a most disconcerting irritation. The cowboy, as she drove up to a halt, did not noticeably move, until Bonita blushingly drew back, to come out of the gate. Then he stared at Madge, rather satirically she thought. Was there not a single man in the whole vast earth who did not fall for every pretty girl he saw, regardless of her color? It had not taken Lance Sidway long to contact the little half-breed coquette of the range. Madge chalked up another mark against the cowboy.

The succeeding moments, outside of Danny Mains' kindly welcome—Madge did not take Bonita's to heart—should have bored Madge, if she had been running true to form. But she was off her stride and she knew the reason, and therefore looked at that reason with rather scornful eyes. Her mental alertness quickened, however, when Ren Starr's car was sighted, and Bonita precipitately fled.

The stab Sidway had given Madge, along with the look he gave her, silenced Madge, and gave rein to whirling thoughts that refused to recognize her wrath. She nursed it, yet succumbed to curiosity, and got out of the car to listen to the short talk of the men. Rustlers! Verily her home-coming had not been dull. Then the men fell back from Starr's car, Sidway to leap astride Range and gallop off, Mains to run into his house, and her father to get in with her, his fine face stern and dark, somehow recalling her fear of him when she was a little girl.

"Step on it, Madge."

"Oh, Dad! What is it? I heard some of your talk. Trucks! Rustlers!"

"You bet you did. . . . Madge, these boys have made me feel like my old self. Sidway got a line on these cattle thieves. All in a day! Won't Nels jump at that? Won't he be pleased? And Starr ran out with news of a truck raid on our cattle tonight."

"Truck raid! Who ever heard of such a thing?"

"Sidway got it, just like that. Keen as a whip, that cowboy. And Starr's a running pard for him. . . . Madge, I have a hunch things will look up for us this summer."

"Darling, are you telling *me*? . . . What will you do?"

"I must tell Nels first."

"That old—ranger! Oh, Dad, he'll be for guns! horses! ropes!"

"You bet. Madge, before the night is over we'll hang some of these truck drivers and cattle-raiding greasers."

"I want to go!"

"Nonsense, child. You might get hurt. . . . Let me out here. I won't be up for supper. Tell Mother."

Naturally Madge expected her mother to be greatly perturbed, but was agreeably surprised.

"This will wake up your father and Nels, too," rejoined her mother, with satisfaction.

"But, Mom! . . . Dad swore they'd *hang* some of them. They will have to catch them first. Oh, wouldn't I like to go? . . . It means a fight. Crooks these days use machine guns. Dad might be hurt. . . . And Sidway. He's a reckless devil."

"Madge, your father and Nels and Danny Mains will be a match for all the crooks in the Southwest. Don't worry about them. Rustlers will give them just the impetus they need. And cattle raising will probably be the better for it."

Nevertheless Madge did worry. She read and worried and waited until long after her mother had retired. Then when she did go to bed she could not sleep. She listened. But there were no sounds except the lonesome chirping of crickets and the murmuring of running water. This Lance Sidway had certainly injected some vim and vigor into the dead old ranch. His fine eyes, shadowed, troubled, and then blazing with scorn, haunted her as did that taunt about gangsters. She hated him, but she deserved it. Her conscience wrung that from her. Indeed he had kept the rendezvous that day, and bad luck have it! he had seen Uhl meet her, get into her car. And being Hollywood-wise he had caught the cut of that gentleman all in a few minutes. Not this fact, but his scorn was what galled Madge. Still if he had been so burned up by her friendship with an underworld character, why had he learned her name, where she lived, and conceived the brilliant idea of meeting her at her own home? The answer was that no matter whom she knew, what she had done, he must have conceived more than a mere interest in her. But was that the answer? Madge conceived the idea that there was a remote possibility it was not.

Chapter Six

LANCE stood back in the shadow of Nels' cabin, a little abashed at his agitation, as he compared it to the coolness of these Arizonians. He did not want them to see that he was an unfledged cowboy, so far as rustlers were concerned.

"Wal, I reckon you fellers better have a smack of grub an' a cup of coffee with me," Nels drawled, as Stewart ended his brief story.

"Reckon I hed, at thet," rejoined Mains. "My two Bonitas would be too interested in thet confab we hed by the house."

"We'll all sponge on you, Nels," said Stewart. "Pitch in, fellows."

"All set 'cept fryin' some more ham. You cut it, Danny. . . . Whar's Sidway? Come heah, cowboy. . . . Gene, this truck rustlin' is shore two-bit stuff. Kinda oot of our experience. Let's get the cowboy's angle on it."

"Suits me."

"Sidway, you oughta be up on this automobile cattle stealin'. What'll we do?"

"We'll intercept this raid, of course," replied Lance, realizing that he was on the spot and forcing a calm and serious front when inwardly he was quaking. It reassured him that his wide sombrero hid his face.

"Hev a slice of ham. I can cook, cowboy. . . . Wal, how'd you intercept it?"

"I'd like Starr in on this with me," replied Sidway.

"By all means. You young bloods put your heads together," said Stewart.

"I'm with you, pard, an' I've got some ideas," returned Starr, nonchalantly. "But I cain't talk an' eat.'

Lance thought with all his might. It was a situation in

which he wanted to make good. But the fact that these old cattlemen, who had fought rustlers and Mexicans for over a score of years, put the responsibility up to him and Starr seemed more stultifying than inspiring.

"Starr, what hour of the night will that highway be most free of traffic?" asked Lance.

"About three in the mawnin' thar's a quiet spell. Sometimes fer two hours not a darn car goes by."

"That will be the time the thieves will load," concluded Lance.

"I agree. And even then it's pretty risky. Old-time rustlers wouldn't be that brazen," said Stewart.

"Boss, we gotta deal with a new breed of criminal," added Starr.

"Like as not the drivers of these trucks won't be regular range characters. These men will be city crooks, stealing cattle as a blind. They are gangsters. Probably hop-heads."

Stewart's leonine head swept up and he transfixed Lance with penetrating eyes.

"Cowboy, I heard you use that word hop-head less than an hour ago?" he queried, sharply.

"Yes sir . . . You—you may have," replied Lance, startled. But despite his qualm he kept his head. "I can explain it."

"Very well. Go on. What's a hop-head?"

"It's the name underworld characters give to men addicted to opium or heroin. They smoke or eat opium. Heroin they mostly inhale by smelling from the back of their hands. It's a powder."

"Wal, the hell you say, cowboy?" ejaculated Nels. "Them hop-heads must be kinda tough nuts, eh?"

"Brutal killers. No mercy! No respect for law. Rats, the police call them."

"Boss, they'll shoot if they're cornered, an' if they have machine guns, it'll jest be too bad," interposed Starr.

"They must be ambushed, or at least surprised," went on

Lance. "They'll be waiting or driving along slow at the place nearest the highway—most convenient to pick up the cattle."

"Thet's less than forty miles from where we're talkin'," said Starr. "I spotted the blackest bunch of cattle on my way oot. I can drive fairly close. We'd hev to walk the rest of the way."

"I was going to suggest that," resumed Lance. "But not to drive too close. These raiders, whose job it is to round up the cattle, could hear a car. . . . They will be mounted—acquainted with the range—probably living on it."

"In cahoots with the truck drivers. Pard. You said a mouthful."

"Reckon he did thet same little thing," observed Mains, in dry subtlety.

"Wal, Gene, the kids ain't so pore," said Nels. "If yore through eatin' an' talkin' let's go. When we git down thar on the flat we can figger the rest."

"What's the hurry, Nels?" asked Stewart.

"Wal, I ain't trustin' them hop-haids to wait till mawnin'. Why, I reckon they'd jest as lief rob us in broad daylight."

Soon after that the five men, armed to the teeth, passed down the road in Starr's car, driving without lights. They had reached the village, passed the main street, when approaching Mains' house, Sidway's keen eyes, accustomed to the dark, espied two mounted riders close to the fence.

"Hold it, Ren," he whispered. . . . "There! . . . Down the walk past Mains' house. Two horsemen! . . . They're moving."

"My gosh, I see them," replied Starr. "Gone now. Listen. . . . Heah them hoofs? Good fast trot."

"Boys," interposed Mains, "it ain't nothin' to see hawsemen around heah. They ride up bold as hell an' then again they sneak up like Injuns. Bonita's the reason."

Lance bit his tongue to keep from bursting out with the news that he had seen Bonita's dark form glide across in front of a yellow-lighted window. To his mind neither the riders nor the girl had moved without significance of secrecy. Lance resolved to make up to this pretty *señorita* for two reasons.

"Drive on, Ren," said Stewart, presently.

Below the village some few hundred yards Starr steered off the road down the slope. In the dark he had to go very slowly, a procedure difficult to accomplish on account of the grade. A vast dim emptiness stretched away under the stars. Far down, double pin points of light, moving along, attested to the presence of a car on the highway. Lance asked Stewart how long that road had encroached upon his range.

"Six or seven years, if I remember. Used to bother old-timers. But that feeling has gone into the discard with the cattle business."

"It'll pick up again and be better than ever," declared Lance.

"Ren, stop every little way, so we can listen."

It was a silent night, not yet cooled off from the day's heat. The rustle of sage and the low hum of insects accentuated the silence. Stars were growing brighter in the darkening blue. Gradually the men ceased talking. Once down on the flat Starr had easier driving. Presently he ran out of the sage into the wash where on the sand and gravel the going was smoother and almost noiseless. Starr must have halted a dozen times at Nels' order and the five had listened intently before Lance heard cattle bawling.

"Reckon we've come fur enough. What say, Gene?" queried Nels. "Let's pile oot."

"I think I know about where we are," said Gene, peering about in the gloom. "Still pretty far from the road, that is, where this wash goes under. But the road curves in to the west."

"Cattle all aboot," observed Nels. "An' they ain't skeered, thet's shore. Let's mosey on till we heah somethin'."

Guardedly and slow, with senses alert, the men zigzagged through the sage, working southwest. Grazing and resting cattle grew more numerous. After what Lance believed was several miles' travel Nels halted them near a rocky mound.

"Fur enough, till we heah or see somethin'. You cowboys climb up thar."

The eminence appeared to be rather long and higher toward the west. Lance signed to Ren that he would climb the far point. He did not, however, get to do it, for a hist from Starr called him back. Lance joined Nels and Stewart who stood under Starr.

". . . Aboot a mile from the highway," Ren was saying, in guarded voice. "Three big double lights comin' from Bolton. Trucks. They're close together. Movin' slow."

"How do you know they're trucks?" asked Stewart.

"Cars an' lamps an' such hev been my job fer a year an' more, Boss. These belong to trucks, an' you bet the ones we're expectin'. Jest creepin' along. An' thet's a level road."

"How fur away?" queried Nels.

"Cain't say. Mebbe three miles, mebbe six."

"Nels, down along here about even with where we are now there are several benches that run close to the road and break off in banks. It would be a simple matter for trucks to be backed up against these banks and loaded. In some places you wouldn't even need a platform. And my cattle are tame."

"Wal, we're some sucker cattlemen," drawled Nels, and sat down with his back to the bank. "Set down an' let's wait fer Starr to find oot somethin'. Sidway, you got sharp ears. Go off a ways an' listen. It's a still night. Listen fer cattle thet air disturbed."

Lance did as he was bidden, conscious of growing excitement. These ranchmen evidently gave him credit for more and wilder experience than he had had. He felt that he must rise to the occasion. Presently there would be some sharp and critical work for all of them and he nerved himself to cool hard purpose. From time to time he heard Starr's low voice.

It was some time, however, fraught with suspense, before Lance's range-trained ear caught the faint trample of hoofs and occasional bawl of cattle. Whereupon he ran back to report.

"Good!" declared Stewart. "How about you, Starr?"

"I reckon I heahed but wasn't shore. I am now. Not so all-fired far, either. . . . Boss, jest wait, I'm watchin' them trucks."

Starr did not speak again, and the others listened intently. The faint sounds of moving cattle augmented. Presently the cowboy whispered sharply: "Boss, the trucks hev stopped—jest a little to the right of us. . . . Lights go out! . . . No, by damn—the trucks air turnin' . . . backin' off the road this way, or I'm a born fool."

"Wal, look like it's all set," said Nels, getting up. Stewart followed his example.

"Them rays of light flash across the highway," went on Starr. "'Pear to be linin' up. . . . Fust lights gone out! . . ."

"Come down, Ren. We'll be moseyin' along. . . . Danny, you come with us. Gene, you go with Sidway. Work straight down to the road an' foller along it. We'll aim to slip up behind the *hombres* who're doin' the rustlin'."

In another moment Lance was gliding cautiously along at Stewart's heels. They progressed fifty steps or more when Stewart halted to listen.

"But Nels didn't say what to do!" whispered Lance.

"It's a cinch we'll break up the raid. But our object is to capture at least one each of the riders and drivers."

Lance silenced his misgivings and conjectures, and transferring his rifle to his left hand he drew his gun. Stewart, he had observed, packed two guns, and Lance thrilled at the way he wore them. So different from the movie bad men! They stole along slowly, avoiding the larger sagebrush, careful not to scare cattle, listening at intervals. The hum of a motorcar off to the east distracted Lance's attention from the now audible moving herd. Presently he saw the lights and he and the rancher watched them grow and pass not far below, and go on out of sight. That car was making fast time. No doubt it did not see the trucks. Soon Lance followed Stewart out of the sage upon the highway, black and glistening under the stars.

"We're farther this way than we thought," whispered Stewart. "That bunch of cattle are down to the road. . . . Hear that?

. . . We've got to hand it to these truck rustlers for nerve. Right on the highway! Not leary of noise."

"To hell with the ranchers, eh?" replied Lance, with a little husky laugh. He felt the heat throb in his pulsing veins.

"They wouldn't put a guard out, as the old rustlers used to. . . . Let's hurry along."

Stewart strode so swiftly that Lance could not hear anything while they were moving. But presently they halted; the trample of hoofs and bawl of cattle became plainly audible. On the third halt Lance distinctly heard the thump of hoofs upon a board floor.

"——!" swore Stewart. "Loading already! Won't that make Nels snort? It should be getting hot over there. But Nels would move slow."

After another hundred steps or so Stewart led off the highway into the sage. Lance divined that the rancher wanted cover to drop behind in case the truckmen flashed their lights. Nevertheless it was not long before Stewart went down on all fours to crawl. This was tremendously exciting to Lance. The thump of solid hoofs on wood drowned all the other sounds except an occasional snort or bawl. The cattle were being moved with amazing celerity and little noice.

"Beats me," muttered Stewart, then crawled on. They had scarcely gotten even with a point opposite, where a high black bulk loomed up squarely above the horizon and marked the position of the trucks, when huge glaring lights gleamed out of the darkness. Lance flattened himself beside Stewart. A low fringe of sage on their right saved them from detection. But Lance's throat contracted. A harsh low voice, a sudden bursting of an engine, into whirring roar, a grind of wheels left no doubt that a truck was starting. It moved quickly down to the road, and turned so that the lights swerved to the right, leaving the men in darkness. Then the truck stopped and the driver called. Stewart jerked Lance to his feet, whispering: "We've got to move. Careful now. Keep your head."

His voice, his presence stirred Lance as nothing else had

ever done. Stewart ran along the sage and up on the road to the truck. Lance, sharp-eyed and tense, kept at his heels. The engine was purring. Reaching the front of the car Stewart jerked open the door and commanded: "*Hands up!*"

Lance over Stewart's shoulder saw the big gun go prodding into the driver's side. "Agg-h!" he ejaculated, and lifted his hands off the wheel.

A quick grating footstep on the other side of the car caused Lance to crouch. A man came swiftly round the front.

"Beat it, Bill—we're held up!" rasped the driver.

But this man cursed and swept up his arm. Lance having him covered, had only to pull the trigger. His shot preceded the others only by an instant. Lance saw his action violently break, his gun burst red. A crash of bursting glass, a thud of bullets preceded Stewart's staggering away from the truck to fall. The driver, with hoarse bellows of alarm, shoved his power on so quickly that the cattle in the truck banged against the gate. Then the truck roared down the road.

The horror that gripped Lance at Stewart's fall nearly overcame him for a moment. Then strident yells, the flashing of lights and roaring of engines added to his fighting fury. Nimbly he leaped beyond the broad flares. And as the second truck whizzed down upon the road he emptied his gun at the front of the first one. The splintering crash of glass, the lurching of the car, the loud yells told that his bullets did some execution. Both trucks gained the road. As they roared on shots rang out from the bank. Then Lance, resorting to his rifle, aimed above the red rear light of the last truck, and sent ten shots after it. Lowering the hot rifle he stood a moment, shaking, wet with cold sweat, realizing all shots had ceased. He caught a clatter of rapid hoofs, the crowding of cattle, then a ringing voice:

"Hey, over there," called Nels. "What'n hell was yore hurry?"

"Nels! Come—quick! Stewart's . . ." yelled Lance hoarsely.

"Keep your shirt on, cowboy," intercepted the cool voice of

Stewart. Then Lance saw his tall dark form against the lighter gloom.

"Oh—Ste—wart. I was afraid," gasped Lance.

"Hello. Where are you, fellers?" shouted Danny Mains, and then followed Starr's cheery voice. "Busted, by thunder!"

"Here," called Stewart. Presently the three loomed on the road.

"Gene, you let 'um git away," protested Nels, hopping mad.

"Trucks vamoosed in spite of us. How about the riders?"

"Wal, we was creepin' up behind, all set, when you opened up the ball."

"Did you identify any of them?"

"Hell, we didn't even see them. Slick an' fast ootfit, Gene. Makes me more curious."

"I ain't so damn curious as I was," growled Danny Mains, enigmatically.

"Pard, you shore done a lot of shootin'," declared Starr, peering into Lance's face.

"Here's what happened," explained Stewart. "Sidway and I got here just as that loaded truck came off the sage. When it turned on the road, we jumped and ran. It stopped. I opened the door and stuck my right gun in the driver's ribs. He yelled in spite of that. Then his pardner came running. Bill, the driver called him. Bill sure saw me. For he came up with a gun. I threw my left on him but it struck the car door, low down. Sidway shot this fellow—broke his aim—or sure as God made little apples he'd have killed me. At that he hit me. His bullet knocked me flat."

"Gene! You shot? Whar? Not a body hit?" exclaimed Nels.

There was a moment's silence, during which the cold began to creep into Lance's marrow.

"Don't know where," returned Stewart, calmly, as he felt of his body and shoulders. "I'm bleeding. Busted glass cut me. That *hombre* saw my body outside the door and believe me he threw his gun on it. But Sidway's shot knocked him off.

Maybe the bullet didn't hit me at all. Maybe it did, because I'm bleeding all over my face and head."

"Aw, then it cain't be serious," declared Nels, with relief. "An' Sidway hit this *hombre*?"

"Bored him plumb center," replied Stewart, grimly. "He stood just inside the light. I saw him drop like a sack. He's lying here somewhere."

Starr produced a flashlight and with the two men began searching the immediate space, while Lance fought the strangest, most sickening sensation of his life.

"Heah! . . . Daid, I'll tell the world!" rang out Starr. "Lousy-lookin' little bastard! One of them hop-haids."

"Search him, Ren, and drag him off the road. . . . Sidway, you're too damn good a shot. Dead men tell no tales."

"Wal, if you ask me, our new cowboy is a man after my kind. Gene, don't call him fer shootin' fast an' straight."

"I was kidding. But at that I wish Sidway had only crippled him. . . . What'd he have on him, Ren?"

"Automatic tight in his mitt. . . . Watch. Knife. Cigarettes. . . . An' this wad of long green. Fellers, will you look at thet! A hundred dollar bill on the ootside!"

Lance gradually dragged himself closer to the trio, and discerned Starr on his knees beside the dead man, a slack spare figure, terribly suggestive, showing in the flashlight a crooked visage, ghastly in hue and contortion.

"Wal, you lousy hop-haid," broke out Starr, in genial levity, "bumped up agin the wrong hombre, didn't you? . . . Lay hold, Danny, an' help me haul him over heah."

The cold gripe on Lance's internals slowly lessened; and he helped it pass by a desperate effort to conceal what he felt to be his squeamishness before these ranchers. He thought he could get by in the dark.

"Sidway must have stung more than this hombre," Stewart was saying to Nels. "He shot the front glasses out of both cars. And he sure cut loose with his rifle as they drove away. I heard the bullets hit that last truck."

"Wal, thanks to him, it didn't turn oot so pore. Mebbe thet money will more than pay fer the cattle they rustled."

"Boss, reckon I'll hev to drive back to Bolton in the mawnin' an' report this execution to the sheriff," said Starr, joining them.

"Yes. And I might have to see a doctor."

"Lemme look." Starr flashed his light upon the side of Stewart's face which he turned for inspection. Lance saw with concern that the rancher was bloody enough to have been struck by a load of shot. The cowboy wiped the blood off, and peering closer he ran his fingers over Stewart's cheek and temple and neck. "Hell! You ain't been shot atall, Boss. Jest a blast of glass, I reckon. . . . Leastways I cain't find any bullet hole. . . . Gosh, I'm glad them glass bits missed yore eye."

"Feel here—back of my ear."

"Ah-ha!—Shore, he creased you thar. . . . Hot as fire, huh. Thet was made by a bullet, Boss."

"A miss is as good as a mile. . . . Sidway, I owe you something."

"Oh, no!—He—he just missed you. I was too—too slow," replied Lance, thickly.

"I've been shot at before, boy. I saw him jerk and his gun spurt up. He'd have bored me."

"How aboot moseyin' along? Thet's a long tramp fer a man who never trailed rustlers on foot," said Nels, plaintively.

As they moved up the highway Starr dropped back to Lance's side. He put a hand on the other's arm. "Pard, you didn't tell me you was some punkins with a gun."

"I'm not."

"Hey, you might josh me, but not these men. You pulled a fast one, Sid. An' Gene Stewart seen you. Wait till I get a chanct to tell you some stories about Stewart an' Nels. Hell, man, they've seen the wildest of western days. An' Nels was a Texas ranger before he ever hit this country. If you know yore West! An' Gene Stewart, or *El Capitan* as his handle was them days, was not only a tough cowboy but a real gunman."

"Ren, I hope this night's work will end the truck rustling," said Lance, lamely.

"Wal, it might, if them *hombres* was ordinary cattle thieves. But who'n hell can figger these hop-haids. Anyway, pard, you've cinched yore job, believe you me. An' I'm gonna ride with you."

"That'll be swell. I'm glad. We'll get along fine, Ren."

"Gosh! I jest happened to think!" ejaculated Starr, stopping in the middle of the highway to take a pull at Lance. "I'd give a heap to be in yore boots."

"Why—what's hurting? Don't you think, usually?"

"Will you be sittin' pretty with Majesty Stewart? . . . Fust stunt—right off—savin' her dad's life! Pard, she adores him. My Gawd, the luck of some gazabos!"

"Lord! . . . Starr, if you're my pard don't tell—her—please," exclaimed Lance, his weakness making him prey to another emotion.

"Wal!—Why, shore, Sidway. I won't tell her. But how about Gene? An' thet gabby old Nels— Pard, if I was you I'd shore want her to know."

"We've clashed, Ren. She misunderstood my coming here. Thinks I'm a liar. Laughed at me—when I denied it. . . . Vainest girl I ever met!"

"Hell! What of thet," returned Ren, bluntly. "She's also the loveliest, the sweetest, the finest an' squarest. Get thet, buddy?"

"Yes, I get *you*—you dumbbell! I see if I'd speak my mind about this glorious creature, you'd sock me one."

"Forget it, pard. You're a little upset. I ain't wonderin' at thet. You reckoned Stewart was daid an' seein' him come back to life would excite anybody, outside the fight."

Starr gave Sidway a friendly pat on the back and then let him alone. Presently they reached a culvert over the wash, and turning here, they followed the pale line of sand into the sage. The sand dragged at Sidway's feet, but the exertion helped restore his equilibrium. The distance back to the car seemed interminable and proved how, on the way down, the excitement had made it short. They found the car at length and were soon bumping over the uneven ground. Starr had no incentive now to drive slowly and noiselessly. He certainly gave his passengers a rough trip back to the ranch.

Lance went to bed at once. For half an hour Nels and Mains, dressing Stewart's wounds in the adjoining room, kept Lance awake, thinking one moment and going over the adventure the next. When quiet settled down, he soon fell asleep.

Upon awakening, Lance heard Starr and Nels talking while they got breakfast. Presently Starr pounded on the wall between, jarring the house. "Hey, Oregon, air you daid?"

"I'm up," replied Lance.

"Wal, you're quieter'n hell if you air. Waltz out. I gotta rustle to town pronto."

"Ren, send for my baggage."

"Shore, pard, an' what else?"

"I'll see."

When Lance entered Nels' bunkhouse to have breakfast he sensed such a great transformation in himself that he felt certain his friends would exclaim about it. But they did not notice any difference in him. During the meal they did not once mention the affair of last night. All in the day, for them, thought Lance! He essayed a cool and quiet demeanor which he meant to make permanent.

"Nels, what'll I do today?" he asked.

"Dog-gone if I know, son," drawled the other, scratching his gray head. "They're all goin' to town. Go wrangle yore hawse an' I'll ask Gene when he comes down."

Umpqua had made the most of the huge grassy pasture. Lance found him in the extreme far corner, more than a mile from the corrals, and rode him bareback to the corrals. After rubbing him down and saddling and bridling him, Lance led him up the lane to the court. Stewart, his head swathed in white bandages, stood by Madge's car talking to Starr. As Lance passed the open door of the store he heard Madge's rich voice, breaking with a singular note, and it gave him a wild impulse to run. Starr hailed him, and then he and Stewart approached.

"Hope you're okay, Boss," said Lance, eagerly.

"Mornin', Sidway. Reckon I feel like a nigger who had to have the buckshot picked out of him. Would you like to go to town with us?"

"Not on my own account, sir. Thanks. There's a lot I can find to do here." Lance said this at the same moment he heard Nels' clinking slow step behind him and a lighter pace that stopped his heart. But he did not turn.

"Starr will come back soon," went on the rancher. "It might be a good idea for you and him to fix up your quarters. Nels said they had gone to rack."

"How about the cattle?" asked Lance.

"They have been left free to run the range, and as you saw, have worked low down. Danny and I will be driving a big herd to the railroad soon. Maybe next week. I'll make that deal in town today. As for immediate jobs, I want you and Ren to repair the water flume and the telephone line pronto."

"Yes, sir. I'll get started on them today."

"Nels, did you make out your list of supplies?"

"Majesty writ it oot fer me."

"Say, what have you been tellin' that girl?" demanded Stewart.

"Me? Why, Gene, nothin' atall," drawled Nels, innocently.

"You old liar! Look at her!"

Lance wished to do this with an almost irresistible desire. But he sat down on the edge of the porch, dragging Starr with him, aware that the others had stepped into the store.

"Ren, you'll not forget my baggage?"

"Shore, pard. Anythin' else? Say how's yore bunkhouse fixed up? I didn't look."

"It's not fixed up at all," replied Lance. "No mattress, no chair, no mirror, nothing to wash in or with. No towels. I've been using Nels'."

"Wal. mine cain't be no wuss . . ."

"Ren, buy what you need today," said Madge Stewart, from behind them. She had not gone into the store at all. Manifestly she had heard their talk. "Whatever is this ranch coming to?"

"Aw, you heah, Miss Majesty. Good mawnin'," replied Starr, with confusion, as he stood up to turn toward her. "About the ranch—wal, I'd say things was lookin' up."

"Lance Sidway!"

Arising stiffly, Lance wheeled to doff his sombrero and greet her in apparent composure. But the tone of her voice and then the look of her played havoc with all his resolves. At this juncture Stewart and Nels came out of the store.

"Nels, do you think I dare ride in with Madge?" quizzed Stewart.

"Wal, I'd jump at the chance."

"You old traitor! Why, you never could be hired to ride in a car. Do you remember Link Stevens driving that big white car of Madeline's?"

"My Gawd, do I? But I'll bet Majesty would hev druv rings around Link."

Madge was looking down upon Lance. The fairness of her face appeared enhanced by the scarlet upon her lips. In truth Lance saw that she was pale and that her eyes were unnaturally large, glowing, dilating, with a violet fire. Then she seemed to float down the steps and entwine her arm in Lance's, and lift her lovely face to him, that in the action flushed a hue to match her lips and then went pearly white.

"You saved Dad's life!"

Lance had prepared himself for he knew not what, though not for this close proximity, the tight pressure of her arm, the quivering feel of her. "Oh, no, Miss Stewart. Somebody has exaggerated."

"Nels told me," said Madge, intensely.

"I might have known," went on Lance, trying to be cool and nonchalant. "Nels is swell, but you know he. . . . Starr told me what an old liar he is."

"Heah!" yelped Starr. "Don't you get me in bad. I never said thet . . ."

"Miss Stewart, please . . ." interposed Lance. "You mustn't give me undue credit. I was there—and I'm glad—I made myself useful. I didn't want to kill the man . . ."

"*You killed him?*" she cried, aghast. "Oh, Nels didn't tell me that."

Lance spread wide his hands to the watching men, as if to say "Now see what you've done." But it was not the revelation that distracted him.

"So you're bound to be our good angel!" she exclaimed, softly, and shook him gently.

"Really I—you . . . it was—it's not so much."

"Nothing! And you killed a robber who'd have murdered my father? I wonder what you'd consider *very* much. . . . Come away from these grinning apes, so I can thank you."

She led him out to her car and still clung to his arm. "It's impossible to thank you," she went on, her voice breaking. "I can't even try. But I'm unutterably grateful. I'll do anything for you."

"Thank you, Miss Stewart. . . ."

"My friends call me Majesty," she interrupted, sweetly.

"I—I appreciate your excitement and feeling. It's kind of a tough spot for you. I hoped they wouldn't tell you. But they did . . . and I won't let you make too much of it."

"Too much! Aren't you glad?" she rejoined, incredulously.

"Glad? That I was there—with him? Good heavens! Of course, I am. Greatest kick I ever had!"

"Nels told me you were a bad *hombre* to meet in a fight. That you reminded him of an old pard, Nick Steele. But that you were different from the old-time bragging gunmen . . . modern, modest—a new kind to him, but dangerous, and just what my father needed—just what *I* needed . . ."

"Nels is a sentimental old jackass," burst out Lance. If she would only let go of his arm, move her soft warm shoulder away from his!

"It bothers you," she asserted, quickly. "We'll skip it. . . . Come into town with us."

"Is that an order?"

"Oh, no. Just a request."

"Thanks, but I've plenty of work to do here."

"I'll say plenty. . . . Lance, I hated you yesterday."

"Are you telling me? But really I'm sorry I was so rude."

"I forgive you. Let's be good friends now. You're here, I'm here—and my friends are coming. You'll like the girls. They're peaches. Full of fun—and great sports. It will embarrass me if we are at odds."

"How could that be? I'm only your father's cowboy."

"Don't forget that *I* saw you first," she taunted. "You're *my* cowboy. They'll all make a play for you, especially that red-headed Bu Allen. She's a devil on the make. They'll hear of your—about you—make you a hero. I want you to be good friends with me."

"I will be, of course. A friend like Ren Starr," qualified Lance.

"But I mean more than that. Ren is swell. Only he's a hired hand."

"So am I. I won't forget my place."

"Aren't you being just a little snooty?" she inquired, subtly changing, and she released his arm.

"Aren't you kidding me?"

"No," she flashed, loftily.

"Then isn't that your line?"

"I haven't any line, Mr. Sidway."

Lance felt utterly helpless in two conflicting ways—that he simply could not help rubbing the girl the wrong way, any more than he could resist her lovely person and insidious charm. He wanted her to hurry away so that he could think. In another moment she would see that his heart if not his will was prostrate at her feet.

"I'm afraid you had better fire me right here and now," he said, glumly.

"Perhaps I had," she returned, her purple eyes glowing upon him, as if visioning afar. "But Dad needs you. And he wouldn't let you go."

"I'd go anyhow. Just you fire me."

"No. I'll not do it. . . . Listen, big boy, you gave me some dirty digs. And I've been catty. It's fifty-fifty. Here's my hand for a new deal."

"Miss Stewart—as Ren says—you're one grand girl," rejoined Lance, unsteadily. "It's unconceivable that I could withhold my hand, if you offered yours. But I can't forget so easily as you evidently do."

"I see. You can't take it?"

"Do you still believe I found out who you were—where you lived—and came out here to—to . . ." he queried, hotly, and ended, unable to finish.

"Why, certainly I do."

"When I swear on my word of honor that I didn't?" went on Lance, passionately.

"Yes," she retorted, almost with like heat. "And I'd think more of you if you'd not lie about it. This word of honor stuff! . . . I thought it was a swell stunt. I was tickled pink. I'll still think it grand of you if you'll only stop bluffing. What more could you want?"

"I must seem ridiculous to you. But I'm neither a callow college youth nor a thickheaded gangster. I'd expect a girl to *believe* me. Else I couldn't be her friend. You're just kidding me. You'd play with me in front of your college crowd—and let me down afterwards. Why, you even have nerve enough to try to get my horse!"

"Yes I have, Lance Sidway," she blazed at him. "I've nerve enough to get him, too, at any cost—unless you show yellow and ride away!"

Lance bowed and turned away toward the bunkhouses, forgetting the others and afraid to go to Umpqua. He heard her call to her father, and presently the sound of the cars wheeling away. In that moment of passion he divined if he approached

Umpqua it would be to ride away from that ranch. And he flung himself upon his bunk to shut out the sunlight. Neither pride in himself nor loyalty to Stewart accounted for that victory over himself. The paralyzing and staggering truth was that he did not ride away because he could not bear to leave this beautiful and tormenting girl.

Chapter Seven

EARLY and late Sidway was out on the road job, overseeing the Mexican laborers, while Starr and Mains, with the *vaqueros*, repaired the telephone, and then drove upwards of six hundred head of cattle to the railroad.

No sooner was the road fit for heavy traffic when it appeared all the trucks in Bolton came along loaded to capacity with the crated furniture and bales and boxes that Madge Stewart had sent from Los Angeles. There were four small trucks and two large ones. The contents, Lance calculated, must have cost the girl thousands of dollars; and the sight of them aroused an unreasonable resentment in him. What business was it of his? Yet he could not help thinking of her all the day and half the night. That fact lay at the root of his intense dissatisfaction rather than her extravagance at such a hard period for her parents. Lance was determined that Madge must not know this. He was always fighting against an acceptance of her faults.

On Saturday afternoon of that busy week Lance was glad to see Starr drive up with Stewart and Mains in his car, and an empty truck behind.

The road job was finished, very much to Stewart's satisfaction, and he paid off the Mexicans, and sent them back to town.

"Well, I reckon we're ready for Madge's outfit," said Stewart, eyeing his cowboys.

"Who is, Boss?" queried Lance.

"Not me, neither," added Starr, making a wry face. "All summer long! Gene, they'll drive us nuts. . . . An' shore one of them swell college sprats will cop my girl."

"Oh, Bonita, you mean," returned Lance, laconically, as

he rested against the car. "Ren, I haven't noticed—so much—that she is your property."

"Sid, you double-crossin' son-of-a-gun! I might have knowed it."

"Swell kid!"

"Look heah, Sidway, hev you been after my daughter, too?" demanded Danny Mains.

"I've seen a good deal of her while you were away. I knew you didn't approve of Ren."

"Danny," interposed Stewart, "cowboys are the same now as we were. Only a good deal better. I think Bonita is better off for friends like Starr and Sidway."

"Wal, I reckon," agreed Danny, dubiously. "On'y I'm afraid they might do some mischief to Bonita's several *vaquero* beaus."

"Mischief! Say, Danny, you ain't got me figgered," replied Ren, doggedly. "I love Bonita an' hev asked her to marry me."

"Ren— So that was it?" ejaculated Lance.

"So that was what?" queried Starr, suspiciously.

"I don't want to embarrass you here, pard."

"Ren, you'll excuse my cantankerousness," said Mains, simply. "I didn't hev you figgered."

"Starr, this here Oregon ladies' man is not only stepping on your preserves, but he's kidding you," rejoined Stewart, with a laugh. "Hook her up and let's go. Sidway, it's a good job well done. . . . Oh, yes, I've a message for you by phone. Madge wants you up at the house to open boxes."

"Boss! I'm a tired man," expostulated Lance. "And Umpqua needs to be worked over. Up and down this dusty road for a week!"

"Haw! Haw! Haw!" laughed Starr, fiendishly.

"All right. I'll tell Madge not tonight."

Starr grinned knowingly at Lance and drove off. From where they had caught up with him it was only a short ride to the ranch. Yet it seemed a long and thoughtful one for Lance. It began to look as if Madge Stewart either meant to try him with odd stable-boy jobs or else she wanted him to be unable to avoid her, as he had tried so hard to do. The former made him furious and the latter made him weak.

By the time he had put Umpqua away it was dark, the store was closed, and bright light shone from Nels' window and door. A drowsy breeze blew in from the range, moved down by the cooler air on high. Frogs were croaking in the lake. Lance washed his grimy hands and face before he went in.

"Jest in time, son. Come in an' get it," said Nels, cheerily.

"Pard, what say to a swim in the lake after supper? She's bank full already," suggested Starr.

"Okay by me. But, boy! that water is cold."

"An' you from Oregon!"

It turned out to be warmer water than Lance was used to at home, and he enjoyed the bath. On the way back he realized that Ren had something on his mind. Lance clapped him on the back.

"What's on your chest, buddy?"

"It's Bonita."

"Say, Ren, I was surprised at what you admitted to Danny. I had no idea you were serious. I'm sorry, old man."

"You like Bonita?"

"I'll say. She's some kid."

"Pard, did you kiss and hug her?"

"Ren! Have a heart. Would you expect me to tell?"

"Wal, in my case, yes. You see, pard, I want you to help me win thet kid. I cain't do it alone."

"Okay. Yes I did—a little. But it was no cinch. And I liked her the better. She's a charming girl, Ren. I honestly think she'd make a swell little wife. But there are a lot of guys who're after her, and not all of them with your good intentions."

"Some of them Mexican *vaqueros*."

"Yes. But town fellows, too. And I'm suspicious of them. I've a hunch some of them might know something about that rustling."

"My hunch, too. We'll find out. An' pard—listen! If you'll

help me with this black-eyed little girl I'll shore play yore game with yore proud Majesty."

"My God!—Ren, have you gone nutty?"

"Nope. I'm cool as a cucumber right this heah minnit."

"But man! *Me* aspire to that . . ."

"Why, hell, yes. Pard, I seen her look at you thet day, an' if she's not stuck on you—mebbe unknowin' to herself—then I am nutty an' what hev you?"

"You are—Ren—you are," replied Lance, frantically. "I'll make that Bonita kid think you're a prince. But, pard, forget your pipe dream about the other."

"Faint heart never won fair lady," returned Starr, lightly.

That night Lance had a dream of a cherub-faced cowboy leading him along flower-strewn trails to a bower where a goddess with golden hair awaited him with white arms extended. At breakfast he was silly enough to tell Ren and Nels about that dream.

"Dreams come true, sometimes," declared Ren, stoutly. "Hey, Nels?"

"Shore they do. An' this one of Lance's has a pertickler bearin' heah," observed Nels, without glancing at Lance.

"Yeah? And how d'you figure that?" asked Lance, scornfully.

Nels and Ren both laughed and Lance's face crimsoned. Luckily at that juncture a message came from Stewart requesting the cowboys to come up to the house, not dressed in their Sunday clothes.

"That means work. And it's Sunday!" complained Lance, honestly and fearfully divided between bliss and panic.

"Aw, you know you're piflicated," replied Starr, cryptically.

"I am—sure, but what is piflicated?"

"Wal, as I remember from past mournful experiences, it's a kinda prolapsus of the gizzard. Heart trouble, pard."

Upon ascending to the ranch house the cowboys, with Nels accompanying them, found a busy and excited household. Front porch and part of the patio were packed with crates, bales, boxes, trunks, packages. Stewart, in his shirt sleeves, apparently in a trance, was helping the beaming Denny Mains carry furniture into the house. Mrs. Stewart, flushed and radiant, was bustling about with the servants. Bonita was there, red-lipped and pretty, her arms full of linens. And Madge, in slacks and a backless waist, cool and sweet and smiling, evidently was boss.

She put Lance and Ren to opening crates. For a couple of hours they worked diligently at this job, and after they had unpacked everything, they carried boards and boxes and burlap and paper out to be hauled away on the morrow. The next job was to move things into the patio rooms. Lance observed that these were light, high-ceiled rooms, with colored adobe walls, and shiny floors. He had a glimpse of Madge's rooms, and was reminded of some of the luxurious motion-picture sets he had seen in Hollywood.

At noon they had lunch on the patio porch, and it was a merry occasion. Lance, looking at Mrs. Stewart, no longer wondered how Madge had come by her beauty. She was a western girl, but her mother's eastern breeding and distinction had been augmented in her. Lance had to admit that parents and daughter made a delightful trio, and also that the girl's singular zest and enthusiasm motivated them.

After luncheon everybody worked harder than ever. Nels was wearing his long spurs, that stuck in dangerously as he knelt to hold a pillow in his teeth and slide it down into a slip. Nevertheless in housekeeping matters, Nels proved serious and efficient. Madge presently gave Starr and Bonita tasks to perform together, while Stewart carried and unrolled rugs and his wife oversaw his disposition of them, and the moving of furniture. Lance propounded the question as to whether he had naturally gravitated to tasks with Madge or she had arranged it that way. But the time came when he no longer doubted. That fixed his distant exterior, but it added more and more to the tumult within.

The tasks she set him, and completed with him, would never be remembered. As the minutes sped by he seemed hardly conscious of anything besides her presence—her intense and zestful activity, her requests and suggestions, and her talk in between, the intimacy that she seemed not to notice but which he felt so subtly, the play of her lovely features and the changing expressions in her violet eyes, her laugh, her smile, her grace, her disheveled golden hair falling over her face to be brushed back with a beautiful hand.

And at last, how it came about he could not say, they had finished all present tasks, and she was offering him a cigarette.

"No thanks," he said, easily.

"Don't you smoke?"

"Sure. Once in a while."

"Lance, you're one swell assistant. I think I'll promote you, if . . ."

"To what?"

"Oh, major-domo or gigolo—or just cavalier."

"It'll be all I can do to make good as a cowboy. That is—here!"

"How modest and cool you are! I'd like it, if I could be sure you were sincere. You don't ring true, darling."

He had no reply for that. They had come out into the patio, and Lance was walking slowly toward the back, with apparent composure and the respectful demeanor of a cowboy toward the boss's daughter. She walked with him, cigarette in hand. Somewhere near by Starr and Bonita were quarreling, but Madge gave no sign she heard them. Lance felt that he must escape at once, or he would betray what he knew not. Yet the bitter paradox was that another self of him longed to linger there.

"Oh, I forgot. There's a nice room at that end of the patio. I want you to have it."

"But, I—thank you, Miss Stewart. I have my bunkhouse lodgings."

"Yes. I peeped in there one day while you were out. Nels showed me. Rotten for even a cowboy. And you're a gentleman, Lance."

"Thanks again. But I'm satisfied down there."

"I expect you to help entertain my guests."

"*What!*" He was tremendously surprised, and could say no more.

"Why should you be so surprised? Because you've been rude to me and I've been selfish?—That's nothing. We can give, and take it, too. . . . These boys and girls will be tenderfeet. I must have some real western he-man around on occasions—especially where my horses are concerned. I'd like to trust you with that job."

"But your father wants Ren and me to ride the range, build and dig and what not."

"So Dad told me. Ren can attend to that with the *vaqueros. I* want you."

"Are you giving me an order?"

"I am inviting you—*asking* you to be a friend—a good sport," she retorted, her eyes flashing.

"You are very—kind. But in that case I must refuse."

"Don't you like me?" she demanded, incredulously.

"Miss Stewart, that is a personal matter," he replied, looking straight ahead.

"You *do* like me," she asserted.

"If you put it that way, I'm afraid I must be rude again. You are mistaken," he rejoined, and his voice sounded curiously strange to his throbbing ears. But he was telling the truth. He did not like Madge Stewart because he loved her. The silence grew almost unbearable. He steeled himself against sarcasm, anger, wounded vanity. When they reached the wide green-bordered exit from the patio, when she stopped, he simply had to look at her. The last thing he expected was to see her eyes brimming with tears. She looked by him, out over the slope to the range. Her wide eyes were softly blurred, dark with pain.

"Lance, I can take it," she said, presently, and lifted her cigarette to her lips. It had gone out. "Have you a match?" He produced one, struck and held it for her, and she blew a cloud of smoke, with apparent unintention, into his face. When the blue cloud cleared away he could not have believed she could possibly have looked hurt.

"Anyone can start something. But it takes a real sport to finish."

Did she refer to an affair with him or the acquisition of his horse, or was it the passionate pride of a woman in herself? He answered by saying that he feared he, at least, had undertaken something he could never finish, and bidding her good night he left her. On the way down he took a short cut off the back road into a trail, and lingered on a secluded spot, from which he could see the flaming range on fire with sunset. The critical hour of his life had struck. He loved this girl, and the emotion seemed a coalescing of all his former fancies and loves, magnified into an incredible passion too great to understand or hate or resist. It did not require to be brooded over and analyzed and made certain. Like an avalanche it fell upon him. It was too terrible in its fatality, too transporting in its bliss, too great to be ashamed of. But it must be his secret. He swore he would die before he would let this man hunter and love taster, who like a savage princess exacted homage, this frail, spoiled, lovely creature know that he loved her.

Before dusk settled down thickly, Lance had fought out the battle, losing in his surrender to the catastrophe that had overtaken him, but victor over his weakness. Nevertheless he realized anew that he should straddle Umpqua and ride away before another day dawned. As he was not big enough to do that he did not blind himself to the peril that played and led him on.

No matter how troubled and hopeless he felt when he lay down at night, when morning dawned, with all the exquisite freshness and sweetness of this country, and the golden light over the range, he seemed to be transformed, renewed, to be glad of life and youth, and the nameless hope that beckoned him on.

Returning from his tasks at the corrals he found Madge and

Nels puttering around her car. She wore a blue hat, blue gown, blue gloves—everywhere she appeared as blue as her eyes.

"Heah, son, come an' help," called Nels. "I don't know a darn thing aboot these enjines."

Madge's look of annoyance vanished as Lance strode up to the car.

"What's the matter?"

"The damn thing won't start," she said, smiling.

"You have a mechanic here. Cars are Starr's specialty."

"He's gone. Will you oblige me?"

Lance leisurely lifted the hood of the engine, to see at a glance what was wrong, and in a moment adjusted it.

"How easy for *you*!" she flashed. "I'm terribly grateful. . . . Won't you ride in to town with me?"

"What for?"

"Well, it might go on the blink again."

"Not a chance."

"All right. Then—just for the ride," she returned.

Lance returned her look with a feeling that he knew he was the only man on earth who could have refused her and who must suffer the anguish of despair because he had done so.

"I'm sorry, Miss Stewart. I've no time. Your father relies on me for certain things. And I'm glad to relieve him of many labors—if I can't of worries."

"Noble of you, big boy! . . . Strike a match for me. I have my gloves on," she rejoined, and leaned over the door with the cigarette between her lips. Lance had to step close, and he executed her request, but to save his life he could not have stilled the quiver of his hand as he held the match. She could not have seen it, however, for her unfathomable eyes were fastened upon his face. Then, with a merry good-by to him and Nels, she drove away. Not until she had gone down the slope did Lance realize he had watched her. Evidently Nels had done the same.

"Wal, son, she's kinda set on disturbin' you," he drawled.

"Nels, I'll never last here," he replied, poignantly.

"Shore you will. We all like you, cowboy, an' thet applies to Majesty Stewart, too."

"Hell no!" ejaculated Lance, borrowing Starr's expressive language.

"Sidway, I've knowed thet girl since she was borned," declared Nels. "You don't figger her atall. You made her mad at you fust off. I reckon thet was good, if you're as nutty aboot her as Starr swears you air."

"Nels, did he tell you that? I'll sock him, by thunder!—Isn't there anything or anybody on this ranch but that girl?"

"Wal, she seems to be the center of things, whirlin' them like a dust devil."

All day long Lance glanced up from this and that task to see if there was a car raising the dust down on the valley road. Nevertheless he accomplished three days' work in one, so strenuously did he apply himself. When he went in to supper, Starr sat there, owl-eyed and pretending innocence. His entrance evidently disrupted some kind of a eulogy Nels was delivering to Stewart.

"Sidway, I've got to hand it to you," said the rancher, warmly. "You're a glutton for work."

"I don't hate work, sir."

Starr sat up in mild reproof. "Heah, you queer duck from Oregon, you aint no hawg fer eatin', I'll tell you thet. An' if you keep on doin' ten greasers' work on an empty stummick you'll be an angel in heaven."

"Been off my feed lately," Lance admitted, after the laugh subsided.

"Sidway, are you any good at figures?" asked Stewart. "My accounts are in a tangle. I never was any good at them. Nels can't add two and two to make four. And Starr never went to school."

"Aw, Boss! The hell I didn't. I can read an' write some."

"Stewart, your daughter can, I'll bet. It must have cost you a lot to educate her. Why not make her your bookkeeper?"

"I wouldn't have Madge see what a poor business man I am for anything. . . . Can you straighten out my accounts for me?"

"Be glad to, Boss. I had a course in bookkeeping. I'm not so hot at it, but ordinary figures are not beyond me."

"Nels, I'll bet our new range hand is hot all around," interposed Starr.

"Ren, he started well. But any fool can start. It's stickin' to the finish that counts."

The cowman's lazy drawl of humor recalled Madge's subtle expression of the very same thought.

"Shall I come up right away?" asked Lance.

"No. I'll fetch the books down. I had to hide them from Madge. She came home full of the Old Nick. She'd be curious, and maybe offended, if she found out about it."

When Stewart was gone, Ren stared solemnly at Lance. "Pard, did you get thet? Full of the Old Nick!"

"Are *you* going to begin again?" burst out Lance. "You're most as bad as Nels. Give me a rest about Madge Stewart."

"Rest! You cain't have a rest. Never again so long as you live! Thet's what Bonita did to me, only not anyways so bad. . . . Pard, I smelled hard likker on Majesty's breath!"

"Yeah? When did she come home?"

"Couple hours ago. She was sweeter'n a basket of roses. But I got a scent like a wolf's."

"What of that? She drinks. All these college girls drink. It's nothing. No more than cigarettes."

"Shore. I read the magazines an' go to the movies. But, pard, it's different in Majesty's case. It worries me an' Nels."

"And why? You're wasting your time."

"Son," interposed Nels, gravely. "Gene Stewart was the hardest drinkin' cowboy on this range. He was a drunkard. For ten years he swore off. Thet was on account of Madeline. Then he drank again—oncet in a long while—an' he does now. When he said Majesty come home full of the Old Nick, me an'

Ben hed the same idee. Did he mean drink? An' is he afeared his girl has inherited his weakness for strong likker?"

"Oh, fellows, the boss didn't mean that," expostulated Lance. "I'm sure he didn't. He just meant mischief. . . . My God, that'd be a tough spot for Stewart! He's one grand guy."

"Wal, you said it. Pard, if she asked you to ride in town with her how'n hell did you keep from it?"

"I've got a job and a sense of responsibility. Besides, she just wants to make a—a chump out of me."

"Son, don't you let her," declared Nels.

"Wal, I hope to Gawd you can keep from it," added Ren, fervently. "Say, Sid, there'll be high jinks goin' on if them girls air the least like Majesty. Comin' day after tomorrow."

"Lord help us!"

"Son, it shore looks like you'd hev to be the Lord. Fer all of us air under her thumb," said Nels, so very earnestly that Lance could not laugh.

"That's telling me, Nels," replied Lance, and went to his own room. He stumbled over something soft, then ran into a chair that had not been there in the morning. He could not locate his table. Even in the pitch blackness the room felt different and smelled differently.

"What in the deuce has come off?" he muttered, and taking out his matches, he struck one. This colorful clean-smelling room could not be his. Yes, it was—because he heard Nels and Ren talking through the partition. Burning his fingers in his astonishment he struck another match to light the lamp. But where was his plain, cheap, stinking lamp? Here was a shining one of brass with a big white globe. Rugs on the floor, curtains at the two windows, a dresser with a fine mirror, pictures on the walls, a new three-quarter bright-blanketed bed where his bunk had been, a washstand with colored ware upon it, and towels the quality of which no cowboy before had ever felt, a comfortable Morris chair beside his table, and . . . but his roving gaze encountered a striking photograph in a silver frame upon his table. Majesty Stewart! With a groan he took the picture and fell into the chair, to stare down upon the lovely face, the speaking eyes, the bare neck of this girl who had bewitched him.

"Damn you! damn you!" he whispered, softly. It seemed a long while before he became aware of whispers and low laughs in Nels' room.

"Hey, pard, air you daid?" came through the wall.

"No! But I wish I were," shouted Lance.

"Why fer, you big stiff? . . . You oughta see my bunk-house. My Gawd!—Pard, what's thet fairy-guy we used to read about when we was kids? Aladdin! Thet's the *hombre*. Wal, he's been here. . . . Nels told me the servants fetched all this truck down today, an' Bonita fixed the rooms up. An' a swell job she did!"

At that juncture Stewart stamped into Nels' room. Lance hid the picture, and hurried out, and into the ranchman's presence. "Here you are, Jack-of-all-trades," said Stewart, gayly, and he opened a ledger on Nels' table. "Balanced proper up to this page and date. And there's a year and more of figures. Sidway, if you make sense of these I'll be obliged."

"I'll hop to it, Boss."

It was midnight when Lance straightened out those accounts. The last entry was of seven hundred and thirty steers sold at thirty-five dollars a head—payment not yet received. Among the bank statements, papers and correspondence were a batch relative to Madge Stewart's income and expenses. Over a period of time a yearly income of sixty thousand dollars had diminished until at the present it had shrunk to a few thousands. The correspondence indicated that from time to time bonds and stocks had been transferred from Madeline Stewart's account to that of her daughter.

"Gosh! I wonder if Stewart really meant me to see these," pondered Lance. "All as plain as print! Mother and father sacrificing themselves to the extravagance of spoiled daughter! And she doesn't know it!—Can you beat that?"

Lance's troubled mind yielded to the exhaustion of a hard

day and toilsome hours with figures, and he slept. Ren's pounding on his door awakened him. After breakfast Stewart appeared and Lance brought him the ledger.

"All done, sir, and not so bad except for—for these," said Lance. "Accounts, you know, of your daughter."

"*Sidway!* Did I leave them in this book?" ejaculated Stewart, utterly discomfited.

"Evidently you did. Of course, I went over them. I'm sorry, sir."

"If she ever found this out . . ."

"Stewart, she won't from me," interrupted Lance, hurriedly, hoping to relieve the rancher of embarrassment. "And—as for your own accounts, sir—they're not so bad as you led me to believe. When you receive the money for that batch of cattle sold the other day, you can pay your debts and have around five thousand dollars left."

"No!—Sidway, you're—you're . . . . it'd be too good to be true."

"Maybe you did not figure out just what you'd receive for the cattle."

"I didn't at that."

"Well, it comes to twenty-five thousand, five hundred and fifty dollars. Quite a lump sum, sir."

"I must have made a big mistake on the wrong side."

"You evidently did."

"I was thinking most of Madeline," replied Stewart, his dark eyes softening. "Sidway, I reckon Starr is right about you."

"That knock-kneed windbag! Now what'd he say?"

"I don't remember it all. One thing stuck, though. He called you a whiz."

Lance felt that he had never received a compliment that had pleased him more. He went to work that day and drove Starr to distraction and dragged him home a cripple.

"Look at me, Nels," whined Ren, wet with sweat, grimy and ragged.

"Hey, Sid, who's this heah nigger you fetched in?" drawled Nels.

"It's me, Nels. Me!—Worked to death by thet fiend. An' what I hate most in all this world is diggin' postholes!"

"We finished that corral, didn't we? Now we can have some peace when Manuel and Jose wrangle Miss Stewart's horses. . . . Oh boy—tomorrow!"

"Me for the hills!" ejaculated Ren.

Lance was waiting for Starr the following night at sunset. Inside Nels was banging pans in unusual excitement.

"Pard, what'n hell's wrong with you?" demanded Ren, staring.

"Behold a—a—devastated man!"

"Wal, whatever'n hell thet means you shore air it. . . . So you obeyed them orders?"

"Yes. They were Stewart's."

"An' you had to ride in town with Majesty—all alone—and meet her friends—all them peaches we jest know air comin' —an' be a swell lady's guy?"

"You said it!"

"My Gawd, how tough! Jest the rottenest break ever. Wait till I bed down my hawse an' I'll be ready to be deevasstated."

After supper Ren got up to help Nels with the dishes and he said: "Okay now, pard. Shoot! I reckon I'm strong enough now."

"What do you want to know?"

"Tell us aboot Majesty's outfit."

"Well, the boys are all nice clean-cut college chaps. You'll like them, especially the big football player, Snake Elwell. He's a regular fellow."

"Aw, nix on the fellers. It's the gurls Nels an' me want to heah about."

"Six of them, Ren. *Six!* And they might have been picked for a swell movie. . . . The gang arrived at ten-thirty. They stayed in town until three. Five awful hours! If I performed one job, there were a hundred. They probably were kidding me or Madge, for the whole bunch of crazy women went after me. Poor little me! While the boys hung around Madge. They ate and they drank. Can that crowd lap up the booze? I'm telling you. And they had to see everything and everybody in Bolton."

"Swell. But thet ain't tellin' us how they stacked up."

"Can't you wait till you lamp them?"

"Nope. Me an' Nels hev artistic feelin's."

"Well, here goes—the way I got it. Allie Leland first, evidently Madge's best friend, a slim stylish girl with gray eyes, the peach of the bunch, I'd say, though not in looks. Next Maramee Joyce, brown beauty built like Jean Harlow, a knockout. Next a little southern girl, looks like sixteen but must be twenty-two. Dark, vivacious, with a smile that would drive any man nutty, and a sweet southern accent. Nels will fall for her. Then Pequita Nelson. Part Spanish, Ren. Creamy olive skin, great dreamy sloe-black eyes, willowy and graceful. Blue-blood, pard. . . . Then Selma Thorne, a blonde that, if you never saw Madge, would do the trick. And last Beulah Allen. . . . Whew! Ren, here's a peach that's a composite of honey, dynamite and autumn leaves of red and gold. Pretty! Why, she's so pretty I couldn't take my eyes off her. Red-headed, roguish-eyed, and a shape! What's more she's a devil clear down to her toes."

"Pard!" gasped Ren, utterly fascinated. "What'n hell air we up agin? It was bad enough with only Majesty heah. We shore air a deevasstated outfit."

"Ren, you should have heard the whoop those college tenderfeet let out when they saw Bonita."

"Ahuh. Wal, I'll be liable to shoot a laig off one of them," growled Ren.

Work on the ranch for Lance and Ren, except an occasional and brief overseeing of laborers brought out from town, practically ceased. Their jobs took on manifold aspects. They had to drive and to ride, especially the latter. The only girl guest who knew anything about horses was Dixie Conn. Madge's horses were all too spirited for tenderfeet. Lance and Ren disagreed as to Madge's own ability to handle several of her mounts.

"Say, Ren, you're all wet," protested Lance. "She was a swell horsewoman once. Nels vouched for that. But she has been to college for four years. She's forgotten a lot. Besides she's out of condition. She's soft, if you get what I mean."

"Cain't you lay off yore grouch?" complained Ren. "Majesty is okay."

"So far as looks are concerned, yes. She looks grand. And that's all you see. Ren, you ought to be back at that garage."

The expression of Starr's face became so peculiar, and a giggle of Bu Allen sounded so gleeful that Lance turned toward the wide stable door. Madge had entered and she had heard him. Likewise had Rollie Stevens and Nate Salisbury, who were with her. The others appeared coming down the lane.

The purple fire in Madge's eyes was no new catastrophe for Lance. As a matter of fact, he had never seen it blaze for anyone or anything except him. Nevertheless this time, as always, it stimulated him to battle. Perhaps he labored under the delusion that he was right, but so long as he believed so he would not give in.

"Ren, saddle Dervish for me," ordered Madge, quietly.

Lance stepped forward and laid an ungentle hand on the cowboy. "Miss Stewart, please forgive my interference. But you should not ride Dervish—just yet. You—he . . ."

"I heard you express your opinions to Ren," she interrupted, in a tone that made Lance feel as if he were the scum of the earth. "You can save your breath."

"That I won't do so long as I am a cowboy on this ranch," replied Lance, coolly, as he found himself. "I have a duty here —to your father—and through him to you. . . . Dervish is a bad actor. He has not been worked out. Besides he does not like you, Miss Stewart. It's dangerous for you to mount him."

"Majesty, listen to Sidway," interposed Rollie, his fine face earnest. "That horse looks skittish to me."

Dixie Conn backed up Stevens, and the other girls apparently fell in line. This, Lance knew, was only adding fuel to the fire. He believed that if they only had advised it, Madge would have been amenable. But Lance Sidway was waving a red flag in her face.

"Ren, do as you're ordered," said Madge.

"Miss Majesty, mebbe Lance is right about this."

"I know I'm right," Lance said, earnestly. "Nels agreed with me. He saw you on Bellefontaine the other day, and Bell isn't half the horse this Dervish is. May I repeat what Nels said to me?"

"Why, yes, if it pleases you so much," rejoined Madge.

"He told me to keep you off the wicked horses if I could."

"Nels! The old traitor! He taught me to ride."

"He said also that when you were sixteen there wasn't your beat in this state. . . . Coming from Nels, Miss Stewart, that is the very highest compliment."

"And *you* think sixteen is so far back in my past that I've forgotten how to ride?" queried Madge, with sarcasm. "Well, I'll show you!"

"I didn't say that. I think, though, you act like sixteen or under. . . . Will you force me to go to your father?"

"You wouldn't dare!"

"Yes, I would."

"Go ahead. It'll be a relief to be rid of you. By the time you find Dad I'll be far out on the range."

"Miss Stewart, he will hold me responsible if you are thrown."

"So that's it? Thinking of your job! It's not too sure, at that."

Lance gave up, and went back to saddling Pinto. Starr, at Madge's order, led the slender racy Dervish out of his stall. Lance heard the cowboy curse under his breath. He also heard

Allie Leland, and some of the other girls, taking his part against Madge. And Lance's ears burned with something besides resentment. All these guests of Madge's had been fine to him, and Bu Allen more than friendly. Lance put Pequita Nelson up on Pinto, and hurried on to saddle Leatherstocking. The young men were having the fun of saddling their own horses. Lance liked this bunch of college boys better than he had anticipated.

At last all the girls were up except Madge and she was leading Dervish out into the open. Ren was with her. Lance hurried to get astride Umpqua. The others, except Allie Leland, rode out toward the range.

"Sidway, go with the others," called Madge.

He waited to see her put a foot into Starr's hand and go sailing upon Dervish. She was not in the least afraid of him. There was a red flush in her cheeks, a smoldering fire in her eyes. Lance had to admire her for more than the superb and lovely figure she made on the roan. Then Madge and the Leland girl passed him to join the others. Dervish acted all right, Lance thought, but Madge was holding him in. But could she hold him if he broke into a run or could she stay on if he wanted to pitch? Lance gambled that she would fail in the latter event, anyway. Starr joined him and they loped to catch up with the others.

"Ren, you four flusher, why didn't you stand by me?" queried Lance, with irritation.

"By thunder, I should of," he replied, contritely. "But Majesty always kids me along—makes me reckon I'm a helluva feller."

"Yeah? Well, if you'd come strong, we might have avoided a risk."

"She'll ride thet nag."

"Gosh, I hope so. She handles him great. But Ren, damnit! That's a horse—a mean horse! And she can't weigh more than a hundred and ten."

"Fifteen, pard, and she's strong. I'll admit, though, I forgot she hadn't been ridin'."

"All right, let's go. I'll try to make Madge think I don't care a damn if she breaks her neck. . . . Fact is, I—I don't. But I'll keep an eye on her."

"Me too, pard. Ain't they a swell lookin' outfit? I wish Bonita was heah. Majesty said I could ask her. But I knowed I couldn't see anyone else, then . . . hey! . . ."

Lance rode away from the loquacious cowboy and steadied down conscientiously to his job. Once out in the grass and the sage there was much less danger of accidents. The girls had listened to reason, if their hostess had not. And except Dixie Conn, they were all too scared of horses to try any stunts. Dixie and Madge forged ahead, and Lance kept a position that would enable him to overtake Dervish, if he bolted. But nothing happened across the sage flat to the pine knoll five miles away. Madge led them up to the top of that, then down, and over the rolling range land toward the foothills. Half an hour of lope and trot brought them to the slope.

"Majesty," screamed Maramee Joyce. "For Pete's sake—hold on! I'm dying!"

"I've got that—awful stitch in my—side," cried Selma Thorne.

"We'll rest," replied Madge, merrily. "But how in the world will you girls ever make it up into the mountains?"

"But you're—not going soon?"

"Ah! this is swell, Majesty!"

"Majesty, let's leave these tenderfeet behind on that trip," suggested Snake Ewell, good-naturedly.

"What? You big hunk of protoplasm!" exclaimed Bu Allen, her pretty face scarlet, her roguish eyes snapping, her red hair disheveled. "Why, astride that horse you look as much like Sidway as I do like a rodeo queen."

At length when they were rested Madge gave the word: "Let's go! And step on it!"

As they swept off with merry screams and shouts Lance, with an eye ever on Dervish, saw that he meant business. He balked. And when Madge laid on the spurs he began to pitch.

Lance in a few jumps had Umpqua beside her, but as he reached for the roan's head Madge cried: "Let him alone!"

"But he'll pile you up."

"He will not!"

As bucking horses went, Dervish would have been mean for any rider. But to Lance's surprise Madge stayed in the saddle. Bent double, red-eyed and infuriated, the roan bucked all over the flat, and failed to dislodge the girl. She had her spurs dug into him and sat her saddle as if a part of it.

"You're riding him, cowgirl!" yelled Lance, carried away with her spirit and the spectacle she made.

Then Dervish, succeeding in getting the bit between his teeth, bolted away across the valley, in the opposite direction from the ranch. It took only a glance to see that the roan was a runaway horse and that he would eventually get the best of his rider. Lance spurred Umpqua after him. By now the others were a couple of miles distant toward the ranch, and they were not yet aware of Madge's predicament. The roan was fast. Lance had to urge Umpqua into his top speed to gain at all. And he saw that it was going to be a race. Madge fought her mount with all her might. If she heard Lance yell to let the horse run she gave no sign. The girl had evidently been jolted by the bucking, and now she was spending the last of her strength. She would be thrown.

Then after a grueling run Lance drew close to the roan. Madge showed signs of distress. She was beginning to sway.

"Drop your bridle!" yelled Lance. "Grab the pommel! Hold on!"

She heard him and obeyed. That saved her from an immediate spill. Umpqua thundered closer and closer until his nose passed the roan's flank. But again Madge was swaying. She was near a fall and the ground was rocky, and rough with hummocks. Desperately goading his horse, Lance gained inch by inch, until he stretched out a clutching hand. She had the sense to shake her feet loose from the stirrups. But that loss of stability broke her seat in the saddle. She was in the air when Lance caught her in a grip of steel and swung her up before him.

"Oh!" she screamed, wildly. "You're tearing my flesh!"

Lance let her go, to slip her into the crook of his arm, and hold her across his saddle. Umpqua was excited, too, and hard to slow down.

"Whoa! Steady, old boy!" called Lance, over and over again. "We've got her. . . . There, Ump!—Easy now—easy!"

At length Lance halted the horse and then turned his attention to the girl. Her face lay high up on his left arm, near his shoulder, and it was white. The lipstick on her strained lips made a startling contrast.

"Gosh—I'm—sorry I had to hurt—you," he said, haltingly. "But I—couldn't help it. That damned—roan can run. Lucky to catch you—at all."

"How strong you are!" she exclaimed, her eyes, darkly dilated, upon him. "You had the muscles of my back. I'll bet I can't wear my new formals very soon."

"Shall I get down? Can you ride my horse?" asked Lance, hurriedly.

"I feel very comfortable where I am. . . . Lance, I deserve it. I was wrong—bullheaded—vain. You were right. . . . Now does that soothe your wounded vanity?"

"My feelings don't count. But I don't remember that vanity entered into it."

"Damn you anyway, cowboy!" she exclaimed, broodingly, passionate eyes upon him in speculation.

"That's not very kind," returned Lance, beginning to weaken under another kind of strain. She was resting in his arms, her head now on his shoulder. A little color began to creep into her cheeks. Lance almost collapsed under a terrific longing to kiss her.

"For *you* to be the one always to catch me in the wrong—do me a service! . . . It's a tough break."

"Miss Stewart, I had a hunch about this horse."

"For the love of Mike stop calling me Miss. Why don't you cuss me out?" she replied, hotly.

"To tell the truth I—I don't know why," answered Lance, lamely. He sensed that fatality for him consisted in being with her, and this close contact was insupportable. If he did not get away from it instantly he could not answer for himself. She was in his arms and if she did not like it, she was acting a part. Then Lance saw Starr approaching in a long sweeping gallop, and the others a mile or more behind.

"They're coming," said Lance, in relief, as he carefully slid with her out of the saddle. "Can you stand?"

"I can—if you hold me." And she swayed against him.

"Miss . . . Madge, you're not hurt so—bad," he protested.

"That's what you say. My back is broken."

"Nonsense!" cried Lance, in alarm, and he turned her round to feel of her. "It's just bruised—sore. I must have pinched you."

She squealed as he felt to see if he had broken a rib.

"You're a swell western girl—I don't think. Can't you take it?"

"What do *you* think, Lance Sidway?"

"God only knows!" he responded, with an inward groan. "Here's Ren. And the others are coming. Sit down. I'll ride after Dervish."

He found upon releasing her that she could stand easily enough.

"What'n hell come off?" shouted Starr, as he leaped from his saddle.

"Only me," laughed Madge.

Lance thankfully galloped off to catch Dervish, now contentedly grazing half a mile away. What a girl! He was slipping—slipping. Then his softer agitation burned away in a tumult, some of which emotion was wrath. He had not had half a chance. To save her life, or at least, a nasty spill, was just his hard luck. All in a second to find her in his arms! Hell! What was a girl like that for? Her lying lovely eyes would make an imbecile out of a cigar-store Indian. Yet there seemed to be something so sweet, so square about her. If only she had not hated him, maybe he never would have known of her other nature! But that would have been worse. At length he caught Dervish, and by the time he had returned to the waiting group he was outwardly his cool self again.

"Did you beat him?" asked Madge.

"No. I never beat horses."

Ren glowered at the sweating roan, as he stood meekly, his racy head drooping. "Wal, I'll beat him some day, believe me."

"I wonder—why is he so kind to dumb brutes," said Madge, cryptically. "Listen, friends. Sidway saved my neck. After I refused to listen to him—insulted him! I am a cat. Now you shall see me apologize."

She turned to Lance in one of her bewildering flashes. "Lance, I am sorry. I beg your pardon. You were swell to keep your temper—and stay a gentleman. I'll tell Dad. And I'll not get on Dervish very soon again—if ever."

"That's just fine," replied Lance, heartily. "Now you ride Umpqua home. He's gentle and easy."

"What will you do?" she asked.

"I'll ride Dervish. He's worked off his edge now." He helped her mount and shortened the stirrups while the others expressed their relief in various ways. The girls, especially, had been frightened. The boys, except Rollie Stevens, quickly recovered their spirits. Then just as the cavalcade got into motion, Bu Allen said slyly:

"Lance, if I ride Dervish some time will you be a hero for me?"

Chapter Eight

THAT night after supper, when Starr, in the next room, was exaggerating the story of Madge's adventure on Dervish, and Lance sat in his big chair gazing at the beautiful photograph, there came a soft step outside and a tap on his door. Hastily hiding the picture of Madge, and with a leap of his heart he called: "Come in."

The door opened to disclose Beulah Allen on the threshold. She wore a henna gown that matched her hair, cut to expose her creamy arms and neck. Her charm appeared considerably magnified.

"Good evening, Lance. Here I am," she said, archly.

Lance awkwardly returned her greeting, then: "So I see Who's with you?"

"I'm alone. I had a scrap with Snake, so I thought I'd hunt you up."

"Swell.—Only, what'll Snake do to me?"

"He hasn't any strings on me. We've been engaged several times and broken it off as often. Tonight is the last."

Lance had arisen, and now he stood looking at her, fully aware of her seductiveness, and half inclined to yield to it.

"How swell you are here! Madge got a kick out of dolling up these rooms. Isn't she a peach? Always playing Santa Claus!"

"Indeed, she's very kind. Which reminds me—in the excitement today I forgot to thank her."

"She hates to be thanked. . . . Aren't you going to ask me in?"

"No. But I'll come out," replied Lance, and taking his sombrero he joined her and led her off the porch. She took his arm and remarked that the night and the full moon were made for love.

"Yeah?—But how about a guy, who if he fell, would be down for good?"

"You?"

"I'm telling you. Beulah, you're one attractive kid. I like you. I'll be glad to help you with your riding—as you asked me. But don't get me in bad with Snake Elwell. He might beat hell out of me."

"I don't know about that. Snake can run with a football. But he gets hurt easily. Always crippled."

"You little devil!" laughed Lance. "Honest now, isn't Snake in love with you?"

"Yes," she admitted, reluctantly. "But he's not alive."

"Beulah, I've met a lot of young fellows. Elwell is not flashy. He's a rough diamond. He's a regular guy. If you liked him well enough to be engaged to him you oughtn't to play fast and loose with him."

"I don't."

"What do you call this? Coming to my quarters after me?"

"Lance, if you must be serious, I came because I felt a little out of it tonight. There's an odd girl, you know. Snake belongs to the same fraternity as the other boys. But I don't belong to Majesty's sorority."

"Oh, I see. . . . But she wouldn't slight you?"

"No. She's a thoroughbred—a real sport. And I'd be crazy about her if she'd let me. She's just a little aloof with me. And I'm as proud as the dickens. So when Snake made me mad, I beat it to you."

"I'm sure flattered. Let's walk down to the village cantina, and have a Mexican cone."

It was dark except for starlight. Lance thought that the ground was hardly uneven enough for Beulah to hang onto him so tightly. But after a while he put his arm around her. When they reached the cantina, with its open vine-covered porch and dim lights, he did not remove his arm in time to escape Bonita's black eyes. She was there with a group of young people, and her escort was a Mexican lad Lance had never seen. He was of the *vaquero* type, a born rider, lithe of form, lean of face, and he had small glittering dark eyes. As Lance passed the table where they were sitting his keen faculties grasped Bonita's jealousy and her friend's uneasy lowering of his face. It strengthened his suspicion that some of these admirers of Bonita could have shed some light upon the rustlers.

"Hello, Bonita. Ren is looking for you," hazarded Lance, with a meaning glance. When her dusky eyes dilated widely he knew he had hit some kind of a mark. Before he and Beulah had finished their ice cream, Bonita left with her escort. The incident determined Lance to pay more attention to Danny Main's pretty daughter.

It developed that Beulah had an intense interest in motion pictures, about which Lance talked at length, and in fact all the way up the hill to the ranch house. She led him in through the corridor to the brightly lighted living room, where Madge and part of her guests sat at two card tables, and the others grouped around Stewart and his wife. Most of them were dressed in white. Lance had to bear the sight of Madge supremely lovely in filmy blue.

Their entrance put a stop to games and conversation. Beulah, flushed and radiant, made the most of the situation. It invoked various greetings, all full of fun and interest.

"Beulah, you look stunning," observed Madge. "What's your recipe for such glamour? My cowboy! . . . Where'd you pick him up?"

"Oh, Lance came up after me," returned Beulah, sweetly. "He took me to the village—for a cone."

"For a which?"

"Cone?"

"You mean ice-cream cone?"

"Yes. It was swell. I'd have liked one of those Mexican drinks we had in town, but I guess Lance doesn't buy drinks for girls. . . . We saw that pretty Bonita. Say, she's got IT!"

"Come on, Barg," spoke up Nate Salisbury. "Let's drive down and grab a cone." And the two young men went tearing out.

"Mr. Sidway, do you play bridge?" asked Madge, politely.

"I tried it once. Didn't get the hang of it."

"Do you play any game—that is, *card* game?"

"Poker."

"Of course. Ren plays poker. We'll have you up some night."

"Thanks a lot. I'll hate to take your money. But I'll come. . . . I'm glad to see you okay, after your run on Dervish."

"I may look okay in front. . . . See, you ironfisted cowboy!" And Madge arose to turn her back. The V-shaped opening in her gown extended clear to her waistline. About half way down, disfiguring her lovely back, showed black and blue marks of a ruthless hand.

"I'm sorry!" burst out Lance, his surprise and regret checking other feelings. "That's terrible. . . . But, Miss Stewart, how could I help it?"

Madge's slow smile might have promised much. However, at this point, Stewart called the cowboy: "Sidway, I've had several versions of this runaway. Madge wouldn't say anything. From the looks of her back, though, I'd say you laid hold of her hard. Nels whitewashed the accident. Starr didn't see it, nor did the others. Come now, what's your story?"

"Mr. Sidway, take this chair here," interposed Mrs. Stewart, beckoning Lance to a seat beside her. He felt the penetrating kindness of her eyes.

"Thank you. . . . Well, really, there wasn't much danger. For a western girl!" replied Lance, deprecatingly, with a casual gesture. "Dervish began to pitch. Mad—Miss Stewart stayed in the saddle. Then he nailed the bit and lit out. Ren had gone with the outfit. I chased Dervish across the flat. He can run, that roan. I caught up with him—and grabbed her—a little roughly, I'm sorry to say."

"Did you forget my instructions?" queried Stewart, his kind eyes twinkling. "I forbade Madge to ride Dervish. And I told you not to let her get on any bad horse. You're a judge of horses, aren't you?"

"Not so good. I—I'm afraid I forgot, sir," returned Lance, not meeting Stewart's eye.

"Dad, your cowboy is a liar," spoke up Madge, in her rich voice, that now had a little ring. "In fact he's an awful liar. . . . He advised me not to ride Dervish. He insisted that I must not. He made me furious by threatening to hunt you up. But you know your little Madge, Dad. . . . Dervish worked out fine as long as I held him in. We rested a while. When I mounted again he began to pitch. He made me see red, and hurt me—took it all out of me. Finding he couldn't unseat me, the devil beat it up the valley. I stayed on somehow. After a while I heard Umpqua pounding at my heels. And Sidway yelled: 'Let him run! Hold on!' But for that I'd have gone off. The rocky ground scared me stiff. My arms went dead. I lost my stirrups. Just then, as I pitched out of the saddle, Sidway caught me. He certainly put his brand on me. . . . But, Dad, he saved me broken bones, perhaps a crushed face—maybe my life!"

Lance groaned in spirit to be thus made out a hero, yet her eloquence radiated through him, and added another link to the chain that was fettering him.

"Sidway, modesty is a becoming trait, but hardly justifies your lying to your boss to save his willful and wayward daughter," said Stewart, mildly.

"Dad, don't rub it in," called Madge, mirthfully. Then, taking up her cards, "Where was I, Allie?"

The card players settled down to their game again. Mrs. Stewart began to ask Lance about Oregon, and she was so gracious and interested that he found himself telling her of his boyhood home, of his mother and sister, about that sister's malady, and how he had left college to take Umpqua to Hollywood, how wonderfully the great horse had made good, how he loved him and would not part with him for the world, and finally how he had set out for Arizona and New Mexico.

"Majesty Stewart! You trumped my ace!" exclaimed Rollie Stevens, incredulously.

"She's transported!" declared Allie.

"Listening to Mr. Sidway," chimed in Maramee, with a giggle. "Majesty, you're not very flattering to us."

"Caught with the goods!" cried Madge, leaping up with a blush, and slamming down her cards. "I hate bridge anyway. . . . Turn on the radio, you all. Or play the Victrola. Dance! What'd you come here for? . . . Mom, please surrender Mr. Sidway to me for a little. I want him to talk to *me*!" And approaching Lance she tugged at his sleeve. He arose, bowed to Mrs. Stewart, and allowed himself to be led toward the door.

"Madge, take a coat or wrap, if you're going into the patio," advised her mother.

"There's one in the hammock, Mom."

Rollie Stevens called forcefully after them. "Majesty, I'll cut in—what do you call it—pronto."

"He will, the sap!" whispered Madge. "But we'll fool him." The patio was silver-bright under a full moon. The fountain tinkled, there was a stir of leaves, and peep of sleepy birds. Madge caught up a white coat from the first hammock and gave it to Lance. He helped her into it, and turned up the wide collar, and buttoned the upper buttons, his fingers clumsy, while she stood still and gazed up at him with eyes he felt but dared not meet. Then she took his arm and led him along the wide porch, where the shadows of foliage played black on the tiles. Lance was helpless in the thrall of the moment.

"Lance, it's coming to you right now—while I'm hot under the spell," declared Madge. "Beulah Allen has fallen for you. They all saw that. I saw it long ago. What did you do to her? She sailed in positively regal. That was for my benefit, Lance Sidway. Only yesterday I told the girls you didn't neck. What a liar you've made me out! . . . They all like you. Dad doesn't throw a fit over every fellow who comes along, not even a cowboy. And Mom! . . . Young man, do you know you couldn't pull a greater stroke here than that? I listened. It couldn't be a line. All that about your sister! Oh, Lance. . . . Mom likes you! That is the last straw! My lovely patrician mother!"

"She was just—moved by my—my service to you," said Lance, unsteadily.

"No. Don't start that stuff. This is serious," she rejoined, and halting beyond the last archway, she turned to him in the white moonlight. In that light, shining from the pale oval of her face, her eyes held the sum of all beauty. "Isn't it a pity—I don't like you?"

"Maybe that is lucky for me," he returned, huskily.

"Lance, are you engaged to any girl in Oregon?"

"No—indeed."

"Are you fancy-free?"

"Yes," he lied, glibly enough.

"You made a play for Bonita. Oh, I know. She gave you away—and herself. I was brazen enough to pump her. . . . Lance, do you know Ren Starr has a terrible case on Bonita?"

"I found that out pronto."

"You were only playing with her?"

"I didn't admit that."

"Aren't you?"

"Not since I found out about Ren."

"Listen, these college friends of mine, particularly Barg and Nate, are nuts over that little Mexican hussy. She's half white, yes, but the Latin blood dominates."

"Bonita isn't quite all that," rejoined Lance, stoutly.

"She is. And I'm a jealous cat. But all this is for Ren's sake. . . . You seem to be as big as that mountain there. Are you big enough to play Ren's game—to keep these college devils away from her? They're on the make. One or the other, most likely Nate, will get her."

"I'm afraid I'm not quite so—so big as that," answered

Lance, led on and on by the deadly sweetness of her, and by the infernal power of his bleeding vanity.

She released his arm and averted her face. Like a cameo the perfect profile shone as if cut out of marble. The night breeze stirred her golden hair. "I'm disappointed in you—again."

"Why should you be, Miss Stewart?" he queried, stiffly, fighting a struggle almost vain. "I'm human—the same as you. Just no good!"

"How dare you!" she cried, wheeling with a startled movement. "Smile—when you say that."

But Lance did not smile. She had wanted to be serious and he had told her the truth. Without a word she left him standing there. Lance stepped into the black shadow of the wall, his thoughts whirling, his conscience stinging, his judgment at fault, his love valiantly championing this perverse and wayward beauty. A thousand wild queries did not lodge in his mind, let alone find an answer. There was not any answer to anything. Why had she asked those direct thought-provoking questions? How easy to escape from her if she were only like Beulah! But Madge Stewart had the insidious power to make men believe in her sincerity. Her look was enough to lift any poor masculine fool to the seventh heaven—to be convinced that he was the one man!

Lance's endless ravings were disrupted by approaching voices. Two people were coming down the patio path. Then Madge's silver laughter, a little mocking, froze Lance to the spot. They came clear to the inside wall.

"Majesty, you drive me mad," came in Rollie Stevens' subdued voice. "You know you have no use for that cowboy. You told me so. Yet for days now you've been rotten to me, on his account! Oh, I get it! Sidway hasn't fallen for you—and that's piqued your vanity. Besides you want his horse. Why don't you give the fellow a break? He's a real man. He's not a sap. But pretty soon he'll fall for you, even if he knows you're not on the level with him."

"Rollie, I might be in earnest," she scoffed.

"Rot! Why, Majesty Stewart, only a month ago you said you—you might marry me."

"That was a month ago, darling. An age!"

"Majesty, you can't marry a cowboy," he expostulated, incredulously.

"Rollie, I hadn't thought of that. But—why couldn't I?"

"You're a lady of quality, a talented girl. Why he's not of your class. Admitting Sidway is a fine chap—I like him, Majesty—you couldn't marry him. Oh, to talk of it is preposterous."

"All right. Skip it. . . . Rollie! don't kiss me right here in the moonlight."

"I'll bet he did," he returned, hoarsely.

"Who?"

"Your cowboy!"

"He never even thought of it."

"My word!—Majesty, can you expect me to believe that?"

"No, I don't."

A slight scuffle followed, a protest from the girl, then the soft sounds of kisses.

"Rollie, you needn't tear my clothes off. Pick up my coat. And remember, my back is too sore for hugging."

"Darling—it maddens me—to taste your lips. I'm just wafted . . ."

"New kind of lipstick! All over your face. And mine too."

"Majesty, honest to God—didn't that Sidway even kiss you?"

"No, Rollie. He didn't even try, I'm ashamed to admit."

"He could have kissed you! All the boys kiss you! It was campus talk!"

"You jealous sap! Surely he could have—and they do. I rather like it. And besides what's a kiss?"

"You know what it leads to, Majesty Stewart."

"Yeah? Well, it never led me anywhere in particular yet, except to muss my dress and make-up, as you've done."

"I'm sorry. But you drive me wild. . . . Kiss me good-night, sweet. A real one, like you used . . ."

"There, little boy. Let us go back. I am cold."

Then soft footfalls and subdued voices faded away. Lance plunged down the trail like a blind man. He had his answer.

Every morning Lance awakened under the shadow of impending calamity. What was going to happen next? Or what would Madge be up to doing? It did not make the slightest difference to Lance, only he seemed to be the one doomed to encounter her in moments of stress.

Things happened to Madge's guests. Pinto ran off with Beulah; Pequita, who was a poor swimmer, fell or was pushed off the platform into the lake, and nearly drowned; Maramee was kicked in the ankle so badly that she could not ride; Allie lolled around all day on the sandy beach and was blistered by the sun. In spite of the fact that Stewart insisted on Lance's keeping a close watch upon the girls, accidents happened.

According to Starr the long-looked-for camping trip in the mountains was approaching; and that, for two lone cowboys, was a job too big. Starr told Lance that he was trying to persuade Madge to take the *vaqueros* and a cook.

The boys went off on larks of their own contrivance, and on one occasion became lost less than ten miles from the ranch. Another time they slipped off to town and did not show up at the ranch until late the next day, for which jaunt Madge called them "a lot of bums."

When, however, the least little thing or something more serious, such as Dervish's bolt, happened to Madge, Lance seemed always to be on the spot. This morning he was morosely counting the occurrences, and wondering if the last two had been strictly bona fide, yet nursing a sense of guilt because of his doubt.

There were endless jobs. He was laboring on a corncrib. Ren had taken the boys fishing. And just about the time Lance forgot his woe, there came a wild clamor of screams from the big barn.

"Sounds scary. Now what the hell?" he muttered, darkly, and strode for the barn. The first screams might have been mirth, but those following sent Lance into a run. He dashed up the runway.

The girls were in a pandemonium of fright, shrieking, pale as death and wild-eyed. It could not be an ordinary circumstance. Missing Madge from the group Lance yelled: "Shut up! —Where's Madge? What's the matter?"

"Oh!—Oh!—she'll be killed!"

"Save her, cowboy—for God's sake!"

"If she falls . . . it . . . it'll be terrible!"

"Where is she? What is it?" yelled Lance.

"Girls, if you tell him—I'll hate you," cried Madge, piercingly from somewhere. "Lance Sidway, you get out—of here! Don't you dare look!"

At that juncture Beulah Allen ran to Lance. "She was swinging on the hay rope—from one loft to the other. . . . Sitting on the noose! . . . Something gave way—and up she went bang against the roof. . . . There!"

"That's out for you, Bu Allen!" raged Madge.

Then Lance saw Madge up under the roof, hard against the wheel. The noose evidently slipped from her hips, up to her armpits, and had stripped her that far. But Lance saw only those terrible eyes and the scarlet face.

"*Go away!*" she shrieked.

"Madge, you're in great danger," flashed Lance. . . . "Grab the wheel!"

"I'd rather die—than—have you . . ."

"I didn't look at you—directly," fumed Lance, angrily. "I didn't *see* you. I wouldn't give a whoop to . . . didn't you ever meet a gentleman? . . . hang on!—Help me, girls. Make a pile of hay right under her—so if she falls. . . ."

Frantically he began to drag huge armloads of hay from the loft, flinging them to the girls. They worked with a will.

Then Lance dashed to the windlass. It was an old-fashioned hay-fork contrivance, and the heavy reel, owing no doubt to a swinging rock wired on it for a balance, had slipped to jerk her aloft.

"All right," shouted Lance, as soon as he had loosened the rope and taken a strong grip. "Let go the wheel up there. . . . Down you come. . . . Hang on to the rope now."

"You're squeezing me—to death," cried Madge.

Madge reached the floor and the rope went slack. A chorus of tender and commiserating exclamations came from the girls who had surrounded Madge. Bu Allen met Lance with a twinkle in her eyes.

"She's not hurt much. I'll say she got squeezed *once* hard enough."

Lance made no effort to approach the circle around Madge, who evidently lay prostrate on the hay. He had been forced to expend breath as much through emotion as effort. Bu put a sympathetic hand on his arm. Lance received the impression that the girl, despite her sophistication, was someone to like.

"Girls—is—she hurt?" panted Lance.

"Not that we can tell," replied Allie, who knelt on the hay. Maramee had Madge's head in her lap. Her abbreviated costume had been decently arranged.

"Where's that dragon killer?" asked Madge, her voice weak, but spirit apparently undaunted.

Bu Allen dragged Lance over to the pile of hay, where Madge lay, white as a sheet.

"You would!" she exclaimed, with inscrutable eyes on Lance.

"Would—would what?"

"Be the one to catch me in that stunt. I used to do it when I was little. It never occurred to me to look at the windlass. I'm an idiot. . . . Sidway, please promise you'll not tell Nels or Dad, or even Ren."

"It never happened, Miss Stewart," rejoined Lance, soberly.

"Help me to the car," she replied, and with Allie and

Maramee's assistance arose painfully to her feet. "The knot on that damned noose stuck into my back."

The girls helped Madge in, and then piled in themselves, with Allie at the wheel. Madge leaned over the door and took hold of the dusty edge of Lance's vest with unsteady fingers.

"Did I thank you?"

"No. But that's not necessary," returned Lance, hurriedly.

"I ought to be decent enough."

"Madge, you said it," chimed in Beulah.

"She's just waiting for something big," added Allie softly. "Anyway, Lance, we all thank you from the bottom of our hearts."

"Lance Sidway, don't you save me any more," said Madge, imperiously. "Not from hayforks, fences, horses, cars—from college youths or gangsters—nor from *myself*. If you do, I'll not be responsible."

"Are those orders?"

"Yes, they're orders."

"Thanks. I'll not be present next time. And I won't attend your funeral!"

The car rolled away.

Lance felt inclined to the conviction that it was his careful avoidance of the girls the next few days which kept him out of hot water. Still he had to hear about their mishaps and stunts from Ren, who had been relegated to the job, and who raved rapturously through supper, and then long afterward, to Lance's disgust. It did not help Lance's mood to realize that he listened keenly when he might have gone out of hearing.

On the third night, however, Ren, for some reason appeared very glum and silent. Nels ventured a few sly queries. And when Lance added: "Has our poodle had his tail pulled?" Ren stalked out and stamped to his room.

"Wal, he ain't often like thet," said Nels, ponderingly. "Reckon one of us ought to make a move, anyhow."

"I'll go, Nels," returned Lance, and lighting a cigarette he went out. Approaching Ren's door and seeing that the light was out, Lance knocked and said:

"Sorry, old man. I was only kidding."

"Shore, I know that. It's okay," replied Ren, gruffly.

"Little off your feed, Ren?"

"I reckon. . . . An' I was made out a turrible sucker today!"

"By whom?"

"Wal, who'd you think?"

"Bonita?"

"Thet little bussy!—Say, she's lost her haid over them boys. I cain't do a damn thing about it."

"Don't try. They're only in fun, Ren."

"Like hell they air!" ejaculated the cowboy, bitterly.

"Ren, I lay off Bonita for your sake. Maybe I shouldn't have. She liked me. And I'm your pal, you know."

"You're damn right you shouldn't. Them boys hev been chasin' Bonita an' her friends pretty hard lately, an' unbeknown to Majesty."

"That's not so good, Ren."

"Good!—It's pretty bad, if you ask me."

"Well, I'll walk down and give the kid a spiel, Ren. . . . But, I forgot. Who made the sucker out of you?"

"Never mind now, pard. I don't want to hear you whoop."

Lance strolled off the long porch across the square, and down the road toward the high wall of poplar trees that marked the village. The night was close and warm. Merry voices up by the lake attested to the presence of night bathers. The strumming of a guitar and the lilt of a Spanish love song suited the summer night. At the corner Lance turned left to go down the long avenue of poplars. Lance passed the deserted adobe houses, then the lighted store, and beyond that the noisy cantina. Here there was no one out under the vine-covered trellis. Peeping in he saw a number of Mexicans, but no girls or white men. Lance crossed the street, and in the deep shadow of the other lane of poplars, he went slowly on toward Danny Mains' house. When he got to the corner he halted in the shadow. The gate was beyond a little ways. Lance thought he would hang around a little before he went in. There were both lights and music in the Mains' cottage. Presently three bareheaded girls appeared, scarfs round their shoulders. The foremost was Bonita. They hesitated, whispering excitedly, and were evidently expecting someone. When Lance called Bonita she gave a start and then approached slowly, while the other girls hung back. He met her at the gate.

"Hello, kiddo. Where are you going?"

"Oh, *Señor* Lance!—I was afraid it might be my brother Manuel . . . I've—we have a date."

"You look it. Sweet as a wild rose! . . . Bonita, have you gone back on Ren and me?"

"No indeed. But I never see you—and him so seldom. He's jealous. Tries to boss me. I won't stand it, Lance."

"Don't blame you. Has he asked you to marry him yet?"

"He has not," she retorted. "But he did say I was so—so bad he wasn't sure he wanted me to."

"Well, that's a tough one. . . . Bonita, have you been stepping out a little lately?"

"Not so very. Tonight's the first time I've consented to go to town. Francisca and Maria have both been. I'm scared. If Daddy finds it out he'll whip me."

"Stay home. Come with me to see Ren. He's blue. Let the others go."

"Lance, if *you* wanted me for yourself I'd break any date. I'd rather. These young college men are too swift for Bonita Mains."

"Listen, honey. Now don't be a little chump. It's all right to go if you refuse to drink. You'll enjoy the movies and dancing."

"They all drink like fish."

"Right." And Lance laughed at the frank girl. He drew her close to him and kissed her. "Bonita, get a load of this. I like you myself—more than these college guests of Miss Stewart's.

But Ren loves you, dearly. I know it. And I'd hate to see you two fail to make a go of it. Now be a good kid. Promise me. I'll make a date with you for tomorrow night, like this, so we can talk."

"I promise, Lance," she replied, happily, her hands on his arm. "I'll not drink tonight. If you can't patch it up between Ren and me, it'll not be my fault."

"Swell! You're okay, Bonita, and Ren is a crabby old sourdough. We'll fix it. . . . Hello!—a car?"

"They're coming. Perhaps it'd be just as well if you weren't seen."

Lance gave her dark head a pat and hurried back into the shadow of the trees. But the car did not come close to the house, and Lance could not ascertain to whom it belonged. The girls ran out and were taken in with merry greetings. As the car went on, Lance thought he saw a figure hanging on behind. Presently, being certain of this, he took to the road and strolled down the hill. He knew that if someone had stolen a ride, he would not stick on for long, not on desert roads at the speed these fellows liked.

This car, however, did not appear to open up, until it reached the level valley floor. Lance kept on, presently reaching the level, where the dry wash and the sand made rough going for a space. At length he gave up and was about to turn back when he almost bumped into someone sitting on the low bank of the road. A little peal of silvery laughter magnified his start.

"Lance Sidway! I was just gambling with myself how soon you'd arrive," said Madge Stewart.

"Well, I'm damned!"

"So am I. Fatally damned to have *you* get me out of every scrape."

"That's a tough break. You're not alone?"

"Yes, I am. Allie was in the plot with me. She was to hang onto the other side. Either she did not get on or she was jolted off. You didn't see her along the road?"

"No. She couldn't have come. I saw only one person hanging on the back of that car."

"You saw me? When?"

"When the car stopped outside Mains' house. I was with Bonita. The other girls waited in the yard."

"Oh! I see. Johnny on the spot!—Did you get who the boys were?"

"No. That didn't interest me particularly. Bonita told me these boys were too swift for her. What Bonita does is probably none of my affair, but I am interested because of Ren. So I urged her not to drink and she said she wouldn't. Bonita is easily influenced if you go about it right. I've been Ren's friend, with her, if you know what I mean."

"I didn't until now," returned Madge, bluntly. "We girls thought the boys were going to the cantina with the girls. I think it lousy of them, especially of Barg Hillcote. Just engaged to Maramee! There I go spilling my insides. . . . Lance Sidway, men are all rotten."

"Yeah!" answered Lance, uncertainly. She had begun to strike him rather singularly, as she had not moved, and she sat leaning back on both hands with one leg up over the bank. In the starlight he could see her lovely face and speaking eyes.

"Maramee would break her engagement with Barg for this. I would. And she's been so happy. . . . I hope to goodness Allie didn't get on and fall off. . . . Surely she'll come soon."

"What's wrong with you?" Lance said suddenly, and he leaned close to Madge, peering at her.

"Guess I got hurt," she replied, with great inscrutable eyes meeting his.

"Where?"

"My foot. This one. Thought at first I'd sprained my ankle. But I'm not sure."

"Let me see." Lance stepped up on the bank and knelt. She had taken off her shoe and stocking. Her white foot and leg gleamed in the starlight.

"Don't touch it!" she cried. But he went right on until she screamed out.

"All right, all right, touchy! . . . Let me see you move it. . . . Flex it!"

"Oh, I can do that. It doesn't hurt."

"Your ankle is okay. You've sprained your instep—or something. But if you keep off it and use hot water frequently, you'll be all right tomorrow or next day."

"I'll have to walk back home."

"No you won't. You can't. Let me get your car."

"But I don't want anyone to know about this, and they will if I come in the car. I'll have to sneak in by the west wing to my room. I'll have to walk."

"Nonsense. I can easily carry you."

She laughed outrageously.

"But I can. I'm strong," protested Lance, earnest, amazed, solicitous. "I can throw a hundred pound sack of grain all over the place."

"Strong? I know you're a perfect Hercules, Mr. Sidway," she said, tauntingly. "But I won't have you packing me around."

Very carefully she stepped, and moved up the slope. Every time her injured foot touched the ground it must have pained greatly, Lance knew. He put a hand under her arm and half lifted her along. They came into a trail, and that appeared to be easier for Madge. When they arrived at the pines, however, she was tottering. But this girl was the kind that could not quit.

"Why won't you let me carry you?" he asked, suddenly. "You did once."

"That's why."

"If you're not the queerest, screwiest girl, I'll eat my hat!" declared Lance.

"Yes, when you haven't one!" she retorted. When she started on, Lance knew she would not make it much farther. And he bided his time, hot and perplexed. Finally she swore and sobbed almost in the same breath. Without a word more he picked her up in his arms and went on. Shifting his hold, so she would carry more comfortably for her, he said: "There. Isn't that better? I hardly feel your weight."

"Better, indeed. But I fear—riskier," she returned in a queer voice.

Lance had to look at her. Before that, all had seemed well. He was relieved to save her pain. Her face lay high up on his right arm, almost on his breast, turned toward him somewhat, and its lovely proximity grew suddenly exciting. She was looking at him with eyes whose expression he could not fathom.

"Riskier!—What do you mean?" he demanded.

"You see I am utterly helpless. You might get a cave-man notion. . . . Really that wouldn't be so bad. But you probably just kissed Bonita . . ."

"I did. For Ren's sake—mostly."

"Ye gods and little fishes! . . . And no doubt it was Bu Allen last night. She came in with her lipstick all smeared up. Radiant. Bold as the very devil. And she didn't deny it when we kidded her about you."

"Miss Stewart, I did not see her last night," protested Lance.

"Oh, for Pete's sake, can the Miss. . . . It doesn't sound natural. . . . And well, if you *had* been with Bu, you'd have kissed her, wouldn't you?"

"That would have depended entirely upon her."

"How chivalrous! If she had been suffering for contact or release—or what have you, why you'd have been a perfect necker. . . . Lance, you give me a pain in the neck."

"I know. But why—why?" he demanded, furiously.

"It must be because you're a liar."

"Well, Madge Stewart, you give me worse than that—and it's because you're no good."

"Let me down. You said that before. I'll die before I—I'll . . ."

"Bunk! You can die all right, after I get you home. I hope you do. I hope you choke on your terrible tongue."

Anger and intense mortification, and some other emotion began to augment in Lance's consciousness.

"The girls think you've the sweetest disposition—that you're the swellest fellow. My God!" And she uttered a tinkling little laugh that cut into Lance like icy blades.

"Your boy friends think the same of you. But they're a lot of sapheads. They don't know you."

"You do!"

"Bet your—sweet life I do. Better than you have any idea," he panted.

"Rest here, young Lochinvar! or you'll fall. I think, after all, you're not so strong. This magnificent frame is pithy—like your head."

Lance groaned under the excess of his burdens. Halfway up to the house, in one of the little bench parks under the pines, he sat down on a boulder to regain his equilibrium, but he did not let go of Madge. He could feel the throb of her against his throbbing. And all at once he happened to think of what she had told Rollie that last night. Under the galvanizing stress of the idea that leaped out of it he arose like a giant and a fiend. He wrapped his long arms closer about her and drew her wholly against his breast. Madge seemed totally calm. Then Lance kissed her, not with any particular feeling, but merely as a preliminary.

"I thought it was about time," muttered Madge.

Then, staggering on under the pines, he kissed her cheeks, her eyes, her hair, her neck—and when at last she protested, Lance stopped her mouth with his, in an endless passionate kiss which magnified all he had ever bestowed in his life.

"Damn—you!" she panted, as he moved a moment to breathe. And she began to pound him—to tear at his hair. "You insult me . . ."

"Insult *you*!—Good God—it—couldn't—be—done," he mocked her, breathlessly. "I heard you say—you rather liked it. . . ."

"You—*what* . . ."

"Mine ought to be—as good as any of those guys—and cleaner, by heaven! and fresher—from lack of promiscuous practice." And bending over, squeezing her face up immovably, he began to kiss her lips like a madman. His kisses choked off her scream. After one frantic and tense struggle she collapsed in his arms. And he kissed her for every step, on under the pines, out upon the drive, almost to the front archway. Keeping outside the drive he passed this, and once in the shrubbery he began again his ravenous tasting of her lips, as if his appetite grew with what it fed upon. But not until he rounded the west wing and reached her window did he realize that her face, her lips, her body had changed. Her eyes were closed tightly—heavy eyelids dreamy, long curled lashes on her cheeks; her lips bowed, open, sweet with a strange fire; her breast pressed on his. Not until Lance lifted her into the open window did he realize that she had an arm round his neck. He lowered her carefully to the floor. Then he leaned on the sill, spent and devastated.

She stirred, and sat up, and laboriously climbed upon the bed. Lance, watching her, expected, yearned for a scourging, bitter enough even for him. But she just looked at him. In the starlight he saw her face as only he would carry it in his heart forever.

"Majesty," he began, in husky whisper, "I . . ." but he could not go on.

Chapter Nine

Madge sat upon her bed gazing tensely out of her window into the gloom where Lance Sidway had vanished. A fringe of her senses seemed to register the drowsy murmur of water, the rustle of leaves, the chirp of crickets, as well as loud voices and gay laughter of some of her guests in the living room. But for all that, her acute senses coalesced on her burning cheeks and neck, her breast, and especially her lips on fire with that cowboy's terrible kisses.

Not all at once could her wit and intelligence throw off that spell. She found herself rubbing her stockingless leg and ankle. The tightness around her foot, the heat, meant injury in some degree, but she felt no pain. Over and above these sensations thundered the truth, clearing in her mind. She had ranged the gamut of incredible feeling—from pique, surprise, shock, fury to a sudden overwhelming tumult of love, of her willful changing moods, her wounded vanity, her temper and upflaring hate, and her softening doubt, her endless misgivings and suspicion, that had kept her up and down for days, only to have this shameful assault leave her undone, madly in love at last, stricken forever.

"I—I can take it!" whispered Madge, with her fluttering hand on her hot lips. She did not weep. She asked no quarter. She had her just deserts. But she was not as he believed—that shot through her with a passionate pang. From the very beginning everything had worked to her detriment. Her imperious demand for that horse? No—that was not the first. Her meeting with the gangster Uhl! That had started her wrong with this Oregon boy. And every single thing afterward had gone wrong—her tempers and her tricks, her insincerity and subterfuge, her nasty tongue and open satire. He must have overheard her saying she rather liked being kissed. That night when Rollie had met her after Lance had infuriated her! But there was nothing to be ashamed of about that. It was true, only on the moment she was torturing Rollie. The cowboy had something these other boys lacked. His recent treatment of her was wholly at variance with that, and seemed inexplicable to Madge. He did not want to kiss her. He did not approve of her. He despised her. He must have possessed some kind of a masculine trait that made her kissing promiscuity intolerable and abhorrent. He was avenging the throng of boys she had kissed and forgotten. There were a thousand slants and angles to this outrageous assault upon her—only one terrible revelation accruing from them! The doom of love, that she had trifled with so regally and callously, had fallen upon her. How impossible to understand! If Lance Sidway had entered her room that moment and snatched her up. . . . But he had not known she had been, at the last, taking his kisses and spending her soul in exchange. And suddenly Madge was possessed of an insane rage. She wanted to kill him. It would not be enough to have him horsewhipped and driven away. He must not live to kiss girls like Bonita and have the sunlight shine in his hazel eyes for some other. . . .

"Oh, nuts!" burst out Madge, baldly, suddenly sick of herself, so weary that the fury drained out of her. "I've put this day of reckoning off long enough!"

Her exclamation must have been heard, for clicking high heels sounded on the stone corridor.

"Majesty!" called Allie, in great eagerness. "Did I hear you?"

"I shouldn't wonder. I was cussing. Come in. I've a story to unfold. What happened to you?"

"Me!—I was thrown in the dust," whispered Allie. "Blinded. I couldn't see a thing. The car was gone and you with it. I felt my way back to my room and washed the dust from my eyes. After that I walked under the pines—down the road—watching for you."

"Funny you didn't see that cowboy carrying me or hear him kissing me. Must have sounded like a decisive battle of the world!"

"*Majesty!*"

"Be careful, darling. I'm a cripple. I fell off the car, too. Hurt my foot. . . . Help me into my bathroom."

There between the two of them, Madge boiled out the pain in her foot, and bound it up, to find then that she could walk without limping. She sent Allie out to find where everybody was, and bade her return to sleep with her. Madge found it good to stretch out in bed, in the dark, and wonder. Presently Allie came back, to feel her way to Madge's side. It was a mutual emotion that caused them to seek each other's arms.

"Your mother has gone to bed, I think," whispered Allie. "Snake was playing checkers with your dad. I told them you were tired. Your dad seemed concerned. 'Madge tired? that's unheard of.' He looked worn himself, poor dear. Majesty, do you know I've an idea he worries about you and us. . . ."

"Skip it!—Where were the girls?"

"In their rooms, lolling, fussing, gossiping. Except Bu. She's down the hill looking for cowboys, so Dixie said."

"Oh!" cried Madge, poignantly.

"What ails you, darling? You act kind of queer and talk worse. You're burning up. I'm afraid you've got fever."

"Fever!—Ha! Ha!—Yes, I've got galloping fever. . . . And the boys?"

"Down playing pool. Wouldn't take the girls."

"Frame-up to shield that trio of heels!" whispered Madge. "All in the know about that date. . . . Darling, get a load of this. Barg and Dawson and Brand were in that car. And down below they took in Bonita and two of her friends. They went to town."

"Majesty! Not really."

"I'll say. What do you think of them, Barg especially?"

"For Barg?—Lousy is too lovely a word. That dirty little bum! Just finally won Maramee, and he pulls such a stunt.

Maramee is so happy. She thinks Barg is perfect. It'll break her heart."

"She must never know. Don't you breathe it."

"But, darling, they don't mean any harm."

"Who don't?"

"Why, Barg and the boys."

"No, I don't suppose they do mean any harm, but it hauls me up, Allie. I've done my damnedest to entertain this crowd. They're swell, only they want to do what they like. Suppose there'd be an accident, or a fight, or they drank too much, and got stuck out all night. That happens, when no harm is intended. What'd my dad say? I grow stiff at the very thought. He's such a peach. He believes I'm so. . . . Oh, hell! . . . What would Danny Mains say? Good old scout. Worships that black-eyed flip! What would that cowboy *do*? My heavens!"

"Majesty! Someone will hear you. Cowboy! You mean Sidway? It's none of his business."

"Isn't it, though? Ren Starr is his pal. Ren has been at Bonita's feet for long. And Lance has been courting her for him. Would he be sore? He was sore tonight, maybe somewhat because I . . . Allie, that cowboy would call the boys down to the barn . . ."

"But, honey, nothing terrible has happened yet. It won't."

"Yes, it has—to *me*," whispered Madge, tragically. "Death wouldn't be half so hard!"

"Majesty, are you crazy? Such talk! What happened?"

Madge hugged her loyal friend close and shook over her. "I fell off the car way down the road. Hurt my foot. I took off my shoe and stocking. Then I sat up on the bank waiting. I knew who'd come. I'd have bet my soul. And he *did* come. Sidway, the darned inquisitive rooster. We talked, and as always in a few moments we were at each other's throats. All before he knew I was hurt. When he found that out he was human for a little bit. I wouldn't let him go for a car or for help, and I started walking up the hill. Hurt? Oh, Lord, did it? Pretty soon he grabbed me up in his arms. I gave him some dirty digs because I knew he'd kiss me. No fellow yet ever got that far with me without kissing me. And I was scared of having Sidway do that. Allie, I—l-liked him too much. . . . Well, pretty soon he did. I never was so mad in my life, just at first. . . . After that I began to like it. I thought he was going to eat me alive. . . . Allie, he lighted some kind of a conflagration in me. If I hadn't been too weak I'd have. . . . Oh!—But I couldn't move. It was only after he tumbled me in my window here that I realized I'd been in a trance of bliss . . . that at last there . . . I'd been kissing him for every kiss he'd given me. It all comes to me gradually. Later I'll remember some of the things he said, and tell you. . . . Allie, darling, I've told you many stories in the dead of night—after love dates, blind dates, hells. But what do you say to this one?"

"Majesty, you *love* him!" whispered Allie, in awe.

"Ha! Ha! So you get that? What wonderful perspicacity, darling! Never mind about me—about the dual rotten nature that has turned on me . . . but what did Lance Sidway mean? Tell me that."

"Madge, it's beyond the bounds of human possibility that he doesn't love you."

"Why?"

"Because he's a man. And you've placed him on the damnedest spots. Seeing you every day and every way. . . . Why, Madge. I was sorry for him the other day at the lake. You in that indecent bathing suit—the boys wallowing you all over the sand! And he stuck there to save our lives if we got cramps!"

"Wrong again. But what did *you* see?" flashed Madge, in a passionate whisper.

"I saw the look in his eyes. You know he has beautiful eyes, when they're soft."

"You're as sentimental as Maramee, and as gullible. That cowboy hates my very insides."

"I can't believe that."

"But, sweet, listen. For God's sake use some brains. Isn't it conceivable that I should finally fall foul of a real man who sees through me—who has my number—whom I can't fool or intrigue or fascinate or seduce—who has fine ideals, and who consequently despises me?"

"Yes, it's conceivable. That'd be a horrible misfortune. . . . But if Sidway wasn't mad about you he couldn't act as he does. Actions, my proud savage! Actions! Any boy or man can rave. But it's actions that count. He's done something, hasn't he?"

"He's done me wrong," wailed Madge, fighting vainly against the sweet madness of Allie's loyal convictions.

"Take the day you were caught in the noose of the hay rope. Madge, do you imagine any man ever recovering from *that*?"

"From—what?" asked Madge, faintly.

"From seeing you—from your chin down—without a stitch!"

"Oh, no! He—he didn't see me . . . he swore he didn't."

"He *did*, Madge Stewart."

"Oh, Allie! I'm so horribly afraid he'll turn out big and fine and noble—despite all—that tonight."

"He was indicating his sex."

"Oh!"

"He was jealous. They *all* kiss you. So would he—and make one swell job of it. I think he's grand."

"You are a traitor, Allie Leland."

"No. You're that, Madge, to yourself."

"Oh, *I* couldn't be a traitor to anyone," retorted Madge, fiercely.

"You are a queen and a law unto yourself. Sidway will not bend to you."

Spent, but still unconvinced, Madge lay there in her friend's arms.

"Darling, have you *ever* been your true self to Sidway?" asked Allie.

"Yes, once. The first time. That campus day."

"Then go back to that. Even if he hates you unmercifully, he'll come around. After we are gone—and we shouldn't drag this grand vacation out selfishly. . . ."

"Gone! I couldn't stay. Yet I must. This is home. I owe it to Dad and Mom. But—alone on the range with that eagle-eyed cowboy! Mom says he is like Dad used to be! Dad is hipped on him. And Nels. . . . Oh, what is the use?"

"Majesty, it'll all work out. But I'm afraid you must suffer more."

"Have a heart, will you? For Pete's sake! I've been dying for weeks."

"Darling, compose yourself and get to sleep," begged Allie, tenderly.

"I'm dead tired. But sleep! What'll I do when I wake up?"

"You mean about *him*?"

"Of course."

"Why be just the same as if nothing had happened."

"You callous woman! . . . Allie—I think—I guess . . ." faltered Madge, finally weakening to tears . . . "I'm licked. . . . I'm afraid—he'll go—away!"

Golden sunlight streaming in at Madge's window seemed inconsistent with the gray gloomy void she wanted to believe was her lot. Allie had gone out in her dressing gown to fetch some coffee and toast. Madge's foot felt stiff, but it was not going to incapacitate her in the least. What she wanted most right at that moment was to be down at the corrals. Would Lance be such a coward as that—to run off for fear she would betray him? What kind of girls had he known anyway? She would not have hurt him in her father's estimation for anything in the world. She was consumed with a desire to see Sidway this morning. To see if the monster resembled in any degree her conception! He should be haggard, drawn, after a sleepless night, burdened by guilt, unable to look anyone in the eye.

Allie returned, escorted by a bevy of bright-eyed girls, all of whom had been in the kitchen.

"Lazy girl! It's ten o'clock," said Maramee, whose sweet face appeared so gay and happy that Madge wondered at the credulity of human nature. They all came in, their colorful print dresses bright around Madge's bed.

"Where are Dixie and Bu?" asked Madge.

"Horse mad. Dixie loves to sit on the corral fence and Bu is crazy to ride everything."

"She'll get piled up," declared Madge, severely.

"Humph! Bu's been piled up, as you call it. But she picks herself up and yelps for more. The cowboys get some kick out of her."

After a little Madge inquired for the boys. Gone, hours before, off on a hiking trip!

"Not really?" ejaculated Madge, her cup halted halfway to her lips. "Not Barg and . . . and . . ."

"Yes, Barg," declared Maramee, happily. "He poked his head in my window and tossed wild roses on my face, to awaken me. Whispered he'd rather have stayed home with me. Oh, he was darling."

"To be sure. Barg's a darling, all right. . . ." Madge was interrupted by the arrival of Dixie Conn, flushed and breathless, no doubt from a climb up the hill.

"Majesty, I thought you were indisposed or something. You just look stunning," said the southern girl.

"Yeah? Thanks, Dix. But you're looking through rose-colored spectacles. . . . Where's Bu?"

"Madge—Girls! That outsider has shown us up. She's dishonored the fair name of our sorority."

"Oh, for the love of Mike—what now?"

"Bu is riding Umpqua right this minute. You know we all tried to coax Sidway to let us ride him. Same as Majesty tried to buy him. Nothing doing! And now she's down there having a swell time on that grand horse. The cowboy is teaching Bu to jump over logs and ditches, and what have you? Was I jealous?

All the same I had to hand it to Bu. She looked great. How'd she ever put that over with Sidway?"

"I've a hunch and I'm going to try it," said Selma Thorne, subtly.

"Say, don't imagine I let any grass grow under my feet," declared Dixie. "I went up to the cowboy, raved about his horse and complimented Bu. Then I said, with all I've got, old dears, 'Lance, I'd almost sell my soul to ride Umpqua!' He said, 'Why didn't you tell me? I can't read your mind. Umpqua loves girls. I'd be only too happy to put you up on him. Hang around, till Beulah is through.' I wasn't dressed for riding as you see, so I asked if I might go down early tomorrow. Then he looked troubled. I hadn't noticed that. Why, he looked just wretched. And he said: 'Yes, by all means, if I'm here. But I expect Miss Stewart to fire me this morning!' . . . Majesty, darling, what has he done now? But no matter, don't fire Sidway."

And then the other girls burst into a chorus of appeals and conjectures and wisecracks that fairly infuriated Madge. She flung pillows at them. "Beat it, you pack of imps! I must have been bughouse to invite you over here. . . . Get out!—*No!* I'm—not—going—to—fire—Lance Sidway! Go climb on his neck and then on his precious Umpqua for all I care. That'd be the way to get there. But I'd die first."

They fled in a fiendish clamor and Madge hid her face in her pillow. It was a bad moment. There were many impetuses toward a magnificent fury, which she viewed with her mind, one after another. But she could not surrender to the one thing that had crushed her—the perfectly inconsequential and natural circumstance of Lance putting Bu Allen up on his horse. The absurdity of her childish pique gradually faded in the stern realization that her happiness, her future, and the welfare of her dear parents, so fatefully bound up in her, were at stake. Well might it be too late! But she would humble herself, crucify her selfish imperious side, absolutely refuse catastrophe. If she had been half as nice to Sidway as Bu Allen had been she would not now be in such extremity.

Madge prostrated herself before her love, which was to betray her pride and spirit. It was too great a thing to deny any longer. But by surrendering she gained some aspect of the wit and self-control she needed at this trying time. Three betrothals among her guests attested to the success of their sojourn at her ranch. That Beulah and Elwell would make a go of it there was no reasonable doubt. Madge decided to shorten and intensify the remaining stages of their entertainment and center her energies upon the trip into the mountains and the dance she had long planned.

This decision would change for her, and therefore her guests, the idle languor of the summer days. To that end, an hour after she left her room, she approached her parents, finding them in her mother's room. Evidently Madge had interrupted a serious talk, and having changed the direction of her mind she looked at them penetratingly, conscious of her neglect this exciting summer.

"Darlings, am I intruding?" she asked, halting in the doorway.

Her mother's sweet response and the light that her presence always brought upon her father's dark face assured Madge of her welcome, and that indeed she had been remiss.

"Mom, you can hide trouble, but Dad can't," said Madge, going to them, and she found that this was not a new thought, only one put aside because it hurt. An unaccountable aloofness, arising from her shame, kept her from sliding upon the arm of Stewart's chair. When had she done that? How little she had seen of him for a month and more! His reserve betrayed it.

"Has my crowd gotten on your nerves?" she asked.

"They have been somewhat trying," replied Mrs. Stewart, with a smile. "But that was only because of our difficulty in adjusting ourselves to excitement and mirth and—well, the life they brought with them. I like them all, Madge. Your favorite Allie is mine, too. And the boys are fine. I'm glad you had them all here."

"Dad?" queried Madge, poignantly.

"After they're gone, I'll tell you, lass," replied her father, then hastily: "Oh, I like them all right. I just mean I must get hold of myself."

"Yeah? I'm afraid I'm answered. . . . Has Rollie Stevens been nagging you about me?"

"No. That young man steers a little clear of me. But he has approached Madeline."

"He has told me he wanted to marry you, darling. Three separate times. And has taken occasion to tell about the Stevens, their position, wealth, and all that. Very correct and a fine young fellow. But, Madge, he wouldn't care to live out here."

"I'll tell the world he wouldn't," retorted Madge, with a laugh. "And I wouldn't have him if he would. So skip that, Mom."

"Madge, then—sc you intend to stay home—a while?" asked Stewart, a little huskily, gazing away from her out of the window.

"Dad!" If she had followed her swift impulse it would have been to throw her arms around his neck. But she could not do it. Her intuition grasped something strange here. "I'm going to pack this crowd off sooner than I had expected. And after that I'm going to stay home for good."

It was her mother Madge looked at, and she divined that whatever had been her thoughtless failings and deplorable shortcomings, they had never changed that faithful heart. If she had lost her father, through the years of absence, and his inability to understand her when she did come back, she divined that would not be a permanent estrangement, because she was kind and loving, and if she made amends for her wildness and settled down to a real love of him, and her future at the ranch, all would be well. Her quiet talks with Nels, too few and far between, had played no small part in the awakening of her conscience. Yet remorseful as she felt, her temper would admit of no reason that she knew why she should arraign herself at these odd moments. It was on account of that cowboy, and because she had been so unaccountably a prey to love for him. She had always known she must love some man with all her being, desperately, once and for good and she had always been looking for him. That might account somewhat for her endless interests.

"Dad, what's on your mind?" asked Madge, after this flashing pageant of thought had left her composed, once more in a way to win back her old confidence. "Nels told me you were worrying over money troubles."

"The gabby old woman!" ejaculated Stewart, impatiently.

"Don't be angry with Nels. I coaxed it out of him. I've intended to go at him again—but I've been so busy with these friends. Besides, Dad, I've troubles of my own."

"You have? No one would guess it. You are the happiest, gayest, most thoughtless of all these young people."

"On the surface. But never mind my trouble now. It's going to keep. . . . What I'd like to know is—when my friends are gone will you tell me everything and let me help? For five years I've spent money like a drunken sailor. It's begun to frighten me a little, Dad, if I thought . . . if I found out I'd been a spendthrift while you and Mom had. . . . Oh, I'd *hate* that so inexpressibly."

To Madge's amaze Stewart abruptly took her in his arms and clasped her so closely that she could not breathe. And over her he said to her mother. "Madeline, Nels knows our girl better than we do." Then he kissed her hair, her cheek, and rushed out.

"Mom!" she cried, going to her mother. "What have I done? . . . Is it? . . . Oh!"

"Darling, your conscience and your heart have spoken," replied her mother, earnestly. "I knew they would. I have never doubted. It is no small thing for a rich and popular girl to return from college, from a great city, to the old-fashioned life of a ranch. Don't distress yourself further now. Devote yourself to your friends. When they are gone we'll face our problems. You have eliminated the only one that concerned me."

"Mother! Whether or not I loved you—and my home? . . I'll never forgive myself."

"What is it you girls say? 'Skip it!' . . . Madge, you will not accept young Stevens?"

Madge did not need to avert her eyes, because they were blind with tears. "No, Mom. I like Rollie, and I've played with him. He has done the same with other girls while courting me. Rollie is a playboy. He couldn't stand this lonely range. But I can, Mother! . . . And I want a handsome brute who will beat me!"

"The latter is inconceivable," returned her mother, mildly. "I hope no such contingency arises. I do not want to see the ranch blown to bits or be shaken by some cataclysm."

"You overrate me, darling. I'm a very meek little girl this morning."

"You are certainly strange."

Madge's original idea had been to ask her father's advice about taking her guests to the wild fastness up in the Peloncillo Hills, famous as a stronghold of the great Apache chief, Cochise. Before her school days Madge had ridden to this place with her father and the cowboys. She had never forgotten it, and it had been one of her cherished hopes to give her friends a camping trip there. For some inexplicable reason she found that she was cooling on the project, but she was too stubborn and fearful to analyze the cause. To abandon the trip after having exalted it continually for weeks did not quite suit Madge. She would have welcomed a reasonable excuse for not going, and as she considered the plans, that idea amplified. If she remembered correctly the ride up to Cochise's stronghold was long and arduous, and not for tenderfeet. That very fact had been an incentive. She had vowed that her friends would get one experience of the real thing.

Whereupon Madge, feeling that there was safety for her in numbers, filled her car full of girls and drove down to the store. Nels was there, chipper as a grasshopper, and ready to sell the girls anything from cigarettes to calico. Three separate times Madge's contingent of friends had bought the store out, to Nels' joy.

"Where are the cowboys?" asked Madge.

"Lance is diggin' postholes. An' thet's a job he hates as turrible as any other cowboy. Ren says every time Lance does somethin' awful he goes oot an' digs postholes."

"Sort of a penance?"

"Must be. I seen Ren aboot somewheres a minnit ago. I'll yell fer him."

It developed that Ren was very easy to locate and soon stood, sombrero in hand, his sunburned face beaming, before Madge and her friends.

"Mawning, cowboy. Where's your side partner?"

"Wal, Miss Majesty, he's drunk or crazy or somethin'," replied Ren, with a grin. "Woke me up before daylight, an' heah's what he said, kinda loud an' ringin'. 'Ren, I'm goin' out to dig postholes fer thet new fence. If anybody about heah wants to hang me or hawsewhip me, I'll be out there. Savvy?' "

"How very thoughtful of him," remarked Madge, resisting a deep vibration that was more than thrill. "What's he—done now?"

"Dog-gone if I know. But it musta been turrible. I says 'Lance, you think you're funny?' An' he says 'About as funny as death!' An' he stamps off, without any grub. Why, he's worryin' pore Nels to death."

"How would you and Sidway like to do me a great favor?"

"Job or jest fun?"

"It'll be a job. No fun at all! I want you to truck your horses as far as you can from town toward the Peloncillo Hills. Find the old trail up to Cochise's stronghold, and fetch me a report on it and the camp site."

"I'd like it swell, Miss Majesty, an' I reckon Lance would

about pass out to get away fer a spell. But, excuse me, what's the big idee? I was huntin' deer up there last fall. I can tell you most anythin'."

"Ren, be very serious now. Think of my friends. Is that trip going to be a safe and comfortable one for them?" And Madge gave Starr a look that had passed from her to him on former occasions. Ren suddenly looked blank and dropped his head.

"Hell no! it's neither one or the other. But thet's why it'd be grand." Ren hated to abandon the idea.

"I'm a little afraid of it. You see, Ren, I was sixteen when I made it first, had been riding horses all summer and I was fit."

The girls burst out into bitter lamentations. "What're we if not fit? . . . Haven't we been riding horses all summer?—Madge, *we* don't care a damn how hard it'd be. At that, we can beat the boys." One and all they put up arguments hard for the kindhearted Madge to withstand. When they were out of breath, Bu Allen contributed calmly: "Lance told me it's a lousy trip."

"Lousy! What's he mean by that?" returned Madge, on fire in an instant despite the fact that Sidway's inelegant remark was in line with her designs.

"Did I ask him that? He told me a lot of terrible stuff. Said we were all too weak-kneed and soft-bottomed. That's just what he said, the bum. He thinks we're a lot of swell kids, but no good for the West. And that goes for you, Majesty."

"I am quite aware in what poor opinion Sidway holds me," rejoined Madge, cool once more, and her contrariness was such that now she felt a mounting desire to go and show him how soft-bottomed she was. "Ren, you take Sidway, and leave at once. Find out all about the trail and Cochise's stronghold. Good and bad. Then upon your return you will report to me and all the crowd, after which we'll vote to decide whether to go or not."

"Very wal, Miss Majesty, I'm on my way," replied Ren.

"Madge, you're a whiz! Of course, we're on to you. But we think this investigation will make the trip irresistible."

"At least it'd be upon your own heads," warned Madge, then calling Ren back she met him halfway, to ask: "Will you let me know if this plan is acceptable to Sidway?"

Ren regarded her, comically dumfounded. Madge averted her face slightly to go on: "You see, Ren, he may leave any minute. The more I—I need him the more contrary he grows." She managed that demurely, but she was not smiling. Starr's tanned face brightened.

"Miss Majesty, between you an' me we know Lance is daid plumb nutty, an' what it's all about. Fer a time there I kind of feared you wasn't on to him. Wal, I am an' so is Nels. If you don't believe me go to Nels. Shore I'm a pore pard to double-cross Lance this way. He'd kill me if he ever found out."

"Found out what, Ren?" queried Madge, cool and sweet, mistress of herself again, but there was an incredible and unbelievable tumult within her being.

"Thet I give him away. . . . Majesty, Lance is a turrible bluff. He brags about ridin' away. Wal, up to this time he hasn't been able to. He's been mad an' wild, but he jest *cain't* leave."

"You surprise me, Ren. . . . And why?" went on Madge, unable to resist these precious and unreliable words from Lance's friend.

"Wal, you gotta figger thet out fer yourself. An' if you cain't, why go to Nels. I've talked too much. Thet son-of-a-gun has eyes like gimlets when he's close an' telescopes when he's far. He might be seein' us right now. Anyway all he does is watch fer you, Majesty."

"Ren! What on earth for?"

"It's not because you're nice to look at. . . . I've peeped through a crack in the wall between our rooms—an' seen him porin' an' sighin' over a picture. He acted like a man who couldn't help lookin' when he hated to. Thet picture is one of you, Majesty, fer I sneaked in an' took a peep. He keeps it under a book in his table drawer. Now don't ask me no more. I feel pretty yellow. But I'd never give him away onless fer my hunch thet you like Lance a little. Don't you?"

"Like—Lance?" repeated Madge, and all her blood seemed rushing to her head. "Ren, if Lance cannot trust you, how can I?"

"Doesn't make sense. But you can."

"I'll trust you. Yes, I do—like Lance," returned Madge, and to save her life she could not have made it casual. She went back to the house with the girls, playing her gay part, but there had come a complete reversal in her emotional reaction. Ren had vindicated her own deep convictions—that even if Sidway did hate her, he liked her too, against his better judgment and will, surely. Once more alone in her room she endeavored to stem this tide of overwhelming love, that was so great and so humble at the mere words of a sentimental cowboy. It frightened Madge—that flood of feeling. The sweetness of it warned her that this was not the time for surrender. But she had a tiny nucleus of hope around which to build. If she could only clasp to her breast this humble spirit! Time, days and days, would be her ally.

It was getting along into August, with touches of color beginning to show on the hills. Stewart advised Madge that if she was contemplating a camping trip up in the Peloncillos not to waste any more time. And she confided that she was pretty sure that would fall through. Snake Elwell had to return to college soon for fall practice; Allie had planned to motor east with her parents; and the rest of the party were beginning to think of the city. Nevertheless they were enthusiastic over the prospect of that horseback ride.

It chanced that Madge's wish to see Sidway and Starr upon their return, before any of her friends, was denied her, much to her concern. She had been alone with her mother when word came up from below that the boys were in. Madge rushed out the patio way and down the trail. A confusion of bright colors decorating Nels' porch attested to the whereabouts of the girls, and where they were the boys would be also. It was a good long run, and Madge had to halt to catch her breath before she half crossed the square. The horses had just been unloaded from the trucks, and the packs thrown out. Ren was surrounded by her excited friends who were evidently besieging him in unison. Sidway stood a little apart, conversing with Nels and her father. The *vaqueros* were attending to the horses. Umpqua nickered at Madge, and she flew to stroke his dusty neck, while he nosed at her for sugar. She had never ridden him since that first day, but she had won his affection, and she felt a sense of guilt to look up and see Sidway's piercing eyes upon her. Ragged and dark, dusty and unshaved, he appealed so powerfully to Madge that as she approached them she wondered how she could hide it.

"Majesty, they won't say a darn thing," burst out Maramee, and the others chimed in with gay sallies.

At last Madge reached them, and with a hand on Stewart's arm, she faced Sidway, and the grinning Starr. She was keen to feel something proven in them.

"Boys–it took you—long enough," she panted, and smiled upon them.

"Wal, Miss Majesty, you gave us all the time there was," replied Ren.

Sidway's hazel eyes, dark and intent, appeared to pierce through Madge. Not for weeks had she met his full gaze like this, and despite the scattering of her wits, she realized the searching nature of his look, as if he were striving to divine her wishes.

"Miss Stewart, it was well you sent us," said Sidway, simply. "I'm sure it spared you and your friends a real ordeal!"

A groan ran through the listening party.

"Real ordeal! What do you mean?"

"Too severe a physical strain for tenderfeet. A motion-picture crowd would shy at this one—and they do things. . . .

But it can be done, Miss Stewart, and I'm bound to admit, it'd be the trip of a lifetime."

"You don't advise it?"

"I do not."

"Would you take the responsibility if I insisted?" asked Madge.

"Yes, if your father insisted, too."

"Dad, are you with me?"

"Daughter, this issue is between you and Sidway. He has not told me a thing. My advice is to listen *before* you make up your mind. You know how you are, Madge."

Madge transfixed Sidway with a troubled passionate gaze. She did not want to undertake this trip. She rejoiced that Sidway was making it impossible. But there was something about him that dared her to see if she could prevail upon him. She realized that until she could conquer such weakness, she would never be at her best with him.

"Lance, you're on the spot," she said.

"Heavens, when haven't I been?" he ejaculated, and joined Stewart in a laugh. Their understanding and good feeling seemed manifest. Then he bent a glance upon Madge, so clear, so frank, yet so supremely doubtful of her, that she writhed inwardly under it. She divined a thrust aimed at what must be his conviction of a vulnerable point in her which she had no idea she possessed.

"Shoot!" she said, with all her disdain, but she felt dismay before she had been attacked. This cowboy must know something about her, to her discredit, or he could not have affected her that way.

"It may seem superfluous—to you," he said, coolly. "But have you considered the expense?"

"Expense!" echoed Madge. That was the last question she would have expected.

"Yes. Perhaps you have not thought of that."

"I had not. Usually I don't consider what my plans cost."

"Exactly. That is why I presume to mention it. . . . This

trip would cost a great deal. A gang of laborers would be needed on the trail. Two weeks' work at least. The cabin up at Cochise's stronghold has gone to rack and ruin. It would have to be repaired. There are no tents and tarpaulins at the ranch, nor cooking utensils. You would require a complete new camping equipment. We have packsaddles for only a few horses; and, well, would you expect to have this camp on the scale on which you do everything?"

"I'm afraid I would."

"Of course. Then it would be necessary to buy twenty new packsaddles and at least ten pack animals. That would entail hiring half a dozen extra riders. . . . So you see, Miss Stewart, it is quite a big undertaking."

"I see all right," replied Madge, dubiously. To the credit of her friends, they at once turned thumbs down upon the whole proposition, and were so nice and fine about it that Madge regretted her subterfuge. But what was Lance Sidway aiming at? She believed his report implicitly. A half or a quarter of these obstacles would have sufficed. He believed that no matter how unfavorable his report or how exorbitantly the trip would cost, she would decide to go willy-nilly. Then he believed other things that mystified Madge. For an instant she had a bothersome thought that he might feel contempt for her because expense had never meant anything to her. A rebellious impulse to do the very thing he expected died in its infancy, somehow hastened to its death by the singular, almost mocking light in Sidway's hazel eyes. In a flash she saw how she could amaze and undeceive him.

"Thank you, Sidway. I'll abandon the camping trip solely upon your report," she said. "You have been very conscientious and dependable. I appreciate it."

If Lance's scarcely veiled surprise proved Madge's intuition close to correct, his relief and gladness, that warmed out the coldness of his face, augmented the thought-provoking power of that moment. Madge conceived, too, an impression that Sidway's feelings were reflected in her father's dark face.

Could these two possibly have an understanding? Madge drove the perplexing thought away.

"Friends, it's off, our mad ride up into the wilds," declared Madge. "Some other summer! Instead I'll throw the biggest party ever."

Pandemonium broke out among the boys and girls. When they ceased mobbing Madge she suddenly found Sidway towering over her, a stranger to whom her whole being seemed to leap.

"Thank heaven, I won't have to make a report on *that*," he cried. "But, come here!" And seizing her hand he led her aside. "You don't know what I thought and I'll never tell you. Only I'm begging you to forgive me. You are one swell sport! You're a thoroughbred! It's no wonder . . ."

He broke off and squeezed her hand and strode away toward the bunkhouses. Madge stood a second, aware of the cramped fingers she could hardly straighten, and wondering what were the words he had left unsaid. It was not her fault if he had not had a glimpse of all her sides. Madge went back to her father.

"Dad, have you and Lance framed me?" she asked.

"My dear, I've had no part in this—this, whatever you'd call it," he laughed. "Honest, Madge. It looked as if I might have been in cahoots with Lance to queer your trip. But he never told me a thing. Nor did Ren. I think he carried it off very well indeed. Your mother will be pleased."

"Yeah?—What's this Machiavelli mean by pleasing you and Mom? Looks like deep stuff to me."

"Madge, he's just a nice boy, who disapproves of you a lot."

"Dad, he said some strange things, for him. Nearly crushed my poor hand. Look! Then he beat it. He ran off before I could even answer."

"Lass, if this Machiavelli and your dad, or better, old Nels, could get you locked in a room and starved or beaten or loved into *listening* for some hours, you'd come through like your mother did when she decided some momentous questions twenty-five years and more ago."

"Dad!—Starved or beaten or. . . . You are as mysterious as *he!*" And Madge judged that the better part of valor would be to flee. But not until she had plunged deeply into plans for her party did she recover from the confusing thoughts resulting from that surprising contact with the cowboy and her father.

Madge set the date for the party. Invitations were sent to all the range people her father knew from Douglas to Bolton. All the *vaqueros* and *señoritas* known to Bonita and her brothers were invited. It took a whole day to put up the decorations. That night when Madge tried out the colored lights and lanterns the glamorous effect transported even her. Next morning the caterer rolled in with his trucks and minions, and Majesty's Rancho hummed like a beehive. Last to arrive were the sixteen musicians. That was early in the afternoon. Madge went to bed to rest, but she could not sleep. The girls could not even rest. They were in and out all afternoon, and finally when Madge asked Allie to get out a new gown none of them had ever seen, and which she had reserved for this occasion, there ensued a perfectly rapt silence. Bu Allen, of course, broke it. "My Gawd!" she gasped in uncontrollable excitement. "Majesty, you must be married in that!"

"Bu, a girl has to have something beside a gown to get married."

"Not that one. You don't even need a slip."

And so mad were they all that only Madge noted the omission of a man. The thing struck a fatalistic chord in her. She had everything—wonderful parents, lovely friends, wealth, education, ranch, horses, cars, all to make any girl happy—except a man to marry.

But that was the last thing in the world to occupy her mind now. Anyway it was a calamity she could remedy this very night, provided she beat down her obsession for one unappreciative, unresponsive cowboy. Still it had been ingrained in Madge's girlish dreams that no one save a cowboy like her father could ever have her.

Toward the end of that long day Madge slept, and was awakened by Allie and Maramee. They informed her that the lights were lit, the many tables set, and guests were arriving. Madge sent them off to dress and flew to her bath. She was in the midst of her make-up task when they returned, formal and elegant, to draw encomiums from Madge.

"Girls, we'll knock 'em for a loop tonight," said Madge gleefully.

"We?" chirped Maramee.

"Yes, us," declared Madge.

"Darling, I think you mean him," retorted Allie.

They brushed her hair until it sparkled with glints of fire, and then by some magic of deft feminine hands they incased her in the blue and gold gown. For jewels Madge wore a string of pearls, the gift of her Aunt Helen, so beautiful and valuable that she had not risked it out of the safe for years. Allie was silent, gazing raptly at her, but Maramee raved on and on.

"Once in my life!" was all Madge whispered to the image shining from her long mirror, and either she meant that she was satisfied or that she would play that beauty to the limit. Madge went to her mother's room, to be admitted. Her father was there, lean and dark and handsome in his black suit.

"Oh, Mom, but you are a lady of quality!" cried Madge, a rush of warm sweetness piercing her trance. "Dad, isn't she just stunning?"

Both her father and mother appeared incapable of speech on the moment, but their eyes would have gratified a far vainer girl than Madge. "I wanted you to see me first." And she whirled for their benefit. "Now, darlings, this is my party. I've had it coming to my crowd for a year. Unknown to them it is my farewell to them—to college—to that kind of life. Whatever we do, don't be shocked."

And she ran out, through the living room, into the corridor

where she encountered Sidway. In his dark garb he looked so slim and different that she did not recognize him at first glance.

"Oh!—how stupid of me! It's Lance." And she halted under the colored lights.

He started and backed partly against the balustrate, while a dazed and frowning expression altered his face. Then it vanished as he leaped erect, to utter a queer little laugh and make her a profound bow.

"Lance. Do you—like me?" she queried softly.

"Majesty, I used to believe you were a mistake of evolution, but now I know it was God."

"Is that a compliment or a slam?"

"Pardon me. I'm in urgent search of your father. I just found out that the balance of his cattle herd were just rustled. And I'm going to find out who stole them and where they were driven."

"Oh, Lance, how dreadful. But must you tell him tonight?" wailed Madge.

"Come to think of it, no," he returned, brightly. "I haven't even told Ren. Poor kid! It's going tough with him. Love is a terrible thing!"

"It is indeed," agreed Madge, fervently. "But *you* have merely heard or read about that."

She left him, sailing with a swish down the corridor to her room. She had no time to deduce sense from Lance Sidway's queer remarks, and she was glad of it. If she spent ten minutes with that cowboy there would be no triumph for her tonight. What a devastating effect he exercised over her! Some of the girls were in her rooms and the others soon paraded in. Every last one of them had on a new gown! And had they planned for this *pièce de résistance* of Madge's? They were interrupted by the caterer, a handsome Italian in immaculate white. Madge admitted him and drove out the girls. "Find the boys. I'll be with you in a moment."

"I hope you please," he said, rubbing his hands together.

"Corvalo, I'm bound to be. Remember, serve champagne to my party in the living room. Wine to the other tables. As for the punch, it must have an awful wallop. But not an immediate kick. Use creme de menthe to flavor only—to make them like it—leading them on. A soft sweet tasty punch—flowers and music leading to a precipice. Get me, Corvalo?"

He departed with shining eyes and beaming face, as if that order had been one to his liking. Madge went in search of her friends. They had rounded up the boys, who looked cool and natty in white flannels. Their various comments were incense to Madge's heart. Rollie Stevens said: "Murder in the Rue Rancho this night!"

"Come, let's make the rounds," said Madge. "At least I can speak to all these strangers."

"Lamping you will be enough," declared Barg.

Madge found it easier to be courteous and friendly than she had anticipated. The delight of the Mexicans especially pleased her. There were ranch people she remembered, and apparently all the cowboys on the range.

"Pack of wolves!" averred Rollie. "They'd eat you alive Good thing you're under my wing."

"Are you sure you can be trusted to think of *me*?"

The long patio made a colorful and beautiful spectacle. A row of tables extended down the center. Benches and chairs lined the walls. The waxed floors, built in for the occasion, shone iridescently. Colorful lanterns hung from the center of the arches. The gorgeous Spanish and Indian decorations lent a richness and legend to the old rancho. Madge slipped a hand over her heart to still its beating, its muffled pain. What was this pang stealing into her happiness?

Moments for pondering had passed by. The great dinner gong pealed through the corridors and the patio, and was followed by a merry hum. Then the orchestra upon which Madge put such store pealed its exotic music through the house. It heralded the Spanish *fiesta* that was to last until dawn.

Madge, with her college guests, and her father and mother, sat down to dinner in the living room. That table from its hothouse orchids, its silver plate and crystal, to the rare and savory dishes of the sumptuous dinner, excelled anything the ranch had ever known.

Stewart appeared to be staggered with its magnificence. But as the dinner wore on he fell under the spell of his wife's pleasure and Madge's rapture, and the continuous merriment and wit of the college crowd. Snake Elwell and Bu Allen were the first couple to begin dancing. Bu looked ravishing in a white gown that threatened to split at every move. Allie, usually the sweetest of girls who never made a criticism or caustic comment, spoke right out: "Some hot little cookie!" And Madge's father, who heard it, surrendered unconditionally to this group of young moderns.

Madge's keen eyes did not miss anything. Once she saw Sidway and Starr, flushed of face and fire-eyed, peep into the living room. She also observed that her father did not drink his champagne. With dinner at an end, the dancing set in continuously, with only short intermissions. Madge loved to dance, and the first hour passed by on wings. When her crowd happened to congregate, someone remembered the punch, whereupon they flocked to the living room. The long table had been cleared, and moved back to the wall. In the center an enormous bowl of silver and crystal shone resplendent, full of a twinkling liquid that had life and color. An attendant stood ready to serve. Curious and gleeful, Madge drained her cup, tasted and wondered, and listened for comments. She alone knew that innocent-looking punch was loaded with dynamite.

"Say, Madge, where'd you hit on this concoction? Pretty nifty," observed Rollie Stevens, who considered himself a connoisseur.

"New to me, Rollie."

"Soft and minty," interposed Brand. "I'll bet it'll lead you on."

"Tame, if you ask me," said Allie, loftily, and that from her was a source for mirth. Allie could not stand liquor at all.

"Swell punch," observed Elwell. "What do you say, Bu?"

"Hand me another," replied the redhead.

"Majesty, are you kidding us with this stuff?"

"I'm sorry, Brand. But this is my home, you know. And remembering your capacities I wanted something weak."

"Weak or not let's have another."

Madge finally dragged her friends out. While dancing and resting the next hour she contrived to keep tabs on that punch bowl. Just as she had suspected, her friends were succumbing to this insidious drink. Once with Rollie she almost burst in upon her father, Nels, Danny Mains, Starr and Sidway, but she drew her escort back behind some decorations in the corridor. With intense interest and fiendish glee she watched them and listened, holding Rollie back with imperious hand.

Manifestly this group of gentlemen had been in there before.

"Gene, we shore lived too soon," drawled Nels, regretfully.

"Shades of Monty Price and Nick Steel!" ejaculated Stewart. "Nels—Danny, what would our old pards have thought of this drink?"

"My Gawd, I dunno. . . . Fill me up another, waiter."

"Boss, this heah punch is nectar an' honey an' hell all mixed up together," said Starr.

"Where does the hell come in?"

"Wal, I hadn't noticed thet until this last drink, which was my sixth. . . . Pard, how many have you had?"

"Enough," replied Sidway, tragically.

"Why, you dawg-gone kill-joy! Cain't you hold your likker?"

"Ren, I can't hold this liquor—and I can't take it!"

"Lissen, pard. I'm gonna put a couple of these under Bonita's belt," whispered Ren, behind Danny Mains' back.

"Don't. You'll lose her right then."

"Umpumm! Thet's when I'll win her. Pard, Bonita is funny tonight. Been cryin' an' turrible upset."

"Come here, you geezer!" And Sidway dragged Ren out of the room.

"Gene, any drink that can make an old man young again is one to tie to," said Nels.

"I agree with you. But, pards, even if my daughter hadn't sprung some destroying drink on us, I'd have to get drunk with you for old times' sake."

"Wal, ole *El Capitan* again!" ejaculated Danny Mains. "If the ootfit was only heah!"

Madge had heard enough to give her a twinge of conscience. But only gay and rapturous thoughts could abide in her mind. She went back to dancing. Rollie with more drinks than were good for him had begun to grow demanding and bossy. Soon came an added interest in Sidway's presence upon the floor. He was taller than her college friends, slim and erect in his black suit, broad-shouldered, quite the handsomest boy there. He had started in dancing with Bonita, and from her to Bu Allen was only a short step. Then he cut in on the boys and apparently enjoyed thoroughly her girl friends. Naturally she expected him to gravitate to her. But he did not approach her or look at her, an omission that did not go unnoticed. It was rude of him, Madge thought, as she was his hostess, but it seemed between them there was no observance of rules. From that hour Madge's feeling of happiness underwent a change. Visits to the punch bowl kept up her spirits. By midnight some kind of a climax seemed imminent. Her father and his friends, despite their visits to the living room, were still steady on their feet. Stewart appeared to have lost his gaiety. Madge saw her mother apparently remonstrating with him, to no avail. Thereafter Madge did not see her mother. Madge was glad and she hoped her father would retire soon. There would be no fights such as Stewart had known in the early days, when he was *El Capitan*, but Madge knew something was bound to happen, and she repented now that she had been responsible for it.

It came in the nature of a surprise. Bu Allen sat down on

the floor, a cup of punch in her hand, and turned a somersault. She did not spill any liquor. The boys and girls howled at the sight. Thus encouraged, she turned somersaults all across the living room. Nels and Danny Mains were in hysterics; Ren Starr whooped like the cowboy he was; Sidway strode out of the room. Stewart, his face like a thundercloud, threw up his hands like a man who had been vainly fighting facts, and lunged out into the patio.

Madge, frightened at the lightning of his eyes, watched him disappear with a sinking of her heart. Had she gone too far? But she had not known Beulah Allen would disgrace her party. And if Snake Elwell had not violently jerked the girl to her feet and dragged her out Madge felt that she would have had to adopt extreme measures. That event saw the disintegration of the party. The dancing grew desultory, except in the patio where the range guests still held forth.

Finding Barg and Maramee asleep in each other's arms in a corner, and some of the other couples fading from the living room to the benches, Madge realized her party was about over. And it had been a failure. She knew when she had had enough to drink. But in her bitterness, she overstepped her habit. With Rollie she drank two more cups of punch. And as she went outdoors with him, wrapping a mantle around her bare shoulders she realized two things—that Rollie was pretty drunk and that a gaiety had overcome her gloom. Good to have the blue devils fade away! Lance Sidway had not come near her! To hell with him! Rollie was a pal, and on the way out under the pines, Madge not only permitted his extravagant embraces but returned his kisses. She felt just on the verge of being giddy and dizzy. But she did not want to think. After all she could do worse than marry Rollie Stevens.

In an open space, shaded by spreading pines and surrounded by low foliage, they found a bench covered with blanket and pillows. The moonlight streaked through rifts in the branches to lend a silver glamour to the glade. Rollie sat down and drew Madge upon his lap. At first she felt silly and soft at his love-making, and experienced a pleasant glow of excitement.

"You're going to marry me," he said, thickly, between kisses.

"Is that so? Who told you?" laughed Madge.

"I'm telling you," he replied, more violently.

"Rollie, you're drunk."

"If I am it's your fault."

"You all fell for that punch. My secret, Rollie!"

"Yeah? . . . Your line, Madge—secrets! I'll give you another one."

The edge on his voice, accompanying some rough handling of her awakened Madge to the situation. But her lackadaisical good nature was such that she made only feeble resistance to his ardor.

"You love me—don't you?" he demanded fiercely.

" 'Course I love you—Rollie—as a pal—old friend, and what have you? . . . but . . ."

"Nuts! I'm tired of that dope." And the hot kisses upon her mouth and neck grew more violent. Madge was no longer returning his kisses. From that to remonstrating with him was only a short step. It appeared to inflame him. Locked in his arms she was at a disadvantage. A rattling of her pearls alarmed her. The fool would break the necklace.

"Let me—go! . . . You're drunk—boy. . . . this is . . ."

"So're you—drunk," he panted, and pushed her back off his lap upon the cushions. Madge's utterance was stifled by his kisses. She twisted her face away. But Rollie only grew more violent.

Furiously she flung him aside, and sprang off the bench. In the dark she fell over someone she took to be Rollie and had to clutch his arm to regain her balance. He appeared to be sitting against a tree trunk. But there at the end of the bench was Rollie, mumbling and cursing.

"Oh!—What?—*Who?*" screamed Madge, leaning forward

on her knees to peer at this man she had fallen against. He had his hands over his eyes and ears. They fell, and Madge recognized Lance Sidway.

She managed to arise despite a paralyzing dismay, that gave place to a terrific shame and rage.

"*You!*" burst out Madge.

He rose rather slowly and pulled himself erect. A slant of moonlight fell across his face. It was ashen white, and out of it glittered eyes as black as coal and as sharp as daggers.

"Yeah, it's me. Who else in hell could have such rotten luck?" he returned, with exceeding bitterness.

"Lance Sidway! you waylaid me!"

"Don't flatter yourself," he flashed, hotly. "I'd left your drunken outfit. On the way to my lodgings, I stopped here to—to smoke. But after I'd finished, I lingered, like the sap I am. I saw you coming and made sure you'd pass. But you didn't. Ha! Ha!"

"Oh, you lie! And you laugh at me!" exclaimed Madge, beside herself with rage.

"No, I don't lie," he retorted. "But I've the laugh on you, Madge Stewart."

Rollie had clambered up, hanging to the bench, evidently more than ever under the influence of liquor.

"Whosis?"

"Rollie, it's Lance Sidway. He was sitting here all the time," declared Madge.

"That cowboy cad? Conceited jackass! . . . Look here, sir, you spy on *me*. I'll cane the hide off you," shouted Stevens, and he struck openhanded at Sidway.

"Keep your hands off me," ordered the cowboy, shoving him back. "I'm sorry. But I wasn't to blame. I didn't spy on you. You get that?"

"You're a liar, Sidway. You're always spying on Madge. You're stuck on her."

Sidway jerked as if he had been stung. "Stevens, if I were you, I'd be a gentleman about it, which you're not. I wouldn't try to take advantage of her when she was drunk. Somebody ought to beat you good. And by God, *I* will, if you don't let me out of this."

Rollie lunged at Sidway who avoided him, backing against the bench.

"Let him alone, Rollie. You're drunk," cried Madge.

Sidway had no recourse but to stave off Stevens' blows. Finally a hearty slap in the face changed the cowboy's tactics. He seized Stevens by the arms and shook him violently. Then he shoved him back. "Stevens, I warn you. Lay off me, or I'll sock you."

"I'd shoot you if I had a gun."

"Yes, if my back were turned. You're one swell flop, Stevens. . . . Stay away from me, I tell you."

"Lance, get away from the fool!" implored Madge, who was if anything more infuriated with Stevens than Sidway.

"Sure, you would ask that. Me run, to save this guy's face."

"It might save my good name."

"You can't save a rotten egg, Madge Stewart. I tell you I'm the insulted one here and I'm getting sore."

When Stevens belligerently confronted Sidway again, it was to meet no resistance. The cowboy stood motionless in the moonlight, his arms lowered. But to Madge he looked formidable.

"You—insufferable cow hand!" shouted Stevens, furiously and he struck Lance twice in the face.

"Okay, Rollie. Now let's see if you can take it," rejoined Sidway, grimly, and he swung hard on the collegian. The blow sounded solid, meaty, and Stevens went down with a thud and did not move.

"There! Sorry to mess up your lover, Miss Stewart, but as you saw, I couldn't avoid it."

"He lies so still . . . he's so white," cried Madge, in alarm.

"I hope the sucker croaks," rejoined Sidway, brutally.

"What'll I do?"

"Well, you might hunt up your dad and Nels, tell them

what this guy tried to do to you—and watch them hang him."

"What a beast you are, Lance Sidway! It was bad enough to sit there, like a cheap eavesdropper, and listen, let alone . . ."

"Hell! I tell you I'm innocent. I didn't look. I didn't listen—at least until you got so raw in your lovemaking . . ."

"But you should have made your presence known at once," cried Madge, poignantly.

"Right. I'm damn sorry. But I was scared, confused . . . It wasn't easy—for me—Madge Stewart."

He choked over the last utterance, and gazed down upon her with eyes of terrible reproach, which might have softened Madge but for her own insupportable emotions.

"That's no excuse for a gentleman," she retorted.

"No! But for God's sake, do you think you were a lady?"

"Lance Sidway, I *was* and I *am*!" she rejoined, imperiously.

"And I'm a poor, miserable, crawling louse!" he ejaculated, in desperation.

"I regard the appellation as fairly felicitous."

"And you're Majesty Stewart, a law unto herself, a lady of quality, a princess who can do no wrong?" he burst out, passionately. "Listen, you!—That college bum there was not drunk. But his decency, if he had any, was gone. And you were not drunk, either, but your dad would have despised you if he had been here in my boots."

"Rollie forgot himself—I confess . . . But I didn't . . ."

"Bah! Why, for a real man you'd have been a push-over," retorted Sidway, hoarsely.

Madge slapped him viciously across the lips. The next instant his open hand cracked along her cheek and head, and but for the bench would have upset her. Nevertheless, almost blinded by stars and shock, Madge slapped him again, with all her might.

"Regular cat, eh?" he burst out, huskily. "But you can't make a dog out of me."

"I—don't—have—to . . ." panted Madge.

He seized her in powerful hands, hard and hot, and dragged her into a ray of moonlight.

"Majesty—what a travesty that name is!—Madge Stewart, you're going to hear the truth once in your life."

He was suddenly so strangely different, so grimly righteous and ruthless, so white and fire-eyed that Madge sustained a sinking of her heart. She tried to retort with some further insult, but failed of coherence. He shook her as he had shaken Stevens.

"Majesty Stewart! One swell girl, they all think. Proud, blue-blooded, rich. What a mistake! Why you are as false as hell. It was low-down enough before I caught you tonight. Thank God it was I instead of your dad who caught you. He's had enough of you to stand."

"Sidway, what do you—mean?" whispered Madge, and slipping out of his nerveless grasp she sank upon the bench.

"I mean your splendid father and your loving mother are too damn good for you, Madge Stewart."

"Lance, I—I know that."

"But you don't know what you've put them through."

"Oh!—Not—not money trouble?"

"Yes, money!" he bit out, bending over her.

Madge moaned. This it was then that had vaguely haunted her, the conscience which she would not face. She felt it in this man's intensity, in the bitterness of his voice, the fire of contempt in his eyes. This something had given him power over her, and her spirit seemed to be fainting.

"It's fate that I have to tell you this," he went on, swiftly. "Your dad gave me his books to straighten out. He did not know that in the book he had left your bank statements, checks and what not. I went over these, too. And that is how I learned of your rotten extravagance and the way your parents have ruined themselves for you."

"*Oh!* Lance!—don't—*don't!* You are furious with me. I—I don't blame you. But for mercy's sake, don't say any more . . ."

"Listen, girl, I couldn't say enough," he interrupted, adamant to the piteous fear in her appeal. "I love your dad. He makes me remember my own father. And your mother—how sweet and loving and thoroughbred!—All for Majesty. That has been the whole story of this ranch. . . . Madge Stewart, you're not rich. You have no income any more. Three years ago it flopped. And these parents of yours have let you go on, spending like a drunken sailor, deceiving yourself, sacrificing them for your college career, your clothes and cars, your cocktail dates with gangsters— My God! that is the limit. . . . And this party of yours, Miss Stewart, this rare and exotic *fiesta* to your glory—you have pulled it when you were broke. And your dad rounded up the last of his cattle to sell—to cover your debts . . . And tonight when the whole country was doing you honor, dancing to your jazz, drinking your wines and punch—that last herd was rustled."

Madge sank down to hide her face in the pillows. The blow had fallen. And of all blows it was the mortal one which could crush her.

"And now, angel-face," whispered Sidway, almost spent, "your father is ruined—and who'll pay for this party? Would you like Nels and Ren and me to chip in our savings. . . ."

Madge stretched out a shaking importunate hand that silenced him. And it seemed amidst the knell of pride and happiness that had fallen in ruins about her, she heard Sidway's swift footfalls fading away.

Chapter Ten

HALFWAY down the slope Lance halted in his blind hurry. The Spanish music floated softly on the still air; the moon soared pitilessly white. What was it that he had done? He sat down under a pine and battled with his conflicting emotions.

Brutally he had made impossible any longer stay at Stewart's ranch. That long-deferred break seemed an unutterable and immense relief. But his conscience flayed him. "What for?" he whispered, huskily. "Why do I feel this—this. . . . It was—coming to her!" He was glad that he had had the courage to tell her. If she had a grain of good in her the truth would bring it out. Then why this stab in his heart, this clamor of furies in his ears, this still small voice? He would have wanted to tell her like an impassive destiny, letting the iron consequences fall. And he had sunk to the level of a man like Uhl. Perhaps even that philanderer would have been more of a gentleman. Lance struck the low of misery.

Then attending to his smarting lip he found it cut and bleeding. How about that? And the stinging blows might as well have been re-enacted. He had struck her, a hard openhanded slap that had staggered her. Suddenly it all flashed clear. Jealousy had been at the root of that incredible passion. Loving Madge Stewart to distraction, his damnable fate had been to be compelled to cower there in the shadow, seeing, hearing the kisses she had lavished on that college fellow. Lance tried to blot out the sight. That had seemed a sickening mortal blow, but it was his vile speech to her that stuck like a hot blade in his side—the jealous false word for which she had struck him across the lips. At last Lance uncovered the real trouble.

"Rotten of me!" he muttered, under his breath. "My God, how terrible she made me feel! . . . But even half drunk she could take care of herself. I saw that. Yet I . . . Jealousy made me low-down. If she had been kissing *me* . . . it would have been heaven. A tough spot for Lance Sidway! . . . Well, Madge, whatever else you are, you're straight—and I can climb out of hell on that."

Lance stood up, shivering a little at the cool air and the indifferent stars. This was the end of his secret love affair. And there would never be another, he was certain. It did not seem possible that any man, much less he, could see Madge Stewart as he had seen her, and carry her in his arms, and kiss her with such abandon, and then fall in love with another woman.

Lance strode down to the bunkhouse, his mind trying to take up the threads of the information he had forced from Bonita. There was a light in Nels' cabin. Lance's watch said that morning was less than an hour away. He burst in upon the old cattleman, who was in the act of undressing.

"Nels, are you sober?" demanded Lance.

"Hello, son, what's ailin' you—all white an' eyes aburnin'?"

"Hell to pay, Nels. Are you sober enough to get me straight?"

"Sober?—Dog-gone! I don't know. Thet shore was some punch. I jest couldn't stop drinkin' it."

"Swell drink, all right. What'd it do to Danny and Ren and Stewart?"

"Wal, they cleaned oot the bowl. Gene said it was an act of charity on their part. *He* was sober. Gene used to hold more bad likker than any man on the range. But Danny an' Ren were lit up some. . . . Say, what you got on yore chest?"

"Plenty! Now, listen. Pack me some biscuits, meat, dried apples—anything you can dig up pronto. Put it in a saddle-bag. I'll wrangle my horse. And you be sure you sober up while I'm gone."

"Son, I reckon I savvy," drawled Nels.

Lance went into his cabin, and hastily changed into his riding garb, buckled on his gunbelt, and hurried out, to jerk a bridle off a peg on the porch. The night before, because of the strange horses that had arrived, Lance had put Umpqua in the barn. The moment Lance's step sounded on the runway, Umpqua nickered, and stamped his hoofs. Lance looped the bridle round his neck, led him out, and filling a nosebag with grain, he put that over Umpqua's head. Then leading the horse he hurried back to Nels' cabin. There he saddled Umpqua, but left the cinch loose. He decided before seeing Nels to go into his cabin thinking hard what to take. It was necessary to light the lamp. A blanket, his fleece-lined coat, his rifle and some shells, his gloves, money and matches—these he thought would be about all. Then he remembered Madge's photograph. He would take that, for the chances were against his returning, or ever seeing her again. Fortunately the picture fit inside his coat pocket. He wrapped it in a silk scarf and carefully put it away. Funny, he thought, if a rustler's bullet pierced that lovely likeness of Majesty Stewart before it pierced his heart! But even so it could not hurt any more than she had hurt him. Then he extinguished the lamp and went out. The east was breaking gray. Dawn was not far off.

Umpqua was pitching the nosebag to get the last of the grain.

"Nels, come out," he called.

"Heah I am. Been waitin', son, kinda worried."

"Thanks, Nels," replied Lance, receiving the saddlebags. "Nothing to worry about—much."

"No. Wal, you act kinda queer. I've spent my life with range fellers. An' if you're not drunk on thet punch, you're shore drunk on somethin'."

"Yeh? Well, what, old wiz?" rejoined Lance, his swift hands at work over the saddle.

"You're leavin' Majesty's Rancho."

"Ha! Gee, Nels, you're keen. I rather snicker to snort that I am."

"An' on account of Majesty?"

"Yes, on account of Majesty!" ejaculated Lance, flippantly.

"Aw!—Did you quarrel?"

"Look where she split my lip. That little lady has a sock."

"Son, don't tell me she—she hit you?"

"I'll tell the world she did."

"What in Gawd's name for?"

"Nels, it's too long a story. I deserved it and I took it."

"Lance, you're uncommon bitter. . . . I don't mind admittin' thet I had it figgered you—you was in love with Majesty."

"Nels, damn your lunatic hide!" burst out Lance. "You don't mind admitting!—Say, you lying old matchmaker, you've been driving me nuts! You haven't given me any peace for weeks. You wouldn't even let me sleep. 'Ain't I kinda in love with Majesty? She shore is sweet on you!' . . . What kind of talk!—Now, listen, for once, for good and all. 'Kinda in love with Majesty?' Ha! Ha! Ha! . . . I love that good-for-nothing angel so terribly I'm dying for her. Do you get that? I'm stark staring mad about her. I'd shoot myself if I hung around here any longer. So I'm beating it. Now, take a load of that."

"Son, it'll be the turriblest mistake if you run off now," replied Nels, awed and moved. "Fer Majesty's jest as turrible in love. . . ."

"Skip it. You're balmy. You're nuts. You're crazy," retorted Lance, wrenching the words out. It was insupportable to listen to such raving from this simple old man. "Listen to this. All the cattle Stewart had left were rustled last night, right after dark. Must have been rounded up in the daytime."

"What?" roared Nels, changing magically. "Why'n'hell didn't you tell us?"

"Your darling Madge begged me to keep it till tomorrow. Well, that's today."

"Who told you?"

"Bonita."

"Ahuh. How'd you drag thet oot of her?"

"I threw a couple of those punches into her, danced with her, took her out. Well, she spilled the beans, on conditions."

"What conditions?"

"Never mind them, Nels. I won't tell you. And you're not to give Bonita away to Stewart or Ren."

"Humph! You cain't fool them."

"That's not important. The cattle have been rustled by *vaqueros*. Bound across the border. By the Gray Ridge Divide. Where's that?"

"It's thet long gray hill southeast of heah. Aboot ten miles, closest. Separates the range from the foothills of the Peloncillos. There's a cattle trail straight down the valley across the border. Rustlers used it years ago."

"Stewart's cattle ought to be around that divide by now."

"Shore, an' then some. What's yore idee, son?"

"I'm going to find out."

"Good. But don't let yourself be seen from the ridge top. Those rustlers will figger thet the cattle won't be missed right off. But they've got sharp eyes. With two days' start they'd aboot get acrost before we could haid them off. . . . I'll get Stewart an' Danny, an' Starr drunk or sober, an' hit this cattle trail. Meanwhile you locate the rustlers, then ride on in to town. Don't lose no time gettin' an ootfit of cowboys—or any kind of a posse, an' ride hell fer leather to haid these greasers off."

"Use my own judgment as to where I'll cross the ridge?"

"Shore. But if you're smart an' lucky you can cross by the Cochise Trail. Only don't ride down into thet valley onless you're ahaid of the rustlers."

"Okay, Nels. I'm on my way," replied Lance. "Nels, that outfit might get suspicious or something, and hit up the Cochise Trail. Tell Gene and Ren to look for my tracks on that trail, crossing the valley." Then vaulting astride he rode across the square, down by the sleeping village, out upon the shadowy gray range. It was almost daybreak when he struck the wash. By the time a ruddy light showed over the dark mountain barrier Lance had struck the fresh cattle track. It crossed the highway and headed straight for the low slant of gray that marked the northern end of Gray Ridge Divide. Satisfied and thrilled, Lance swerved off the trail to make a short cut, intending to climb the ridge ten miles or so toward the south. It was then only that his mind reverted to the tragedy of his leaving. Madge haunted him, her lovely face white and tragic, her big eyes, and most of all, after he had told her that she had ruined her father, the way she sank down, crushed by amaze and shame. Lastly that imploring hand, mute appeal for mercy. Would she like him and Nels and Ren to donate their wages?—those had been his last words. Too late! Lance writhed in his saddle. As the dawn slowly flamed to a glorious sunrise and the broad daylight drove away his morbid thoughts, he could not understand how he had been so base. He felt that he would be driven to go back to the ranch and explain to Madge how his jealousy and passion had made him a coward and a cad. That would be a betrayal of his love, a refuting of all his scorn. As he rode along, his brooding self-reproach and remorse augmented his error and mitigated Madge's faults. If it turned out that he was to be the means of saving her father's cattle, and perhaps getting himself shot in Madge's interest, that would be all right with him, if only she could know of his repentance.

Lance crossed the valley obliquely and headed up the ridge about five miles south of the point. The sun was high in the heavens when he gained the summit. He took care not to show his horse or himself on top of the ridge. There were rocks and scrub cedars all along, affording good cover. Lance dismounted to reconnoiter. He had to walk a long way north on the ridge before he discovered the cattle. They had been driven into the head of the narrow valley between the foothills and the ridge, and were grazing. The distance was not quite too far to distinguish horses and riders, but Lance had to wait a good while before he made sure he saw them. They should have traveled down the valley to a point almost equal with his position. Lance lingered there until he saw the herd move down the valley toward him. Then he retraced his steps.

Vaqueros had almost as keen eyesight as Indians. But if these rustlers had anticipated immediate pursuit they would not have traveled so leisurely during the night. They had probably calculated upon the cowboys and riders sleeping all this day after the excitement and disturbance of the *señorita's fiesta*. The raid would not be discovered for several days, which would give the thieves time to get across the border. It was a clever and nicely timed move on their part.

Arriving at the spot where he had left his horse, Lance sent a keen gaze back across the valley toward the ranch. He espied puffs of dust some miles out from the highway, about on a line with the cattle trail. He concluded Gene and his riders were in pursuit of the rustlers.

"Okay," soliloquized Lance, with satisfaction. "Pretty lucky for me to worm this out of Bonita. Poor kid! All to save her good-for-nothing brother! Well, I'll keep my word."

Lance mounted and rode along a rough summit trail, which Umpqua had to walk. Lance calculated that he was forty miles from the highway, and close to forty from town. The hour was short of midmorning. He had all the rest of that day, and longer, if need be, to carry out Nels' instructions. Recovery of the cattle looked easy to Lance. He tried to conjecture unforeseen circumstances. If the *vaqueros* discovered they were being pursued they would take to the foothills and escape. Lance eyed those formidable hills, rising and swelling gradually to the rough black summits of the Peloncillos.

"My best bet is to go down to the range and look for a cattle outfit between here and town," Lance told himself, and after thinking of every angle possible he decided to put his idea into effect. There were several ranches along that slope of the ridge, and he might be fortunate enough to meet some riders. To this end Lance headed down the slope.

Lance had enough on his mind to make the miles and hours seem short. Umpqua walked and trotted under the hot sun. As long as he had soft ground to travel on he would not tire. Late in the afternoon Lance arrived at the last ranch along the ridge, and ascertained that an outfit of cowboys had left not long before to round up some cattle south of Bolton. This was good luck, indeed, and Lance set off with high hopes. These riders would very likely camp outside of Bolton.

It was sunset when Lance caught up with a trio of cowboys leading three pack horses, and half a dozen extra mounts. Lance joined them with a greeting and pulled Umpqua to a walk.

"Howdy," returned a lean towheaded rider, fastening penetrating eyes upon Lance. "I seen you coming 'way back. Jest about in a hurry, wasn't you?"

"I'll say. You're the Bar X boys from Spencer's ranch, aren't you?"

"Wal, we're some of them."

"I'm Sidway, riding for Gene Stewart."

"I reckoned you was. My handle's Tim Sloan, an' my pards are brothers, sons of Spencer."

"Your boss told me you were bound south of Bolton to round up some of his cattle."

"We air, if we can locate them. But I reckon they're rustled across the border. Some two-bit outfit been workin' the edges of the range lately."

Lance lost no time accounting for his presence, and the lean rider was so interested that he reined his horse, and halted the cavalcade in the middle of the road. "Hell you say!—Boys, you hear thet? . . . How far back air these raiders with Stewart's cattle?"

"Over the ridge in the valley, halfway at the least."

"An' when was it you sighted them?"

"This morning around ten. Stewart will be behind them, keeping out of sight. And it's my job to get some riders to head them off from this end."

"We're with you, Sidway. . . . Boys, like as not this same outfit has been runnin' off our stock."

"Purty shore, I'd say," replied one of the brothers. "But we'd help you out if there wasn't a chance."

"Thanks, fellows. I'm relieved. . . . And now, Sloan, what do you advise?"

"Wal, them stolen cattle won't get nowhere near this end of the valley tonight. My idee is to camp here outside of town, an' be off before daylight in the mawnin'. How's thet suit you?"

"Fine. It's just going to work out great."

Before dusk settled down the riders halted just on the edge of Bolton near a clump of trees Lance remembered having passed on the trip to the Peloncillos.

"Sloan, will we eat in town?" queried Lance, as he dismounted.

"No. Boss won't stand for thet. We'll throw up some grub here. But we're out of coffee an' butter."

"I'll buy some. Do you think I ought to notify the sheriff?"

"Hell no. This deal is a cinch, an' thet old geezer would hawg all the credit."

Lance strode off into town, his mind thronged with thoughts. He seemed on the verge of an adventure much to his liking. Stewart and Nels were sure to like him better than ever. And proud, wild, volcanic Madge Stewart would surely be indebted to him, whether or not she ever confessed it. Lance had a desire to telephone the ranch. At that hour, with Stewart and his men absent, it was ten to one that Madge would answer. How coolly he could make his report, not omitting subtly to augment the dangers! Did that violet-eyed girl have a heart? Lance had to admit that she had, but he had never touched it. His bitter and final resolve of last night still held, yet he was conscious of a rending of spirit at the thought of keeping it, and leaving Majesty's Rancho forever.

At Smith's Store on the highway Lance purchased butter and coffee, and several cakes of hard chocolate, one of which he put in his pocket. While the clerk was wrapping Lance's purchases the proprietor accosted him.

"Hey, Sidway, when did you leave the ranch?"

"Before daylight this morning. Rode down the ridge looking for cattle."

"Then you don't know Stewart's phone is out of connection? I suspect it has been cut."

"Indeed I don't."

"Well, something's wrong. This morning Mrs. Stewart phoned in an order. I expected some things she wanted by express, so did not call until after they arrived. Then I couldn't get an answer."

"That's not strange. One of the old telephone poles may have toppled over," replied Lance, thoughtfully.

"Yes, it might, but it didn't," returned Smith, bluntly.

"Yeah? How do you know?"

"Mike Scanlon was in not ten minutes ago. He'd been out for a load of dead aspen wood. He said that when he was cuttin' it, out there along the creek, he saw a big black car dustin' along toward town hell-bent fer election. An' it stopped down the road eight or ten miles. Mike forgot about thet until he got near to the highway. Then he tangled up in a wire thet turned out to be Stewart's. It had fallen across the road. Hadn't been cut long, for Mike saw the bright end, where it had been clipped. He thought somebody in thet big black car had done it. Not half an hour ago! Damn queer, don't you call it?"

"Where does this Mike Scanlon live?"

"Up at the end of town, on the other side of the highway. Ask Meade, the garage man."

Lance, hurrying along past the bright red and yellow lights, pondered this news. It clamped down upon him with a presagement far out of proportion to probabilities. Apparently Stewart's telephone wire had not been cut until late in the day. That seemed to preclude any possibility of the rustlers being accountable. A big black car! Lance wanted to talk to Mike Scanlon about that car.

He passed the last bright neon lights. Meade's garage appeared to be deserted. Just at that moment a big black car, with headlights dark, moved slowly down the back road. Lance wanted a look at that car. It was strangely familiar in line and build. He swerved off the highway, crossed the open space to the back road.

"Hi there. Hold up," he called boldly. Manifestly the driver heard him for the car came to a halt. The street lamp behind Lance caught the gleaming faces of men in the front seat.

"Stick 'em up, cowboy!" cut the air with deadly menace. As Lance threw up his hands he recognized that voice. It belonged with the car.

"Okay, Uhl. Up—they are," he replied quietly.

"Come close."

Lance walked to the automobile halting abreast of the front seat. Uhl had his hand in his coat pocket and he was leaning over the door. Lance knew that he faced a concealed gun and that he had to think quickly and right. Uhl was bareheaded. His clean-cut visage shone pale and cold in the light. The driver hunched down over the wheel, as if ready to race. The engine purred. Then Lance caught the gleam of a machine gun on the lap of a man in the back seat. Between him and another man shrank a girl with face as white as chalk and great dark eyes. Lance recognized her with a terrific stop of his heart. For an instant he seemed to reel dizzily, then the cold sickening freeze of his very marrow quickened to a hot gush of blood, and his faculties cleared to a magnified intensity.

"Cowboy, you've been here on Cork's snatch racket?" queried Uhl, sharply.

"Yes."

"What held him up?"

"I don't know."

"We beat him to it! Who wised you and why're you looking for me?"

"Want to tip you off. You cut the wire too late. Sheriff here has blocked you as far west as Tucson and as far east as El Paso. Posse down the road waiting to blow your tires into smithereens."

Uhl burst into vehement curses: "Raggy, —— —— your dumb soul! You —— —— —— hop-head! I ought to bump you off for that loss of time back there. . . . What'll we do?"

"Shoot our way through," rasped the driver.

Lance interrupted in ringing low voice: "Might be okay for Bolton but points farther on the highway will be blocked. No chance in a million. Just as bad east. The wires are hot."

"Fox, what's the dope?" flashed the leader.

"Are you asking me?" curtly retorted one of the men in the back. "Didn't I warn you against this racket? I advise hiding along the railroad track and hopping a freight."

"You're no fox. You're a rabbit. . . . Cowboy, what's your tip?"

"Beat it for the hills pronto," exclaimed Lance, hurriedly. "You can't get through this town by car."

"Hills! . . . I get it. But horses, food, blankets—where can they be found?"

"Cowboy outfit just out of town. You can buy what you need from them and be on the trail in a jiffy."

"Good. Where'll we go?"

"Up in the Peloncillos. Rough wild country. You couldn't be tracked. You can hide for days. As soon as you get your dough you can ride down across the border into Mexico."

"Good tip, cowboy. What about this bus?"

"Send your driver on the ridge road. Give him water and grub. When morning comes he can drive off the road into the cedars beyond the point. And hide there. He could get out later."

"Oke. Will you guide us?"

"Sure. If you slip me enough."

Uhl's gun gave out a metallic clink as he drew his coat over the door. Producing a roll of bills he handed one to Lance.

"Here's a grand."

"Make it two, Uhl. And promise of more if I get you through," demanded Lance, lowering his hands.

"Okay, you chiseler. Jump on the running board and tell the driver where to go."

Lance ran around to the other side of the car and caught on. He directed the driver down the road and away from the town. A campfire blazed among the trees. In a reaction of feeling Lance could scarcely hold on. He imagined he was in a dreadful nightmare. But the car was moving. In the back he saw a gangster on this side with a machine gun across his knees, the same as the other. And on the floor lay another man. Lance puzzled over that. By sheer luck and wit he had met a tremendous situation. Anything to keep Uhl from carrying Madge off to the cities! She would be worse than lost or dead. He divined that Uhl would never release her. If he could steer them up into the hills, Stewart would be on his trail in another day. It was the only chance.

"Here we are," called Lance, as the car approached to within fifty feet of the campfire, out in the shadow.

"Fox, you and Flemm get out and stick up this bunch," ordered Uhl.

It was done almost in the twinkling of an eye. Uhl got out and faced the cowboys. Sloan's comrades, especially the cook, looked comical in their maze, but Sloan himself grew pale and grim.

"No holdup, cowboys. I want to buy horses and stuff to go up in the hills. Here's a grand."

"What's thet?" queried Sloan.

"Ten hundred smackers—a thousand dollars, you dumb-bell."

"What do you want fer thet much?"

"Five saddle horses, some packs, and whatever else we need."

"It's a deal."

Uhl stuck the bill into the cowboy's shirt pocket. "Line them up, Flemm, and keep 'em covered. . . . Come here, cowboy."

Lance strode into the campfire light, quite prepared for the profane ejaculations of Sloan and the Spencer brothers.

"Pick out what we want damn quick."

"Uhl, we'd save time by having these cowboys help me saddle and pack. Two of your men can keep them covered," suggested Lance.

"Oke. Step on it," rejoined Uhl, then repaired to the car. He opened the back door. "Come out, baby."

Madge descended from the car, clad in white slacks and a white sport coat. She made a step toward the campfire, when Uhl seized her roughly.

"Say, you move only when you're told," ordered the gangster, harshly. "Honey Bee Uhl talking—and you get it."

"All right. But keep your hands off me," flashed Madge, with a passion that told her spirit had not been weakened. And she twisted free.

"Oke, baby. But you might as well get used to them. . . . Raggy, throw that college bloke out. Then you grab some eats and drink and beat it."

Lance was as amazed as the other cowboys to see a limp young man pulled out of the car. He appeared dazed or injured, but he sat up, to disclose the handsome pale features of Rollie Stevens.

"Get up and come to the fire," ordered Uhl. And he pushed Madge along ahead of him. "Now sit down, both of you. In a minute I'll talk ransom money to you. . . . Raggy, don't forget to put our bags out of the car."

Lance tried to see and hear everything from where he saddled Umpqua. The other cowboys were saddling and packing with extreme celerity under the guns of the two gangsters.

Lance, thinking to have Madge ride his horse, shortened the stirrups. If a chance offered he might shoot one or more of these fellows and leap up behind Madge to make their escape. In a very few minutes six saddle and two pack horses were ready to travel. He searched for an extra rope and canteen, to tie them on his saddle. He heard the car roar and roll away up the ridge road. Hurrying back to the campfire he said crisply: "Ready, Uhl."

"My God!" cried Rollie Stevens. "It's Sidway. Madge, look!"

"I've had the pleasure," returned Madge, with infinite scorn.

"*Kidnaper!*" shouted Stevens, incredulously. Then it appeared a kind of joy came over him. That infuriated Lance, whose nerves were taut.

"Fetch those cowboys here," called Uhl.

When Sloan and his two comrades were lined up in front of the gangster, he asked, indicating Sloan, "What's your name?"

"Tim Sloan."

"Get this dope, cowboy," went on the gangster, deliberately. "In the morning you notify Stewart I'm holding his daughter for fifty grand. . . ."

"My father can't raise that," interposed Madge. "He is practically ruined. But I can raise half that."

"Baby, will you keep out of this?" retorted Uhl, then turning to Sloan again he resumed. "Notify Stewart I want fifty grand for her, and the same for her boy friend. If my orders are not obeyed, we'll rape the girl, and then kill them both. No bluffing. Send one man on our track with the money. Get that, cowboy?"

"Shore—I get it," replied Sloan, huskily.

"Fox, you keep these fellows covered until we're all in the saddle and out of the light. . . . Sidway, you lead the way with the pack horses. I'll follow with the dame. Fox, you and Flemm drive Stevens between you. Let's go."

"Uhl, I've selected an easy-gaited horse for Miss Stewart," spoke up Lance. "It's a tough trail."

"Yeah? Bet she'll stand it better than any of us. I haven't been in a saddle half a dozen times in my life. . . . Which horse? Come on, baby."

Lance led them over to Umpqua, and took from the saddle the fleece-lined coat he had untied.

"Get into this. It'll be bitter cold when we're high up," he said, and held the coat for her. If he had not been under stress of strongly suppressed emotion he might have recoiled from her convulsed white face and magnificent eyes. But her look of horror and hate strangely changed.

"*It can't—be true!*" she cried, poignantly.

"What can't be true, baby?" interposed Uhl.

"That Lance Sidway is a side partner of *you*, Bee Uhl!"

"Miss Stewart, it happens that I am," replied Lance. "Hurry into this coat. . . . You'll find gloves in the pocket."

Lance blindly held the coat for her and then plunged away. Mounting Sloan's horse he drove the two pack animals into the road, and headed for the dark hills. In a moment or more he recognized Umpqua's gait behind him, and presently heard the other horses following. It was done, and his heart seemed to descend from his throat and settle where it belonged. A cool wind blew down from the heights. The stars blinked as if incredulous. His jumbled thoughts began to straighten out. No use to marvel at where he found himself—at the unaccountable fate which had finally placed it in his power to save Madge Stewart, her honor and her life, and the happiness of her parents. Somehow he would do it. All these dovetailing angles could not be merely coincidences. They fitted, and he felt that he would solve the problem. But he must be governed by cool judgment instead of emotion. To this end he brought sternly to bear all the mentality of which he was capable. And out of the welter of thoughts he fixed upon a determination to be alert and ready on the instant to seize any opportunity to escape with Madge. It would come inevitably. These tenderfoot gangsters, unused to horses and pains, climbing into the wild rugged hills, would sooner or later provide that opportunity. But if it did not come before Uhl resorted to violence with the girl then Lance must be quick to kill him, and call upon her to run for her life while he fought it out with the others. That settled Lance into a cold and calculating mood which transformed him into another man. He was dealing with a matter of life and death—with vicious degenerates from the underworld of crime.

Tim Sloan had a rather complex problem to solve, as far as Lance's connection with Uhl was concerned; but any cowboy would obey the gangster's orders, and then let Stewart decide. Lance knew what would happen and he would not have been in Uhl's boots for a million dollars. Stewart and his men would be Indians on the trail of this gang, and they would shoot them down from ambush or surprise them and hang them from the pines. All Lance's faculties must be concentrated on his task of saving Madge from these merciless fiends.

Several miles out, the road swung to the south, and the Cochise Trail branched off around the lower point of the ridge. The black hills loomed high. A brightening to the east heralded a rising moon. Lance did not need the repeated calls from Uhl to "step on it," and he led across the valley at a trot. The pack horses, with light burdens, did not hold up the progress. In short order Lance reached the point where the trail started up the slope. He dismounted here to wait for the others. Umpqua was close behind. Lance broke the tip of a cedar bush with a vicious twist. He prepared this first sign to make his trail easy to follow.

"How you riding, girl?" queried Lance, as Umpqua came up.

"Swell. I like Umpqua in spite of the bum who owns him. It's going to be some romantic ride," replied Madge, mockingly.

Uhl arrived next, straddling his horse as if he were on stilts.

"What you gassing about?" he demanded.

"I asked Miss Stewart about her saddle cinch," returned Lance.

"Yeah? And what did that little dame say?"

"Ask her."

Uhl did and was promptly told to go where it was hot and that if he wanted to keep her from talking he would have to gag her. Stevens rode up then, accompanied by his captors. He appeared to have recovered somewhat and sat his saddle upright. The other gangsters, packing their bags and machine guns in front, looked as if they would have been glad to get down and walk.

"We begin to climb here," said Lance, "and I'll tighten your cinches." When he worked back to Madge and made a motion at her cinch she interrupted him.

"Keep your black hands away from me. I don't want to be soiled. If my cinch needs tightening, I'll do it," and her voice rang with contempt.

"Black? . . . Oh, I see. Gosh, how dumb I am!" declared Lance, lowering his bare hands. "Listen, you all. This trail is steep. Give your horse his head. Lean forward in bad places and hang onto his mane. When I stop to rest my horses you do the same. That's all."

He slapped the pack animals up the trail, and mounting he followed them. Umpqua, with a loose bridle, kept right on the heels of Lance's horse. When Lance turned to look back he saw Madge almost close enough to touch. The other four riders came on in close single file.

Lance zigzagged after the pack horses, and forbore gazing back again. But he thrilled at her nerve. She was not in the least afraid of Uhl. Lance let the pack horses initiate the rests. They were well-trained animals. Beyond the first foothill yawned a shadowy cedar flat, which led to another slope, long and gradual. When he surmounted it to the summit a full moon soared white above the black domes, transforming night into a silvery luminous day.

"Beastly trail," declared Madge, sarcastically. "I'll have to send a gang of laborers up here for two weeks to work on it. Big expense, though."

"I'll say," replied Uhl, taking her literally. "Tough as nuts But, baby, you ride like one of those circus girls in tights."

"Miss Stewart, you'd better not go to such expense," interposed Lance, satirically.

"Oh, are you a monumental liar?" burst out the girl.

"Shut up gabbing to him," ordered Uhl.

That significant speech for once silenced Madge, and it almost drove Lance into throwing his gun on the egoistic crook. He had kidnaped Madge for more than ransom.

Lance rode on into an up-an-down cedar country with an occasional pine tree heralding the approach to the heights. The air began to have a cool edge. The moon climbed toward the zenith. Presently the trail led into a narrow canyon. It was long and tortuous, heading at last into a mountain meadow, where traveling was comfortable for a while. A black belt of pines loomed ahead, shining in the moonlight. Lance kept eye and ear keen for his followers. Madge appeared to ride easily, but the others were growing crippled. They shifted from side to side in their saddles, let their legs hang, and grumbled intermittently.

Once, under the dark pines, Lance was seized by a savage and desperate impulse. Here was the place to shoot Uhl and ride off with Madge. He almost surrendered to it. He was sure of killing the gangster, sure of Umpqua, but some hitch he could not anticipate might give the other gangsters a moment to rake forward with those machine guns. Lance refused the chance. A better would offer, and he importuned patience.

The forest belt gave way to rough rocky country where Madge, if she had not bestrode a grand horse, would have suffered considerably. The horses labored slowly over shale and up loose slides and through thick brush that tore at them. The moon reached a point overhead; the air had a bite in it; coyotes mourned lonely cries; the night grew far advanced. Here Uhl at last fell off his saddle and walked behind Madge leading his horse. The other gangsters cursed and raved for a halt.

"Sidway, for God's sake, have a heart!" yelped Uhl, finally. "Aren't we far enough? Can't we camp here?"

"No water. No grass. You must go on," replied Lance.

"But we've rode—a hundred miles—already," panted the gangster.

"Seems like, maybe. But we're not twenty miles from town. Better get on your horse again."

Uhl obeyed groaning. Lance would not let them rest, and presently divining that Uhl was dependent upon him and knew it, he turned a deaf ear to appeals and curses and threats alike. And he led on and up through increasingly rough country, until Uhl, with a bellow, fell off his horse.

"Sorry, Uhl," said Lance. "You almost made it."

"Made what?"

"Camp at Cochise's stronghold. Not much further. And a swell place. Water, wood, grass. A log cabin."

"Gimme a—drink—Fox," panted the gangster. "I can walk—the rest."

"I wouldn't ride no furder for Al Capone," retorted Flemm, doggedly.

"Well, you can rot here—for a little shot," snapped Uhl, and he labored to his feet.

"Beat it, cowboy."

Lance led on, riding with his hands in his pockets. On the heights it was cold. Madge would be warm, all except her feet. Stevens appeared to be sagging in his saddle, but Lance could not summon any sympathy for the collegian. After more weary miles of travel Uhl burst out:

"Baby, what kind of liar did you call Sidway?"

"Monumental. But that's weak. He's a colossal liar!"

"Shall I bump him off?"

"Nothing could delight me more, except to see *you* bumped off."

"Say, you're a hellcat, ain't you? But I'll tame you. . . . Hold up, you guide. I want to get on again."

The last miles of that uphill ride were dragging and cruel

to the gangsters. Even Stevens, hurt at the outset in some way, endured the ordeal better. When Lance led into the beautiful wooded park, which inclosed Cochise's stronghold, the moon was low and dawn not far away. He halted the cavalcade under some spreading pines.

Lance's hands were so stiff from cold that he could scarcely start a fire. But that once done, he gathered firewood, and soon had a blaze. White and silent now Madge leaned against a tree. Lance threw his saddle, then flew to the packs. In a few moments he had them off the horses. He carried one to the fire and threw out blankets. Uhl knelt, his shaking hands to the fire. The other gangsters stood over the blaze, guns in hands, still wary and watchful. Their chief might have trusted Lance, but they did not.

"Majesty—aren't you—frozen?" asked Rollie, his teeth chattering. "Come to the—fire."

"My feet—are ice," she whispered.

"Here," cried Lance, sharply. "They can't be frozen. It's not cold enough. . . . Sit here, on this blanket. Lean against the pack. Put this blanket over you. . . . Never mind, I'll take off your shoes."

Her thin shoes and stockings afforded little protection against this frosty air. Her little feet did feel like blocks of ice.

"Rollie, throw a blanket round you and sit close to her," went on Lance. No one seemed to oppose him, and he caught Madge's great dark eyes upon him.

Then Lance leaped to throw the other pack, and unsaddle the horses. He turned them loose. The luxuriant grass and good water in the mountain park were the equal of any pasture. There was not much likelihood of their straying soon, and Umpqua at least would stay. Lance went back to the fire. Madge was asleep, her fair face drooping upon Rollie's shoulder. He too had sunk into weary slumber. On the other side of the fire Uhl lay covered with his head on a log, dead asleep. Fox appeared to have crawled under a pack canvas. Flemm sat on his guard, his machine gun at rest, his eyes like gimlets.

"Cowboy, stretch yourself right there," he said. "Me an' Fox will have a go at this job."

Lance dragged his saddle close, and wrapping himself in his blanket he lay down to make up a little for the loss of two nights' sleep. His last thought was a wondering if he dared risk a snap shot at Flemm, and then kill Fox and Uhl as they lay. Sleep claimed him before he could decide.

Daylight had come when he was awakened by a sound of wood being dumped upon the fire. Fox had taken Flemm's place on guard. The others were locked in slumber. Lance fell asleep again and when he awakened the sun was high. Uhl sat huddled near the fire, his pale face showing the havoc of extreme exertion and privation. Behind him the fox-featured guard paced to and fro, gun in hand.

Lance threw off his blanket and arose to his feet, cramped with the cold.

"Good morning. Kind of brisk up here on top," he said, cheerfully.

"Brisk?—Ha! I damn near froze to death," ejaculated Uhl.

Lance spread his hands to the blaze, and casually looked about. The third gangster evidently was hidden under the tarpaulin. The two victims of the kidnapers were asleep. All Lance could see of Madge was her disheveled golden hair.

"Uhl, it's only a little way to the log cabin," said Lance. "Much better place to camp. Hadn't we better move over? Then I'll cook some meat and make some hot coffee."

"Oke, cowboy. Step on it. I'll follow with these duds. . . . Fox, kick Flemm out of his sleep. . . . Baby, wake up and get wise. This is the last time you'll ever sleep with any man but me."

Lance, with murder in his heart, lifted a pack upon his shoulder, and stepping into the trail he strode for the clearing. He could see it through the big pines, a beautiful glade, with its frosted grass glistening under the sun. Sight of deer made him think of his rifle. That was in his saddle sheath. There might come a chance later to use it. Umpqua whistled from some point near at hand. Lance saw no sign of the other horses. A huge pine tree with wide spreading branches, and some high gray rocks marked the site of the log cabin. Its open door stared like a black curious eye, wondering what was to happen there. All around the stately pines stood up and beyond them rugged crags. This spot had once been the stronghold of the Apache chief, Cochise, at which time the trail was known only to the Indians.

Depositing the pack under the pine, Lance hurried back for another load. Halfway he met the gangsters. Lance swerved off the trail into the brush. He had a reluctance to meet Madge Stewart face to face. Yet the part he was playing sustained him with a kind of rapture. Perhaps he was afraid she might see through him. Most certainly he must look a queer kind of villain. Returning to the glade with the second pack, which he had opened, he set that down with the other, and then proceeded to build a fire. This done, he went back to fetch his saddle and the blankets that had been left.

Flemm, the meanest looking of the gangsters, manifestly distrusted Lance, and for that matter, the situation itself. He sat apart, holding the machine gun across his knee.

Lance spread the tarpaulin on the grass and proceeded to empty the contents of a pack.

"Rollie, you're one of these worthless rich guys, I know," said Lance, not without sarcasm. "But if you'd condescend to help me, we'd have breakfast sooner."

"I'd starve to death before I'd associate with you in any way," declared the collegian.

"Yes, and you'd let Madge starve, too. If you and she were left alone on your own, she'd soon get your number."

"Don't address me again, you two-faced scoundrel. You're a dirty rat, Sidway, and your pleas won't get you anywhere with Miss Stewart or me."

"What would you call yourself for night before last?" queried Lance, in bitter scorn.

Stevens' pale face flamed red, but it was fury more than shame that strangled his speech in his throat.

"Cowboy, you said a mouthful," interposed Uhl, caustically. "What'd this swelled-up sap pull on my baby?"

"I don't know whom you mean," snapped Lance.

"Well, then, Miss Stewart."

"That's none of your business."

"Yeah?—See here, cowboy. Don't let this dame work on you. Flemm swears you're sore because we beat you to this snatch."

"Bee, I tell you he's not on the level," interposed Flemm.

"Sidway, you're not on the spot with me," went on Uhl. "You've done me service and I'm for you. But don't strain things on account of a pretty skirt. That doesn't go with me. . . . What'd this swell sap do to Madge Stewart that burned you up?"

Lance was quick to see how jealousy and heat had imperiled him, and therefore the girl. Despite his calculations he had erred.

"Chief, you wouldn't think it much," Lance said, with an outright laugh. "I happened to see Stevens trying to take liberties with Miss Stewart."

"Did he get away with it?"

"I'll say he didn't."

The gangsters' explosion of mirth was no compliment to Madge. Lance resisted a strong impulse to look at her then. No doubt she would be something unforgettable to see.

"Skip the dirt about me, you poor fish!" she interrupted shortly.

Suddenly Lance felt her close to him, and then heard her light step. He was on his knees on the tarpaulin fumbling among cans and parcels, and he was aware that his hands shook.

"Did anyone see the sack I had with me last night? Coffee and butter."

"If it was a snake, it'd bite you," spoke up Madge, sweetly.

"There, under your nose!—Lance, can I offer my services as assistant cook?"

Lance sustained a slight start. "Are you—any good?"

"Pretty good—in *that* way."

"Can you mix biscuit dough?"

"Swell. Nels taught me."

"Go to it. Here's flour, salt, lard, pan. Fetch some water. I'll heat the Dutch oven."

Uhl showed interest in the proceedings. The other gangsters grinned sardonically. Stevens sat dejectedly with his face in his hands. Lance cut strips of bacon into a skillet all the while bafflingly aware of the going and returning of the girl, and then her agitating presence close beside him, on her knees. The shine of her hair, the fragrance of her, the vitality of her, and more than all that nameless and irresistible attraction seemed propelled into his senses. Hurriedly he arose to rake red coals out of the fire, to put on the oven to heat, and the coffeepot to boil, to fetch more firewood, and to find other tasks. It was the eyes of Uhl and his allies fixed upon the kneeling girl that drove Lance to look at her. She had thrown off the heavy coat, and knelt in her thin slacks, her round, gold-tanned arms bare, her beautiful voluptuous form revealed in all its devastating allurement. Lance cursed under his breath. This gangster was a ghoul for both money and flesh. Madge was in deadly peril, yet seemed oblivious of it. Lance's calculation had been that by midday Stewart would be on his trail. That would fetch him to the mountain clearing late the coming night or at dawn. What might happen before then? No matter what happened, Stewart and his men could be expected to waylay or ambush the gangsters and kill them. No doubt Tim Sloan and the Spencer boys would be with them. It was all up with Uhl right that moment. They would not escape these relentless rangers. Gene Stewart would experience a throwback to his wild frontier days. But they were hours and miles away. And Lance had to escape with Madge before nightfall. These thoughts revolved in his mind as he performed the tasks of cook around the campfire.

Presently breakfast was ready, and it was Madge, not Lance, who called: "Come and get it!" Kneeling over the fire had caused her cheeks to burn red, and it was only in her deep somber eyes that there was any sign of physical or mental distress. They all sat or knelt to eat and drink, except the cursed Flemm, who patrolled his short beat. Fox brought him food and drink.

"Baby, I didn't think it was in you," declared Uhl, devouring one of the hot biscuits.

Then Lance discovered that as she did not reply, nor deign to glance at the gangster, he took offense at her indifference. Evidently he had a tremendous egoism. "Get this, baby," he flashed, in cold passion. "Soon as I thaw out and get some sleep, I'll change your damned snooty manner." With that he stamped away into the pine brush beyond the clearing. Stevens appeared to shrivel up at the significance of that threat. Madge gazed intently at Lance, her wonderful eyes, hypnotic in effect, searching his very soul. She was delving into his depths. What did she imagine she saw there? She was strangely uncertain of her convictions about him. Her present bad conceptions might be warring with good ones of the past. Lance nearly betrayed himself before her tremendous appeal. But he was aware that the beady and fox-eyed gangsters were watching, too. Kneeling once more, Lance bent over the utensils, and began collecting them preparatory to washing. Presently Uhl returned.

"Flemm, I'll give you a rest for half an hour. Then I want to sleep. God, that sun feels good!" Then he turned to Madge. "Baby, you can go into the cabin."

She hurriedly acted upon the order.

"Uhl, hadn't I better look up the horses?" queried Lance.

"Horses? I forgot them."

"They've strayed. I didn't see any tracks going down the

trail. So they must be around. You realize how important horses are, don't you?"

"By God, I do now! . . . Here, Stevens, you wash up that mess. Cowboy, find those horses."

Lance, making a show of anxiety and hurry, strode off. Circling the clearing he found Sloan's roan and near by his own horse Umpqua. No sign of the other animals. Lance did not bother to hunt tracks. He made a detour and came up within sight of the camp, and sat down on a log to peer through the foliage. He could see the cabin. There, watching intently, he brooded over the situation. Presently he saw Flemm rejoin Uhl. The three gangsters held a colloquy, which was unintelligible to Lance. But they did not appear concerned. Once Fox pointed at Stevens, who knelt with his back turned, laboring over his task. Again Uhl made a passionate gesture toward the cabin, at which Flemm threw up his hands in resignation. Then Uhl lay down on a blanket in the sun and went to sleep.

Lingering there for some time Lance finally retraced his steps.

"Found only two horses," he informed Flemm. "The rest have wandered off. I'll have to saddle up to find them."

"Wait. If we waked up the boss now he'd bump you off."

"But every hour they may stray farther away."

"Okay by me. I'd a hell of sight rather walk."

Whereupon Lance proceeded to wipe the utensils for Stevens. "Rollie, this is a tough break," he said. "Don't take it so hard. You'll come out okay, except for loss of some dough you won't miss."

"I don't mind the money. I fear for Majesty. It was all my fault—that we were caught by these ruffians. I persuaded her to come out—lied to get her, in fact. And we were held up."

"Sidway," interrupted Flemm, sarcastically, "you don't strike me as a snatch scout. . . . Cheese it!"

Lance wisely refrained from further talk, though he gnashed his teeth. When the chores were finished he cut and packed firewood, mostly bark from dead trees. After that he cut great armloads of spruce boughs and dragged them to camp.

"Sid, there's somethin' rotten about you, but it ain't in this camp stuff," commented Fox.

"Ha! He learned all that in Chi," laughed Flemm.

"Say, tenderfeet, if you're stuck up here for a week, you'll appreciate soft beds," replied Lance.

"Week! What in hell's eatin' you? Two days is my limit," retorted Fox.

Lance strode off, ax in hand, groaning over a thought of what complications would evolve among these violent men in another day. He cut armloads of spruce, and packing that back he approached the door of the cabin, and without a glance at the gangsters, made bold to enter.

To his amaze Madge had been waiting, surely watching for him, for she leaped at him.

"Lance—*darling*," she whispered, and circled his arm with two steellike hands.

He let the load of spruce fall with a sodden swish. Her extraordinary loveliness must have been due to intense spirit and emotion. Her face was like a pearl—her eyes glowing purple.

"Are you crooked or honest?" she added.

"Crooked—as hell!" he gasped.

"I fear it. . . . But still you must save me from *him*—and get the ransom. I'll pay anything. . . . He means to attack me—keep me! . . . For God's sake—for Mother's—for mine—save me from that!"

"I'll try. . . . Keep your nerve. Watch!" he whispered, huskily, and turned to stride out. Before facing the gangsters he thought it best to go into the woods and cut more boughs. Recovering his poise he packed another huge load back to camp. Presently he said to Flemm.

"It's getting late in the afternoon. I ought to be wrangling the horses."

"Yeah. An' what's that?"

"Hunting them."

"Set down an keep your shirt on. Or you might peel potatoes an' what have you."

"*Uhl!*" yelled Lance, suddenly.

The gangster leader roused out of his slumber with surprising quickness, and sat up, blinking.

"These guys won't let me hunt for the horses. I found only two. I ought to ride around these woods and find them."

"Hop to it, cowboy. But don't forget we want supper soon."

Lance ran to get his saddle and bridle and blankets, tingling with the vibration of his nerves. All day he had pondered over the need to saddle Umpqua. Once astride the horse he felt that the critical hour was near at hand. Riding off out of sight he returned to the point where he could watch the camp. The heat of the day was waning, and sunset burned in the west. Lance saw Uhl, bare headed and coatless, get up to go toward the cabin. And he went in!

That was a signal for Lance to ride back toward the camp. He had to meet the crisis. Terror and panic gave way to fury, and by the time he had reached the clearing he was steel—cold and tight in mind and body. Boldly he rode to the big pine opposite the cabin, and there halted. Flemm and Fox were watching him curiously. With warning gesture, Lance pointed down the trail toward the opening into the clearing. Both gangsters were impelled to leap up and look. On the moment Lance heard Madge's ringing voice: "No! . . . Bee Uhl, I'll pay the ransom. But. . . ."

"Baby, you started it. You got to come through. No dame who ever lived can play with me," he replied, in cold passion.

"I *did* play with you," she protested. "But I didn't mean what you mean!"

"No matter now. You'll come across."

Lance leaped off Umpqua and ran over to the excited gangsters. His manner would have struck anyone into amaze and fear.

"Where's Uhl?" he queried.

"He said he was goin' to love his baby," replied Fox. "What's eatin' you?'

"I rode up high back there on the slope. And I saw two horses down where the trail comes up. First I thought they were our horses. But they had riders and were coming this way."

"Riders! You mean men on horseback?"

"I sure do. . . . There may be more than two. Looks damn bad. You better sneak down the trail, keeping out of sight, and make sure."

"What of?"

"Who it is and what they want."

"Fox, you go," ordered Flemm.

"Okay. But what'll I do!"

"Hold them up. An' use your gray matter."

Fox looked to his machine gun, and ran out to the trail, which he entered, and glided along till he reached the green foliage where he soon passed out of sight.

Lance stepped up on the pack beside Flemm.

"There! Look!" he whispered, tensely. "That little open place, beyond the yellow pine. "See!"

"My eyes must be damn poor. I see nothin' but green," growled Flemm.

"Okay! then see stars," hissed Lance, and swung his heavy gun on the gangster's bare head. Flemm fell soddenly. Whereupon Lance sped across the space to the side of the cabin, listening, watching the door.

He heard a scuffle, then swift light footfalls, then panting breaths, and—: "I'm not—afraid of you—Bee Uhl!"

"Swell! I like my dames to be wildcats," replied Uhl, with something exultant in his voice, no longer cold. "Make me fight for it, eh?"

"You lousy bum! Fight you? I can whip you," cried Madge, hotly.

Lance made for the door. He heard thudding footfalls, a cry, and then a rip of cloth.

"Let go!—Oh, you beast!"

"Baby—I'll strip you—right now," panted the gangster.

Lance leaped into the doorway, gun leveled. Uhl had Madge backed against the wall. The gangster's clawing hands held strips of her clothing. The girl, half naked, was warding him off, like a tigress at bay.

"*Madge!* Duck! Get away from him!" shouted Lance.

The gangster froze a second, then sprang into convulsive action, to catch the girl and get her in front of him. But she was as strong as he and far more supple. A short struggle ensued, the end of which came when Uhl made the blunder of striking her down. Then, even as he half turned, his thin face gray, his eyes hot and clear as molten steel, Lance leaped to get in better line. When his gun boomed the gangster appeared to be propelled against the wall. It upheld him a moment. A great bloody blotch came as if by magic. Lance thought he had shot away half of Uhl's face. He stuck there an instant, a ghastly spectacle, then slid sideways to the floor.

Madge lay apparently unconscious, a bruise on her white temple and a red welt across her bare shoulder. Lance snatched up a blanket, and lifting her flung it around her and carried her out the door. Flemm lay as Lance had last seen him. Far down the trail Fox appeared running toward camp. Lance took a long shot at him for luck, then sheathing his gun, he stepped to the snorting Umpqua, and kicked the stirrup around.

"Steady, Ump! It's me. Hold, you fool horse!"

With Madge in his left arm Lance mounted and drew her across his saddle. Umpqua needed no urging. As he plunged away a rattle of gunshots blended in a continuous volley, and a rain of bullets whistled and ticked through the trees, and pattered on the cabin. But in a few jumps the horse was behind the cabin, and out of danger. Lance held him to a lope along the wall of foliage, into the woods.

Chapter Eleven

No sooner had Gene Stewart lain down and dropped to sleep, some hours after midnight, than he was assailed by nightmares. It was just as well that he had not gone to bed in his own room, for he kicked around pretty violently. And he was in the thick of violent events when someone not a hobgoblin or demon thoroughly aroused him. Dawn had come. He made out Nels standing over him.

"Wal, Boss, you was loco. Never seen you so oot of your haid."

"Hello, old-timer. Been having crazy dreams. Must have been that punch concoction Madge sprung on us."

"Wait till you see Ren. . . . Pile oot, Gene, an' throw on your ridin' things. We've got work on hand."

"Uhuh. So that was the big idea. What's up?"

"Sidway just left on the trail of your cattle. Rustled last night before the ball opened."

"By jacks!—He wanted to tell me last night. But Madge wouldn't let him."

"Might hev spoiled her party. . . . We're to hit Sidway's trail pronto. Danny is wranglin' the hawses. An' I've throwed some grub together. Come along, Boss. We hev Sidway to thank fer somethin' like old times."

Nels clinked out into the patio where his musical footsteps died away. Gene quickly dressed in his range garb, and slipped a comb and toothbrush into his pocket. His gun belt had ample shells, and his rifle was down at Nels' bunkhouse. Then he went to his wife's room and poking his head in the door he awakened her: "Sorry, dear. Nels just called me. We're going after a bunch of strayed stock. May not be back for a day or two."

"So this is what young Sidway had to tell you?" she replied quickly.

"Good guess, Mom. Go back to sleep, and don't worry about what that cowboy starts. He's a finisher."

Going out through the patio Stewart saw two of Madge's guests, boy and girl, asleep in each other's arms in a hammock. They were half covered by a colorful blanket. It was a pretty picture, and Gene thought the girl was Maramee. "Some party!" he muttered, as he strode on. "But dog-gone-it! I had a good time watching them. . . . Only—my girl worries me!"

Clear daylight had come when Stewart reached the bunk-houses. Four horses saddled and bridled stood at the rail. He found his men inside eating. Danny looked grim and dark as he bent over his plate. Starr appeared drunk.

"Boss, throw some hot cakes under yore belt. . . . Ren, you drink thet hot coffee or I'll pour it down you."

"Nels—old manz—I want drink."

"I gave you a bracer."

"Ren, you're drunk," said Gene.

"Whosh drunk? I ain't so. . . . It wash just thet peach juice las night."

Nels forced the cowboy to drink the coffee, and stuffed some biscuits and cold meat in his pocket.

"Boss, let's get goin'," interposed Danny Mains, darkly. "If I don't miss my guess we'll hev hell catchin' Sidway. Thet boy's another Nick Steele."

"Right," agreed Nels.

They dragged Starr outside and threw him on his horse.

"Can you stick on?" queried Stewart.

"You insolt me," protested Ren, swaying in his saddle.

"I'll hold him on, Gene," said Danny, "till he sobers up."

"Bosh, whash in 'ell was thet punch as night?"

"I don't know, Ren. It sure gave me a hell of a nightmare."

"I'm agonna get thet mixtoure from Miss Madge—an' mak million bucks. Washen thet heavern best drink ever?"

"A most deceiving one Ren. It led you on."

"Whash wuz in it?"

"Dynamite, greased lightning, sweet cider and aqua fortis."

"Hell you shay?"

They rode down past the village, Stewart and Nels gradually drawing ahead, while Mains came along behind steadying Starr in his saddle.

"Nels, what's the deal?" asked Stewart.

"Wal, some Mexicans sloped off with the rest of yore an' Danny's cattle. Gosh, but Danny is sore! They was slick aboot it, when every last person in the country was heah last night. I've a hunch how Sidway got wise to the deal. He's a clever boy, Gene. But how he found oot ain't nothin' to us. The thieves drove the cattle acrost to the valley behind Gray Divide. An' they expect to work them by easy stages down acrost the border. It'd been a cinch but fer Sidway. . . . Wal, he's goin' to locate them, then ride on into town an' get help. In the mawnin' he'll haid the rustlers off in thet narrow valley. Our part is to ride in behind the ridge an' trail them down, keepin' oot of sight. By this time tomorrow I reckon we'll be smokin' them up."

"Hardly, in that open valley," replied Stewart. "They'll see us and slope. Which suits me, though I'd like to throw a scare into them."

"Wal, we'll get the cattle back, an' mebbe thet'll end this two-bit rustlin'."

"Nels, as long as westerners raise cattle out on the range there will be stealing."

"Kind of a disease. . . . Look, Gene, heah's the trail, plain as plowed ground. An' there's the track of Sidway's hawse."

"I see. . . . Nels, do you remember when I gave my great roan Majesty to Madeline and beat it for Mexico to get myself shot?"

"My Gawd, yes," declared Nels, fervently. "All thet past seems to be gettin' clearer in my memory. . . . Gene, I'll bet Sidway gives Umpqua to Madge."

"Not that cowboy. He's got too much spunk. He's onto Madge," replied Gene, a little sadly.

"Wal, I reckon thet won't make no hell of a difference. There ain't a man in the world who could resist thet girl long."

"If you put it that way," agreed Stewart, pleased with the old cattleman's hint.

Once across the highway the four riders settled down to a steady trot, and in two hours had reached the rocky point of the ridge. They rode around cautiously. The gateway to the valley was wide, and on the ridge side thick with sage and brush.

"Let's hold up heah," suggested Nels, and reined in. "Ren, air you so bleary-eyed yet you cain't see nothin'?"

"Nels, I can see a hawse ten miles an' a steer more'n thet—an' a gurl with a red bonnet twice as fur," declared Starr, swaggeringly.

"All right. Climb up the slope heah an' see if you can spot the cattle down the valley."

"My Gawd!—Climb in these high-heel boots?"

"Come on, Ren. I'll go, too," offered Stewart. They did not ascend the rough brushy slope more than a hundred feet when Starr made good his brag. Then Gene saw a long black band, moving like a snake, down the valley.

"Eight or ten miles?" asked Gene.

"More'n thet, Boss. Jest moseyin' along."

They retraced their steps and reported to Nels. "Wal," said that worthy, "I reckon we better keep travelin'. We want to be on their heels when Sidway haids them back in the mawnin'."

"Ren, don't I remember there's good water down this valley?" asked Gene.

"Shore you do. Nice rocky creek haids aboot where them cattle air now."

"That'll be far enough for us. We'll camp there. . . . Walk your horses and keep your eyes peeled."

They rode on in single file, somewhat separated. The sun

rose hot; a flock of buzzards circled high over the locality where the herd moved, indicating death to a calf or heifer. Coyotes slunk through the sage, another indication of meat on the move; the black domes of the Peloncillos sank behind the gray foothills.

Stewart's memory was busy. He recalled his early days with Nick Steele and Monty Price, and others of Stillwell's famous cowboys. And that reminded him of Madeline's brother Al, who had married Florence Kingsley, and had moved to Colorado to take charge of a ranch she had inherited. They had prospered. Stewart wondered if it would not be a good plan to ask financial assistance of Al. Something had to be done as soon as Madge's guests left, or he would lose the ranch. Madge would have to be told of the impending ruin, and Stewart hated the thought. But he must do it. Madge was wonderful, adorable, irresistible, but she was on the wrong track. Hours wore away while Stewart revolved memories and problems and hurts over and over in his mind.

Some time late in the afternoon Stewart and his men arrived at the head of the creek and halted to make camp there. It was an ideal spot, with grass and sage, and cottonwood trees, and dead cedars near by on the slope.

"Wal, I'll boil a pot of coffee," drawled Nels, "an' what with our meat an' biscuits we won't fare so bad."

"Rustle then, for I'm almost asleep this minute," replied Gene.

"We ain't none of us had a damn wink of sleep," added Starr.

"Why, Ren, I had to kick you onmerciful this mawnin," protested Nels.

"Thet wasn't sleep. I was unconscious from Majesty Stewart's punch. . . . Boss, don't you never let thet gurl make thet drink again. My Gawd! if college eddication is responsible fer thet—wall, when I marry Bonita an' we hev a dotter, she ain't goin' to get any modern schoolin' atall."

"Ren, your philosophy is sound," declared Stewart, ruefully after the laugh had subsided. "But it can't be adopted."

"An' why'n th'ell not?"

"Because these days girls will do as they please whether they have education or not. They are going to have equal rights with men."

"Wal, Gene, thet'll make a better world," interposed Nels.

"Nels, never in yore born days, did you know anythin' aboot wimmen, much less a dotter," observed Danny, pessimistically.

"Dan, do you mean a dotter is a turrible burden?"

"More'n turrible'n awful."

"An' if you had it all to live over again would you kept single, so you couldn't hev no dotter?"

"I ain't sayin' thet."

"An' you, Gene, would you rather never hev had Madge?"

"Nels, old pard, ten thousand times no," burst out Stewart, somehow glad to express himself. "Madge has been a joy. And will be forever."

"Thar yore talkin'. She's life—beautiful life—an' thet cain't be perfect."

They talked and had their leisurely and frugal meal round the little smokeless campfire, while the sun set, and shadows appeared under the slopes. Stewart made his bed with saddle and blankets, and scarcely had he stretched himself when a subtle glue touched his eyelids. Late in the night he awoke, saw Danny replenishing the fire, fell asleep again, to be roused at dawn by an ungentle boot.

"Come an' get it," said Nels, cheerily. "I've a hunch we've a day ahaid of us."

Before broad daylight they were on the move. When the sun arose, Danny and Ren rode up the slope to locate the cattle, but failed to do so, owing to a projecting cape that ran down into the valley. This was some miles ahead. Before they reached it Ren sighted dust clouds.

"On the run already," declared Nels.

"Looks like it," admitted Stewart.

"They're pretty far yet, Boss," added Ren.

"Wal, there ain't no use in our haidin' the cattle off, when we want them to come this way."

"No. But how about the rustlers?"

"If they got haided off below, we won't see hide nor hair of them."

They rounded the cape and rode at a trot fully five miles farther before Ren sighted cattle. They were headed up the valley and evidently had been running, but had now slowed down. They rode on, keeping sharp lookout for riders on the slopes, and presently had to take to higher ground to let a scattered herd pass.

"Aboot seven hundred, I'd say," observed Nels. "Reckon thet's all of them. Not winded much. They'll be home tomorrow."

"Wonder where'n hell them rustlers rode?" complained Ren. "I ain't feelin' swell, an' I'd shore like to shoot at somebody."

"Suits me," replied Danny, relieved. "Killin' Mexicans even from acrost the border wouldn't set good with my family."

"Danny, we don't know them rustlers was greasers," declared Ren, too casually.

"No. But I was afeared they might be."

Stewart suggested they ride on to meet Sidway, and whoever he had with him. Very soon Ren sighted three riders, whereupon Stewart ordered a halt.

"Lance ain't in thet ootfit," declared Starr, presently. "Say, they see us, an' air ridin' to beat the band."

Stewart was curious about the three horsemen who were evidently in a hurry to reach them. In very short order they arrived, three lean cowboys, ragged and dusty and hard-eyed. Stewart recognized them.

"Howdy, boys. Where's Sidway?"

Stewart thought Sloan's intent eyes searched his with undue fire, and he wondered what was coming.

"Mawnin', all," returned Sloan. "Stewart, you don't 'pear all het up aboot this raid—or nothin'."

"I'm well satisfied, thanks to you boys. Did you get a line on the rustlers?"

"They seen us far off an' bolted. We couldn't make them out."

"All right, that's that. Where's Sidway?" rejoined Stewart, sharply, suddenly sensing some untoward circumstance.

"By now Sidway must be at Cochise's stronghold, guidin' some gangsters who'd kidnaped your girl Madge an' a young fellow."

A blank silence ensued. But amaze did not long obstruct Stewart's faculties. He had sensed catastrophe. Sloan's tan had lost a shade. His eyes smoldered.

Nels flung a clenched hand at him. "Sloan, what you sayin'?"

"Listen, all of you. But don't waste no time restin' here. Come on. Ride close an' let me spill it. . . . Yesterday a little before sundown, Sidway caught up with us on the road to town. He told us about this cattle steal an' asked us to help him haid them back this mawnin'. Me an' the Spencers was glad to help, of course. We made camp jest outside of town. Jest about dusk, Sidway walked in town to get some coffee an' butter. Not long after, but it was dark, a big black car came up, an' Sidway was on the runnin' board. We was held up by two men with machine guns. Then their boss got out an' bought my hawse outfit fer a thousand dollars. They was a gangster outfit an' Sidway 'peared to be on good terms with them. I didn't get wise to the kidnapin' till Miss Madge an' the young feller was dragged out of the car. Then I seen it plain as print. . . . Now, to make it short, one gangster drove the car away, up the range road. Sidway an' us fellers, under them guns, saddled an' packed. Then thet pale-faced gangster ordered me to wait till mawnin', an' notify you to send one man up the Cochise Trail with fifty thousand dollars fer Miss Madge an' the same for the young feller. An' if his orders was not carried out Miss Madge would be raped, an' both of them killed. . . . It was hard fer me to wait till mawnin' but with your telephone wire cut, I couldn't find out if you'd left, an'

I knew you'd be comin' along here after the cattle. So here we are."

By the time Sloan had concluded, Stewart's horror had mounted to a ruthless and terrible wrath. Starr's face had grown a leaden white, and he appeared incapable of speech. After a brief paroxysm of emotion Nels interrupted Danny Mains' curses with a terse query: "Gene, what do you make of Sidway?"

"What do you?" countered Stewart, huskily.

"I got it figgered. When he went in town he seen thet car with Madge in it. He must hev been slick enough to scare them kidnapers off the highway, to take to the hills."

Sloan interrupted impatiently: "But, Nels—Stewart, it looked like Sidway was one of thet gang."

"It shore did," corroborated the Spencer boys in unison. "Their boss *knew* him."

"You all think Sidway was in with the gangsters?" queried Stewart.

"I'm afraid, sir—we do. Why, we stayed awake half the night talkin' it over. These kidnapers are pretty smart. They take their time. We figger Sidway must have been sent on ahead—planned the job—rode away the day it was done. But we jest couldn't figger this cattle steal in the job atall."

"Sloan, I'll grant it looked that way to you," rejoined Stewart, tersely. "But you don't know Sidway. I tell you the idea is preposterous."

"All right, sir. I only hope an' pray you're right."

Then Ren Starr exploded. "I ought to throw my gun on you," he roared. "Sidway's my pard. He's as true as steel. He *couldn't* be in a deal like this. How in hell he ever got mixed up in it I can't guess, but you bet your life it's damn lucky for the girl an' us. He'll *save* her. An' you'll have to apologize to me fer thinkin' him a crook."

"I'll do thet now, Starr," returned Sloan. "But be reasonable. Things looked queer. Circumstantial evidence, you know.

. . . An' Miss Madge!—*she* believed Sidway was one of them. You should have seen her—heard her call him."

"My—Gawd!" gasped Starr, totally overcome by that information.

At last Nels broke silence: "Gene, I knowed thet cowboy would hev his chance. It jest worked oot thet way. An' I'd gamble my bunk in heaven on his honesty, an' his nerve an' sense to beat thet gang. He *knew* we'd be on his trail. Why, the last thing he said was, in case, look fer his tracks. Them gangsters air tenderfeet. Once up in the hills they'll be lost, an' easy fer thet slick cowboy. He'll lay fer his chance, an' as shore as we're right heah he'll hold them somehow till we come, or get away with her, or do something to save her from them."

"Boss, thet's it—one of Nels' hunches," affirmed Starr. "But, my Gawd, we got to rustle!"

"Sloan, you boys will go with us," asserted Stewart.

"You bet your life!"

"Nels, we'll cut off the trail halfway up, and work round to the west side of Cochise's stronghold. We might get there ahead of them. It'll be a drill for tenderfeet. They'll be all in. We've got time. We *must* make it before dark. . . . Now, all of you—ride!"

Riders and horses were wet with sweat, and practically spent when that long climb up the mountain had been accomplished by sundown. A halt was made in the deep forest west of Cochise's stronghold, at a point they all agreed was scarcely a half mile from the clearing.

"Ketch your—breath, fellers," panted Nels, as he removed his chaps.

"Men, in case they're here . . ." began Stewart.

"They air heah," interrupted Nels. "Didn't we foller their tracks over two thirds of thet trail? Didn't Sloan ketch two of his hawses makin' fer home? Sidway would make the gang stop heah, even if it wasn't the logical camp."

"All—right, then," Stewart rasped. "We'll slip up on them. Then what?"

"Stewart, they're gangsters with machine guns. I'd say shoot 'em down on sight."

"Hell, yes," agreed Starr.

"Wal, I don't know," added Nels, ponderingly. "Shore we never—dealt with any of this ilk—before. I'd say hold 'em up. If they don't hold up pronto then bore 'em."

"By all means before they can turn machine guns loose in our direction," replied Stewart, grimly. "But I want to talk to these *hombres* first—and then see them kick at the end of a rope."

"Boss, it's a better idee at thet," agreed Ren, savagely. "But my gun finger is shore itchin'. . . . If we only find—Madge alive an' unharmed."

"We will—shore," declared Nels, passionately. "I may hev lived to be old an' soft, but somehow I gamble on Sidway. He loves thet girl an' he'll ootwit the slickest kidnapers there ever was."

"Nels, that faith has kept me from collapse. First time in my life I've weakened. But it's—my girl!" exclaimed Stewart, low and thick under his breath.

"Come on," ended Nels. "Keep even an' in sight of each other. No noise!"

A pine-thicketed slope led up to the gray crags. They entered the mountain enclosure through a gateway between the huge monuments of stone. The clearing lay beneath Stewart's strained eyes, a green and gold park marked by great pines scattered about, and shining with appalling beauty under the sunset glow. A thin column of blue smoke halfway across made Stewart's heart leap. Ren pointed to a roan horse grazing in the open meadow, and Sloan whispered that it was his horse Baldy.

At a motion from Nels they stealthily began their approach down to the level. Every few rods Nels halted to listen. Stewart could hear only the sough of the wind in the pines, and the murmur of distant running water. The place seemed locked in an unearthly silence.

Suddenly Ren startled Stewart and all of them. He held up a pregnant hand.

"I heah voices," he whispered.

He must have possessed extraordinarily sharp ears, for all of his companions shook their heads. Hardly had they started forward again when the boom of a gun made them statues. They listened with bated breath.

"No forty-five Colt," whispered Stewart.

"Sidway packs a forty-four Smith an' Wesson. Sounded like it," replied Nels. "Come on, we gotta see this."

Before they had taken a dozen swift steps a rattling biting volley halted them.

"*Machine gun!*" whispered Sloan, in great excitement. "Have I heard them? I'm tellin' you!"

The continuous volley appeared to come from their right down the trail. Accompanying the rattling was a swishing cut of bullets through foliage and then a pattering on solid wood. It ceased. And Ren leaped up in the air, trying to see over the green brush.

"Heah 'em?—Hawse hoofs!"

"Shore as Gawd made little apples!" ejaculated Sloan.

Stewart was quick to catch a soft rapid thud of hoofs, a crash of brush, a cracking of dead twigs, then thudding hoof-beats dying away.

"Thet was when, Gene!" hissed Nels, his gray eyes like points of flame, and he motioned them on.

Despite the intense suspense, Nels had the cool judgment to advance very slowly, without the slightest sound. Stewart swallowed his harrowing fears and doubts. Then swift foot-falls close in front made him, and all of them, aware of the nearness of the trail. Nels crouched down and stealthily separated the small pines to slip through. Starr followed suit, as did the others to left and right. Stewart saw the roof of the old cabin over the tips of the brush.

"Flemm!" shouted a hoarse voice. "What happened?"

"He crowned me," replied another man, hotly.

"Who? Not Stevens?"

"No. It was that two-timin' cowboy. He lied about seeing horses down the trail. Ruse to get rid of you. Then he beaned me."

"That shot in the cabin?"

"I didn't hear any."

"You know Uhl went in the cabin to the girl?"

"Yes. I saw that."

"Well, there was a shot in there, all right. Sidway went in and bumped Bee off. That's it. For I saw the cowboy come out with the girl in his arms and jump on his horse. I let loose my gun, but I was running—and didn't connect."

The faces of Nels and Ren appeared to shine upon Stewart, a singular transformation from grim dark passion to an ecstasy of gladness. Stewart felt the same so powerfully that he was overcome. But his tremendous relief was counteracted by a hateful query—had Sidway gotten in that cabin in time? Again Stewart's passion to rend and slay dominated him. He crawled softly after the others, until he bumped into them.

They had arrived at the edge of the clearing. Ren's hard hand pressed Stewart's shoulder. Peering through the foliage he saw that they were scarcely fifty yards from the campfire. Two bareheaded young men, with corded livid faces, stood facing each other. Both held machine guns. The taller, a dark-haired individual, was bending his head to the other, no doubt for examination. Beyond them on the ground sat young Stevens, apparently uninjured, but plainly shocked with terror. Then on the moment the gangsters whirled at a piercing shout from the cabin. A third man appeared, a slim-built fellow, with a bloody face. He staggered toward them, a ghastly spectacle, but assuredly instinct with life and desperation. His curses rang through the forest clearing. Then he confronted the astounded gangsters.

"That ———— fake cowboy shot me . . . got away

with her!" he yelled, wildly. "I'll kill you both—you ———— hop-heads! What in hell were you doing?"

"He fooled us, Bee," replied Flemm. "Made us believe he saw horses. Sent Fox down the trail. Then he crowned me."

"I wish to God he'd smashed your empty pan!"

"Looks like he emptied yours. Better let us wash you off. Looks like what you used for brains is oozing away."

"It's only blood. He grooved me . . . here . . . Christ, how it burns!—Wipe me off."

Fox laid down his gun and picked up a towel from the pack. He dipped it in a water bucket, and wiped off the blood to disclose to the watchers the visage of a white, hard-faced criminal whose passion and experience seemed greatly beyond his years.

"HANDS UP!" thundered Nels.

"*Stick 'em up, gangsters!*" rang out Starr's voice.

Uhl and Fox lost not a second in elevating their hands. But Flemm whirled with his machine gun bursting into flame and rattle. Almost instantly his distorted visage went blank and he pitched forward. The machine gun sputtered into the ground, scattering gravel, then fell from the gangster's stretching hands. Stewart saw smoke issuing from Starr's rifle. Then Nels, gun low, ran out, to be followed by the cowboys. Mains came out from the right. When Stewart emerged from the foliage Sloan was disarming the gangsters.

"Heah, gimme thet rope, Spencer," yelped Starr. Receiving it he spread the noose, and pitched it deftly over Uhl's head. The gangster had courage or else he did not get the significance of Starr's move.

"Wait, Ren!" ordered Stewart, and strode over to Stevens. "Are you all right, boy?"

"Yes—sir. I—guess so," faltered Stevens. "Thank God. I was about—dead of fright."

"Sidway made off with Madge?"

"He did, sir, but—but . . ."

"Was she—all right . . . too?" queried Stewart, hoarsely.

"I'm afraid—not. . . . I heard her fighting—*him!*" And Stevens pointed a shaking finger at Uhl. "She'd fainted—or was dead—when Sidway got on his horse with her. . . . But, Mr. Stewart—even if she was alive—she's as bad off with him . . . for he's one of—these gangsters!"

"Yeah, that's correct," interposed Uhl, darkly. "Sidway belongs to Cork's snatch gang. He tricked me. He wants the ransom and the girl for himself. I'll get him for that if it costs me a hundred grand."

"Haw! Haw!" burst out Sloan, sardonically.

"Gangster," added Stewart, coldly. "If you knew Westerners you would not concern yourself about that."

Ren Starr confronted Rollie Stevens. "Say, did I heah you make a crack about Sidway bein' one of this outfit?"

"Yes, you did. He's hand in glove with these kidnapers. And he has betrayed them. He's . . ."

"Shet up, you white-mugged college dude! What'd you go to college fer? Haven't you any sense? My pard *saved* the girl."

"You're a thickheaded fool."

"I reckon I'll have to bat you one . . ."

"Hold on, Ren," interrupted Stewart, sternly. "Make allowance for circumstances. It does look strange. But we'll clear it up presently."

The gangster Flemm was dead, shot through the center of the forehead. Stewart ordered Sloan to take charge of the machine guns, and Starr to search the gangsters. Nels stood with his gun on Uhl, and not for many years had Stewart seen such an expression on that lean face. Then Stewart strode to the cabin and went in. There was a pile of spruce brush on the floor, but it had not been disturbed. Searching around Stewart saw tracks of Madge's little feet in the dust, and he could read from them that she had run and fought. He also found a splotch of blood in a depression, where no doubt Uhl had fallen, and had lain until he came to. There was little more to be learned in the cabin. The dreadful pang in Stewart's breast did not subside. But how grateful he was that Madge was alive and in the keeping of a man!

Upon Stewart's return to the group, Ren pointed to several automatic pistols evidently salvaged from the gangsters' effects.

"You boys can have those. Save Uhl's for Sidway. I imagine he'd like to keep it."

"How about these, Boss?" asked Ren, and handed Stewart several wads of greenbacks. On one, the outside wrapper had a denomination of one thousand.

"Peep into thet, Boss. All the same. What these guys call grands."

"Well!—These gentlemen seem to deal in large numbers," said Gene, sarcastically.

"Stewart, that dough is yours if you pass up this snatch," said Uhl, suavely. He seemed to lack comprehension and fear. And his assurance, even before the grim and silent Nels, was remarkable, and could have come only from supreme egoism and ignorance. Stewart knew that no power on earth or in heaven could stay Nels' hand. These vultures had dared to frighten, and probably harm, Nels' one treasure, and that had been Madge since she had first ridden his knee.

"Thanks, Uhl. You can afford to be generous, for you won't need that money where you are going."

"Boss, he doesn't get it," declared Starr, contemptuously. "Let me hev the fun of tellin' him." And the cowboy gave the lasso a jerk that made the noose close up like a snake round Uhl's neck. The gangster spread the noose and flung it off his head.

"Cowboy, I never forget faces," he snarled. "I've put men on the spot for less than that."

"For the love of Mike!" shrilled Starr, astounded and resentful. "Boss!—Nels!—Danny! Did you heah this guy? He'd put me on the spot!"

Stewart realized that his comrades as well as he were profoundly impressed by this new type of desperado. Absolutely, Uhl was convinced he would get out of this predicament. His ally, Fox, was an older man and less assured. No doubt he had always been a tool. Uhl, young as he was, indubitably had been used to imperious and unlimited power.

"Say, you opium-eatin' nut, air you so dotty you think you'll get out of this?" yelled Starr, red in the face. It struck Stewart that the cowboy voiced a tremendous antagonism toward the cold-faced, steel-eyed gangster, while Nels maintained a silent ruthlessness. Stewart knew Uhl was as good as dead, yet had not the slightest divination of it. Stewart felt that he had an intense curiosity about this species of gunman. His own inflexible hate, now that fear for Madge had somewhat subsided, was controllable.

"Let me talk to this *hombre*, Ren. . . . You boys tie up the other one," he said, as he stepped close to the gangster. Nels had never swerved his gun an inch from its first deadly alignment. "Uhl, you implicate Sidway in this kidnaping of my daughter. How come?"

"He's a scout for Cork. I know that bird. I met Sidway in Yuma. He drove one of my booze trucks."

"Ahuh. One of those trucks you sent back with stolen cattle, eh?"

"Me steal cattle? That's a kick," replied Uhl, with a laugh of contempt.

"All the same your drivers did, probably on the sly. Sidway drove an empty truck to Tucson. It had been full of cattle. He was held up by men who expected to find bootleg whisky. Later this truck and others like it parked off the highway near my ranch to be loaded with stolen cattle. They got away with one load. Sidway killed one of your men."

Uhl gave vent to a rage that convinced Stewart of his innocence of complicity in the raid. Such curses Stewart had never heard in the dens of the frontier.

"What's more, Sidway is not what you think him," went on Stewart. "He's just a slick cowboy. He knew you—outguessed you—led you up here to your death."

"He was going to kidnap Madge himself," snapped Uhl, but his certainty seemed weakening.

"Your mistake. Why would he want to kidnap her when he's going to marry her?"

That random shot of Stewart's broke down the gangster's stubborn convictions and betrayed the terrible nature of the man. If he were capable of love for a woman, he must have felt it for Madge Stewart. At any rate Stewart decided the gangster had been obsessed with some violent passion for Madge and that an insane jealousy possessed him.

"Marry her—yeah?" he choked out, his face purple, his neck convulsed, his eyes not those of a human. "He's welcome—to the rag—I made her!"

Stewart knocked him flat, but had the self-possession to turn aside Nels' quivering gun. It seemed impossible, however, to control Starr, and suddenly Stewart had no desire to. Starr dragged the gangster to his feet.

"You bastard," he hissed, his visage gray and set. "You'll never live—to brag of thet again!"

"Stand aside, Ren," ordered Nels, piercingly.

"No, Nels, you ain't gonna bore him," shouted Starr, hoarsely. "An' we ain't gonna hang him. We'll hang his pard, an' make him look on, but by Gawd! I owe somethin' to myself heah!"

Starr slipped the noose over Fox's head and jerking it tight he threw the end of the lasso over a sturdy pine branch, and caught it coming down. "Heah, Sloan, an' you Spencers! Get in on this. An', young feller, grab hold of this rope behind me, an' pull, if you're half a man. . . . If you don't I'll beat hell oot of you. . . . PULL! . . . Ahah! Them yells choked off! Yellow clear through! . . . There, tie the end, Sloan."

Stewart averted his eyes, but he could not escape the grotesque jumping-jack shadow on the ground, or the expulsion of breath from the condemned and executioners, the scrape of boots and jangle of spurs, and lastly the incredible spectacle of Stevens hauling on the lasso. For the moment the collegian had answered to primal instincts, and his red visage was as beastly as those of his fellows.

But suddenly Stewart swerved his attention to Uhl. The gangster had watched the hanging of his lieutenant, and his face, his look, his mien were vastly but incalculably transformed from what they had been.

"What do you think of our necktie party, gangster?" demanded Ren, leering at him. "Thet's how we do things in the West. . . . I'm jest damn sorry I cain't hang you an' watch you kick. But yore swagger gets my goat. So Mister Bee Uhl, kidnapin'—bootleggin' gangster gunman, you're gonna go up agin my game!"

"Heah, Ren—none of thet. Hang him," said Nels, speaking for the first time.

"Umpumm, old pard. I wonder you ask it. . . . Where's thet popgun of his?" Ren snatched it up from the pack and held it gingerly in contempt. "What do you think of thet toy, Nels? These guys in the movies shoot through their coat pockets. Okay! . . . Where's his coat?" Starr took that up and slipped the little automatic into the right coat pocket.

Stewart had answered to the same strange antagonistic passion that beset Starr. No doubt Nels also was under its influence or he would have shot the gangster and made an end of the thing. Nels had been a gunman in his day; and later cowboys, who packed and shot guns, were wont to view with contempt the exploits of the modern killers with their automatic and hidden firing. They were simply murderers. An even break was Greek to them. But Ren wanted the test.

"Listen to reason, cowboy," importuned Stewart. "I savvy you. But even a little risk . . ."

"Risk, hell? There won't be none. Anyway, Boss, neither you nor Nels must hev this crook's blood on yore hands."

"What's the difference whether it's you or me or all of us?"

"On account of Madge. An' if you elected to take him to jail—why Sidway would ride down there an' shoot him in his cell. Thet wouldn't do either, Boss."

Nels appeared to be struck mute and Stewart had no ready answer. At that moment Starr reminded Stewart again of Monty Price. The advance of time did not change the hearts of these firebrand range riders.

Starr drew his gun, and kept it in his hand while he helped the gangster into his coat.

"There! . . . Stewart, you fellers get back pronto. . . . Now Uhl, don't move a hand." Starr backed away from him for perhaps twenty feet. "Turn around, Uhl."

The gangster did as he was bidden, exposing a front that was sickening to men who held courage and nerve as Stewart held them. Blood had again begun to stream down the side of Uhl's temple and cheek.

"Ten—grand—if you'll . . ."

"Bah!" interrupted Starr, piercingly. "You're talkin' to an American cowboy." Starr sheathed his gun and held his hand out, his fingers clutching at the air.

"Nels, you give the word. . . . Come on, kidnaper! Let's hev yore game."

"Ready!" rang out Nels. "*Shoot!*"

Stewart's gaze was riveted on the gangster. In a flash he jerked his right hand down into his coat pocket. As the corner of his coat suddenly pointed out to bark and smoke, Starr's gun crashed and in a second again. The ganster's bullet sputtered up dust and gravel. Between the shots his visage underwent an indescribable change, and as he fell the terrible instinct to survive left his body.

Darkness found Stewart and his men around a campfire in another spot, several rods from the cabin. Nels was cooking some supper. And he was speaking:

"Wal, Gene, I cain't see any sense in tryin' to trail Sidway in the dark."

"Hawses all in, Mr. Stewart," interposed Sloan. "We'll have to rest up tonight at least."

Stewart endeavored to subdue his impatience and dread, knowing how right his comrades were.

"Anyway, wait till Red comes back," added Nels, and presently called them to supper. While they were sitting there the cowboy returned. In the campfire light his face showed white and set, without the violence that had distorted it.

"I found Lance's trail," he said, eagerly. "Used my flashlight. He had Ump goin' some when he struck into the trail. But he soon slowed down. I follered the tracks till they turned left off the trail."

"What'll he do?" queried Stewart, sharply.

"Beat it fer home. Thet guy an' thet hoss—nothin' to it, Boss, if Madge is okay."

"Does he know how to get down out of here?"

"Wal, we rode all over when we was up heah."

"Ren, you take his trail at daybreak," suggested Nels.

"Shore. I'd thought of thet. But mark my hunch, Sid will beat us home half a day."

"Set in an' hev a bite."

"Nels, I sorta ain't hungry."

"Wal, eat an' drink anyhow. It's been a tough day."

"You boys go after our horses and hobble them out for tonight. And Sloan, you'll hunt up the rest of your horses tomorrow," asserted Stewart.

"They'll be around close. Seldom thet stock will leave this grass an' water."

Stevens set propped against a pack, with a blanket around him, his hair damp on his pale forehead.

"Rollie, you had a hand in that lynching," said Stewart. "How you feel?"

"Pretty scared—and sick yet," he replied, weakly. "But it—isn't my part in that hanging. That was great."

"Fine. Brace up now. Everything is okay. And we're d—— lucky."

Very little was spoken after that and nothing at all about the tragedy. The cowboys brought a pile of firewood to last out the night. Stewart asked one of them to fetch the cut spruce in the cabin, and he made his bed upon that. Starr was the only one who did not smoke. He stood back to the fire, his head bent. Stewart appreciated how he felt. The night wind set up its dirge in the pines and coyotes barked off in the distance. Despite his extreme fatigue Stewart could not sleep at once. The stars seemed to mock his troubled mind.

Chapter Twelve

UHL's striking Madge down had less to do with her collapse than the appearance of Sidway in the cabin, with his darkly stern visage, his deadly voice, and the bursting red boom of his gun.

She did not wholly lose consciousness, for she felt him lift her and wrap her in a blanket and carry her out. More clearly then she heard a string of shots and the spang and thud of bullets all about, and felt herself swung upon a horse, and the violent jars of her body as he plunged away.

A vague, almost blank interval succeeded. When her mind cleared again she was being carried comfortably upon a pacing horse over a level trail. Through the big black pines she saw the stars shining, and then a dim outline of Sidway's face and bare head. That thrilling reality brought back vividly the fight with the gangster, his half stripping her, and the brutal blow he had dealt her, and then Sidway's startling and fatal intervention. Sidway, no matter why, had saved her again, and this time from a horrible fate—an insupportable shame and inevitable death. Her thoughts grew so wildly whirling that she had to disrupt them by talking.

"Lance," she whispered. Apparently he did not hear her.

"Lance! . . . We got away." She felt a strong vibration pass through him.

"Hello! You've come to?" he returned, hastily.

"Yes. But I wasn't altogether out."

"I haven't had time to see. . . . Did he hurt you?"

"Lance, I was holding my own with him—when he struck me. I wasn't afraid of him—till then. . . . I suppose he could have beaten me helpless?"

"Then . . . Uhl didn't—harm you?" queried Sidway, in a halting husky voice.

"No, not outside the blow. Lance! You—*killed* him?"

"Yes."

"You *saved*—me?"

"Yes."

"From something hideous. He never meant to let me go for ransom. He'd have kept me. . . . Merciful heaven! What an idiot I was—to flirt with Honey Bee Uhl!"

"It takes a lot to cure some girls' egotism," returned Sidway with an intonation she could not define. He seemed far removed from her, somehow.

"I'm cured—Lance."

"Listen, baby!—Excuse me. I fell into Uhl's way of speech. . . . The day will never come when you won't look at a man."

"But for goodness sake! I have eyes. I can't hang my head—never look."

"A look from *your* eyes is enough."

"Yeah?—For what?"

"To incite a man to madness—kidnaping—outrage—murder."

"Oh!—Not a *real* man. What do you mean?"

"I mean, Miss Stewart, that whether you have guilty intent or perfect innocence, when you look at men with those eyes, you play hell."

"I observe, Mr. Sidway, that my marvelous eyes failed to play hell with you," she returned, sarcastically.

"Only because I was wise to you."

Madge had no quick retort for that, mainly because there seemed some hope for her with this young man of dual nature. They rode along the trail in silence. But she watched him from between narrowed eyelids. If she had not been spent and in pain she would have found this situation vastly intriguing. At length Umpqua exchanged his pacing gait for a walk. Evidently the mountain clearing had been passed. Presently Sidway turned off the trail to the left, and had to pick his course.

The forest gradually grew less dense, and therefore lighter. Thickets of pine and spruce reached above Sidway's head, and in places had to be carefully threaded. It became evident to Madge that they were traveling downhill. At length the cowboy halted as if undecided how to proceed.

"Lost?" inquired Madge.

"I'll tell the world," he replied, with a queer laugh.

"I'd just as soon you made a halt till morning. I'm about done for."

"My idea exactly. . . . Soon as I hit a level spot."

He zigzagged down the slope for a while, and eventually stopped, to slide out of the saddle. Madge could not help feeling that he handled her as if she were a child. He set her down, back against a tree, which Madge observed to be a cedar. There were still big pines about, but scattering, and the presence of cedars denoted lower altitude.

"I'm freezing to death," she said.

He stripped the horse and haltered him to a sapling. Then from his saddle he untied a blanket, and other trappings. This he doubled and wrapped around her. Then he tore sheathes of bark off the cedar, and snapped twigs and dead branches, with which he started a fire not far from her feet. The crackling of wood and leaping of red flame changed the moon-blanched gloom. While Madge stretched her hands to the heat, Sidway opened a saddlebag.

"Here's some meat, biscuits, dried apples, and a piece of chocolate. . . . Yes, and a little salt. Are you hungry?"

"I could go for a *filet mignon* in a big way."

"Daresay you could. Sorry I can't furnish one."

"Very well. I'll have a biscuit and a piece of meat. . . . Thanks. Where are we, Lance?"

"Up in the Peloncillos."

"How far from that camp?"

"Miles, I'd say."

"I wish you could have gotten Rollie away from them."

"Well, I expect trouble enough, without your boy friend."

"Trouble?—You'll not have any with me," she returned, all at once cognizant again of the double role he played. "Lance, you're after that ransom yourself!"

In the light of the fire she saw a dark tide sweep across his face. His somber eyes regarded her as if somehow she had recalled to him her true character. He let out a mirthless laugh.

"You guessed it, Majesty," he replied, grimly.

"I will gladly pay you. . . . What will those gangsters do with Rollie? His people are rich. They will pay. But it'll take time. Meanwhile Dad and Nels will be on the rampage. That demand of Uhl's will drive him crazy. He can't pay it. I'll bet they are on our trail now."

Sidway had averted his face and he made no reply, facts that excited Madge's speculation. Suddenly a wild conviction bore crushingly upon her. "*Lance!* Ransom or no ransom—you mean to—to keep me?"

"You sure are some guesser," he declared, bitterly.

"My—God!—You can't—be so low."

"Men as a rule are pretty bad *hombres.* Don't you think you deserve it?"

"Yes—yes! Oh, I've been a heedless, vain and selfish thing! . . . But, Lance, I—I haven't been rotten . . ."

"Are you telling me?" he queried, turning his back on her.

"Yes, I am. I never. . . . Oh, what you must think me! . . . Lance Sidway, you killed that devil Uhl just so you could have me—take me yourself?"

"You said it, baby."

"Don't call me *that.* I'll hate you."

"I thought you did already."

"I didn't. But I shall."

"Okay by me. More sport if I have to beat you."

"Beat me! You've already done that."

"Miss Stewart, I think you hit me first."

"Yes I did. For the dirtiest remark any fellow ever dared make to me"

"Struck me at the moment as strictly merited."

"Oh, the way we quarrel! It gets my goat! . . . What do you intend to do with me?"

"You're so damn smart—why don't you tell me?"

"I can. . . . You've fallen for this temptation, Lance Sidway. Too much easy money in sight! And a chance to get even with me! . . . I suppose you'll tie me in a cave—starve me—beat me . . . till you get that money."

"I declare," he interrupted, as she choked over her words, "you grow better all the time. Wise girl! College girl, you know!"

"Oh, damn!—Lance Sidway, you'll have to marry me!"

She might have struck him, judging by his shrinking start. "I'll refuse to pay that ransom or move out of my tracks unless you swear you'll marry me."

"Very well, if you think that important," he returned, in a queer voice.

Madge, in the wildness of that agitation, thought she must make the best of a bad bargain. She loved him, whether he was a crook or a cowboy, a Dr. Jekyll or Mr. Hyde, a strange combination of virtue and vice. It ran through her mind that he could not forever stay immune, that she could win his love, and reform him. That might be the retribution meted out to her for her imperious and willful ways. After all he had saved her. She could not hate him. If he beat her she would fight back, and perhaps, womanlike, love him the more for his brutality. There was a queer streak in her, she feared, or at least one strongly primitive.

"You are fagged out," he said, presently turning. "I'll make a bed for you."

He broke an armful of cedar brush, laid it flat, and put a saddle blanket on that. Then he arranged his saddle for her head. As she moved over, half crawling, the folded blanket fell, and the one wrapped around her half slipped off. Madge made no great haste to wrap it around her again.

"What's the odds?" she said, moodily. "You've seen me

almost naked twice." And she lay down to stretch out wearily, her eyes upon him, as he bent to cover her with the extra blanket. She made the discovery then that if the moonlight did not deceive her, his face was white.

"Now it's settled, let's talk . . ."

"What's settled?" he interposed.

"Why, I suppose you'd vulgarly call it my hash. . . . I intend to make up for the ruin I unwittingly brought upon Dad and Mom. I suppose you'll block that."

"Too late! I'll need the money."

"But you needn't be a hog. You seemed to like them. Can't you be sport enough to let me make amends?"

"Sure, I liked Gene. And your mother is . . . swell! . . . But they won't need the money after you've gone."

"Mr. Sidway, when you were snooping over my securities and bankbooks, did you get a line on what I was worth?"

"I did, you bet. It used to be about a million!"

"Yes. But that won't do you much good now. I can sell my pearls and other jewels for a hundred grand—as your gangster pards call it. I'll do that on one condition only. You let me split with Dad and Mom!"

"Okay! Fifty grand will do for our honeymoon—at least until the dicks get me."

"Oh, you were wanted by the police even before this," cried Madge, despairingly. Then she grew enraged and flung at him: "How can you be so—so fine—so— Oh, so many things, and still be such a beast."

"Mystery of life, baby," he retorted. "How can you be so sweet—have such an angel face—such soulful, eloquent, lovely eyes—such a winning way with everyone, when at heart you are just no damn good?"

"You've about convinced me," she said, darkly. "Perhaps this will either kill or cure me. . . . But beating me, as no doubt you will, depriving me of the home I'd just begun to love, packing me off like this to misery and—and God knows what else—perhaps it'll reform me. . . . Yes? No?"

"I wouldn't limit your possibilities any more than I'd believe one word you said," he returned, passionately.

"We're certainly two of a kind," she retorted. "But let's not be fourflushers. If you're not big enough to reform yourself, and me, then be big enough to be outright bad. And not a two-faced liar such as you are!"

That stinging speech appeared to wither him. Presently he began to gather firewood and pile it conveniently. Madge had an intense curiosity in regard to him, and tried hard to keep awake. But she was utterly exhausted, and felt her eyelids falling again and again until they shut for good. She seemed scarcely to have slept any time at all when she was awakened. Sidway was shaking her, and not gently.

"Are you dead?" he called, with something besides impatience.

"Oh!". . . The gray dawn, the piercing cold, the ghostly pines quickly regulated her bewildered senses to actuality. "*Buenos dias,* darling. No, I'm not dead—yet."

"Don't call me that," he almost shouted, most unreasonably. "I'm liable to slap you good."

"Well, you put one black and blue brand on me. Why not another?"

"Get up. Move around. Eat something," he ordered, peremptorily.

Madge found the first desperately hard to accomplish, and the second no easy matter, and the third impossible. Her hands were numb and her feet blocks of ice, until she almost burned them in the fire. Sidway went off somewhere in to the woods, presumably to hunt his horse. Madge could easily have escaped from him then. But that would have been absurd, even if she had wanted to. She walked away from the fire and back again, and presently found that exercise relieved both cold and cramp. At length the cowboy returned with his horse, which he saddled and bridled.

"You'll have to ride," he said, brusquely.

"Thanks. You're very kind to your squaw—darling."

"But not in that blanket. Here, put on my coat."

"No. You'll need that yourself. I can ride with this blanket around me. Only my hands and feet are cold now."

"Warm them pronto, while I tie these things on."

When presently Madge mounted into the saddle she found the stirrups had been shortened to fit her. Without a word Sidway took hold of the reins and led Umpqua down the slope. He took long strides and a slanting zigzag course, down through the cedars. Broad daylight had come and gradually the nipping air and the frost lessened. Madge kept her hands in the folds of the blanket and endured the acute pain of cold feet. Gray shaggy foothills appeared to surround them; the heads of ravines slanted down between these, to widen into narrow valleys; through the trees Madge sometimes caught glimpses of a hazy void. When the sun rose it appeared to be in the wrong direction to her, and if her calculation was correct, Sidway was taking her down across the border into Mexico. He never spoke, never glanced back at her, but strode on, down and ever down, like a man who was lost and did not know nor care where he was going.

Madge's thoughts did not change materially from those which had had their inception in the dark hours of the night before. She could not save herself, or help herself, and any romance or thrill she might conjure up were welcome. In the sunlight of day, however, her disappointment in Sidway and her disillusion grew more bitter hourly. She felt her strength failing, and a consequent gloom and sadness wore on her antagonistic and unquenchable spirit. The time came when she would not have cared what happened, if she could only rest. The cedar trees gave place to brush, which offered no protection from the sun, now climbing high and growing unendurably hot.

"Lance, I'm—spitting cotton," said Madge, at last breaking silence. "Must have—a drink."

"So am I. But hang on. I see green willows below. There's water."

When at last Sidway found water it was none too soon for Madge. There was nothing to drink out of and Madge said if she got off the horse she could not climb back. Whereupon the cowboy, regardless of the fact that she had let the hot blanket slip down, lifted her out of the saddle, and after she had slaked her thirst, he put her back. Madge had never known before the sweetness and life in cold pure water. There were many things she had never appreciated.

Sidway led on tirelessly, always down, but it appeared to Madge that the slopes were less precipitous and the zigzags far longer. She grew so weary that she sagged and swayed in the saddle, and so hot she wanted to fall off and perish, and so miserable that she had hardly strength left to hold the remnants of her garment around her. Nevertheless she would have endured more before entreating him to find some shade and let her rest. She hated him now. She could have killed him. To make her love him hopelessly and terribly, to heap the shame of her horrible selfishness upon her head were indeed enough, without adding this endless insupportable ghastly ride. Madge clutched the pommel and her blanket with sore and hot hands, and sat with closed and burning eyes, wearing to collapse. Minutes or hours dragged by until she seemed not to feel any more. Still she was aware when the horse stopped.

"Look, Madge!" rang out Sidway's voice.

Madge seemed impelled by more than his command. Opening her eyes she saw that they had halted upon a promontory, a level summit of the last foothill. A blue and gray range land not far below, clear and close in the sunlight, appeared to leap up at her. Across its sage-spotted floor moved a long line of cattle, wearily wending their way. Like a black ribbon some miles out stretched a road with speeding automobiles, flashing sunlight from their glass windows. And beyond, over the blue sage loomed a green timbered knoll, from the top of which, half concealed, peeped a white ranch house that Madge knew.

"The cattle herd you see working back belong to your father and Danny Mains," said Sidway, imperturbably.

"That's the highway! . . . there's—my home!" faltered Madge, fighting a sudden dizziness.

"Thought you'd recognize it," he drawled, lighting a cigarette. "I'm sure tickled with the way I came straight down, in a swell short cut, from Cochise's stronghold."

"*Lance!*" She could not hear her own voice.

"Okay. What now?" But he never turned to look at her.

"You're taking—me *home*?"

"Certainly, you poor fish!"

"You're not—what I took you for?—Liar—two-faced—cowboy—kidnaper . . . gangster?"

"No, Miss Stewart. I hate to disillusion you—spoil your pipe dream. It's just too bad, for you're such a swell romancer. You concoct such lovely things about me and my motives. But they didn't pan out, as you see."

"Oh, my—God!—Then you didn't kill Uhl—to—to abduct me, but—but to save me?"

"Right. Your comprehension is at least encouraging. You may be a bright girl yet."

"You don't want—a ransom?"

"Madge Stewart, I'd starve to death before I'd accept a dollar of your money."

"Oh—oh—I . . . What you've done—for me, for Dad and Mom! . . . And I?—Oh, how little—how miserable—you've made me! Oh, the shame! . . ."

Uttering a sharp cry she swayed in the saddle.

"*Madge!* Hang on!" she felt pierce her fading sense, and then, as she fell into his arms, all went black.

When Madge recovered consciousness she found that Sidway was carrying her in front of him, and traveling at a fast pace across the range. Only vague thoughts accompanied her sensations of faintness and pain, and these faded. Then she went through stages of sleep or semiconsciousness, until at last she recovered sufficiently to make out that it was sunset and that she was almost paralyzed.

"Lance . . . how far?" she whispered.

"Almost home," he replied, cheerily. "I'm glad you came to . . . Brace up now. So you won't scare hell out of your mother and the girls. . . . Here, I'll have to wrap you up again, for you're sure in a state of nature."

"Oh—you cowboy!" And she turned in his arm, to sink against his shoulder, reviving anew to life and pain and love, and realizing that there would be nothing worth living for without him. Wide-eyed she lay there, her cheek against his hot dusty vest. They began to climb and entered the pines. A little later Sidway halted the horse in front of the house and yelled: "Hello, inside! It's Sidway! . . . And here's Madge all in, but okay!"

He stepped off with her in his arms, and mounting the porch, encountered a group of wild screaming and questioning boys and girls, and behind them her white-faced mother and the servants.

"Mrs. Stewart, she's *all* right," Sidway assured her. "Let go, girls." He carried her into the house and to her rooms, finally to lay her down on her bed. "*There!*" he ejaculated, poignantly, and straightened up as the others flocked in, eager and wide-eyed, all talking at once.

"Mom!" And that was all Madge could say as her mother knelt to envelop her in loving arms. But she gazed with blurred eyes up at the faces of her friends, crowded around the bed. It was a little while before Madge could answer coherently.

"Mother!—Darlings! I'm well—and safe. You're to thank Sidway for that. . . . I'm just done up. Oh, what an adventure! . . . About Rollie?—I don't know—I don't know. . . . Lance, tell them what it's all about."

Sidway turned away from the window. "Stevens was all right when we left. I'm sure Stewart with his men will have rescued him by now. They'll be back tonight, or tomorrow surely."

"Rescued!" they all cried in unison.

"We were kidnaped," whispered Madge. "Rollie and I went down to the village. That gangster Uhl!—I *knew* him. I'd met him in Los Angeles. He'd found out where I lived. He and his gang kidnaped us . . . And that night Sidway bobbed up—to perform another miracle. He also knew Uhl—and he fooled Uhl—tricked him to leave his car—and ride into the mountains. . . . Lance was the guide—and I thought—but never mind that. He led us up—to Cochise's stronghold. Uhl had sent word to Dad to—pay ransom. . . . Uhl meant to—to . . . he was vile—and Lance had to *kill*—him—to save me! . . ."

Sidway interrupted the chorus of wondering and awed exclamations. "Her voice is gone. Stop making her talk, and fetch her something to drink," he said, hastily. "Mrs. Stewart, Madge is naturally excited about all this." He briefly outlined the history of the adventure, ending, "Now, it's a sure bet that Sloan joined Stewart and they cut loose after us. I think you may expect them back with Stevens by tomorrow."

"Sidway, how can we ever thank you for this?" exclaimed Madge's mother, fervently. "What a relief! . . ."

"Mom, don't let him leave!" cried Madge, frantically, as Sidway started out. "He'll ride away . . . and never—let me thank him."

"Why, child!—Sidway would not do that."

"Wouldn't he? Much you know! . . . Lance, promise me . . ."

Then the girls added their entreaties to hers, until Sidway, red of face, assured them he wanted only to go down to his bunkhouse to clean up, and that he would come back.

"You'll have supper here," added Mrs. Stewart.

At this juncture Barg elbowed his way to Madge's bed with a silver flask, and a glass.

"Nothing doing!" cried Madge, her voice still weak. "I'm on

the wagon—for good. . . . Get me some water first—then hot coffee. . . . And I'm starved."

But despite the assiduous attention of her friends and mother Madge could not keep awake very long. She slept until late the next day, to find that a relaxation had set in from her strenuous and harrowing experience. She was too weak to get out of bed. Allie, who had slept with her, told Madge she had never before looked so lovely and languid and fascinating.

"That bruise, though—I think you'd better hide it," added her worshipful friend.

"Not on your life!" retorted Madge. "That's where Bee Uhl socked me. . . . It might serve to soften the heart of a certain callous and soulless person."

"Majesty! . . . Is it *that* bad?"

"Oh, Lord!—Allie, it's terrible. A million times worse than before—before . . ."

"Before what?" whispered Allie, intensely excited.

"Before he slapped me the night of my party. Oh! wait till you get an earful of that. . . . Before he saved my life. . . . Before I took him for a gangster and a crook—and God only knows what else I called him! . . . Allie darling, I'm terribly afraid it's hopeless."

"Moron! Of course it will be, if you persist in this inferiority complex. But if you *get* to HIM . . ."

The other girls trooped in, clad in colorful pajamas and slacks, and made much of Madge. The boys hung at the door and out in the patio, and then her mother entered. Madge, for once in her life, was coddled and nursed, and paid enough compliments to last a month. But the one person Madge wanted most to see did not present himself. She was too proud, too hurt to ask for him. Why could he not be kind enough to come to see how she fared after the long ride? No doubt Sidway was anxious for the return of Stewart and the others. Madge hardly expected them so soon, and not at all without Rollie Stevens. Late in the afternoon, however, when gold shafts from the setting sun filtered through the foliage at her window, Madge was greatly excited to learn that Rollie had returned safely.

"Drag him in—no matter how he looks," cried Madge, who knew Rollie's weakness.

"He's a sight," replied Nate. "But we'll get him."

Presently there was a merry hubbub outside. Then Rollie came in, supported between Nate and Snake Elwell. Allie, who sat beside Madge on the bed, uttered a shriek. Madge was too overcome for mirth. The collegian's appearance presented grim evidence of the hardship and fright he had suffered.

"Oh, Rollie!—I'm so—so glad! . . ." burst out Madge.

"I'm glad myself, especially to see you home safe. . . . That blighter turned out a hero instead of what you and I took him for?"

"Yes, Rollie."

"He's one swell fellow—I'll tell you," gulped Stevens, gallantly.

"But, *Dad!*"

"Your father is all right, Majesty. He's coming up, with Sidway. The boys drove me. . . . Excuse me now, Majesty. I'm a mess."

Then, as Rollie left, Dawson Metcalf called in at the door. "Steady, Madge! Hold everything! Here come your dad and the hero!"

The clinking of spurs on the stone patio path sent strange little shivers all over Madge. She squeezed Allie's hand and she felt her heart weakly swell in her throat. Then her father entered her room, followed by someone Madge saw only vaguely. Sight of her father stalking in, dusty in his rider's garb, dark of visage, somehow recalled Madge's earliest memories. What a piercing gaze he bent upon her! Never had she met his eyes like that. What thought had been in his mind? After that strange look, his eyes and face softened, and he held her shaking hands and kissed her.

"Well, lass, I'm happy to see you safe at home," he said, with deep feeling.

"Oh—Dad!" And Madge sat up to cling to him and hide her face. There was more than the aftermath of her adventure in her instinctive action. Had she nearly lost him?

Stewart laid her back upon the pillow. "You're pretty white, Madge. And that's a nasty bruise on your temple. How'd you get that?"

"Honey Bee Uhl paid his respects—that way." Her eyes fastened upon Sidway, who stood at the foot of her bed, looking with grave eyes down upon her. It was not only his clean shave and change of garb that made him look so different. Madge thought she had never seen him so handsome, so fine, so disturbing to her heart and mind. She had wit left to realize that she should control her spoken thought, but so great an emotion that she did not care what she said. Her remorse seemed insupportable.

"Lance," she said, beseechingly, "come here—beside Allie—and let me thank you."

"What for?" he asked, smiling.

"Well, saving me from Uhl—killing him, for *one* thing."

"Madge, you and I were mistaken. I didn't kill him."

"No!"

"Daughter, though you both thought so, Sid isn't responsible for that," interposed her father. "Or I either. It was Ren Starr. That cowboy seemed unusually wild, even for him. Effect of that punch you served the other night! . . . Well, Ren shot Flemm when he held them up. That gangster turned on us with his machine gun spitting fire. Then Uhl came out of the cabin, all bloody. Sid's bullet had grooved his scalp. I had some words with Uhl. He was a queer duck, quite beyond me. While Nels held a gun on him, Ren and the other boys hanged the third gangster. And they forced your college boy friend to help. What do you think of that?"

"Heavens!—Rollie help hang a man—even a gangster who had kidnaped *me*?"

"It's a fact. He pulled on the lasso like a regular cowboy."

It would have been extremely embarrassing then for Rollie, had he been present, to hear the outburst.

"We intended to hang Uhl, of course," resumed her father, presently. "But Ren wouldn't hear of it. He forced Uhl to fight—gave him his gun and an even break. Killed him, Madge! . . . Well, I've told the sheriff all about it, and that lets us out. . . . Madeline," said Stewart, addressing his wife, who had come in to stand with Sidway, "it's a good thing this sheriff is not like Pat Hawe, my enemy sheriff of our early years here. . . . And to conclude, we will have our cattle back in another day. All's well that ends well. Let's forget it."

"But, Dad," said Madge, her voice soft and low, "it—hasn't ended well, yet."

"How come? Sure it has."

"I haven't thanked Lance," rejoined Madge, turning the full battery of her eyes upon Sidway, knowing she did so, but deeply sure of her sincerity.

"Well, do so, then," declared Stewart, with a laugh, as he arose.

"I don't need—want to be thanked," said Sidway, with inscrutable eyes upon her.

"Darling!—I . . ."

"There! Let that do," interrupted Sidway, holding up an appealing hand. "It's an inconsequential word for you, Madge. You call your friends 'darling,' both boys and girls. You call Nels and Ren darling, and your parents, even your horses. So, evidently it's just a convenient word that places the lucky one within the charmed circle of your intimates. I accept that gratefully as your thanks for my little service. And it's enough."

Madge stared up at him while the others laughed and made mirth out of it. What a speech for Lance Sidway! He was keener, wittier than she had ever realized. Had he the faintest conception of her remorse? Could not the cool smiling enigma see how she regarded him? There came a culminating rush to Madge's uncontrollable emotion.

"Beloved!" flashed Madge, with a passionate defiant elo-

quence. "Is that less impersonal?" she added trying to make her tone flippant although she felt her face burn red.

Sidway appeared very far from being prostrated by that exquisite epithet. Turning to her father he spread wide his hands: "Gene, I told you she is flighty. Out of her head! I noticed it yesterday toward the last of the ride. No girl ever pulled a gamer stunt. That night ride up on the mountain, then half another night down, then all day in the hot sun—why, it was a grand performance. Not to say fighting off that thug in between! It's no wonder she's cracked under the strain. . . . I think we all ought to get out of here. She needs rest, nursing, quiet."

"Right you are, Sid. Come, beat it, all of us, except one or two of you girls to care for her."

They filed out, except Allie and Maramee, who piled back upon the bed. Someone shut the door.

"Oh hell!" cried Madge, wildly. "Was there *ever* such a man? . . . So I've cracked!"

"Majesty," murmured the incorrigibly romantic Maramee, "It's the most delicious love story there ever was in all the world."

Madge made the following day a quiet and recuperative and thoughtful one. Her guests were due to leave next day and she felt that she would be both sorry and relieved to see them go. The truck loaded with baggage departed early the following morning. And at one o'clock three cars took aboard a hysterical bevy of girls and a merry wisecracking complement of boys. Farewells were prolonged. And at last, when it seemed all had been said, Bu Allen hailed the somber Sidway in a high-pitched penetrating voice.

"Lance, old darling, if Snake Elwell gives me the gate, I'm coming back to go for you in a big way."

That sally elicited a roar of mirth, in which Lance had to join. Madge's rather weak response was a little insincere.

"But, old red-top, that will be swell," retorted Sidway.

"Cowboy, you don't think anyone else around here has a look-in with you?" went on Beulah, demurely anxious, with a sly glance at Madge standing big-eyed and disconsolate on the porch.

"Not a chance, Bu."

Then with a chorus of: "We'll be seeing you!" they were off. Madge watched the cars wind into the green pines and disappear down the slope.

"That's over," she said, with a sigh.

Sidway, with Nels and Ren, had slipped away unobserved. There were tears in her mother's eyes. Her father bent an abstracted gaze below, watching to see the cars come out from under the slope.

"Darlings, let's get it over," said Madge, and locking arms with her parents she led them in.

"Get what over?" queried Stewart, with a start, and her mother looked suddenly concerned.

"Now, Dad! Don't try to fool your little Madge." Forthright then, she plunged abruptly into a confession of how it had come about that Sidway had told her of the impending ruin, if she did not retrieve the situation. She tried to spare the cowboy, but not herself. The quarrel they had had, and the vicious slap she had given him, surely justified him in losing his temper to bitterly flay her.

"You slapped that cowboy, Madge?" queried Stewart in surprise and concern.

"I'll say I did. You may have observed his cut and swollen lip."

"Yes. . . . What did Sidway say to that?" asked her father curiously.

"He slapped me back."

"No!"

"I thought he'd jar my teeth out of their sockets. But I hit him back with all my might. Then he said he refused to let me make a cat and dog fight out of it. . . . Well, that, of course, happened before he told me where to get off. . . .

Dad, dear—Mom darling, this pass that my extravagance and stupidity—and selfishness—have brought you to, has almost broken my heart. I shall make amends. I'll pay it all back. I've wired L. A. and New York, too. I can raise a hundred grand on my jewels. I don't need them. I seldom wore Aunt Helen's pearls. I shan't miss them. . . . Dad, will that money save us, with plenty to spare?"

"It would—lass," he replied, a little huskily, and his arm tightened round her.

"Madge, dearest," spoke up her mother, her poise for once broken. "I *knew* you would do just this. If Gene had let me tell you long ago!"

"Dad was trying me out, Mom. It's settled then. . . . I've had a ghastly lesson. I'll make up for it, my darlings. . . . Dad, I never could hope to be your ideal western girl, nor ever in Mom's class as a lady of quality, but I can be a square shooter and I will be."

"Lass, we might argue over that western girl idea," returned Stewart, his dark eyes alight. Her mother folded her in loving arms, and by these simple things Madge seemed to grasp a great joy that had almost eluded her.

"Oh, yes, Dad . . . there's one other thing," said Madge, turning in her mother's arms. She essayed to be composed and casual, with dubious success. "Can I rely on you—on your keeping Sidway here? He—I. . . . At least I can thank him—reward him somehow."

"Madge, I don't think that'll be at all difficult," replied Stewart, but he did not make clear whether he meant keeping Sidway there or rewarding him.

"I'm almost—happy again," said Madge, yielding to tears, "but still feel kind of wobbly and I'd better—lie down."

"It might be a good idea to talk that matter over with Nels," added Stewart, smilingly. "He and Sid are thick as hops."

Madge fled, yearning to ask just what matter her father meant, but she did not dare. How perilously close was she to betrayal of her secret! Her father's evasive eye and significant words, her mother's softened face and restrained sympathy—these were hard to resist. But Madge had a little pride and spirit left. In her room, which had again taken on its old tranquillity and speaking silence, she salvaged something of her old self.

Next morning, biding her time, until she had seen Lance and Ren ride away, Madge waylaid Nels in his bunkhouse.

"Wal, Majesty! I shore was wonderin' when you'd remember yore old Nels."

"Darling, I've never forgotten you," she said, tenderly. "It's just that I've been knocked out—and lots on my mind. . . . And I knew when I *did* see you I'd have to talk turkey."

"Aboot who, lass? Wal, I reckon I know. An' it's aboot high time."

"Nels! He's not leaving?" queried Madge, hurriedly.

"Wal, he talks aboot it a lot. An' he's purty sad these days. Ren rags him all the time aboot you. Lance says he'll stay till Ren an' Bonita air married."

"Oh, Nels! Is that settled?"

"It shore is. An' Ren is one dotty cowboy."

"I'm happy over it. . . . Oh, what shall I give them? It must be something wonderful."

"Wal, lass, if I had my say, I'd want to see another marryin' pretty pronto."

"Nels!—You're so sudden. Have a heart! . . . You mean. . . ."

"Lass, I'm confessin' somethin'," replied Nels, earnestly. "I'm gettin' along—close to seventy. An' I've had a long full life. Lately my heart has been warnin' me thet I might not hev long to be heah. An' I couldn't go satisfied an' happy if you wasn't . . ."

"Oh, Nels!—Don't! don't!" implored Madge, poignantly, and she flew to throw her arms around his neck and lay her face against his hollow bristling cheek. Don't think such a thing!—It'd break my heart.—Nels, you're my second dad. You taught me everything. . . . You must not go away—and leave me."

"Wal, honey, I reckon there ain't any reason to be onduly scared. I was jest preparin' you. . . . An' thet fetches me to the somethin' nearest my heart. It's this turrible love affair between you an' Lance."

"Turrible one-sided. . . . Yes," choked out Madge, hiding her face.

"One-sided?—Not onless you don't love him."

"Oh, dear old Nels!" was all she could say, clinging to him.

"Majesty, the boy is dyin' fer you. He's got it wuss than I ever seen any boy in all my life."

"How do you know?" she cried, desperately.

"Wal, a blind man could see. But, lass, I'll give him away—double-cross him—if you say his case is not hopeless."

"Nels—darling . . . it's not—*quite* hopeless," she whispered.

"Aw, thet's fine!—Wal, Lance has told me time an' again, an' this last time, the other night, he jest cried in his misery. It seems you hurt him turrible by believin' he was a gangster—a kidnaper—an' Gawd knows what. . . . Lass, I cain't understand how you—so smart a girl—could ever make thet mistake."

"I did! I'm not smart. But I know *now*—and *that's* killing me."

"Wal, he's the finest youngster yore Dad an' me ever met. Thet's all of thet. An' he loves you so much he suffers awful, I could tell you the things he does thet'd make you ashamed an' sorry. But this is enough. He told me thet he loved you so much he couldn't stay heah an' he couldn't leave. Now Majesty, I've told you—I've betrayed him. What do you say?"

"I can't say—much—when—I—I'm crying. . . . But I—I love him more—than he loves me—and I'm dying of longing—and shame. . . ."

"Thet's enough, lass," interrupted Nels, vastly disturbed by her weeping. "It's gonna be all right. . . . What you must do is be clear enough to break his pride. He's stubborn as a mule."

"Break his pride! You mean—make him confess—he loves me?"

"Sartin I mean thet. An' you've gotta do somethin' onheered of an' powerful sweet thet won't give him no chance on earth."

"Nels, I'll do—anything," cried Madge, wildly. "But what?"

"Wal, thet's more than I can tell. You'll hev to figger thet yourself."

"I'll do anything—anything . . ." Madge repeated.

"Wal, thet makes me happy," burst out the old cattleman. "Majesty, run home now an' cudgel yore pretty haid fer a grand idee. Somethin' onheerd of—turrible lovin'—amazin' an' sweet thet won't give Lance no chance atall. An' spring it on him pronto."

"You darling old matchmaker—*I will*," promised Madge, and almost blind with ecstasy, she ran away, up into the solitary pines.

After dinner that night, during which she had been rapturously gay, to the wonder and delight of her parents, Madge put on one of her flimsiest, most shimmering gowns, with high-heeled white slippers to match. Wearing a long dark coat over this she stole forth upon what seemed to her the most momentous and thrilling venture of her life.

She went by the patio and down through the pines by the trail. At this hour she knew Nels, her father perhaps, and surely the cowboys, would be at the store. As if by magic all her old imperious confidence, tempered this time by a secret humility and gratitude and love, returned in full force. She could not lose, and that gave a tremendous zest to her venture.

Her blood raced with her thoughts and her heart throbbed high as she gained the level, and like a shadow glided across to the bunkhouses. Lance's was next to that occupied by Nels. She tiptoed down the porch, close to the wall until she came to Lance's open door. The yellow lights of the store cast a glow out upon the open. She heard low voices and Sidway's laugh. That gave her pause. Could he be so deeply and miserably in love, as Nels had sworn, and laugh like any other fancy-free cowboy? What if that sly Nels had framed her? The thought was terrible. But nobly she cast it aside as unworthy of a chastened and humble girl. Anyway the die was cast.

Madge took off her clicking high-heeled slippers and stole into Lance's room and laid aside the long coat. Feeling around for his chair she found it and curled up in it, shaking with excitement. Presently she dimly espied her picture on his table, and that overjoyed her.

It was done. She was there, in his room. Beyond Lance's finding her there she had not thought. This was far enough. Of all the things in the world, this was the last Lance Sidway would think of. It did not matter much what he did, when he found her there, unless he took her by the heels and dragged her out. He was capable of that, Madge thought.

Voices and jingling spurs enjoined silence. The men were approaching. Madge would have preferred that Lance came alone. For a moment she fought a wild need to laugh. How her blood was gushing through her veins!

Heavy footfalls upon the porch jarred the log cabin. Madge sat as quietly as a mouse, her heart pounding. She hoped Lance would not come to his room while the other men were in the bunkhouse. Still, no matter! She did not care what happened. Nels had cured her malady. She had all the cards in her hands.

The men, apparently three in number, filed into Nels' room.

"Strike a light, Nels," said Stewart.

"It's pretty darn warm," rejoined Sidway. "I won't light my lamp."

"Wal, Sid, you won't need to," added Nels. "Reckon you got kind of a glow aboot you."

"Nels, I've a mind to bounce something off your dome," declared the cowboy, irritably, and then he laughed.

"Son, I'll smoke one of your cigarettes," said Stewart.

How Madge shook at that laconic epithet given Sidway by

her father! Poor Lance! They were all in league against him. not a ghost of a show to escape!

"All right, we're set," went on her father, seriously. "You're determined to ride away tomorrow?"

"Yes, Gene—I am," replied Lance, sadly.

"There's a future here for you. This ranch will pay again some day. I'm glad to tell you that I'm going to pull through this tough time. Madge is helping me."

"By God! I *knew* she would," cried Lance, passionately, as if verifying something to a doubtful side of him. "I'm glad, Gene. It's worried me a lot. Not that it's any of my business. . . . She's swell. She's a Stewart, all right."

"I had that hunch myself."

"Wal," drawled Nels, "I always told you *hombres* thet Majesty was true-blue, a western girl at heart, an' one grand thoroughbred."

There ensued a momentary silence, during which Madge feared they might hear her heart beat, so thickly and swiftly did it pound in her ears.

Then Stewart spoke: "Son, please tell me why you don't want to stay here at Majesty's Rancho?"

"Gene, it can't be possible you don't know," retorted Lance. Then his laugh cut a little coldly, with a hopeless note. "Gene, to come straight out with the truth—I'm so mad over your beautiful daughter that I can't stand being any longer where I can see her."

"That's blunt and to the point," returned Stewart. "I'll speak the same way. I'd like you to be my son. . . . Have you asked Madge to marry you?"

"Good heavens—no!" ground out Sidway, apparently tortured.

"Why not? Faint heart never won fair lady! I don't recall being very shy with Madeline. Was I, Nels?"

"Hell no!"

"Madge hates the very sight of me," declared Lance, abjectly.

"Don't believe it," declared Stewart, vigorously.

"Son, I reckon you air wrong aboot thet," drawled Nels.

"Oh, you fellows will drive me to drink. Let's make an end of it. I know you like me, and you've been swell to me. I love you both. But that has nothing to do with it. Madge is the one. And she loathes the ground I walk on. It's no wonder. I've had the rotten luck to save her in humiliating circumstances. She is as proud as a princess. I've rubbed her the wrong way. I've bucked her in everything. Perhaps the last straw was her finding out that I had seen her bank statements and credits. But that wasn't my fault. Worse than that, my knowing about her flirtation with that gangster, Uhl . . ." Suddenly Lance broke off, panic in his voice. "I didn't mean to tell you that—to give her away. I could kick myself."

"Son, you're not giving Madge away. I savvied that. And then she told me."

"She did? Holy cats!"

"She just casually spoke of it, as if for her it was okay. That has been bothering me. . . . Just how far it went!"

"Wal, Gene, thet doesn't bother me none," drawled Nels.

"But it should," flashed Stewart.

"Gene, one day Majesty talked to me for a long while. She was in one of them bare bathin' ootfits, an' I jest couldn't look at her atall. An' she got to tellin' me aboot the girls an' boys, an' these new modern ways. We air old-fashioned, Gene. An' this world has moved along. It's changed. Somehow I seemed to savvy Majesty, an' since thet day nothin' she ever did or might do could bother me."

"Why didn't she confide in her father, too?" asked Stewart, jealously.

"Gene, you may not believe it," put in Lance, "but Madge was afraid of you. Loved you—craved your respect. I know."

"All right. You and Nels are hipped on this girl. You just can't see anything wrong. . . ."

"There wasn't anything wrong," interrupted Sidway, with heat, "unless we except her flirtations and extravagances. Not in this day!"

"What's the age to do with it?"

"I don't know, but it has a lot."

"Sidway, speak right out, will you?" importuned Stewart. "It seems we three all worship this strange girl. Well, Nels is set and safe in his worship. I don't want to embarrass you. I know you'd lie like a gentleman to protect her. And so would I if I were in your place. I love Madge and nothing can change it. Still I wish. . . . Oh, hell, I don't know *what* I want. But it's a deep and bitter need, I assure you."

Again there ensued a silence, except for Nels' cough, and the tapping of his pipe upon the table, while Madge sat there, strung and tense, her heart bursting.

"Gene, I get you," spoke up Lance, with finality. "You want your old idea of respect back for Madge. I tell you, on my word of honor, that you may feel that respect. Madge Stewart has never done one single thing that she would hide from you—that she could not look you in the eyes and tell. Sure she is modern, sophisticated. She's a college girl. A radical, when it comes to mid-Victorian standards. . . . But, get this, both of you. Even if she had been what you old fogies would call bad, it'd make no difference. Not to me! Not to anyone who knows her! Madge Stewart is like Helen of Troy. Their value is as incomparable and incalculable as their beauty, their minds and souls, their great power to create love, to give, to be a joy to all who come in contact with them."

"You win, son," came Stewart's quiet voice, a little husky. "Then, even if Madge were what you swear she is not—you'd make her your wife, if she cared for you?"

"My—heaven! Gene, you're thickheaded," declared Lance in despair. "Yes! *Yes!* And consider myself the luckiest fellow in the world—as I'd be the happiest."

Madge could not bear any more. Slipping out of the chair she picked up her slippers, and softly went outside, to appear in the open doorway of Nels' room. She paused a moment, then entered.

The smile of beatitude that shone resplendent on Nels'

visage, the sudden sinking of Stewart into a chair, as if his legs had suddenly grown weak, and Sidway's backing into the wall for support,—these reactions sustained Madge in this emotional climax of her life.

"Dad—Nels—Lance, did I happen in opportunely?"

"Madge! Where did you come from?" demanded Stewart.

"From Lance's room. I've been in there listening to you."

"For God's sake! . . . Are you crazy, girl?—What were you doing there?"

"Waiting for Lance. I'd framed a little stunt. But you've upset it."

"Yes. And what were you going to do—when he came?"

"Dad, I hadn't the slightest idea. But I know now."

She approached Sidway, in so poignant a joy and surety of her power to bestow happiness, that his pale and working face did not deter her from prolonging his torture a little longer.

"Lance, if I don't put on my slippers I won't be so tall, and I can look up to you better. See!" And dropping them she stepped closer, to look up into his eyes.

He stood like a statue, his gaze somber and unbelieving. But her glance quickly descended to his vest, where her hands, quivering almost imperceptibly, touched the frayed edge, and a spot that lacked a button. She was not quite ready yet to let him read what her eyes would surely say.

"Cowboy, you need someone to look after you," she went on, sweetly. "Did you know I could make buttonholes and sew on buttons?"

"No. I couldn't imagine it," he returned hoarsely. "Did you learn that in college?"

"Mother taught me. . . . I can mend socks, too. And make my own clothes, and I know how to cook and bake, too."

"You're—a—remarkably accomplished—young lady."

"Thank you. I wondered if you had found it out. . . . Are you interested in my waiting for you—in your room?"

Evidently it was utterly impossible for Lance to answer that. He divined something his intelligence repudiated.

"Well, as a matter of fact, I forgot. You and Dad and Nels spoiled my plot. Let's skip it."

She began to slide her gold-tan hands up the edges of his vest, and her eyes traveled with them. Then, in a flash, her arms encircled his neck, and she gave him her eyes, with all her heart and soul in them.

"I have much to thank you for," she said, eloquently. "But even more than for my very life. I want to thank you for what you told Dad just now."

"Madge, please—don't," he rejoined, unsteadily. "You're excited again. . . . I don't want thanks."

"Wrong again, darl . . . No, darling is out. I must find another word. . . . Lance, I'm not excited. Just in a transport," and her hands slipped by one another, so that in another moment her arms were clasping his neck.

"Did it ever occur to you that I might have fallen in love with you at first sight—that day at the campus in L.A.?"

"It—certainly—didn't!" he gasped.

"Well, I did. And then wondering where you were, and if I could find you again, and then discovering you here where we have misunderstood each other and fought like cat and dog—all this while, Lance, it's grown worse, until I'm dying more for you than you are for me."

"Madge—for God's sake—for my sake. . . ."

"It's for all our sakes, but mine mostly. Lance, I need more than you need. . . . Aren't you going to hug me? Can't you see the real thing? Can't you take it?"

"No! . . . Gene—Nels, get her away," he implored, hoarsely, his face the hue of ashes. "She is getting even with me. It's her revenge. . . . She's acting."

"Son, a moment or so ago you very chivalrously championed this girl," declared Stewart, with a rare smile. "I've a hunch she's serious."

"Wal, Lance, I reckon you better believe her—an' take it—

an' hug her all to oncet," drawled Nels, supremely nonchalant. "Com-mon, Gene." The two walked out, but Madge was beyond noticing.

"Listen, Lance," she began again, lifting her lips until they were close to his. "If I should happen to throw another party—a *wedding* party, for instance—there would not be any punch. And. . . ."

"Wait! Give me—a break!" he panted, his arms encircling her, and almost crushing the breath out of her.

"I'm giving you—a break," she whispered. "Only—don't break—my ribs." She could no longer endure the beseeching incredulous love light in his eyes, and hastened to her surrender.

She felt her willful spirit fading away in a deep and overpowering rapture, and the kiss she gave him almost prevented one last expression of her mischievous self.

"Sweetheart. You know I swore I'd have Umpqua," she said, softly, at his lips.

He drew back startled, with questioning eyes. "Darling, you couldn't be—so—so," he replied, huskily . . . "just to make me give you Umpqua?"

"But that oughtn't be so hard—giving Umpqua—along with yourself," she whispered, tremulously, and as she blindly sought his lips again, it seemed the end of their travail.

"Majesty! . . . You can have him—and me forever," he said, with incredulous bliss. "I adored you . . . my heart was broken. . . . But I'd live it all over again—for this!"

W9-CNZ-300

PRAISE FOR

FREEDOM'S DOMINION

"Jefferson Cowie has a knack for publishing instant classics: books that change historians' conversations. This is his most extraordinary yet. With eloquence and with brilliance, he delves deep into the annals of a specific place, Barbour County, Alabama, in order to excavate the foundations of America's darkest and most enduring story: how 'freedom' became a national alibi for cruelty, inequity, and reaction. As soon as I finished reading it, I wanted to start over and absorb it all over again." —Rick Perlstein, author of *Reaganland*

"Cowie has given us a deep history of the long war on the federal government—especially when it came to policies advancing class and race equality, of the evolution of white grievance politics, and of a new way of thinking about the psychic structure of American Exceptionalism. With eloquent, precise prose, Cowie clears away the cobwebs to reveal a national malady long in the making."

—Greg Grandin, Pulitzer Prize–winning author of *The End of the Myth*

"A fascinating book, *Freedom's Dominion* takes us to the states'-rights stronghold of Barbour County, Alabama. Barbour was the birthplace of Governor George Wallace, whose infamous defense of segregation described integration as tyranny, segregation as freedom, and equal access to the ballot as a threat to individual rights. Wallace's views illustrate the confounding interdependence of ideas about freedom and oppression in American politics—as does Barbour County's long history of state-building rooted in antiblack violence, white supremacist rule, and Indian land dispossession. *Freedom's Dominion* offers a searing account of that history that leaves one wondering whether American freedom can ever be disentangled from the causes it has supported."

—Mia Bay, author of *Traveling Black*

"*Freedom's Dominion* covers centuries of American history in Eufala, Alabama, from the violence of settler colonialism through the ascent of arch-segregationist George Wallace, the region's most famous native son. Cowie is interested in how people in power—almost always white men—used claims of freedom to dominate and enslave others, and how they articulated domination as resistance to a tyrannical federal government. This history has urgent implications for how we understand white supremacist and anti-government politics today."

—Kathleen Belew, author of *Bring the War Home*

"Cowie's *Freedom's Dominion* is a magisterial narrative history of white grievance politics. Cowie reveals the origins of these often hypocritical and confounding perspectives in which those who stole, enslaved, and segregated would themselves claim to be victims of federal overreach even as they oppressed so many others. Cowie's terrific book explains the Southern roots of that racialized ideology and reveals how one of the most influential segregationist rhetoricians of the 1960s helped repackage this powerful form of regional white-identity politics for the rest of the nation."

—William Sturkey, author of *Hattiesburg*

"Gripping and haunting. Cowie's meticulous accumulation of detail and candid assessments make for distressing yet essential reading. This is history at its most vital."

—*Publishers Weekly* (starred review)

FREEDOM'S DOMINION

ALSO BY JEFFERSON COWIE

The Great Exception:
The New Deal and the Limits of American Politics

Stayin' Alive:
The 1970s and the Last Days of the Working Class

Beyond the Ruins:
The Meanings of Deindustrialization (co-edited)

Capital Moves:
RCA's Seventy-Year Quest for Cheap Labor

FREEDOM'S DOMINION

A SAGA OF WHITE RESISTANCE TO FEDERAL POWER

Jefferson Cowie

BASIC BOOKS
NEW YORK

Basic Books
Hachette Book Group
1290 Avenue of the Americas, New York, NY 10104
www.basicbooks.com

Printed in the United States of America

First Edition: November 2022

Published by Basic Books, an imprint of Perseus Books, LLC, a subsidiary of Hachette Book Group, Inc. The Basic Books name and logo is a trademark of the Hachette Book Group.

Library of Congress Control Number: 2022940794

ISBNs: 9781541672802 (hardcover), 9781541672819 (ebook)

LSC-C

Printing 1, 2022

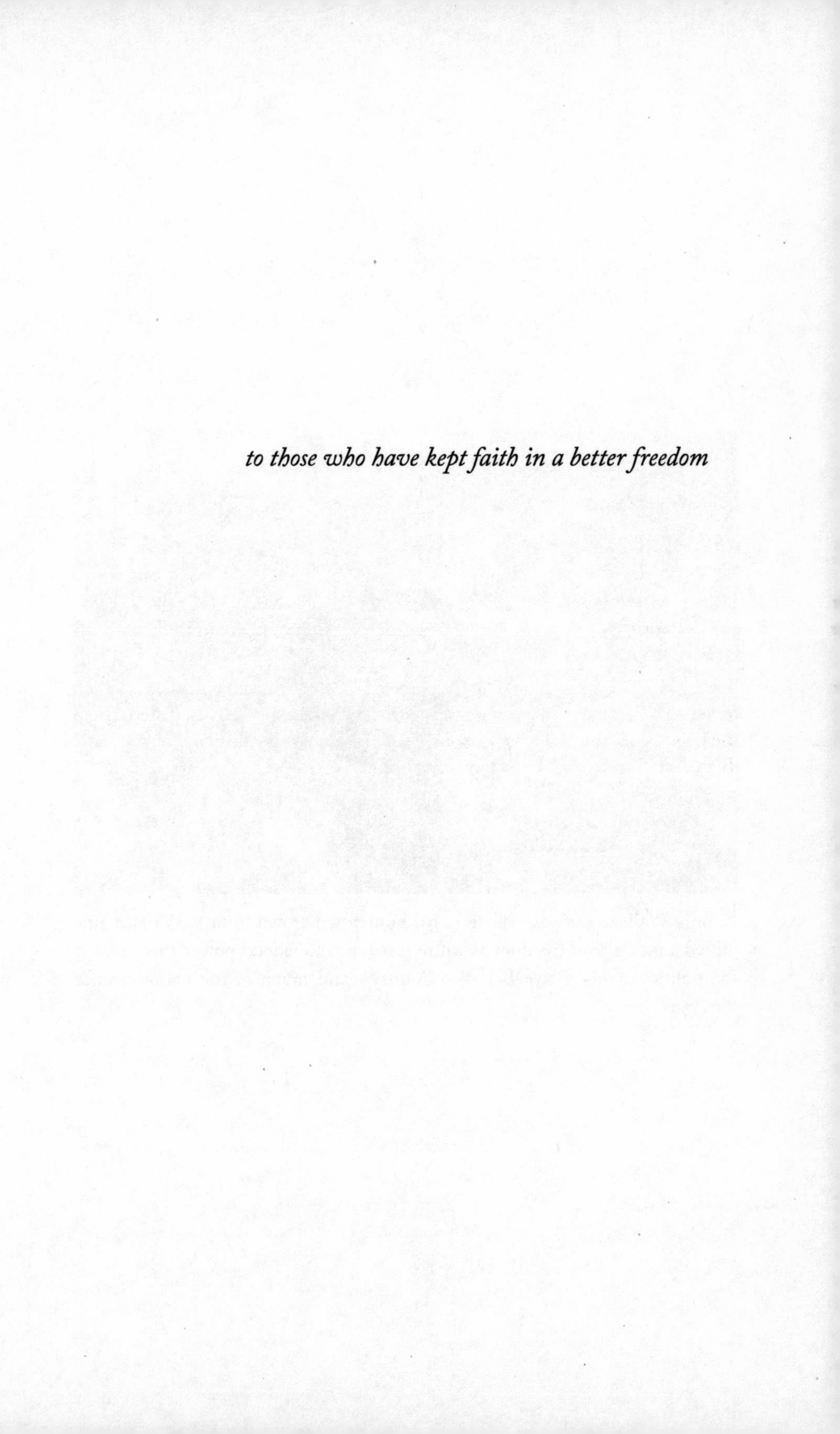

to those who have kept faith in a better freedom

George Wallace campaigns before his hometown crowd in 1958. Wallace amplified a message of freedom as white resistance to federal power that defined the politics of his native Barbour County—and much of the nation—since the 1830s.

The great force of history comes from the fact that we carry it within us, are unconsciously controlled by it in many ways, and history is literally *present* in all that we do. It could scarcely be otherwise, since it is to history that we owe our frames of reference, our identities, and our aspirations. And it is with great pain and terror that one begins to realize this.

—JAMES BALDWIN, 1965

CONTENTS

BOOK FOUR: Democracy

Creek Lands, the Alabama Black Belt, and Barbour County

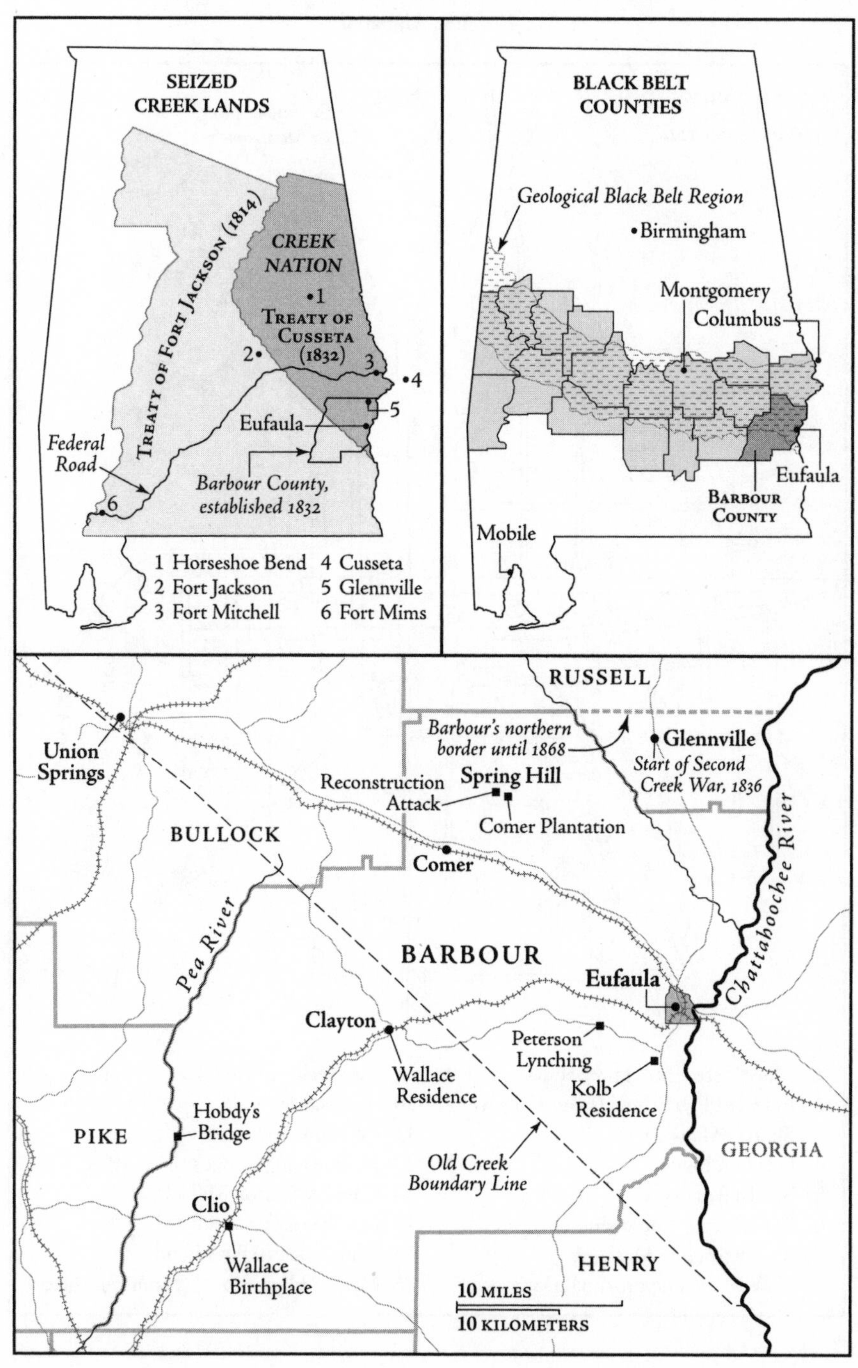

SEIZED CREEK LANDS
CREEK NATION
Treaty of Fort Jackson (1814)
Treaty of Cusseta (1832)
Eufaula
Federal Road
Barbour County, established 1832
1 Horseshoe Bend
2 Fort Jackson
3 Fort Mitchell
4 Cusseta
5 Glennville
6 Fort Mims
BLACK BELT COUNTIES
Geological Black Belt Region
Birmingham
Montgomery
Columbus
Eufaula
Barbour County
Mobile
RUSSELL
Barbour's northern border until 1868
Glennville
Start of Second Creek War, 1836
Union Springs
Reconstruction Attack
Spring Hill
Comer Plantation
BULLOCK
Comer
Chattahoochee River
Pea River
BARBOUR
Eufaula
Clayton
Peterson Lynching
Wallace Residence
Kolb Residence
Hobdy's Bridge
PIKE
GEORGIA
Old Creek Boundary Line
Clio
Wallace Birthplace
HENRY
10 MILES
10 KILOMETERS

Eufaula, Alabama

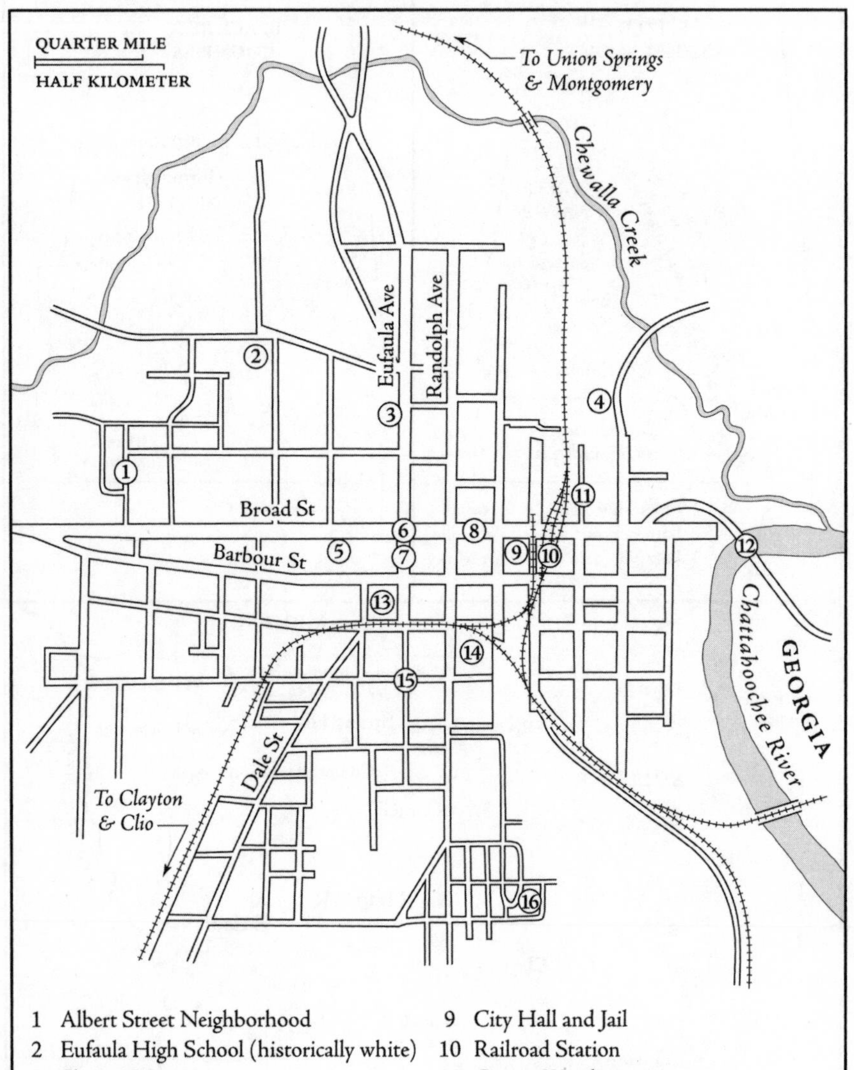

1	Albert Street Neighborhood	9	City Hall and Jail
2	Eufaula High School (historically white)	10	Railroad Station
3	Shorter Mansion	11	Cotton Warehouses
4	Freedom House	12	Horace King Bridge (1839–1924)
5	Sparks Residence	13	Cowikee Cotton Mill #1
6	Confederate Monument	14	Cowikee Cotton Mill #3
7	Reconstruction Massacre	15	Southside Neighborhood
8	Slave Market (approximate location)	16	McCoo High School (historically black)

INTRODUCTION

George Wallace and American Freedom

GEORGE WALLACE, EVER proud and defiant, tightened his fighter's frame as he assumed the spot where Jefferson Davis was sworn in as president of the Confederacy over a century earlier. Chin forward, chest puffed out, the new governor stood high on the rostrum, flanked by undulating waves of red, white, and blue bunting. A Confederate flag adorned the podium before him. When he began to speak, Wallace's lips curled around his famous cocksure Southern drawl, his vowels gliding and stretching toward some secret past. The new governor seemed to transcend time—a man as much from the nineteenth century as from the Space Age. January 14, 1963, was the coldest day in almost any Alabamian's lifetime, and the fog of the governor's breath rose into the winter air. The man who would go on to become the firebrand of the modern conservative movement seemed to breathe history and exhale ghosts.[1]

The new governor began his infamous inaugural with an homage to the specifics of place. Thanking the "home folks" of his native Barbour County for giving "an anxious country boy" a chance, he called out no fewer than twenty-five locations in that county on the banks of the Chattahoochee River—Haigler's Mill, Spring Hill, Baxter's Station, Horns Crossroads, Baker Hill, Eufaula, and his own birthplace, Clio (pronounced here with a long *i*, as in "Ohio"). Like his audience, Wallace understood history in terms of place as well as time: settings of rich soil, old churches, familiar streets, sharecropper shacks, opulent mansions, and buried ancestors. Such places of enduring independence and eternal innocence, Wallace would argue, needed to be defended from the ominous storm of federal forces forever gathering just over the horizon.

Wallace's angry finger jabbed at legions of imaginary enemies before him. The audience hung on every word. His well-trained boxer's fists flew. The crowd roared. As Wallace moved on from his tribute to Barbour County, the register of his voice changed. It became louder, less dignified, even forced. Then came words that split the frozen Alabama air like fire: "Segregation now, segregation tomorrow, and segregation forever!" Each syllable, written by a Klansman no less, got its due. That one race-baiting line shot around the country and riveted the nation's attention. It remains the most famous sentence of George Wallace's life.

History recalls Wallace's inaugural address as a set piece in the larger drama of defending Southern segregation, which it was. But the speech was about something even more profound, more enduring, even more virulent than segregation. Aside from his infamous "Segregation Forever" slogan, Wallace mentioned "segregation" only one other time that afternoon. In contrast, he invoked "freedom" twenty-five times in his speech—more than Martin Luther King Jr. would use the term later that year in his "I Have a Dream" address at the March on Washington. "Let us rise to the call of freedom-loving blood that is in us," Wallace told his audience, "and send our answer to the tyranny that clanks its chains upon the South." Those rattling shackles of oppression were forged by the enemy of the people of his beloved Barbour County: the federal government.

After the inaugural, the crowd dispersed down Montgomery's capitol hill. Many in attendance still had white carnations pinned on their lapels to proclaim their resistance to integration. As they spilled down toward Dexter Avenue, there on the corner, in plain sight from the governor's office window, stood the sturdy redbrick

Baptist church where Martin Luther King Jr. preached until 1959. In the dark, wood-paneled basement of that house of worship, King and his many allies planned parts of the Montgomery Bus Boycott after NAACP activist Rosa Parks's strategic refusal to give up her bus seat in 1955. By Wallace's inaugural, King had decamped for Atlanta to build his growing national campaign for civil rights. Yet Wallace, too, was building up a national presence, hell-bent on combating the very same federally ensured equality that King and his allies sought. Except what King believed to be the path to freedom, Wallace believed to be a wall of federal tyranny. The new governor tapped into something fierce. "Wallacism," King explained on national television later that spring, "is bigger than Wallace."[2]

During the fight over the Civil Rights Act in 1964, Wallace's criticism of federal overreach became even more enflamed: the legislation was an "act of tyranny," the "assassin's knife stuck in the back of liberty," an assertion of government overreach with "more power than claimed by King George III, more power than Hitler, Mussolini, or Khrushchev ever had." By promoting national laws to end racial segregation, the "federal force-cult," Wallace claimed, was trying to push the white South "back into bondage."[3]

George Wallace, famous as a defender of segregation, believed himself to be a fighter for freedom. From the American Revolution to the ongoing civil rights struggle, Americans have come to associate the concept of freedom with the fight of the oppressed for a better life and a better world. Few ideas are as central to the American mythos. It is easy to ignore or dismiss Wallace's call for freedom as little more than ideological window dressing for his racism. The real story, however, is far deeper and more complex. Even superficial familiarity with American political discourse reveals that this word, *freedom*, is as vague as it is ubiquitous, as contested as it is omnipresent, as reflexive as it is inescapable, as oppressive as it is liberating. What the world heard that cold January day was a politician in a long history of local politicians, one with a preternatural capacity to channel the currents of Southern—and national—history into the nation's most cherished ideal.[4]

Americans, Wallace believed, would forever continue the fight of their Jeffersonian ancestors against centralized tyranny. "We intend," he declared at the inaugural, "quite simply, to practice the free heritage as bequeathed to us as sons of free fathers." He tapped into what one historian has called an obsessive "fear of an imminent loss of freedom" displayed throughout Southern, and American, history. Wallace's words are hard to differentiate from generations of similar calls to protect local ideas of American freedom. Patriotically rooted in the United States' revolution against colonial monarchy, these cries subsequently turned against the US government itself. An 1851 issue of the *Montgomery Advertiser*, for instance, found white slaveholding Alabamians to be "the most oppressed, insulted and plundered of all" in their struggle against federal power. Protecting their freedom to enslave others meant they had to fight tirelessly for "the maintenance and perpetuation of those great principles of civil liberty transmitted to us by a glorious and venerated ancestry."[5]

Since federal authority often proved to be an essential, if often fallible, means of redress for nonwhite people, generations of leaders like Wallace saw federal authority as a threat to their social order. Wallace therefore spent his career repeating an enduring and widespread American promise to keep federal power at bay. His brand of freedom was not just ideological residue of the revolutionary generation, but a means to maintain local white political and economic power. Freedom from what whites deplored as federal "tyranny," therefore, ironically provided license to practice actual tyranny in countless places like Barbour County. From the theft of Native lands to the suppression of modern civil rights movements, conflict between federal power and local autonomy forged a peculiar ideology of white freedom: an ever-evolving freedom to dominate others.

This book is about the idea and practice of a specific kind of freedom in the very place George Wallace elegized in his speech—Barbour County, Alabama, and its main town, Eufaula. A place of grand, tree-lined boulevards, enormous antebellum-style mansions, once bustling commerce, and a dizzyingly rich political history, the town once sat high upon on a bluff above the Chattahoochee River, an elevation submerged, since the 1960s, by a federal dam. The serpentine waters of the river, marking the divide between Alabama and Georgia, flow down to Apalachicola Bay, carrying cotton to the great ports of the world. Here the stately homes in the southeast corner of Alabama are known by the names of deceased locals who made their fortunes as cotton planters and merchants—and controllers of local politics—who found themselves in constant battle with federal authorities to obtain their land and maintain their political and economic power. From the once famous bluff, the town dissolves westward into the enormous spreading plains of plantation cotton, grown in the rich black soil of the northern part of the county. The southern half of the county, below the famous region known as the Black Belt, hosts the poverty and hardscrabble lands that gave birth to George Wallace.

Stories of this obscure place of "surpassing charm," once hidden behind veils of Spanish moss or beneath thick oak boughs bending to the weight of history, reveal a microhistory of the largest and most central conflict in American political history: that over the meaning of American freedom. A close examination of Barbour County reveals how a racialized, domineering version of American freedom evolved through two centuries of local battles with federal authorities. A focus on a single place allows for a full exploration of why and how appeals to American freedom so often serve as an ideological motor for practices of domination of other people's land, labor, and political power. The dramas here, small and large, illustrate how racialized anti-statism became a core aspect of American freedom.[6]

Historians have long recognized the oppressive tensions that gave birth to American freedom but have rarely addressed the grinding persistence of the problem. They have observed the comingled contradictions between freedom and slavery, noted the paradox of those claiming freedom for themselves but oppressing others, and puzzled at the contradictory tensions in American ideologies, but rarely have they recognized that oppression and freedom are not opposites. In the United States, freedom and oppression are mutually constructed, interdependent, and difficult to separate. As African American historian Nathan Irvin Huggins put it, "Slavery and freedom, white and black, are joined at the hip." From the founding fathers of whom Wallace spoke, to his own day and down to ours, land dispossession, slavery, power, and oppression do not stand in contrast to freedom—they are expressions of it.[7]

Where did this idea of American freedom as freedom to dominate come from? Turning back thousands of years, we can see how ancient ideas of political freedom emerged in slave societies. In ancient Athens, as the classicist Moses Finley put it some years ago, we saw the "advance, hand in hand, of freedom and slavery." Without a large body of people to whom freedom was denied, the historical sociologist Orlando Patterson argues, there was little need for the concept of what became Europe's most cherished value. Freedom, argues Patterson, was founded not "upon a rock of human virtue but upon the degraded time fill of man's vilest inhumanity to man"—the capacity to enslave.[8]

Patterson sees the structure of Western freedom as having three notes that compose a single cultural chord. The first note is the most obvious: freedom as the absence of constraint on one's latitude to act. We might consider this the realm of individual liberty, the type of absence of constraint that is cherished by Americans and the most romantic version in ideology and practice. The second note is "civic freedom"—the ability to participate in the governance of one's community. We call this democracy. We are civically free to the degree that we share in the decisions of the political community.

The third, and most ominous, note in Patterson's chord is an idea of freedom that means not simply the absence of slavery but the power to enslave. Patterson explains that an individual engaging in freedom as an expression of his—and only in recent decades has it been anything but *his*—singular sovereignty "has the power to restrict the freedom of others or to empower others with the capacity to do as they please with others beneath them." Such a framework begins to explain why cries for American freedom so often exist in an uncomfortable embrace with concentration of power, racial bigotry, religious intolerance, misogyny, land hunger, violence, and a belligerent form of gun rights. By recognizing discrimination, white supremacy, economic power, and the capacity for violence as dimensions of what "freedom" has always meant, we gain a fresh perspective on central problems of American ideology and practice. A core dimension of freedom is an expression of power.[9]

The ancient concept of freedom became something more specific, more virulent, in the United States through interactions with Indigenous lands and African labor. If we can step away from gauzy, almost religious, celebrations of the nation's founding, some distinctive problems in American history become salient. The United States was born at a unique confluence of two streams of global history: settler colonialism and chattel slavery. In global history, there are settler colonial societies and there are slave societies, but few societies are both. Even fewer are founded on a premise so deeply wedded to the combined ancient republican values of freedom and democratic governance. At its heart, this book offers a long historical answer to the short question posed by the eighteenth-century English poet and essayist Samuel Johnson: "How is it that we hear the loudest yelps for liberty among the drivers of negroes?"[10]

Americans celebrate their independence from British colonial rule as the fountainhead of their freedom, yet they proceeded to use their freedom to seize the continent and replace the existing people with both themselves and human beings stolen from Africa. After the expulsion of Indigenous people of the South was underway, Choctaw leader Levi Colbert asked if the "spirit of liberality and equality which distinguishes the United States from all the Empires" was merely "jealousy and defence of their own particular rights, an unwillingness to be oppressed themselves?" The answer to his question reveals a foundational American irony. Independence from colonial rule has often meant not an absence of tyranny, but the opposite: the right to practice tyranny in the name of the universal philosophical category—freedom.[11]

By design, the US Constitution limits federal authority to very specific levers of action. Seen by many at the time as having gone too far in centralizing power and undermining local democracy, the Constitution was created amid widespread paranoia about conspiracy, corruption, and political "enslavement" to tyranny. In Jeffersonian democracy, government was to be small, local, and participatory, a source of vigilance against the abhorrent tendencies of political corruption, centralization, and aristocracy. The real source of what legal scholars call "police power"—the ability to regulate and enforce behavior in the name of the welfare of the people—rests officially with the various states. The federal government is therefore consciously designed, and popularly understood, to be a thing of restraint, while state and local governments are given broad latitude of action. Most key political questions have historically been left to the states, and some of the most dramatic episodes in political history, as George Wallace knew from his time in Barbour County, occur when federal power threatened the autonomy of local and state authority.[12]

Crucial to understanding how freedom works in the American context is grasping what James Madison called the "compound republic." A productive tension, he believed, was built into the American system in which local, state, and federal arenas form an integral, political whole. What scholars flippantly call "the state" is really a messy geopolitical clash over order, rights, and freedoms. James Bryce, the nineteenth-century analyst of the American state, described the compound republic as being "like a great factory wherein two sets of machinery are at work, their revolving wheels apparently intermixed, their bands crossing each other, yet each set doing its own work without touching or hampering the other." Yet the set of machines did not simply touch but crashed, their gears grinding and gnashing, the belts flying off, and, in the case of the Civil War, the spinning energies of the flywheels violently smashing into each other. *Freedom's Dominion* is not so much a community study of Barbour County as it is a close analysis of those conflicting kinetic energies of the compound republic as they unfold in one place over time.[13]

If a political entity has legitimacy in the eyes of its citizens, its coercive powers are accepted—or at least tolerated. Citizens grant authority to ruling powers to maintain civil order, to provide for the well-being of the people, to regulate social and economic behavior, and to defend against outsiders. Faith in a government's legitimacy and reciprocal obligations between state and citizen emerge alongside other bonds of social cohesion, such as tradition, ideology, shared experience, ethnic purity, or others. In the case of the American compound republic, where Washington's power was designed to be limited, such bonds often find strongest expression at local and state levels of government in opposition to federal authority.

As Wallace exclaimed so fervently, when the federal government opposed visions of local white sovereignty, it grew to become an enemy—even *the* enemy—of "the people." Federal power became the looming usurper, the illegitimate actor, the violator of white American freedom. The federal government rarely took an unambiguous stand for minority citizenship, but frequently it stepped in just enough to whip white elites into a frenzy of racialized anti-statism that spread rapidly and wildly under the banner of freedom. When rare victories for nonwhite peoples happened, they often required tremendous interventions by federal authority that did, arguably, break with the limits enshrined in constitutional tradition that men like George Wallace were trying to defend.

Even the hint of federal authorities mustering their forces could breed zealotry and violence. Should federal power even minimally imperil local capacity to, for example, appropriate Indigenous lands, exploit chattel slavery, or otherwise reorder labor and race relations, it posed a direct threat to local (white) autonomy. Federal authority, when it meddles in local affairs, is cast as an illegitimate source of coercive power that must be resisted—sometimes with deadly force. More often than not, federal power was egregiously positioned against the interests of nonwhite people, except when it was not, and then invocations of white freedom grew ever more strident. The local struggle against the illegitimacy of federal power then took the form of a dynamic racialized anti-statism: an ever-evolving catalyst in the political chemistry of American freedom.

In many histories of local resistance to racial reform, the idea of "white supremacy" is deployed to explain the prevailing state of affairs, the motives of the local powerbrokers, as well as deep historical roots and present-day echoes alike. *Freedom's Dominion* seeks a more specific and grounded explanation given that the overt use of the phrase "white supremacy" was not popularly adopted until well after the Civil War. The Barbour County story shows the deeper and more continuous and evolving ideological and rhetorical underpinnings of white domination. Those defending racism, land appropriation, and enslavement portrayed themselves, and even understood their own actions, as part of a long history of freedom. This is also why they were quick to pick up the fight of their ancestors against federal authorities who dared interfere in the practice of their birthright of freedom, the most American of creeds.

The heroes of this tale are the actors on the ground who battled to achieve better lives for themselves and their families—and a more just union for all. The protagonist, however, is a body much maligned on both the left and the right: the federal government. Often it was the only hope there was for those seeking to preserve their land, to win the vote, to avoid being lynched, or ultimately to gain their civil rights. Not surprisingly, this protagonist turns out to be clay-footed, two-faced, weak-kneed, and often ineffectual. For local movements for democracy to win and flourish, however, required the backing of the federal government—often including the use of force. The terrible fact is that what some feared and still denounce as "bayonet rule" is what others simply called citizenship. The argument here is that defending the civil and economic rights of all people cannot be left to local enforcement. "A government without force," argues the Reconstruction historian Gregory P. Downs, "means a people without rights."[14]

Freedom's Dominion is a story of rough continuity, recurring conflict, and ideological regeneration across time in one place. In Barbour County, freedom served as an ideological scaffolding that supported most every form of domination discussed in this book—Indian land dispossession and removal, mob political violence, lynching, convict labor, Jim Crow, resistance to school integration, and the fight against voting rights. Whether popular wisdom emphasized the social, political, or economic dimensions of white freedom, the patriarchal masculinity inherent in what Patterson calls the "freedom to limit the freedom of others" remained constant and powerful. It still does. To explore the varied expressions of freedom within this broad continuity, this book focuses on four periods of racialized antistatism and conflict with federal power. Each unfolds as an epic unto itself—with theft, riots, killings, political intrigue, corruption, and war.[15]

In the first period, federal troops attempted to remove illegal white intruders from Creek Indian land that had been guaranteed by a federal treaty in the 1830s. From the very birth of Barbour County, the federal government's attempt to prevent white settlers from invading the Creek Nation made it the literal enemy of white settlers' freedom to access land: the core of the Jeffersonian ideal. *Preventing* the theft of Native lands seemed to contradict much of the essence of Jacksonian-era politics—even if those protections were designed to rein in and control white freedom in the strategic interest of promoting a long-term strategy of land dispossession. The federal defense of Native American rights against white intruders, argued one speculator at the time, struck "at the very root of the tree of Liberty" by subverting the interests of the states and the rights of "the people." Within the compound republic, a vigorous alliance emerged between the newly created county and the young state of Alabama; together they squared off against the federal government. The result was talk of nullification, secession, and even civil war in the name of preserving the freedom to dominate local lands.[16]

The story then shifts to Reconstruction in the 1860s and 1870s, when US troops backed the right of African Americans to vote in one of the most important stories of federal intervention in US history. It took unprecedented military, legal, and political reach for the federal government to ensure the rights of freedmen through laws and amendments that could not have passed outside of the wartime emergency and extraordinary postwar political opportunities. Reconstruction did work when it worked, but it failed when the political and military power necessary to back the rights of the freed people wavered. The subsequent white assault on the federal guarantee of Black voting in Barbour County was understood as fighting the "flagrant and dangerous invasion of the *ancient conservative principles of personal liberty and free government*." The result was the bloody "redemption," as white Southerners called it, of their freedom in the form of a murderous coup against Black voters.[17]

The third section begins after Reconstruction, with federal power in repose. Here the consequences of federal inaction become glaring, and this book reinterprets themes like convict leasing, lynching, the Jim Crow state constitution, and labor relations within the framework of a local white sovereignty largely unconstrained by federal power. Here was the highpoint of overt claims of white supremacy in some of its most naked and least contested forms. Access to white power, though hardly economic resources, was redistributed from the plantation elite to all white people in the Jim Crow era. With the coming of the New Deal, however, Southerners willingly accepted monies from the new federal bureaucracy but kept a watchful eye on incursions into the Southern racial order. The growth of the federal government lay the groundwork for white Southerners' later abandonment of the Democratic Party as it attempted to protect the citizenship of African American people. The governor from Barbour County in the 1940s, for instance, fought fair employment practices for African Americans, proclaiming, "When the government at Washington, thru* its executive, or judicial branches, undertakes to force upon a State a standard which it does not and will not accept, it is a denial of freedom."[18]

Finally, the book turns to the modern civil rights era and the blinkered but crucial federal support for civil and voting rights that tipped the balance of power in the compound republic, thus attempting to nationalize both the Bill of Rights and the right to vote. White

* Author's note: I have preserved the original spellings of words, which are often unorthodox or noncontemporary, as they appear in the source documents. For the sake of clarity, in a few cases I mark such a spelling with "[*sic*]" where it might otherwise appear as if it were a typo or error. Whether marked or not, all unorthodox spellings have been checked against the original to ensure accuracy.

people of Barbour County found clever ways to fight the integration of schools and thwart the rising power of the right to vote among its people. As local African Americans finally began to see dependable federal enforcement of their rights, George Wallace rose from the backwoods of Barbour County to deliver his fight against the scourge of federal power to the national stage. In so doing, he tapped into generations of concerns that local white people's freedom was yet again under siege by federal powers.

Wallace transformed national politics by making his version of racialized anti-statism into a central component of modern conservative politics. All citizens across the nation, he urged, needed to enroll in the fight against federal courts, federal troops, federal economic planning, and federal political control. He understood the national draw of this local problem as early as his 1963 inaugural. "And you native sons and daughters of old New England's rock-ribbed patriotism, and you sturdy natives of the great Mid-West, and you descendants of the far West flaming spirit of pioneer freedom," he intoned, "we invite you to come and be with us, for you are of the Southern mind, and the Southern spirit, and the Southern philosophy[;] you are Southerners too and brothers with us in our fight." Regardless of where one called home, Wallace claimed, "the heel of tyranny does not fit the neck of an upright man."

When the governor concluded his address, he declared that the South had to lead the nation back toward Jeffersonian values, back toward states' rights, back toward freedom. He knew not just the South but the entire nation yearned for a revival of its freedom. "We, together," Wallace concluded, "can give courageous leadership to millions of people through this nation who look to the South for their hope in this fight to win and preserve our freedoms and liberties."

These stories are not simply regional tales lost in the dark, overgrown thickets of the past. They are quintessentially American histories—inescapably local, yet national in theme, scope, and scale. As George Wallace made clear with his inaugural litany of Barbour County places, the very specificity of his home opened onto elements of everyplace. There, on the ground, broad theories dissolve into the everyday complexities and contradictions of lived experience that make up this story. What we learn is that federal power has proven itself, quite consistently, by design and by practice, to be inadequate to the basic claims of citizenship of its people. One of the great ironies of American history is that federal power has a far better record of breeding anti-statists than it does disciplining them. As a result, the battles being waged today echo those fought two hundred years ago. In each of these fights, we see immense effort required even for small victories that have been too often defeated, erased, or rolled back by time. This book stands as an argument for a vigorous, federally enforced model of American citizenship that is not afraid to fight the many incarnations of the freedom to dominate. To do so requires changing our story of federal power, democracy, and American freedom.

Like many good tales, this one begins when a stranger comes to town. A single rider approached a village of white settlers in the summer of 1832. The white residents had seized prime land on a bluff overlooking the Chattahoochee River, known among the Native Americans as Eufaula Town. There the white intruders had built a settlement in violation of a federal treaty signed with Creek Indians. The interlopers drove the Eufaula Creeks from their ancestral home, seizing their crops and depriving them of their means of subsistence.

The approaching rider was a federal marshal. Before he left, he burned the white settlement down.

BOOK ONE

Land

CHAPTER ONE

Marshal Crawford's Orders

UNITED STATES MARSHAL Robert L. Crawford might have ridden tall and commanding in the saddle, the crispness of his uniform and the curve of his hat defying the soggy July humidity of southeastern Alabama. Or perhaps he traveled slumped over on his horse, wilted by the heat and defeated by the thankless job of a US Marshal trying to keep federal order in the rough and frenzied land grab known as "Alabama Fever." It's not hard to imagine him stealing an occasional nip from a flask to dull the misery of it all, growling outbursts of rage against the Lord and the entire American experiment as he patrolled the Federal Road that sliced through the swampy tribal lands of the Creek people. For all we know, he proudly embodied the power granted to him as an extension of federal authority in the Old Southwest, responding to the call of service and public virtue in Jacksonian America. Like many in the US Marshals Service at the time, however, he probably simply enjoyed a ripe plum of federal patronage, possibly procured through his father, a judge down in Mobile, and pursued his federal position with vigor and professionalism.

Truth is, the historical archive reveals little as to what sort of person Marshal Robert L. Crawford might have been. We do know that, in the spring of 1832, the United States War Department gave him a difficult, probably impossible, task that he pursued with impressive diligence. His superiors in Washington sent him into battle to pursue the federal government's reputation and good faith, "well knowing that your feelings will prompt you to aid the oppressed."[1]

The "oppressed" in this case were the Creek people. His orders were to protect the Indians with "vigilance and energy" from the onslaught of white intruders pouring into Native lands in eastern Alabama, then known officially as the Creek Nation. Those orders outright opposed the land-grabbing frenzy that infected and defined Jacksonian America. Sent neither to remove nor to relocate the Indigenous people, Marshal Crawford had been dispatched to do the near impossible: drive white trespassers out of a five-million-acre crescent of land in eastern Alabama that, by federal treaty, still belonged to the Creek people. "The Indians must be protected, and the white trespassers must be driven off," the War Department ordered.[2]

After a generation of genocidal war, President Andrew Jackson himself sent down the directive to defend the terms of the Treaty of Cusseta and push white intruders out of the Creek Nation. This was an area roughly the size and shape of New Jersey, set aside specifically for the Muscogee Creek people. The land hugged the western flank of the Chattahoochee, a river that formed the boundary between Georgia and Alabama.

In an age defined by the deportation, expulsion, and extermination of the Native American people, Crawford was sent to stem one of the fiercest tides of human migration in world history. The opposition he would face from the clamoring hordes of white intruders would, in the long run, destroy Crawford's will. Whatever "feelings" he may have had for the "oppressed" at the start of his job descended into despair about the federal government's capacity to control the freedom-loving white land grab in the Creek Nation. Neither he nor his superiors knew, or could even imagine, that they were launching a century of fighting over the nature and reach of federal power in Barbour County.

Crawford's orders were aggressive and clear. "I am directed by the President," wrote Secretary of War Lewis Cass to Crawford in April

1832, "to instruct you to repair to the district, ceded by this treaty, and give notice to all [intruding] persons, except those, allowed by the treaty to remain till their crops are gathered, to remove within as short a period as practicable, having due regard to their local position, and other circumstances." The length of time granted to the intruders to pack up and get out, "you will fix, and publickly make known." All the white intruders on Creek land were to be gone by that fall.[3]

"In the execution of this delicate trust I recommend to you to be as conciliatory, as may be compatible with the object to be attained," wrote Secretary Cass. "Apply force only when absolutely necessary and then after having fully explained to the parties their own duties, the rights of the Indians, the obligation of the government, and the instructions you have received." There would be no punishment beyond eviction from the Creek Nation. "When a person is removed beyond the boundary line," he directed, "he will be left entirely free." In contrast to Cass's naively clinical directions, Crawford's time in southeastern Alabama gave him the sense that the situation was volatile and confusing—a place in which it was "frequently impossible to arrive at the facts."[4]

That spring, Marshal Crawford published notice in three newspapers, setting the public date for removal of the white trespassers as July 15, 1832. By that date, he declared, all whites had to evacuate the Creek Nation, with the exception of those who had not directly stolen their lands from the Indians. Those intruders squatting between Creek developments could remain until their crops had been harvested. Then they too had to evacuate the region. As the secretary of war explained, Crawford just had to make it clear to all concerned parties "the obligations of the government, and the earnest hope of the President"; this should be enough to "induce every citizen to remove within the time prescribed."[5]

Should moral suasion fail to pry European Americans off Native American lands, the secretary of war also placed the federal troops at Fort Mitchell, some forty miles up the river, at Marshal Crawford's disposal. However, the civic virtue of the people, he seemed to believe, would be sufficient to carry the day. "I will not permit myself to doubt, but that the valuable cession made by the Indians, and the publick faith, which has been plighted to them, will furnish motives sufficiently powerful to produce this desirable result." Local imperatives would have to give way to the national government's "solemn obligations with the Creeks," Cass explained, as "every principle of justice and good faith" on the part of the federal government was at stake.[6]

Secretary of War Cass could not begin to fathom the obstacles in Crawford's path, though the marshal already sensed what was coming. "Removal of these few would be attended with considerable expence, and rumors to them," Crawford warned the secretary in the understated tone of official correspondence of the nineteenth century. Driving hundreds or even thousands of white intruders from the five million acres along the Chattahoochee could prove overwhelming—and dangerous. Perhaps Crawford had seen a certain foreshadowing of his own fate up in neighboring Pike County. There, a local grand jury indicted the commandant of the US garrison at Fort Mitchell, one Major Philip Wager, for issuing a proclamation demanding that all white persons failing to produce permits or not married to Indians were to leave Creek lands in fifteen days. The tension was already sharp between intruders, bolstered by an unruly democratic spirit and protected by both state and local governments, and federal authority supported by an armed force it was loath to use. Crawford, who stood between the intruders and some of the most valuable land in the world at the time, most likely figured it was about to get a whole lot worse.[7]

Crawford began his work in a place commonly known by its Muscogee Creek name, Eu-fau-la Town. It was one hundred and fifty feet above the banks of the Chattahoochee River, whose waters passed by on their way to Apalachicola Bay and into the Gulf of Mexico. Between the site's access to global markets and some of the finest cotton growing soil in the world, the little spot proved precious to white invaders. The southern boundary of the Creek Nation sliced diagonally right through Barbour County, with Eufaula at the lower tip. That made the tiny settlement a good geographic point to begin a sweep northward to rid the region of intruders.

Creek villages tended to be tidy operations, typically close to the types of moving waters for which the Anglos renamed them from their native Muscogee. The many Creek towns in Alabama and Georgia followed similar layouts. Each had a central gathering place surrounded on four sides with open-air cabins staked out in cardinal order. Each was lined with benches, which helped foster the town squares, or *talwas*, as places of civic and commercial life, where trading, games, lounging, and socializing took place. Public ceremonies, political decisions, and the meeting of dignitaries all happened in the square. Many satellite communities of kin living in compounds scattered widely around the township supported and looked to the *talwa*, which comprised the primary point of loyalty and political life for the loose, even fragmented, confederacy of Creek peoples.[8]

Upon arrival in Eufaula in July 1832, Crawford found those tidy squares overtaken by "some of the most lawless and uncouth men I have ever seen. Some of them refugees from the state of Georgia and for whom rewards are offered." The white intruders, Crawford reported, had not only "taken the Indian lands from them & burnt or destroyed their houses & corn, but did violence to their person." They had whipped and beaten the Creek people. Stolen their lands. Forced them to flee into the forest, leaving them in desperate shape, scattered forty and fifty miles away from their homes. Whatever ambivalence the marshal may have had about his mission dissolved into disgust upon confronting the white ruffians. "The extreme hostility existing between the Indians & these intruders forbid a compromise of any kind taking place," he reported back to Washington; "nothing but absolute expulsion would do them." Crawford quickly recognized the job was too big for one person. Figuring that "rough men, required rough treatment," he called upon a detachment of federal troops from Fort Mitchell.[9]

The intruders' belligerent "threats & menaces" only stiffened Crawford's resolve, until, in the sweltering heat of a hazy hot July, he ordered federal troops to lay torches to the white settlement. They burned a number of cabins and a particularly large warehouse, presumably for the cotton riches the whites hoped to produce, that was still under construction. Other cabins he ordered torn down. The Eufaula Creeks even requested that Crawford burn their own cabins, which the intruders had stolen and occupied, to ensure that the interlopers would have neither motivation nor means to retake the hamlet. The marshal not only returned the land to the Natives, he went so far as to force the return of the land taken *between* various Creek plots spread around the *talwa*, land the treaty originally ruled should remain in the intruders' hands until after the harvest, at which time they should be expelled from the region. Crawford's exasperated men kicked them out, however, then turned the existing crops, already coming in strong at midsummer's height, over to the Creek people.[10]

For a moment in the summer of 1832, as the sun beat through the smoky haze and flames of buildings burning the moisture out of the sticky Alabama air, it appeared to be the end of the intruders' settlement in Eufaula. The partisans of a virulent local freedom, hungry for land, wasted little time in reorganizing to defy federal authority and take back what was "theirs."

When news spread that the federals burned the town, political melodrama, rumors of savagery, and demands for revenge boiled up around the state. Using Alabama's official new name of the town, the headlines of the *Enquirer* newspaper of nearby Columbus, Georgia, blared, "Storm, Capture, and Burning of Irwinton!!!" The paper claimed a fight with the federals was now imminent and reported rumors that the "independent freemen" of the settlement had equipped 140 "brave and haughty settlers of the youthful town" to fight the government's intrusion on the freedom of whites to settle the land. A "night of commotion and gloom" ended with dawn revealing a "town deserted and desolate" after Crawford's actions: "The few remaining stragglers who had lingered behind to preserve some valuable piece of property from destruction, and those who, in their anxiety and impatience to be off, overloaded their wagons, and were lodged on the side of the adjoining steep were kindly accelerated to an eminence, from whence they saw their devoted town fall a prey to the devouring flames." No mention was made of those who fled into the woods, vowing to return in defiance of the federal troops. "This terminated the storm, capture, and burning of Irwinton," the paper lamented in the summer of 1832. "Short its existence, but brilliant its history." The maudlin history of white victimization at the hands of federal troops had begun.[11]

William Irwin, the planter, military officer, speculator, and politician for whom Irwinton was named, complained directly to the secretary of war about the federal assault on local rights. The burned warehouse had not been near any Indian improvements, he argued, making the troops' attack on it a federal crime against the people. The citizenry, in fact, issued a warrant for the arrest of the military officers who performed that dastardly deed.

Unsubstantiated stories and outright lies quickly followed. Irwin alleged that a federal soldier, acting on orders, ran his bayonet through the sheriff, which "sevearly wounded one of the best Citerzins of that County." The sheriff, Irwin pointed out, "Is a man of Good Reputation and the Ground Is stained with his blood." The apocryphal story probably came from the Montgomery paper, which repeated the fact that the small hamlet was set on fire but included the claim that when a warrant was issued against the federal marshal, the issuing deputy sheriff "was pierced by a Federal bayonet." There is no evidence that this happened, but the rumor of martyrdom in defense of the state of Alabama against federal intervention was a perfect set piece of political theater that would be restaged for generations to come.[12]

Despite the local uproar, officials in Washington City backed Crawford's actions in Eufaula and elsewhere. The War Department commended the marshal, explaining that they found "nothing to censure, but much to approve, in the manner in which you have executed the duties entrusted to you." His superiors unfazed by the local uproar, Crawford proceeded in his quixotic efforts to stem the flood of land thieves.[13]

No sooner had Crawford begun his march northward from Eufaula than he reported, with considerable frustration, that the intruders "returned with a reenforcement," this time "armed, and threatening to defend themselves." The intruders seized the land that had been returned to the Creeks and swore to fight anyone who tried to take it again. The county sheriff also showed up to serve writs of trespass on Marshal Crawford, the commanding officer of the troops, and the Creeks who remained on the land. The Creeks remained at the mercy of the whites. The Eufaula chief explained that just a few weeks after removal, the invading European Americans forced the Creeks to hide in the woods with no means of subsistence and no possibility of justice from the state of Alabama.[14]

Crawford grew impatient, realizing that if Washington allowed any exceptions to the law they would face the "utter impossibility" of keeping large numbers of intruders at bay. In December 1832, six months after his burning of Eufaula, Crawford demanded more troops. A lot more. "It is entirely useless to go into the [Creek] nation with a less number than two hundred men," he wrote to Washington; "they might possibly be driven off with less, but they would be back, before the troops had gone five miles."[15]

Meanwhile, the reconstituted white intruders of Eufaula pleaded directly to the secretary of war to stop their removal. Tensions between Natives and whites, they argued, were exaggerated. The settlers merely occupied a port (a "deposite") that served the "indispensable" economic interests of all people—not just the intruders—and the land had very little agricultural value to the Creeks but tremendous cotton producing potential for the whites. To this, they added a jurisdictional argument: the state of Alabama had extended its purview over the Creek Nation, and that jurisdiction protected the legality of the intruders' land claims. The state had appointed commissioners to stake out the square mile of the town, and that, the citizens believed, "fully authorized" them to occupy and develop the land. Because of this, they "humbly petition your honor to suspend orders for our removal from this village." Backed by the the people and government of Alabama and in ready defiance of federal authority and Crawford's efforts, the new town sprang back to life like cotton flowers in the spring.[16]

The problem, as even President Andrew Jackson would later admit, was that to allow any intrusion was to create a dangerously porous boundary that could turn a trickle of white settlers into a flood. As the sword of federal authority in the Southern District of Alabama, Marshal Crawford understood the dilemma better than anyone. As he pointed out to the secretary of war, "I found it impossible to make any limit to intrusion." If one settler was let in for any reason, it meant the entire mission of halting violations of treaty rights was vulnerable. "I conceive an intrusion in part, to be an intrusion in the whole," Crawford explained in terms that echoed the Creek chiefs' increasingly frantic appeals to the federal government.[17]

The Treaty of Cusseta, signed just weeks before Crawford had received his orders, was just one of many agreements that followed Jackson's Indian Removal Act of 1830. That act allowed the government to exchange land west of the Mississippi for Native lands in the East. The terms of the Treaty of Cusseta essentially privatized the five million acres along the Chattahoochee known as the Creek Nation, premised on giving individual plots of land to the Creek people. Indian families would get their plots legally deeded to them, but the hope in Washington was that the Creeks would sell their lands and move west of the Mississippi—Jackson and Cass's undeniable main objective.

Yet for the Indigenous population, the core of the Treaty of Cusseta was not the "opportunity" to move west as advocated by President Jackson and Secretary Cass, but Washington's commitment to drive white intruders out of the region and to prevent any land transfers or in-migration for five years. The dual nature of the treaty was such that, in addition to inducements to move west, there was an alternative plan: the guarantee of private parcels of land to the Indigenous population.

Under the Treaty of Cusseta, a federal survey was to be performed, and then individual allotments of 320 acres were to be granted to each Creek family (or orphan) and 640 acres to each tribal chief and town headman who selected to remain in the nine-county area known as the Creek Nation. The plots that Washington promised would be legally deeded plots, in Anglo-style land ownership, which could be worked or sold as the owners saw fit. In addition, annual annuities would be paid to the Creeks for twenty years. Moreover, the treaty guaranteed that the Creek people would have *five years of federal protection* from white intruders or land sales while they organized and prepared for their transition from a tribal to a privatized land structure. In order to check the swindlers and intruders, all land sales would not only be blocked for five years, but then they could only be conducted through an agent appointed by the president himself. The treaty offered the hope of remaining on the land, but at the cost of the end of Creek national sovereignty.[18]

The last Creek strongholds east of the Mississippi. The Muscogee Creek people were driven from the eastern portion of this region in 1825 under the Treaty of Indian Springs, a deal so fraudulent and corrupt that the Creek National Council vowed never to give up any more land to white settlers. After the Treaty of Cusseta (1832), the Creek struggled against an onslaught of white intruders to preserve their right to remain in the parcel west of the Chattahoochee. This region includes Barbour County at the southern tip.

Secretary of War Lewis Cass and President Andrew Jackson, who had personally invited the Creeks to Washington that spring to negotiate the Treaty of Cusseta, were the main architects of the land privatization scheme. They believed that once the allotments were surveyed and deeded, the Creeks would sell them for a good price and move west. Both saw the treaty as an equitable move that accomplished two goals: it honored remaining Creek land claims and would eventually build toward their master plan to relocate as many Indians as possible west of the Mississippi. The government banked on the idea that the only way for the Creeks to preserve their tribal traditions and withstand the economic pressure of the settlers would be to move west. It was, as one historian put it, a "market-based removal" treaty for the transition to white domination of the region.[19]

Though the agreement was a long way from perfect in the eyes of the Creeks, the federal promise to remove the whites, transfer ownership to individual Creeks, and protect the region from intruders for five years stood out as a welcome respite from decades of conflict and war. It seemed to many to be the Creek people's last hope. Some semblance of Creek community and culture might survive in eastern Alabama—if the federal authorities proved willing to enforce the land privatization scheme of their own design.

Lacking legal capacity for self-governance under the laws of the state of Alabama, the chiefs understood their position perfectly. "Our only alternative is protection [provided by] the United States." The more desperate their circumstances became, the more they looked to the federal government to stop the white flood and recognize their rights. The worst fate for the Creeks would be if they were left at the mercy of the wild and unruly new state of Alabama. Short of a full-scale Creek war on the white population, which most recognized would end horribly, the survival of the Creeks depended upon the extension of federal authority over them and their land. State jurisdiction would mean the end of the Creek Nation.[20]

In practice, the treaty set the terms of conflict for the next five years. European Americans saw the agreement as the beginning of open season for seizure and colonization, part of their Jacksonian destiny under the Indian Removal Act. Native Americans believed it to be a five-year, federally enforced respite from white intrusion, followed by legal transfer of land ownership to tribe members. The rub between the Natives' legal truth, weakly backed by the United States government, and the Americans' ideological fiction, enforced by the state of Alabama, would eventually mean war.

In the buildup to the treaty, Secretary of War Cass tried desperately to convince the Creeks that they would be much happier running their own affairs west of the Mississippi. In a letter to the Creek leaders, he noted honestly that their "condition is deplorable," "health and morals ruined," and that they had become "debased, indolent, and improvident." The white invaders had deprived them of land and thinned their game, leaving the Creek people "absolutely starving, or subsisting upon the bark of trees." All of this was true. Their best choice, as he saw it, was to head west where they would be undisturbed, where they could run their own affairs, where they could "flee from the evils of your present position and to seek comfort and plenty." Yet, Cass affirmed, that's just how he saw it. The choice was theirs. "If you wish to go, every liberality shall be extended to you. Money, provisions, agricultural instruments, domestic animals, schools, teachers, in short every thing which can... [provide] assurance of permanent prosperity." "But if you choose to remain, so be it. No one will compel you to go, no force will be applied. You are as free to stay as we are."[21]

To the great frustration of Jackson and Cass, the vast majority of the Creek people chose to stay. What federal authorities in Washington did not understand was that Cass's list of misery was exactly what made the American Indians want to stay under federal protection, not uproot and go west. The Indigenous people of Alabama saw the treaty as their last best hope to preserve what remained of their lands, their community, and their traditions. Privatization seemed to be a tidy solution, but Jackson and Cass had no idea that it would create the opposite reaction of their desire: it would deepen the sense of hope of remaining home. Despite the challenge to tribal ways of life, the individualized land ownership scheme of the Treaty of Cusseta held out the promise that some elements of their lives might remain as they had. At bare minimum, with a five-year transition period, they could think, prepare, and organize for a new future.[22]

Yet the excitement among European Americans generated by the treaty foreclosed even a market-based transition period. Whites, choosing to believe that the treaty ended sovereignty and opened up the Creek Nation to settlement rather than closing it with federal protection, flooded across the border in a frenzied land grab that defied federal promises made to the Creeks. This was not a unified horde of whiteness, however, but a crazy quilt of competing interests among affluent speculators, on-the-make settlers, and poor roughs in search of a plot to call their own. Each saw land as central to their liberty, and federal authority and Indian rights as antagonistic to their goals. Each sought refuge under the mission of the state of Alabama, which sided with them and against the Indians and federal power. Each wanted the federal government and its protection of Native Americans out of the way.

Without bothering to wait for the federal census or the survey, speculators sent land agents in with large supplies of whiskey and cheap goods. The agents pushed the Indians to buy on credit, often taking land title as security and betting that the Natives would be forced to sell off their allotments to pay their debts. Speculators opened hundreds of grog shops along the Chattahoochee, ultimately destroying hope, fortitude, resistance, and Creek land ownership. The regulation of whiskey was beyond federal purview, Cass argued, though the federal marshals recognized that curtailing alcohol was imperative for the Creeks' survival. Using every angle imaginable to get Native land, including ploys as simple as having imposters pose as local Creeks in order to sign away lands they did not own, the speculators ran roughshod over federal promises to protect the Creeks. The Native Americans had no standing in local or state courts and found themselves swindled at every turn. Soon, the land rush Crawford had been sent to stop became a torrent.

The most insidious aspect of the swindles was the land companies' use of African American slaves as interpreters who would receive rewards for finding unsold allotments. As one government agent put it, the slaves were sent after land titles, "to hunt the reservees down like malefactors or wild beasts, and to follow them incessantly wheresoever they might retreat to avoid importunity and persecution, and never cease hampering them, till from mere disgust, not a few have committed suicide, and many more have sold for very inadequate prices." By using slaves as fronts for their thievery, the speculators insulated themselves legally. Enslaved people, lacking citizenship standing, could not legally testify even if wrongdoings managed to make it into the courts.[23]

Reports of beatings, theft, burning of property, killings, kidnapping of Indian wives in order to obtain land rights, and the "floating" of legal land rights from one person to another without permission all plagued the good marshal's removal efforts. Indebtedness crippled the Creeks' capacity to do anything—including moving west. As one of the census takers in the area reported, "Whenever a party of Indians shall be ready to emigrate, bail writs, under the laws of Alabama, will be served upon almost every head of a family." He continued: "The jails of Alabama will be full of Indians, or the Indians will have to surrender their reservations" as well as anything else "they may possess which is of any value, to release themselves from custody." The plague of whiskey made it all the more horrible and complicated. The choices were obvious but not easy. The federal government either had "to remove them, protected by an armed force" or drain their coffers paying endless claims ginned up by the intruders. The Creek people swamped the federal government with complaints of intruders' land frauds, while the intruders wrote a deluge of complaints about Marshal Crawford's violation of their rights.[24]

Meantime, the Creek Council laid out their desperate situation to their only ally, the United States War Department. "Instead of our situation being relieved, as was anticipated," the council explained, "we are distressed in a tenfold manner. We are surrounded by the whites with there fields & fences. Our lives are in jeopardy. We are dayly threatened for fear we should make choice of there improvements, we are prevented from building new Houses or clearing new fields. We have for the last six months lived in fire, yet we have borne it with patience. Believing our Father the President would comply on his part, what He had pledged himself to do." Even though they were "crowded with white people," "oppressed by the laws of Alabama," unable to build houses, and facing threats to their lives, they chose to stay. Although ethnically and geographically divided, the Creeks knew what they wanted: "There is not a dissenting voice among us who wish either to sell or move west of the Mississippi."[25]

The report of the chiefs in Eufaula stood out as particularly dire. In October, several months after the burning of the white settlement, local Indian Agent Major Thomas Abbott reported, "After much privation and fatigue I am about finishing the census of the heads of families . . . of the Eu-Fau-la Town of Indians." He'd met with the principal chief and a gathering of local headmen, he explained, and they had grievances they wished to convey to Washington. "They complain bitterly of the treatment they have received at the hands of the *intruders* and of the abuse which still continues to be heaped upon them." Their list of problems was "endless," and "they say they have ample testimony that their sufferings are great." A principal of the public council stated, "with much feeling," that "many had nothing now to eat and that, he was assured, without timely assistance from the government members of them must perish, for want of sustenance, of hunger." Points of fact were corroborated by many of those gathered from both observation and personal experience. "They insisted that I should write to you as their agent, immediately, with the request that without delay you would endeavor to procure for them some alleviation of their distress, by representing their conditions hopefully to the commandant of the troops at the Fort and induce him to order on some part of his force to their assistance." Starvation was imminent. "Without some such immediate protection afforded to them, before their corn is entirely taken from their fields, they say they will not have a grain left and starvation must be the inevitable consequence for they dare not now return to their dwellings, being like wild beasts hunted and driven from them."[26]

Other federal agents professed immense skepticism that anything the federal government could do at that point would win over the Native population by 1832. As John Brodnax, a trader, planter, and "Indian countryman," as the Europeans who lived closely with the Natives were called, declared, "Nothing we can say will be believed" by the Creek people. "They can no longer be persuaded to repose confidence in our promises, nor to entertain a hope of the realization of the prospects we would hold out to them. A melancholy experience of the past has instilled into them the gloom of despair for the future." Even Crawford's dramatic actions in Eufaula could not change the culture of profound mistrust among the Creeks. The Indians' position bordered on the impossible. Yet they knew, and professed, that the best—indeed only—option was to hold out hope for the federal government, which made promises it broke regularly, to defend them. Otherwise, they were left to be ransacked by waves of intruders protected by the Alabama government.[27]

Rather than bending to the will of the intruders, the War Department chose to redouble its efforts to protect the Creeks. "It is obligatory on the Government to protect the Creek Indians in the enjoyment of their land until their removal," Secretary of War Cass reiterated to Crawford. "Your best exertions are particularly required to put an end to their lawless and disgraceful practice of intrusion. The necessary military aid will therefore on your requisition be furnished for this purpose; and you will moreover cause the District Attorney to prosecute all those who shall have the temerity to return after their expulsion." This should be done "with vigilance and energy." He made clear that "the Indians must be protected, and the white trespassers must be driven off, and if possible punished in order to prevent a repetition of such illegal and reproachful conduct." These commands, the War Department emphasized, are at "the direction of the President." By the spring of 1833 the Office of Indian Affairs promised Crawford more troops "at whatever place you may direct, and to assist you in expelling intruders and preventing their return."[28]

The many battles, skirmishes, murders, and usurpations that ensued between the white settlers and the federal troops after the Treaty of Cusseta became known as the "Intruders' War." But intrusion had been going on for a very long time. Those who would build the slave-based empire of cotton capitalism were, indeed, as the Creek called them, the *Ecunnau-Nuxulgee*: "those greedily grasping after lands." And it was difficult to imagine it stopping. As white intruders poured in, "the fires of their encampments made the woods blaze in all directions," explained one observer of the migration of white people west. "The people will soon sweep over the Chattahoochee, and, after settling on the best lands in the Creek Nation, presently to be in the market, they will fill Alabama."[29]

Marshal Crawford's struggle would be the beginning of a series of federal protections, however flawed, of Creek—and later African American—people that would not be forgiven by the white population of Alabama. Even when the president, the War Department, and the Marshals Service all sided with the Creek people, the white intruders refused to tolerate the federal government's curtailing of what they militantly regarded as their rights and freedoms. White Americans did not elect General Andrew Jackson, the "people's president," to be kicked off of Indian land by Old Hickory himself.

CHAPTER TWO

Land, Liberty, and Jackson

TALL AND THIN AS an ax handle, Andrew Jackson's body must have creaked with agony upon every move. His sinewy frame carried countless injuries, large and small, festering from a lifetime of war against his two biggest enemies: the Indians and the British. His face featured a permanent scar delivered by the sword of a British officer—punishment for his boyhood resistance to being forced to clean the redcoat's boots while a prisoner during the Revolutionary War. He bore discernable scars from the smallpox he contracted while in jail for his offense—all before he was even an adult. A bullet remained lodged in his arm from a duel, and another was inoperably embedded near his heart and lungs.

Jackson's body was the corporeal archive of his pugnacious soul. The bullet caused him "violent pain" on a regular basis, with bouts of blood gurgling into his mouth, as well as probable poisoning from the ball leaking lead into his system. He could barely eat. Plagued by malaria and recurring bouts of typhoid, typhus, and dysentery, his merciless battle wounds scarred his internal organs as much as his outward appearance. His teeth were painfully rotten. Given the mercury he took to cure his malarial fevers, and his faith in "bleeding"—that is, removing bad humors by letting blood out of the body—his cures were probably as deadly as the frontier battles he fought. Making matters even worse, when he took office in March 1829, his heart was still broken by the passing of his beloved wife, Rachel, that December.[1]

Jackson grew from a backwoods orphan into a man of tremendous sorrow, anger, and determination. American voters, excited by the democratic and territorial expansion Jackson embodied and fought for, raised him up as the champion of the people—the white people. His rhetoric incendiary and manners crude, he won as the candidate of the frontier common folk, and his victory relocated the geographic center of American politics south and westward. The franchise expanded state by state to include almost all white men, those with property and without, allowing Jackson to finally displace that intellectual, Harvard-educated, Yankee, son of a president John Quincy Adams, whom Jackson and his supporters believed had stolen the previous election from him in the notorious "Corrupt Bargain" of 1824.

In Jackson's undisputed victory in 1828, the entire South went for the general as did most of the mid-Atlantic. He won every county in Alabama on the promise of redeeming the nation's freedom from the republic's political aristocracy. He had, after all, been responsible for the creation of the state in the first place. He unleashed a new nationalist, expansionist form of popular white democracy. The Jacksonian vision was about access to land, which meant access to opportunity and equality. He built upon Jefferson's "Empire of Liberty," the exploitation of an expansive western space into which democratic freedoms would unfold. It would turn out that even the old Indian fighter would prove too cautious in the face of the voracious popular hunger for land and the freedom it promised. The "people" dashed ahead of their leader, and the man they put in the White House turned from democratic hero to federal villain.

The press deployed various naturalistic metaphors to describe the crowds drawn to the new president's inauguration: "a mountain of heads," "a moving mass," "a stream of many tides," "like bees in the act of swarming." As Senator Daniel Webster remarked, "Persons have come five hundred miles to see General Jackson; and they really seem to think that the Country is rescued from some dreadful danger." After the ceremony, Jackson's well-wishers famously took over the White House with their drunken enthusiasm. "I never saw such a mixture," said Supreme Court justice Joseph Story. "The reign of King Mob seemed triumphant." Whether they celebrated a Democratic champion of the people or the American Caesar remained to be seen—and much debated. As Arthur J. Stansbury snorted, "It was like the inundation of the northern barbarians into Rome, save that the tumultuous tide came in from a different point of the compass."[2]

The torchlight parades for liberty, the urgent chants reverberating through the city streets, and the melodrama of the penny press became the symbols and tools of mobilization in the newly popularized democracy. The number of white male voters quadrupled between 1824 and Jackson's victory in 1828, unleashing a new, raw, and visceral emotional dimension to American politics. A belief in the causal relationship between liberty and equality—that one begot the other—became the shifting essence of republican faith. Jackson was the man for the moment: the supposed foe of privilege, the enemy of elitism, and the embodiment of the idea that freedom meant land, and land meant freedom from economic dependence on other white men. Jackson's presidency expanded the currency of white freedom to such a degree that the smallest obstacle to the forward march of liberty would be confronted in hyperbolic terms. A threat to freedom was a threat to democracy and a betrayal of the revolution or worse: the beginning of servitude of the white race—slavery being a metaphor always at the ready in the early republic. In the South, where slavery existed as both foil and foundation for freedom, the polity was even more devoted to Jackson than the rest of the nation.[3]

By the time of Jackson's inaugural, the United States was the most democratic place on Earth, but white Americans connected their liberty and sovereignty to the subjugation of others. The blend of independence and domination, freedom and sovereignty, fought for by Jacksonian whites, itself depended upon a social hierarchy. At its foundation lay an unruly subjugation of others. The rough and unruly combination was leavened with a violent victimization, as the

Jacksonians saw power and corruption moving everywhere among them, threatening their position, denying them their land, and justifying their vengeance. They sought their sovereignty and freedom beyond federal law, while, ironically, their racialized anti-statism prevented them from controlling the wild tides of the very market revolution that generated such popular and widespread anxieties.[4]

Andrew Jackson demonstrated a lifetime of determined, merciless hostility to the Native Americans who possessed the American lands that promised white liberty. His animosity was such that Indians dubbed him "Sharp Knife" and "Pointed Arrow" for his fierce battles against them. Others, who had witnessed his maniacal approach to subjugation up close, simply called him "Old Mad Jackson." Even more than his famous veto of the Bank of the United States, which held out the hollow promise of redeeming the nation from aristocratic corruption, Andrew Jackson's most important presidential act was his dogged pursuit of the bill for indian removal—his primary goal and "signature" policy.[5]

Yet Jackson was more than a simple destroyer of Native Americans and their lands. Much as he longed to push Native Americans west of the Mississippi to provide land for white settlers, another part of his thinking saw removal as a twisted act of preservation: the only policy that would ensure the Native Americans' survival against the inevitable drift toward the Euro-American domination of the eastern half of the continent. In Jackson's first annual message to Congress, he pointed out that the tribes of the Northeast were already extinct, and a similar fate was on the horizon for the southern tribes. "Humanity and national honor demand that every effort should be made to avert so great a calamity," he believed. Such arguments can also be viewed as political maneuvering, as the Indian Removal bill was not inherently popular—in fact, it generated a storm of political controversy and opposition. Jackson wanted the land foremost. And if he could allow Indians to survive out west, all the better. But the land came first.[6]

As a military leader, Jackson had occasion to police white settlers in actions akin to Marshal Robert Crawford's efforts in the Creek

Nation. From early on he showed little tolerance for white men who squatted on Native American land in violation of federal treaties. Such white "troublemakers," he believed, placed the lives of other settlers at risk and stripped Indians of faith in the treaty process. Even though he was dead set on Indian removal as his eventual goal, the means could not simply be wanton land hunger and endless frontier skirmishes. There had to be order, discipline, and a certain Jacksonian justice to the process. In part, this attitude allowed Jackson to believe the fiction that, if done properly, removal beyond the Mississippi could be achieved in a "voluntary" manner by the tribes. In part, he also fundamentally believed in authority and the rule of law, and the connection between civil and military rule—even as applied to white people. He also knew that squatters, once kicked out, tended to return unless they were fully prosecuted for their transgressions. In confronting these white "robbers," he believed his orders were "to take all persons and stock, found trespassing on the Indian Territory, and deliver them over to the civil authority for prosecution." Despite his belief in the rule of law, Andrew Jackson reserved the greatest share of his wrath for anyone who opposed Andrew Jackson.[7]

The new president's national fame originated with his victory against, nay, wholesale slaughter of, the Creek Indians in Alabama in 1814. That war began as a division within the Creek Nation over what to do about the invasion of white settlers into Georgia and Alabama—fight them or live with them. The conflict ended at a famous sharp twist in the Tallapoosa River in a horrific confrontation with Jackson known as the Battle of Horseshoe Bend.

For many years the Creeks, a loose and decentered confederation of tribes, had successfully navigated pressures from competing empires in the colonial era—Spanish, French, British, and, ultimately, American. As an alliance of towns and clans, the Creeks governed themselves and controlled the interior of their lands while European empires struggled for power on the edges of their territory. For more than two centuries, their economy had been dominated by trade in deer skins, but with the deer population exhausted, the Creeks took to settled agriculture. By the dawn of the nineteenth century, Creek life and fate had become enmeshed with competing and cooperating peoples in the area: frontier whites, Blacks, and other tribes. "The territorial borders of Creek country never formed an impermeable boundary to people, goods, animals, plants, microbes, or ideas," concludes historical anthropologist Robbie Ethridge. "All kinds of traveling parties were trekking through Creek country: pack-horse trains, Indian warriors, Indian hunting parties, white immigrants, banditti, Indian countrymen, free Blacks, Black slaves, government officials, military personnel, renegades, and herders with their animal flocks."[8]

By Jackson's time, most Creeks had settled into agricultural and ranching lifestyles, and a few lived on large farms. Some even possessed larger, slave-based plantations, but most farmed on a subsistence basis. People of European descent continued to regard them as landless wanderers, in part because of their resistance to using the plow. At the urging of the federal agent Benjamin Hawkins, the Creeks divided into two administrative groups, the Lower Town Councils and the Upper Town Councils. This codified a vague set of geographic and social divisions among what is better understood as a "decentralized, multi-ethnic polity." Their identity as a nation, however divided, slowly took form as Euro-American encroachment pushed them closer together. Moving the mail through the 1806 Federal Road that cut straight through Creek country from Fort Mitchell to Mobile quickened interactions with people of European descent, but it was cotton and land speculation that most transformed the Creeks' world. What was once a cultural crossroads became overwhelmed as European Americans flooded in, and the Creek people divided over what to do.[9]

One day in 1810 the mystical Shawnee leader Tecumseh showed up in Creek lands on his itinerant voyage to deliver a fevered message: all Native peoples needed to come together to preserve their land, reject white culture, and return to the ways before the coming of the Europeans. The Great Spirit had told him and his brother, the Prophet, that all Indians must unite against their true enemy, the white men, who were seizing their land, destroying their culture, denying their freedom, and kicking and striking them as they did "their black faces." As he spoke to the Upper Creeks about this mission, "his eyes burned with supernatural luster, and every limb and muscle quivered with emotion." His mother was a Creek, and his connection to his audience ran deep. "Brush from your eyelids the sleep of slavery, and strike for vengeance and your country!" he demanded of his cousins. "Let the white race perish!" he proclaimed. "Back whence they came, upon a trail of blood, they must be driven! . . . burn their dwellings—destroy their stock—slay their wives and children, that the very breed may perish."[10]

Tecumseh convinced many Upper Creeks of his shamanistic, messianic mission to turn back the European invasion or face the coming apocalypse. The fire of resistance burned through the villages, and a band known as the "Red Sticks" for their choice of weapon—war clubs painted red—launched a violent struggle to drive out the invading whites. Many accepted Tecumseh's belief that the Great Spirit would protect them from the white man's bullets in their holy effort to purge the land of intruders. The Red Sticks even believed themselves empowered to kill nonbelievers among their own people. This meant waging a civil war against their accommodationist brothers. The emerging Creek War therefore cut in many directions: a geopolitical struggle against white intruders and a civil war among the Creeks torn over what to do about the white invasion. The Lower Creeks, including much of the Eufaula, tended to be more enmeshed socially and economically with the white settlers and rejected the plea for violent resistance. When the War of 1812 broke out, the Creeks allied with the British, forming an intolerable alliance of enemies for Andrew Jackson.[11]

The Fort Mims massacre changed all. The Red Sticks had raided a number of white settlements, but their 1813 raid on Fort Mims in Alabama galvanized white opposition after a particularly horrific slaughter of hundreds of people—military, civilian, women, and children. While an enormous military success for the Red Sticks, the destruction of Fort Mims united white Americans on their assumption that Native Americans were bloodthirsty savages who needed to be destroyed. General Jackson rallied the troops. "Your frontier," Jackson proclaimed, "is threatened with invasion by a savage foe! Already do they advance towards your frontier, with their scalping knives unsheathed, to butcher your wives, your children, and your helpless babes. Time is not to be lost! We must hasten to the frontier, or we will find it drenched in the blood of our fellow-citizens."[12]

Events at Fort Mims launched Jackson's ruthless retaliatory campaign that sliced through the dense forests of eastern Alabama, ending at the Battle of Horseshoe Bend. The Creek rebels, believing the dramatic U-shaped loop of river offered them good defensive protection, had barricaded access to their position on the peninsula with impressively tight fortifications. It quickly became evident that what at first appeared to be an impenetrable position turned out to be a death trap. By barricading themselves on a spit of land, the beleaguered and desperate Creeks surrendered their core strategic advantages: their skills at guerrilla tactics and their capacity to melt into the forest when necessary.

The Tennessee militia, complete with idols of Americana among their ranks—including Andrew Jackson, Davy Crockett, Sam Houston, and the Cherokee leader John Ross—assaulted the barricades directly, while placing their Cherokee allies in lines on the other side of the river bend to shoot Red Stick warriors who attempted to flee across the river. Of the estimated one thousand Creek warriors, only two hundred survived the slaughter. Jackson's men are said to have kept the body count straight by cutting off and collecting the noses of the fallen Red Sticks. Soldiers later recounted making bridle reins from the flesh of their dead adversaries. "We have retaliated for the destruction of Fort Mims," General Jackson wrote in understated terms to the governor of Tennessee about one of the bloodiest battles between the United States and Native Americans in United States history.[13]

Andrew Jackson demanded a merciless and rapacious "conqueror's peace." Not surprisingly, when he called for negotiations only a small faction showed up to "negotiate." These were led by William McIntosh, who had not only opposed the Red Sticks from the start but had built substantial economic and political power by siding with the European Americans, maneuverings that earned him the contempt of the Creek majority. Jackson, rather than differentiate friend from foe, simply took land from everybody with the fraudulent claim that the signatures of McIntosh and his associates were enough to claim complete acquiescence and compliance of the Creeks.[14]

The Treaty of Fort Jackson was signed in August 1814. It stripped the Creeks of twenty-three million acres of land, including, most viciously, much of the territory of the Lower Creeks, even though they had allied with the European Americans in the conflict. Jackson justified the taking of the land as payment for an "unprovoked, inhuman, and sanguinary war," as the text of the treaty put it. When Jackson's Creek allies complained that they were being punished for the actions of a minority, he argued back that they should have stopped the Red Sticks. Creek law held that ceding land to the United States without the consent of the entire Creek Nation was punishable by death, and McIntosh would ultimately pay that price. In 1825, hundreds of Red Stick warriors surrounded his house, set it ablaze, and opened fire in unison on the notorious traitor as he fled his burning home.[15]

The enormous chunk of land taken at the Treaty of Fort Jackson filled most of the borders of modern Alabama and Georgia, except for a swath of land surrounding the Chattahoochee on both sides. Intense pressures for the Creeks to move out of Georgia culminated in the Treaty of Indian Springs in 1825, which surrendered Creek lands in Georgia, also signed under circumstances of fraud, lies, and bribery. The treaty was one of the very first issues President John Quincy Adams faced as he took office. Recognizing the fraudulent deal for what it was, he refused to honor it. Georgia governor George M. Troup, mad for states' rights, threatened military resistance if Adams did not accept the unabridged terms of the 1825 treaty. Adams backed down and avoided a regional conflict, if not a civil war.[16]

The land that remained for the Creeks was one large, five-million-acre wedge along the banks of the Chattahoochee stretching from

Eufaula northward. This had long been the heart of Creek civilization, and the watery network of tributaries that laced the area was how the Muscogee people got the Anglo name "Creeks." This was the region Marshal Crawford would be sent to defend against white intruders.[17]

Andrew Jackson followed the Battle of Horseshoe Bend with his forward march to victory against the British at the Battle of New Orleans in January 1815. Together these victories cemented his national reputation and his path to the White House. By 1820, he could look back upon a career that forced the Indians to cede much of Georgia, almost all of Alabama, much of western Tennessee, and a sizable chunk of Mississippi to the United States. His blood-soaked rise to national power helped ensure Jackson's sweep of the electoral college, and Adams out of office, in 1828.

In President Jackson's first address to Congress, he laid out his lifetime goal: the Indian Removal Act. Despite its title, the act did not directly relocate any American Indians, but it allowed the president to trade federal lands on the western side of the Mississippi, which the Native peoples would supposedly own forever, in exchange for their ancestral lands in the East. It provided a federal budget for removal, and provisions for aid and assistance in "voluntary" relocations of American Indians to US territory west of the Mississippi. But the law would require specific negotiations and treaties to convince and coerce the American Indians to actually make the move. "Our ancestors found them the uncontrolled possessors of these vast regions," Jackson proclaimed in his championing of the removal bill. The Indians receded "from river to river and from mountain to mountain" as whites swarmed their lands, "until some of the tribes have become extinct and others have left but remnants to preserve for a while their once terrible names." The United States could do better. "Humanity and national honor demand that every effort should be made to avert so great a calamity."[18]

From Jackson's perspective, the collision of peoples in the South was as dangerous as it was inevitable. Only out west, Jackson believed, far from the reach of whites, could the Indigenous peoples live "free from the mercenary influence of White men, and undisturbed by the local authority of the states." While some politicians opposed the plan on humanitarian grounds and demanded a degree of respect and equality for the Native Americans, most opponents of the act failed to come up with a cohesive alternative. Merely muddling through with the old policies of endless skirmishes and battles was no answer.[19]

The most generous read of Andrew Jackson rests on the assumption that, as Old Hickory's sympathetic biographer put it, "removal was meant to prevent annihilation, not cause it." Yet, Jackson had demonstrated a continuous pattern of being viscerally hostile to Indigenous people while claiming the mantle of caring paternalism. He was an "iron-fisted patriarch" with both slave and Native. He promulgated the idea that these were not supposed to be forced removals at bayonet point but negotiated and compensated "voluntary" relocations. Yet that idea was a myth. The horrific story of the removal of the "Five Civilized Tribes" and the Trail of Tears are the most notorious outcomes. Whatever the best version of intent may have been, as events unfolded, the "voluntary" dimensions of the treaty process devolved into violence, coercion, murder, theft, and swindle, which in turn became part of the broader pattern of what would be called today nothing short of a massive ethnic cleansing—even genocide. Contemporary observers express disdain for Jackson, but, seen in the light of Barbour County, the white citizens were even more aggressive in their freedoms to steal lands than old Hickory himself.[20]

The Indian Removal bill was a tough sell, even though most of Congress could agree that life for Native Americans in the South was brutal and murderous. Congressman Joseph Hemphill tried to tamp down Jackson's sense of urgency. Seeking to delay the removal process and send a delegation to investigate the suitability of western lands, he sought to make Congress, rather than the president, responsible for the Indian question. The history of removal thus far, he believed, justified only caution and generosity:

> Against the aborigines who once possessed this fair country, what complaint have we to make? In what degree are their scalping knives and tomahawks to be compared to our instruments of death by which we have overthrown their once powerful kingdoms, and reduced the whole fabric of their societies, with their kings and queens, to their present miserable condition? How little did they expect, three hundred years ago, that a race of human beings would come from beyond the great waters to destroy them.

The old Federalist Henry R. Storrs of New York was also suspicious of Jackson's justifications for removal. If the real reason for the bill was to give Indians a free choice in their fate, he could support it. "No philanthropic man can look at the condition to which these unfortunate people have become reduced . . . without fervently wishing that they were already removed far beyond the reach of the oppression—and, I was about to say, the example of the white man." But he knew a land grab when he saw one. "There is one plain path of honor. . . . Retrace your steps. Acknowledge your treaties. Confess your obligations. Redeem your faith. Execute your laws. Let the President revise his opinions. It is never too late to be just." Even that most famous of frontiersman and Jackson supporter, Representative Davy Crockett, felt compelled to oppose the bill, despite its popularity with his Tennessee constituents. He called it a "wicked, unjust measure" and "oppression with a vengeance." Despite eloquent opposition from the sincere and the politically motivated alike, the bill squeaked through the House with 102 voting for removal and 97 against the bill. The Senate proved more in tune with Jackson, voting 28 to 19 in favor.[21]

The Native Americans could not possibly have relished the presence of federal troops in their lands, but what remained of the Creek Nation depended upon whatever federal military presence they could obtain to protect them from the onslaught of white intruders. The US Army—and the army alone—could help the Creeks prevent a major war with intruders. The Lower Creek chiefs read the future of their survival with absolute clarity: their only source of protection would be the federal government. As they wrote to President Jackson in 1830, two years before the Treaty of Cusseta:

> Our condition as a free people is one which is to be lamented by all the Humane part of the community; We from our infancy have been taught to exercise our feelings as a *free* and *independent people*, subject only to the Laws and wishes of the United States, such a state of feelings have been our happy lott to experience from time immemorial; but it now appears to us that, that happy fate of ours, so long exercised is about to be sealed; Our white Brothers on each side of us appear to have lost all the good feeling which formerly existed, all appear to have turned their hands to crush us; Justice on our part appear to have forever fled. We can but now rely on the good faith of the proud Americans, for our future destiny, If they withdraw their strong hands from beneath us, we will inevitably fall as a Nation to rise no more. We therefore as a dependant people look to you for protection, and sincerely hope that we as a Nation may prosper and that in a coming day we may be able proudly to say that the American people were our Friend
>
> we rem yur humble & Loving children.[22]

Besieged, the Creeks sought to protect their remaining territory by signing on to one of the deals that Jackson negotiated as an instrument of the Indian Removal Act. In March 1832, a combined delegation of Upper and Lower Creeks traveled to Washington at Jackson's invitation. They parlayed with the War Department and signed their marks on the Treaty of Cusseta, thus ending collective rights to the remaining tribal lands in the state of Alabama. In "exchange," the Creeks would receive legally deeded land allotments, organized around their old town sites, in such a way as to guarantee their cultural survival, albeit under Anglo-American terms of land ownership. The treaty guaranteed the Creeks a five-year period of protection from white intrusion while they made the transition to private land ownership. For the Creeks, the essence of the treaty was bringing the federal government into the business of supporting their claims and driving out the throngs of intruders.

Even by establishing a privatized system of Creek land ownership, Jackson's goal was to push the Creeks west. European Americans would immediately purchase the land from the Natives, his prediction went. If the Indians did not sell quickly, they would have a hard time competing with the settlers once the five years of protection were up. Such competition would inevitably complete the push west. All would, theoretically, make for a peaceful transition—a perfect expression of Jackson's vision for the Indian Removal Act. But the dual agenda of simultaneously protecting Creek property rights and pushing them west of the Mississippi would prove poisonous. The two views of the treaty were at loggerheads, and the treaty failed on every single count.[23]

The president still had a secret weapon in his arsenal to pressure the Indians west: state law. Guaranteeing the property rights of individual Creeks on the state level, in effect, would end the federal legal oversight of Native American lands. "You have become citizens

"Andrew Jackson as the Great Father" (1835) mocked the president's claim to protect Native Americans while he simultaneously took their land under the Indian Removal Act. Shaped by a combination of infantilization and subjugation, Jackson's policies were a confused and bloody mess. A portrait of Lady Liberty trampling despotism, one of Jackson's favorite political themes, hangs over his shoulder.

of Alabama," Secretary of War Cass proclaimed to the Creek chiefs, a threat as much as a declaration. Across the continent, state sovereignty meant abrogating tribal governments, ending tribal courts and laws, forcing Indians to pay state taxes and serve in militias, and holding them responsible for debt—both real and fraudulent. Yet simultaneously, under state law, they would be denied the right to vote, to pursue their legal interests, or even to testify in court. State laws were soon passed forbidding Creeks from hunting, trapping, or fishing in areas in which "Indian title has been extinguished." Finally, in January 1832, when the Creeks still had the status of a nation prior to Cusseta, Alabama prohibited all Creek and Cherokee "laws, usages, and customs" as well as "council, assembly, or convention" that they believed violated the constitution and laws of the state. The only leverage for the Indians was the good faith of the federal government, and that, of course, was a complicated thing.[24]

Like African Americans in the twentieth century, the Creeks recognized "states' rights" as code for the right to rule the state. "The law, if it contains a single provision which can protect the Indian from outrage, or can redress his wrongs when they have been sustained, is, to this extent, unknown to us," the Creek chiefs argued. "We know it only as an instrument by which we are oppressed, and as opposing an insurmountable obstacle against our obtaining redress." The system was inescapable: when disputes arose, the Creeks complained to the president, and they were "told to go to the protection of the Alabama laws—to present our case before an Alabama court." Yet in state cases, the Native Americans were not even allowed to testify on each other's behalf.[25]

As the warrior, strategist, and politician behind one of the most dramatic periods of American Indian removal, Andrew Jackson certainly made a bizarre symbol of hope and faith, however guarded, for the Creek people. But it was in him, and the federal government whose official policy was to push Indigenous people west of the Mississippi, that the Creeks had to devote their faith. Despite the hostility of the courts, the military, and the executive branch, the Creeks had to believe in Jackson and the power of federal intervention—or their ability to persuade both—because that was all they had.[26]

The Treaty of Cusseta would trap the Jackson administration and the War Department in its own self-made snarls and conflicting goals. It promised protections to the Creeks but simultaneously sought their removal and left them subject to state law. On the one hand, droves of complaints from the Creeks made clear that they continued to see federal protection as the answer to their problems. Yet if the federal government acted too strongly on the Native Americans' behalf, white Alabamians might generate an anti-federal backlash that could ignite even broader sectional divisions in the young republic. Jackson needed the white settler colonization project to continue, but he wanted it to happen in an organized and disciplined way that avoided wars with Natives or a backlash with his constituencies.

The Creeks continued to understand their geopolitical position with complete clarity. They had made treaties with the US government, lost the better part of two states to bad faith on the part of the federal government, and now looked to the last remaining five-million-acre plot of land in Alabama as their last hope and salvation. "We removed the bones of our ancestors and our kindred within the property" created by the Treaty of Cusseta, they argued, "the possession of which was thus guaranteed." In the "performance of this last sad duty," they "derived a consolation from the reflection" that they had finally "fixed upon a spot where our ashes might be permitted peaceably to mingle with theirs, and from which we could not be removed." This was their last stand and, nominally, the federal government was on their side. The only humane alternative to never-ending small-scale warfare or plans for forced removal beyond the Mississippi was federal enforcement of individual land ownership and protection for the tribes in the circumscribed areas they still possessed.[27]

That's why Marshal Crawford was in Eufaula just months after the signing of the Treaty of Cusseta. His opponents—the hordes of rough settlers, elite speculators, and their agents—had other plans for the lands of the Creek Nation. Any federal force that dared hold them back would face the wrath of the freedom-loving democratic masses.[28]

CHAPTER THREE

The Killing of Hardeman Owens

In 1833, almost a year to the day after Marshal Robert Crawford burned the intruders' settlement at Eufaula, the War Department ordered Crawford's deputy marshal, Jeremiah Austill, to continue the job of removing white intruders from Creek lands. The white people kept coming, the Creeks' situation deteriorated, and the state of Alabama continued to claim sovereignty. This time, however, the federals sent in a hero.

By the time Austill received his orders he was already a frontier legend. He earned his fame two decades earlier in the autumn of 1813, at the age of nineteen, during the Red Stick War. Camped at the mouth of Randon's Creek where it met the Alabama River, Austill's party spied nine enemy Creeks in a large canoe. Austill and his commander set off in another canoe, described as being paddled by "the old Negro" Caesar. Drawing up alongside the enemy, they engaged the Creeks in a floating battle. Their powder wet, the warring parties set to clubbing each other with rifles and paddles while Caesar strained to keep the two boats together and the combatants within reach of each other's weapons. Austill's small crew eventually triumphed over their much larger foe. They tossed the bodies of the Creek fighters into the river to cheers of the Euro-American soldiers on the shore. The "Canoe Fight," as it became known, sealed Austill's reputation as an Indian fighter and Alabama frontier legend.[1]

Twenty years later, the deputy marshal arrived at Fort Mitchell. Echoing Crawford's findings, he reported his shock at the "deplorable condition" of the Creeks in the area. He noted to the War Department the widespread fraud, theft, and debt that the intruders had used to wrangle the land from the Natives. Uncovering the schemes, he quickly found himself threatened by the intruders with lawsuits if he continued his investigations. Realizing that his federal mandate would hold no weight in hostile local courts, he had little choice but to press on.[2]

Down in Eufaula Town, Austill found matters even worse. There he discovered intruders renting land to Creeks that the Indian tenants actually owned. The Natives' only nonviolent recourse was legal, but court officers examined falsified evidence in state courts that did not recognize Native witnesses. They simply tossed the Creeks in jail if they complained. From there, the Indians had no choice but to forfeit their land claims to secure their freedom. Austill found Eufaula, still called Irwinton, to be "the fountain from which all intrusion and cruelty has originated in that part of the nation." Like Crawford before him, he discovered the settlement "composed principally of a set of outlawed reffugees, who neither respect the law, nor anything else." Driven off once, they had come back even stronger. "It would require a colume" to counter "the acts of cruelty and impositions imposed upon the Indians," Austill reported. "Fifty men would be sufficient to drive them all out but it would take Two hundred to keep them off."[3]

While Austill managed to push some intruders back across the river here and there, and even burned a few more of the intruders' dwellings, the job proved frustrating and overwhelming without a strong display of federal force. The deputy marshal explained to his superiors at the War Department that patrolling a nine-county region with a handful of foot soldiers was simply impossible. If the Treaty of Cusseta was to be taken seriously, then what he and the

Creek people needed was simple: a sizable show of federal force to protect Indigenous land rights. If not that, then he at least needed the ability to arrest intruders and have them tried in federal courts where respect for the rule of law could be guaranteed.[4]

Meantime, federal census takers finally delivered the numbers the War Department needed to proceed with plans to divide lands among individual Creeks according to the treaty. Allotting the land promised to the Indigenous people required figuring out exactly who lived in the Creek Nation. The process had been full of difficulties, in the census takers' words, due "to the blended ignorance, credulity, and cunning of the natives and the schemes of the greedy speculators," all of which had accelerated rapidly in the spring of 1833. It did not help matters that census takers were to count "head of households," but that men of European descent had little understanding of what that might mean in a historically matrilocal society like that of the Creeks. Although some areas needed to be resurveyed, the government's tally showed that the Creek Nation had 22,694 people, including African American slaves. Of those, 6,696 were Creek "head of households" entitled to land. Yet the numbers were difficult to obtain, the census takers reported, since they had been scattered far and wide by the violence and usurpations of the settlers.[5]

If the land ever got distributed according to plan, the Creek families would absorb just over two million acres for themselves as private property. That would leave another three million acres in the Creek Nation for public lands. With the population count complete, the land survey could now follow, which would divide the region into townships and sections that could be guaranteed to the Native peoples. The Treaty of Cusseta still guaranteed a five-year window before the public lands would be made available to outsiders, but at the rate of illegal intrusion, the Creeks' hopes of receiving their promised adjustment time, to say nothing of the land itself, dwindled with astonishing rapidity. Even with the census complete, the weak federal military presence proved little match for a clamorous invasion of white intruders, further emboldened by the fear of losing out in the frenzied, escalating land grab.[6]

Soon, Austill became aware of a scoundrel named Hardeman Owens who would prove a lasting problem to the federal mission. Just north of Barbour County, Creek chiefs complained of a particularly "obnoxious, quarrelsome, and abusive" character. Realizing he could not stem the white tide completely, Austill figured he might at least be able to take care of the most loathsome cases. The Creeks accused the intruder Owens of "taking their fields from them, and killing their hogs and horses, beating the Indians in a most cruel manner." He was said to have broken a girl's arm in a dispute and was believed to be robbing Creek graves and selling the artifacts in his little shop. Surveying the evidence, which Marshal Austill found was "proved by the Indians and several white persons," he decided to pursue Owens.[7]

Austill confronted Owens on the land he occupied, commanding him to leave the Creek Nation by order of the federal government. Owens swore to Austill that he would die before being pushed off "his" land by federal forces. Unprepared to deal with Owens's belligerent resistance on his own, Austill left, planning to return with backup. Some Creek chiefs caught up with him down the road, begging him not to abandon them to Owens's savagery. After Austill left, they said, the intruder had already "drawn his knife on them, and swore he would kill some of them." The deputy marshal then returned with a command of soldiers to arrest Owens. When the intruder showed remorse, begging for his freedom and promising to "leave in peace," Austill took pity and released him. Thinking his mission accomplished, the deputy marshal again rode along his way.[8]

Once again some Creeks urgently caught up to Austill about fifteen miles down the road. As soon as he left, they claimed, Owens threatened them once again, claiming he would "burn their houses and kill all those who dared to come upon the fields taken by him." The Creeks pleaded with Austill to rid them of Owens once and for all. When Austill returned to arrest Owens, he again found him curiously conciliatory. His belligerence toward the federals appeared completely at bay.[9]

Owens "very politely asked us to walk in" to his cabin to discuss matters, Austill reported. Yet when the deputy marshal approached the gate of the house, an Indian stopped him in his tracks. The house, he told him, had been rigged with gunpowder. As Austill bolted from the front of the house, Owens ran out the back. A few seconds later, the cabin exploded. Miraculously, everyone survived. Owens fled. The deputy marshal told the Indians that, should he return, they should capture him if they could and even "shoot him down" if necessary. Austill's act of granting federal authority to Indians to kill a white man would haunt him later on.[10]

Deputy Marshal Austill believed Owens to be "the most daring" and "most dangerous" man he had ever met with. The fugitive remained at large until a detachment of Fort Mitchell soldiers ultimately caught up to him. Finally surrounded by federal troops, Owens still refused to give up, drew his weapon, and took aim at the US Army sergeant in command. Just as the intruder was about to shoot the commander, another soldier, James Emmerson, trained his weapon on Owens, killing him with a bullet to the side of his head.[11]

In death, Owens became something even worse than the rascal he had been in life. The federal troops had created a victim, a fallen hero, a soldier who gave his life to defend freedom, states' rights, and free access to Indian land. Owens was known as a bit of a civic leader among the interlopers. He had been an officer in the Georgia militia, and he was one of the first intruders to invade the Creek Nation after the signing of the Treaty of Cusseta. He also served as commissioner of roads and revenue for Russell County. In death, however, he had his greatest impact as a populist symbol—an innocent man murdered by a ruthless federal government interfering in locals' rights. While the Creeks faced being forever driven from their ancient homelands, at the time literally starving on diets of cooked tree bark, a state and national furor ensued over the killing of one scoundrel by federal troops.[12]

The event could not have been better designed to enrage the passions of the intruders and the authorities of the state of Alabama. A nearby paper declared the killing to be "an act wholly unjustifiable," the logical outcome of Andrew Jackson's policy of intruder removal. The federal troops, whites argued, "place[d] the property and lives of the citizens of that county at the mercy of the malignity or, rapacity of the Indians; and has sent out a file of Soldiers to execute whatever the [Creeks] may dictate." Alabama governor John Gayle accused Crawford of bringing armed federal force in the midst of a "civil and peaceable society" in order to guard the rights of those who, legally speaking, had no rights. He immediately demanded that Marshal Crawford turn Austill over to state authorities to face murder charges as well as the termination of the entire federal scheme to drive the intruders out of Alabama. Gayle protested the outrage of the "murder" directly to the secretary of war, and denied the federal soldiers' right to remove intruders all together. The state courts, he believed, had sole jurisdiction over the land.[13]

William D. Pickett, the solicitor for the Eighth Judicial Circuit, demanded that Fort Mitchell turn over the detachment for prosecution. The fort's commanding officer, Major MacIntosh, countered that the shooter, trooper Emmerson, was in "the lawful execution of his duty" in the killing. "I must therefore decline your invitation to deliver to the sheriff of this county the detachment of soldiers who were present at the time that Owen was killed," he formally replied. The state court of Alabama nonetheless indicted Emmerson for the murder, and the sheriff of Pike County came looking for him for violating the laws of the state of Alabama. Austill and others were named as coconspirators in the murder.[14]

A state grand jury found James Emmerson guilty. They accused him of "not having the fear of God before his eyes, but being moved and seduced by the instigation of the devil" did "feloniously, wilfully" discharge his weapon and mortally wound the right side of Owens's head in such a way as to "kill and murder" him "against the peace and dignity of the State of Alabama." Emmerson's officers—including the hero of the Canoe Fight, Austill—did similarly "feloniously, wilfully, and maliciously incite, move, procure, aid, counsel, hire, and command" his actions. Secretary of War Cass responded by directing the district attorney to move cases to federal courts "wherever it can be legally done" and, failing that, to defend the marshals in the state courts. At the same time, Cass sought to keep peace in the compound republic by instructing Marshal Crawford to obey any suits from the state "without hesitation" and without the "slightest obstacle."[15]

The presence and actions of the federal soldiers became flashpoints in a more sophisticated debate about the triangle of sovereignty formed by the Creek Nation, the state of Alabama, and the United States government. It was not just a case of *imperium in imperio* (a governmental authority within a governmental authority), the defining problem of US constitutional governance; it was *imperium in imperio in imperio* that jammed up all forms of political authority. Federal marshals and troops could not act independently or oversee the relations between the Creeks and whites; the Creek chiefs could not enforce their rights since Alabama claimed jurisdiction; and the state of Alabama snubbed federal authority and saw no gain in asserting any positive control over the situation, as the state's interest lay with the lawless intruders. In place of federal or tribal controls, Governor Gayle and the Alabama Assembly substituted a weak county court system that had little interest in prosecuting whites or limiting the rampant liquor sales that proved effective in loosening lands from Creek ownership.[16]

The killing inflamed sectionalist fevers as Owens grew to become a martyred folk hero, the public grew enraged, militias prepared to march on the federal troops, and Alabama's freedom and honor seemed to hang in the balance. The Unionist *National Intelligencer* editorialized that events in Alabama, and particularly the Owens killing, "threaten seriously the peace of the country." Looking to check risks to the union, the paper argued that the federal government "acted unquestionably in obedience to the laws of the land, and therefore in the strict line of its duty." Federal patrolling of the Creek Nation was "in a manner compatible at once with its own credit and the public peace." In contrast, the *State Rights Expositor* proclaimed its faith that "the settlers, we trust, will remain—aye, remain and defend their lives and their dearest rights." Local papers in Tuscaloosa demanded opposition to federal infringements on state sovereignty and called for Barbour and other counties to organize into military companies for the defense of Alabama. Armed settlers encamped at Pole Cat Springs were supposedly preparing for the arrival of federal troops "with determination to expel them by force."[17]

Events along the Chattahoochee reignited the infamous Nullification Crisis, which had only recently died down. South Carolinians, fearful of federal incursions on their "minority" status, fought what John C. Calhoun called their position as "serffs of the system." They opposed the tariff increase of 1828, histrionically labeling it "Tariff of Abominations." Cotton producers wanted tariff-free access to European goods and markets for their exports and therefore opposed all tariffs, while Northern manufacturers wanted protection for their fledging industrial interests. South Carolinians believed that a given state had a right to ignore federal laws like the tariff, which Calhoun had labeled "unconstitutional, unequal, and oppressive" given its preference for the economic interests of the North. Calhoun made the case that an individual state could nullify federal law if it found the law unconstitutional. A nullifying state could even select to leave the union if federal authority proved too onerous.[18]

Andrew Jackson would have none of it. The president was so enraged that he threatened to lead an army to South Carolina personally and hang Calhoun or any other treasonous fiend who dared to defy the union and Jackson personally. He excoriated nullification as an attempt "to destroy the union" by way of forming "a southern confederacy bounded, north, by the Patomac river," through acts of "wickedness, madness and folly" without parallel "in the history of the world." The power to annul federal law, he said, was "incompatible with the existence of the Union, contradicted expressly by the letter of the Constitution, unauthorized by its spirit, inconsistent with every principle on which it was founded, and destructive of the great object for which it was formed." Jackson's argument that "the Constitution of the United States forms a government, not a league" was an idea on which there was considerable and violent disagreement.[19]

By propping up the economic interests of the slave regimes, the Nullifiers and other states' rights advocates may have been supporting morally reprehensible ends, but they were not out of bounds for the American republican tradition. In many ways, Calhoun's "fears of majoritarian tyranny" made him more of a direct descendent of the revolutionary generation than did Jackson's demand for national unity. As the historian Pauline Maier argues, Calhoun was a statesman of the eighteenth century, "the last of the Founding Fathers" or, as Calhoun himself put it, an individual rooted in "the opinions of the Republican party of '98" with a "rigid adherence" to their principles as "the Rock of our political salvation." His reference to 1798 was to the Kentucky and Virginia Resolutions, written by Jefferson and James Madison respectively. They argued, with regard to the Alien and Sedition Acts, that the states had the right to adjudicate the constitutionality of federal laws on their own. Nullification, it was not difficult to argue, fell under the same legal idea. It was "a reformation essential to the preservation of the Union, the Constitution, and the liberty of the country," as Calhoun wrote South Carolina governor James Hamilton in 1832.[20]

No sooner did Henry Clay's 1833 Compromise Tariff tame the sectional passions of the Nullification Crisis, than the Owens controversy renewed them. The outcome of the "great excitement in Alabama," argued the Unionists, depended upon "whether there is sufficient power in the general government to preserve itself." A small number of Alabama papers, such as the *Huntsville Advocate*, denounced Owens as "an outlaw and a desperado, robbing and committing all kinds of outrages, and with an avarice that invaded even the sanctuary of the grave." These papers saw his killing as an act of "justifiable homicide . . . in the execution of lawful authority, upon one who provoked his fate by unlawful and *armed* resistance." More typical, however, was a fear that paralleled that of nullification: the state had been "humbled" and "the SUPREMACY OF THE FEDERAL GOVERNMENT ESTABLISHED" under the authoritarian Jackson. The subjugation of Alabama was "the darling object of Jackson's heart!" Others, such as the *Charleston Courier*, delivered the ideological fundamentals: Hardeman Owens could not possibly be an outlaw as "'outlawry' is unknown in this country, at least as applied to freemen." Thirty-five years before the firing on Fort Sumter, the Mobile paper whipped up fear that ten federal companies were marching toward Fort Mitchell to deliver Alabama to civil war.[21]

Alabama governor Gayle, an erstwhile Jackson supporter, had been elected on a strong anti-nullification platform. He once urged the "freemen of Alabama to plant themselves on their glorious union—on its preservation depend their liberties." Gayle may not have liked the theory of nullification, but he rapidly turned to embrace the same brand of state sovereignty when it came to controversy over Creek lands. He argued with Secretary of War Cass, claiming that Jackson's order to remove the intruders was fundamentally unconstitutional because those lands fell under the jurisdiction of the state of Alabama not the federal government. By the 1833 campaign season, Andrew Jackson had become a liability for Governor Gayle, and he turned against both the imperious Jackson and the federal government's intrusion in Alabama. Whatever Jackson's commitment to white freedom, it was no longer enough.[22]

The battle of words and ideas between Secretary of War Cass and Governor Gayle became national news. Cass built his argument on the fact that the federal government took "upon itself the obligation of removing intruders from this land, in the same manner as intruders may be removed by law from other public lands," as laid out in an 1807 federal law. For a man who once wrote of Indians as "benighted savages," Cass's list of grievances to the governor simmered with uncharacteristic moral outrage. He complained that "the houses of Indians have been forcibly taken possession of, and sometimes burnt, and the owners driven into the woods, that their fields and improvements have been wrested from them and occupied by white persons, that aggravated injuries have been committed upon the persons of the Indians, and that their horses, cattle, hogs and other property have been forcibly taken from them." The treaty and federal integrity seemed to actually matter to Secretary Cass. "They represent that their crops have been taken from them, and they look forward to a state of starvation, unless some decisive step is adopted in their favor." As Cass forthrightly concluded, "There is not an individual settled upon the ceded lands, who has the slightest legal claim to remain there."[23]

Gayle fought back with a combination of claims of state sovereignty and accusations of federal distortions. Marshal Crawford's field reports, Governor Gayle claimed, were designed "to make an unfavorable impression of the settlers generally," and that the marshal's "prejudices are very strong, that his feelings had become excited." Nine-tenths of the white settlers, Gayle claimed, had never interfered in Indian land or affairs. Not a "whisper of dissatisfaction has been uttered" in the most populous areas. He asked the secretary to consider the misery of the poor freeholder being driven from land and crops after laboring to tame the Southern frontier. As for the enabling 1807 legislation that allowed the federal government to intervene in public lands, he argued that it should not penalize those "who had no object in view beyond their cultivation." Thirty years of legislation, he claimed, had encouraged citizens to settle and occupy public lands, and "this class of our population has always been esteemed highly meritorious." Should the federal government infringe upon the rights of citizens to dispose of their lands as they choose, as the marshal had recently done, then "the whole field of State jurisdiction may be considered as occupied" by the power of the general government. If so, Gayle believed, then the words "state sovereignty" are "but unmeaning sounds, totally unworthy of serious consideration."[24]

Governor Gayle concluded his diatribe: "I respectfully request that this project, so fatal in its tendency to civil liberty, and so directly subversive of the acknowledged rights and sovereignty of the State of Alabama, be abandoned." He pleaded for the secretary of war to "put away, Sir, the sword which has been unnecessarily and too hastily drawn against this large and unoffending community."[25]

Astonishingly, the federal government, under the leadership of President Andrew Jackson, rejected Gayle's pleas, choosing to bolster its efforts to get tough on the intruders' freedom to dominate Creek land. Cass explained to Crawford that the government's lenience had been the source of the problem all along—a position that Jackson would reiterate and one Austill and Crawford had long argued. "The indulgence which the Government has granted to the settlers," Cass argued, could be mistakenly "considered as conferring upon them positive rights." That ambiguity could not stand. The "indulgence" had proven "very injurious to the Indians." Again, Cass decreed that the intruders could harvest their crops but then had to be driven out. The past practice of leniency had proven "utterly inexpedient," producing "the evils" of sectional angers and Indigenous degradation.[26]

The secretary of war backed up his position with an opinion solicited from the US attorney general that he hoped would drive the land question into federal courts. Jackson's attorney general was Roger Taney, who would become a states' rights champion as chief justice of the Supreme Court, and who would later deliver the notorious Dred Scott decision in 1857 that denied citizenship to Black people in the United States. In the Alabama case, however, Taney believed that the federal government had authority over both the states and the Creeks. In the 1807 Insurrection Act, he noted, Congress empowered the president to deploy military force in lands held by the United States government. He also found that the lands of the Creek Nation still belonged to the United States—not to the Creeks or to Alabama. The Indians therefore had no legal right to grant permission to white settlers or anyone else to occupy the lands without the express consent of the US government. Crawford was therefore ordered to report to the district attorney, John Elliott, "the names of all persons who hereafter intrude upon, or who now live upon the ceded land, and refuse to remove agreeably to your requisition, together with the names of the witnesses who can prove the necessary facts." The district attorney would then prosecute them.[27]

Sectional divisions were so high that the United States government began preparations for the military subjugation of the state of Alabama. Major General Winfield Scott, head of the US Army, who would go on to lead American forces in the Mexican-American War, secretly drew up military plans for the invasion. His plans included blockading the state's cotton ports, tactics that would be dusted off for use during the Civil War. At the same time, Scott advised that the administration avoid using troops to fight intruders since this would "excite the sympathies and inflame the passions" of other Southern states. Rumors of the formation of local anti-federal militias boiled up regularly.[28]

The histrionic tale of the Hardeman Owens crisis, well captured by the *Augusta Sentinel*, proved difficult for federal authorities to defend themselves against:

> [If] any American citizen had been shot down by a brutal soldiery, at the command of a mere Deputy Marshal, without trial, without a charge, save that of an Indian's allegation...within a sovereign State, in a boasted land of liberty; when he stated that his State, free as any other State, was surrounded by the army of the United States, ready to commence the work of death, under the force bill, upon the peaceful citizens of Alabama, to favor the speculating views of Government favorites, and the revengeful malice of the Indians; when he despicted [*sic*] the suffering condition of the settlers who had spent their all to make their daily bread in a wilderness, and who were thereby unable to leave their country...shivering in the chilling blast of mid-winter, as they were forced before the bayonets...to leave their homes....What! armies to march through the country at the will of one man, and stationed on the border of States to terrify them into submission! It will not do.

Whatever the story lacked in coherence or rhetorical grace, it made up for in vitriol and populist appeal. And it culminated in a very specific point: "Even the Northern States are awakening on this subject, and the spread of State Right doctrine, every where, is truly gratifying to the friends of liberty."[29]

What did Jackson actually believe in the face of such a story? Some of the president's unfiltered views on these questions can be gleaned from some private marginalia and notes for messages and speeches that he never delivered. As for Governor Gayle's position that federal intrusion was "utterly subversive of our free and happy form of Government," Jackson had no patience. The president responded in unpublished documents with a full-throated defense of the 1807 law that authorized the forcible removal of intruders on federal lands. He also believed the Constitution was clear that no state could "keep troops or ships of war in time of peace." When Enoch Parsons wrote him to question the economic and political costs involved in removing intruders, Jackson privately noted that "a pure government cannot, nay ought not to be influenced by such corruptions." He noted on the letter, in no uncertain terms, that it was the "speculators who has occasioned" the unrest in eastern Alabama—not the Indians and not the federal government. In what appears to be an undelivered draft of a message to Congress, he clearly had no patience with "the intrusion of the lawless white men upon the Creek Indians, committing violence and outrage against their persons & property, in open violation of the late treaty made with that tribe." In the case of the killing of Hardeman Owens, his position was equally clear: Owens was "a lawless violent man" and the marshals were doing their job when he was killed, which was to remove intruders "without discrimination."[30]

There was a presidential irony at work. Andrew Jackson, the Hero of New Orleans, the conqueror of Creek lands, the champion of removal, the president who had wrested the government from aristocratic interests and restored it to the people, the standard bearer of the white common man, had become the enemy of his very constituency and pilloried for his honoring the commitments of the Treaty of Cusseta. For white Southerners, he was now a monger of federal power and an Indian lover. Branded "King Andrew" by his new opponents for his imperious belief in federal authority and his own cantankerous attitude toward dissent, Jackson was punished by the white people of Alabama for siding with the Creeks over the settlers. Supporting Jackson, as Governor Gayle discovered, could prove costly. In comparison to the democratic vitriol of the white people of Alabama, President Andrew Jackson, the notorious "Indian hater," suddenly seemed like a moderate on the question of Native American land rights. Compared to the white Democratic multitudes, in fact, he was.[31]

Jackson was tangled in a web of his own design, but the deeper power of white freedom can be seen in the fate of Marshal Robert Crawford. State law suits were brought against him, and the secretary of war ordered him to "submit to the process without hesitation."

It was dizzying. Ordered to push the intruders out, he also had to balance his orders to do "as little injury to the citizens of Alabama as possible." The man singled out for having the type of "feelings" that would allow him "to aid the oppressed" seemed to give up as he collapsed in fear and exhaustion. There really were only a small number of intruders, he now claimed, rather than the overwhelming numbers he reported before. Any removal, he came to believe, would simply spark further formation of anti-federal militias. The Indians had not really been all that aggrieved, he now argued, and such issues were only a product of a few questionable speculators. Besides, he backtracked, the federal government didn't have enough troops in the region to do the job anyway. Then came what appears to be the real reason for his switch. Like Austill, he had come to fear for his life at the hands of the white population occupying the Creek Nation.[32]

Austill, in contrast, kept the faith. "I feel a clear conscience of having done my duty and no more," he declared, "and they may take my life, but never will they frighten me from the discharge of my duty, nor drive me from the country." Yet he was haunted by fears of a lynch mob. He had been forced to arm himself wherever he went, dreading being taken and "tried by an infuriated set of mad men," convinced that at this feverish point in the drama, "*neither law, testimony, nor justice could save my life.*"[33]

Given Austill's fears, perhaps the greatest irony of the freedom to dominate was that by fighting against it, federal authorities entered the same unsettling and violent legal netherworld of the very people they had been assigned to protect. To the intruders, the United States government was denying them their birthright. To the Creeks, who held on to the last piece of land and dignity available to them in the South, the protections of federal government meant survival. The conflict between white freedom and federal authority, between populist politics and treaty rights, had been set in motion by Andrew Jackson himself. By late 1833, the president realized that he needed help to get out of his predicament—or at least find enough political cover to allow for his escape. He turned to the author of "The Star-Spangled Banner," Francis Scott Key.

CHAPTER FOUR

The Compromise of Francis Scott Key

FRONTIER HERO SAM HOUSTON vowed to shoot Ohio congressman William Stanbery on sight if he ever saw him. It didn't matter whether it was out in the territories, in the more lawless sections of Texas or Alabama, or in the nation's capital—he meant to draw the congressman's blood wherever he found him. And there he was, leaving Mrs. Queen's boarding house on Pennsylvania Avenue one sticky afternoon in the spring of 1832.

Citizens out for a stroll in downtown Washington City watched in horror as Houston seized his opportunity for attack. "You are the damned rascal," he yelled. Lacking his pistol, Houston leapt into action and began mercilessly thrashing Stanbery with his hickory walking stick. A witness testified that the congressman threw up his hands to defend himself against the blows until he managed to run away. In pursuit, Houston jumped onto the congressman's back, and the two of them staggered a number of paces before collectively collapsing to the ground. The congressman screamed what were reported to be "wild heterogenous expressions" as Houston continued his assault. Stanbery, aware of Houston's threats on his life, had come armed with two pistols and a dagger. He pulled one of two pistols from beneath his coat, aimed at Houston's chest, and fired. The gun jammed. The very fact of the pistol further enraged Houston, who grabbed it and resumed pummeling Stanbery. Houston stormed off through the gathered crowd, leaving the Ohioan's beaten and bloody body on the street.[1]

Houston, whose name would one day be synonymous with all things Texan, had stood solidly with Jackson since their days fighting Indians back in Tennessee. Congressman Stanbery, a vocal Jackson opponent, impugned Houston's reputation by claiming on the floor of Congress that Jackson and Houston together had dealt unfairly in federal contracts to provide Indian rations. Houston then sent Stanbery letters demanding that he prepare to defend himself for impugning Houston's honor. Houston then made good on his threat to defend his honor by bloodying Stanbery in broad daylight in the streets of Washington.[2]

Congressman Stanbery wasted no time taking the battery directly to Congress for adjudication. The House of Representatives immediately voted to arrest Houston and indict him for contempt of Congress. By physically attacking a member for what he had said on the House floor, members charged, Houston had interfered with the free deliberations of the House and corrupted the integrity of the political process. The House would be judge and jury in the trial, and vote on Houston's guilt or innocence. In the eyes of the president, the fact that Congress would or could arrest a private citizen—not to mention indict his close friend and political ally—was beyond the democratic pale. A violation of Jackson was a violation of the will of the people. The president, who fought alongside Houston in the Creek War, declared his arrest to be "the greatest act of tyranny and usurpation ever attempted under our government."[3]

To defend Houston in the House trial, Jackson selected one of his allies, Francis Scott Key. His skill as an amateur poet preceded him everywhere he went since his vivid account of the Battle of Fort McHenry during the War of 1812. As British gunboats pounded the fort, Key, trapped on the deck of a ship across the harbor, nervously watched and took note of the "rockets' red glare." His poem, "The Defense of Fort M'Henry," became known nationwide as the lyrics to "The Star-Spangled Banner."

The Stanbery-Houston affair was a small part of a long pattern of physical violence in the national capital. The drama on the Chattahoochee was hardly limited to the frontier. In Washington, duels, canings, mob actions, mortal threats, fistfights, and bullying of various sorts plagued national politics before the Civil War. Deescalating these situations sometimes required a special kind of Washington figure, the rule-following, civility-obsessed types who often chose procedure over virtue or morality. Key was exactly that man, and he would defend his client in Washington with the same lack of grace that he would soon use to broker a deal in the Creek Nation.[4]

He had since become a Washington lawyer and political insider. Once proudly nonpartisan, Key had been persuaded by the vicious divides of the Jacksonian era to see Jackson as the nation's savior. Houston's trial became one of the nation's early spectacles, riveting audience attention as spectators flowed through the House chamber to witness it. Nationwide, reporters, particularly the anti-Jackson press, noted all of the nasty details. Key mostly embarrassed himself. He harangued the chamber for a month of bluster-filled, rambling, arcane, obnoxious, fumbling, and ultimately futile defenses of his client. Houston stood trial in his buckskins, still carrying the same cane he used to attack Stanbery. As one paper reported of the political farce, "From this assault and some things developed in the trial, we should judge that some of our *great* men, so called, are but half civilized, and not Christianized at all." Outsiders viewing the spectacle, the paper continued, "should consider us as a nation of barbarians." Key lost the case and a great deal of his reputation in the fight. Houston faced light penalties before abandoning Washington later that year to join the turmoil in Texas. There Houston became a war hero in the fight with Mexico and eventually president of the independent Republic of Texas.[5]

Yet Key's professional future was secure. In exchange for his efforts to defend Houston and the administration, President Jackson appointed him US attorney for the District of Columbia in 1833. It was a sweet slice of federal patronage that he held on to for eight years. Frank Key had barely started the job when Jackson personally selected him to take care of yet another problem vexing his administration: the need to resolve the conflict over sovereignty created by the Treaty of Cusseta. Tensions were rife in Alabama after the summer killing of Hardeman Owens, and someone needed to arbitrate the competing interests of the federal government, the state of Alabama, and the Creek Nation. Key proved his loyalty and would be that man. Sadly for the Indigenous people of Alabama, Francis Scott Key defended their rights with the same level of acumen that he demonstrated in defending Sam Houston.

Key's official mission, explained Secretary of War Cass, was "to proceed to Alabama" and implement "the removal of the intruders from the public lands ceded to the United States by the Creek Indians in March 1832." At the same time Cass sent Key out west, he reminded Governor Gayle that the federal government remained obligated by its "solemn contract" with the "feeble survivors of a once powerful and high spirited, but now broken and dejected tribe." The president himself desired that "the difficulties which have arisen up on that subject may be terminated with as little inconvenience to individuals as may be compatible with the public faith."[6]

Jackson continued to maintain that the entire conflagration in Alabama arose from a single presumption on the intruders' part. The "very forbearance" of the United States, he argued, "has had the effect of inducing the settlers to believe the Government would not actually remove them from the land." Jackson emphasized that the Indians had the right to occupy, sell, and exercise all rights of ownership to the land. The federal government's role was to serve as "a control over it until they might be supposed to become acquainted with its value" against the speculators hungry for land and willing to swindle this "unfortunate race" for "the most trifling consideration."[7]

The president's messages to Secretary of War Cass, Frank Key, and Governor Gayle all conveyed his conviction that the Indians should most certainly be moved west, but he demanded, at minimum, for them to receive a fair price, awarded to them directly, for the land that would be deeded to them under the terms of the treaty. He also consistently held out the possibility that they might choose to retain the land, use it productively, and assimilate into the white economy and culture, but he was not optimistic about that future. The provision of five years of federal protection seemed to be slipping from Jackson's agenda, but it was still on the books. Until everything was set for the Creeks to receive just compensation or possession as per the Treaty of Cusseta, Jackson maintained, the federal marshals and Francis Scott Key would have to see to it that the white intruders were kept out.

Jackson had even more on his mind. He was bleeding political support. The justifiable killing of one murderous scoundrel had made him appear soft on removal. Having just finished defusing the Nullification Crisis—one of the defining and most constitutionally vexing problems of his administration—the last thing he needed was a reputation for aggressive federal overreach. Although there is no documentation to prove anything either way, Jackson may have dumped the problem on Key in order to give the president enough political cover to escape public wrath. Perhaps Key could find a way to abandon Jackson's promises in a way that the president could not afford to do directly.

When Jackson selected Key to travel to the Creek Nation, he was choosing a person of national prominence. A bit foppish, perhaps, and someone prone to believe his own bloated and pious speechifying, but he was still an important Washington insider, noted attorney, devout Christian, and, above all, "a rank Jackson man." He also happened to be the brother-in-law of Jackson's attorney general and future Supreme Court chief justice, Roger Taney.[8]

Key's views of slavery and freedom might have been thought of as forward-thinking in the first half of the nineteenth century among European Americans. He owned slaves, and he believed in the innate inferiority of African people. He hated abolitionists more than just about anyone else, and his law practice fought for the return of human chattel to those who claimed ownership. But he also regularly represented African Americans in court—typically for free—and criticized the fact that there were seizures of free Black people into slavery as well as open slave markets in Washington. He could not abide the image of slave trading in the shadow of the Capitol.

Key agreed with his friend John Randolph, who criticized Washington City as "an assemblage of prisons where the unfortunate beings, reluctant, no doubt, to be torn from their connections, and the affections of their lives, were incarcerated and chained down, and thence driven in fetters like beasts, to be paid for like cattle." He seemed to have little sense of any contradiction in his willingness to protect free Blacks but despise abolitionists, and protect slave owners' interests but detest the Washington slave market.[9]

Like many European Americans of the era who believed themselves enlightened, Key expressed his racial beliefs through his commitment to the American Colonization Society, a widespread movement of white elites who set their sights on "returning" free Blacks to Africa. With slavery declining in the North, the question of what should happen with free African Americans grew, and so did support for a simplistic solution: get rid of them. Yet when Key thought of colonization, he did so, as he did so much else, in extravagantly utopian ways. He claimed African colonies of freed slaves would be marked by "spires of temples glittering in the sun" filled with the "hum of industry" and happy citizens proud to be descendants of "the nation with the star-spangled banner." When a group of African Americans from Eufaula would eventually make good on the American Colonization Society's ideas by going to Liberia after the Civil War, they would find no such utopia.[10]

Key's "The Star-Spangled Banner" was not kind to slaves either. Key's racial ideology is revealed in lines never sung at today's sporting events: "No refuge could save the hireling and slave / From the terror of flight, or the gloom of the grave." Here he was criticizing those bondsmen who had fled the United States to fight on the side of the British in the War of 1812. At that time, slaves and free Blacks knew that they were far more likely to find freedom under the Union Jack than they were in the song's "land of the free." There was certainly a parallel in the Creeks' belief that they had some hope in embracing federal power and no hope on the state level. Key's first priority was ultimately the health of the young, white republic above all else—just as it would be in Alabama.[11]

Key finished what must have been an arduous voyage to the wilds of Alabama on November 11, 1833. By that time his orders were published in papers around the country, naming him, tellingly, as "the minister of the United States to the state Alabama." Tensions were on the rise. Talk of disunion increased, and papers like the *Mobile Commercial Register* assisted in whipping up the frenzy with false claims such as "We have just learned, from an authentic source, that orders have been issued from headquarters for the immediate marching of ten companies of United States' artillery, completely equipped for the field, to Fort Mitchell, in this state." The fear was that this could "constitute an effective force of fourteen companies" poised to control Alabama. Frank Key soldiered forth, however, his mission from Jackson still clear: to ensure that "the faith of the United States [be] preserved." He believed that he could find the balance between Creek rights and intruder removal so as to calm the situation. The variables in the calculus were complex, however, and he knew that any federal support of the Creeks would be a fraught and tenuous process. Ultimately, Key's job was to help Jackson climb down from a tenuous confrontation between federal and state power. In so doing, the welfare and rights of Creeks would not be his highest priorities.[12]

A couple of days after his arrival in the Creek Nation, Key got his first inkling about what he was up against. In a rural tavern, he overheard the justice of the peace publicly declare that the killing of Hardeman Owens was nothing more than "a base and inhuman murder" by federal troops. Key found that Alabama law had been "grossly abused," but he began to grasp the conundrum he had to solve. If the local sheriff, he figured, has the right under Alabama jurisdiction "to execute the process of her courts, the marshal of the United States has a right, if this sheriff is an intruder upon her lands, to remove him." Obviously, he calculated, "these two rights are in conflict," and the question was "is the Government of the United States to yield?" Alternatively, "these people are all residing here by the indulgence of the Government; shall it not withdraw that indulgence when it is thus abused?"[13]

This clash between federal and local power had produced a more immediately pressing question: What was to be done about the grim fate of the soldiers involved in the killing of Owens? "How these people are to be saved from going to the Montg'y Jail I cannot see," Key wrote, buckling to the demands of local and states' rights advocates. "Nor is there any prospects of getting them out." They could not be handed over to the state, he surmised, as they would inevitably be "convicted & executed or perhaps sacrificed to the fury of the Intruders without a trial"—which is to say, lynched. While the federal soldiers seemed "disposed to remain & take their trial," he was not sure their position would hold. Desertion, he guessed, would be the most likely outcome. If the federal government did not back the soldiers against local and state claims, however, it would forever disarm Washington's authority in similar situations. Failing the soldiers would mean that "neither officer or soldier will ever move again to turn off an Intruder but that they will refuse in a body & take their chance of a Court Martial." Having visited the Russell County Courthouse some "9 miles off in a wilderness," he knew he had to keep the federal soldiers out of state and county courts. The courthouse he found to be a "sort of shantee of rough plank," and the grand jury inside "all intruders & their overseers & the agents of the speculators." The justice of the peace himself was little more than "an obstinate & violent intruder who declares his purpose of resisting any effort of the Gov't to turn him off."[14]

The ironies and complexities of the entire catastrophe did not escape him. The "Court house, clerk's office, Judge, Sheriff & Jury are all here on the U.S. land, by the indulgence of the U.S. and they evidently mean to use this indulgence to prevent the U.S. from using the right of ownership on their own lands & fulfilling the purpose they have intended and declared." The local authorities he found determined. "They say they will not be turned off and this Court & this one Justice of the peace is to arrest & commit your officers & men to jail at their pleasure." Even if it was lawful to remove intruders, Key pondered, leaning in favor of the white locals, it might not have been legal for federal troops to kill resisters. The state of Alabama maintained that Owens was not killed in pursuit of a law, but that "he was killed in pursuance of no law" that the state was willing to recognize. In contrast, if the soldiers were in pursuit of a law without authority, then the case was one of simple murder. But Key found little evidence to back the rumors of armed assemblages of white Alabamians ready to fight the federals en masse, surely calming the nerves of some in Jackson's administration.[15]

Like other observers, he could not turn his eyes from the suffering of the Creek people. He lamented that the Indians were "completely in the power" of the land speculators, at whose coercion and desperation many Creeks had "sold their lands two or three times over for any trifle that has been offered." He remarked on the throngs of demoralized Creeks "going to Columbus with bundles of fodder on their heads to sell, & saw numbers of them in the streets there, where they exchange every thing they carry for whiskey." Yet Key feared that if the federal government sided too strongly with the Creeks it could trigger Governor Gayle to order the state militia into action. He recommended that his superiors in Washington avoid direct confrontation with the governor and do what they could to avoid such calamity. Aware that "the speculators will harass the Indians with the State laws," and aware of what the application of state law would mean for his own mission, he found himself believing "that the only effectual way of saving them will be to buy their lands & send them off."[16]

Key also proved sympathetic to the volatile predicament of Governor Gayle. Key wrote to his brother-in-law, Roger Taney, that the governor's position "is not a little embarassing [*sic*]." The problem was that "if he offends the Nullifiers," as Key referred to the militant states' rights people, he is not sure of "appeasing all the Union men, & if he says he is satisfied with the U.S. he will be sure to offend the Nullifiers." While he believed Gayle was committed to a "pacific course," tempers were running hot. The situation could exacerbate the tense national mood, Key explained, and he would not be "surprized to see all the South & Virginia with them, committing some folly quite equal to Nullification" over the land problems in Alabama.

Key feared for the stability of the nation if his work set off a series of reactions that Jackson could not control.[17]

Having traveled around the state, met with a variety of constituents, and observed the situation in the Creek Nation, Francis Scott Key offered up what became known as the Key Compromise. Put to paper on December 16, 1833, it contained a number of working parts. Given that the land surveys required by the treaties were almost finished, Key's compromise would accelerate the allotment process so that lands would be deeded to Creek heads of households very quickly—just one month later, by January 15, 1834. In a direct violation of the original terms of the Treaty of Cusseta, the settlers on all lands outside of those allotments would no longer be subject to removal. Intruders who had settled on Indian reserves would have the option of buying the land they occupied or scrambling for other nonallotted lands, another violation of the treaty's core commitment to giving the Creeks five years of noninterference. In exchange for these capitulations, the state of Alabama would agree to drop its prosecution of the federal soldiers involved in the shooting of Hardeman Owens. Meantime, the soldiers at Fort Mitchell would agree to be under state-level civil authority in Alabama. Finally, Key secured Gayle's commitment to make "it penal" for any white person "to occupy their reservation without a title made and approved by the President."[18]

The deal maintained the illusion that federal authority still mattered, but did little else. The concessions related to the shooting of Hardeman Owens meant little in light of the fact that trooper Emmerson had already deserted, fearing for his life. Under the Key Compromise, all of the militant demands that Jackson and Cass made, as well as the risks men like Crawford and Austill took, evaporated on the spot. The path around the self-created snarls of the Treaty of Cusseta meant abandoning the Creeks to their miserable fate among the intruders, the whiskey, the fraud, the state jurisdictions, and the arbitrary local authorities. Key had sold out the entire project, substituting the slenderest of pretenses of genuine Creek protection. The resolution of the procedural paradoxes of the compound republic, and, presumably, helping Jackson save face, were far more important than the substance of the disputes—or the fate of the Creek people.

In all this, the governor saw victory. He crowed in a special message to the state that the "highest satisfaction to our fellow citizens in these new counties" has been met by avoiding the "calamity" with the federal power. In avoiding war, "the supremacy of the civil over the military authority has been successfully maintained." The Creeks, he concluded, "have become citizens of the State, and have placed themselves under the protection of our laws, by their own consent, freely and voluntarily given."[19]

When Key analyzed the situation, he singled out Eli Shorter of Columbus, Georgia, to be the central player in the entire system of dispossession that connected everything from politics, finance, and the press into an interlocking directorate of land thievery projected to an industrial scale. Ironically, elite speculators like Shorter were the exact type of person who were empowered by his compromise. The entire racialized anti-statist mood of the era, while claiming to serve the unwashed Jacksonian masses, actually boosted the fate of the unregulated elite. Key set free the richest and most powerful men in the Chattahoochee Valley to devour what remained of Creek lands.

Shorter, or "the Judge" as he was known locally, had already amassed 171 Creek reservations into his Columbus Land Company, and from there his holdings with another partner, Seaborn Jones (they were each also conveniently president of a different bank), mushroomed to an estimated three or four thousand allotments by the time that Francis Scott Key visited. Colonel John Hogan, a federal officer doing his humane best for the Creek people and therefore at odds with men like Shorter, put it most directly: "It seems that no honest man can go into the Creek nation & endeavor to do justice to the Government, the Indians, & his own conscience without being assailed by such men as Eli S. Shorter." Politician and Montgomery newspaper editor James E. Belser explained to President Jackson that Shorter and his associates were nothing more than "land pirates" involved in a "system of villainy" that would unnecessarily drive the Creeks to rebellion and war.[20]

A former gambler who transformed his "itch" into a wild pattern of land theft, Shorter eventually took possession of 275 square miles of Creek land from Barbour County northward. As the western Chattahoochee's most rapacious and shameless speculator, he became about as close to a capitalist villain as one might find in the antebellum era. He had his fingers in many of the twenty-one companies in Columbus dedicated to speculation and dispossession, and his exploits were legendary. He seized land leveraging fictional debts of the owners, forged letters, burned down homes, paid impersonators of Creek land holders to sign over property, championed the federal deportation of Native Americans, defrauded banks, manipulated the buying and selling of contracts, built wholly unregulated trusts, and even chained and tortured people until they signed away their property. In his escapades, he funneled capital from London, Boston, and New York to fuel his swindles of Native Americans in order to help build the slave-based plantation economy to come. And it all worked. Shorter only seemed to fear one thing: federal investigation of the contracts he used to defraud the Creek people.[21]

Shorter developed and deployed the widespread practice of "personation," which meant simply hiring one Creek to pretend to be a different, landowning tribe member. The imposter would then sell the allotment to an agent of the speculator in the presence of a federal agent. The actual landowner never knew what was happening—and since Native Americans had no standing in state courts, they had little legal recourse. Milton S. Booth explained about one incident in Barbour County in which a Creek resident was killed on Thursday evening and his allotment was taken by the following Monday. No matter what the means, Eli Shorter's men took property before the federal authorities could regulate the process or Indian leaders could figure out what to do. Ironically, the speculators actually aggravated federal operations to move the Creeks west, since Indians who felt swindled refused to move without redress.[22]

Ever since the signing of the Treaty of Cusseta, there had grown "an air of urgency in the affairs" of the speculators, but the Key Compromise opened the way for intruders to seize the remaining lands with minimal fear of federal intervention. "*Stealing* is the order of the day," exclaimed Shorter. Big-time speculators proved to be the worst, consolidating the majority of quality cotton lands in the region and leaving only the less productive lands to the scrambling settlers. Shorter sounded the alarm to have his lieutenants fan out and get to work. "Make the most of the time left to you," he demanded; "the *great struggle* should be for the most valuable lands. Every man should now be at his post." He required that his team "*instantly*" put aside all other business and "gather up as many Indians who can be depended on as possible" to impersonate land allotment owners. Money would be no problem, Shorter explained; what they needed were more Indians. His minions were to round up and "drill" and "prepare" desperate Creeks willing to fraudulently sign away lands that did not belong to them in exchange for $10 in goods for each successful plot conveyed to Shorter's land company. "The harvest is nearly over, and perhaps there will never be another such a one," Shorter panted about the dwindling potential for theft in the spring of 1835. Eli Shorter's sense of urgency was all the more amazing given that he claimed to already have *four hundred* desperate Creek Indians hidden in camps in the forests surrounding the certifying agency ready to defraud their brethren. "Now is the time, or never!" exclaimed one his associates. "Hurrah boys! Here goes it! Let's steal all we can. I shall go for it, or get no lands! Now or never!"[23]

Federal authorities might have been able to stop the flow of white "settlers," but without an unprecedented show of force, they could not stop the juggernaut of Shorter's brand of violent capitalist speculation. Dispossession of Native lands was not simply an unstoppable fever, but a process pushed aggressively by economic interests aided by sophisticated financial instruments that stretched from Europe to the banks of Boston and New York to the lands of the Creeks. At stake was some of the most valuable land in the world in the 1830s. The rights and claims of the Indigenous population—and their physical presence, often their very existence—had to be destroyed in order to make this section of Alabama a central player in the global cotton market that it would become.

The wielders of global capital chased after land along the Chattahoochee, enrolling local elites such that global finance, Native American dispossession, slavery, and the cotton economy became links in a historical chain of events. In the state capital of Montgomery, all the talk was of "cotton, negroes, land and money." In the words of the historian Claudio Saunt, Native Americans had been uprooted at the urging of the "bottom-line figures in ledger books and the speculative fervor of U.S. and overseas investors." Opothleyahola, a resident of the Creek Nation, put it more succinctly to a United States agent: "The homes which have been rendered valuable by the labor of our hands are torn from us by a combination of designing speculators, who haunt your office, and who, like the man among the tombs, are so fierce that no one can pass that way." His reference to the evil spirit who confronted Jesus, a monstrous ghost that could tear apart any chains used to restrain him, begins to suggest the power of speculation that could not be subdued in eastern Alabama.[24]

In contrast to the speculators like Shorter, the poor "roughs," those swarms of landless frontiersmen in search of property, independence, and Jacksonian liberty, were not the Creeks' biggest problem. Those ragtag intruders may have been large in number and tough in character, but it was the elite speculators with more money, voice, and political power who were taking over the region—especially in areas with valuable land like Barbour County. President Jackson's posturing as an enemy of privilege and power resonated deeply with those small freeholders. His actions, however, had the broader effect of opening up the pathway for large-scale economic systems that harnessed Creek land and slave labor to the growing of cotton. That cotton fed the voracious appetite of the transatlantic industry spanning from Massachusetts to Manchester.

The curtailing of federal power and cries for freedom were the political means to the speculators' desire: large amounts of land. Shorter, for instance, organized a town meeting to denounce *Worcester v. Georgia* (1832), in which the Supreme Court found in favor of tribal sovereignty (i.e., nationhood), because political independence for the Native Americans struck "at the very root of the tree of

Liberty" by subverting the interests of the states and "the people." He urged resistance to the intrusion on white freedom—"There is no middle course," he proclaimed. Even if Jackson ignored the decision and removed the Cherokee (as he did), Shorter feared what it could mean for the future ability of speculators such as himself to take over Creek lands. "Resolved, That whenever the Supreme Court in the exercise of pretended powers shall transcend the limits imposed by the constitution and violate the rights of this State—it is the right & it is the duty of the State and of the people to refuse obedience to its mandates to maintain those rights," he argued. Shorter also swore up and down that every transaction had been legitimate. When he wrote to the secretary of war, he professed his shock to the rumors and innuendos about his and his colleagues' actions, which he claimed were "basely false and slanderous."[25]

It helped the speculators' cause that Cass and Jackson agreed, upon Key's urging, to also dismiss the existing suits against the intruders who had already stolen the lands. And it all worked. According to the most in-depth calculation of the mess of complicated legal and economic ventures in the Creek Nation, of the 2,142,720 acres originally part of the Treaty of Cusseta, 1,970,324 of them fell to swindlers. Shorter got a sizable, but not the largest, slice of the land-grab pie with his 312,574 acres. When the final war and forced removal of the Creeks was over, and the financial bubble created by land speculation burst in the Panic of 1837, just about everyone pointed their fingers at the elite speculators, who quickly fell from the lofty heights of city fathers to corrupt scoundrels.[26]

The Creeks, once "enspired with an allmost unshaken confidence" in the capacity of the federal government, had become "allmost dispondent of ever finding the promises of their father the president," reported John Scott, formerly one of Shorter's agents, who had turned against him and sided with the plight of the Creeks. Now even the federals were out of the treaty enforcement business. As a changed and conciliatory Jackson wrote that spring to the governor: "I called on the secretary of war . . . and he expressed the fullest confidence in you and his willingness to leave the whole matter (of Indian troubles) to yourself." Gayle could not have asked for more. Marshal Robert Crawford, who burned the white settlement in Eufaula, gave up on the whole business, surrendering to the juggernaut of white freedom. "I feel fully satisfied that this business is fully settled," he reported to the secretary of war.[27]

Having lost faith in the weak and duplicitous promises of Washington, the Indigenous people chose not to go quietly. Exhausted, depleted, and abandoned by the very federal protections the Creeks had been promised—and continued to both hope for and demand—they took matters into their own hands. The Creek people chose to launch one last desperate war on the intruders in the Creek Nation. Less a war than a horrific campaign of terrorism, guerrilla fighting, and bloody mayhem, the Lower Creeks, like the Red Sticks before them, were driven to the sort of wanton violence of which they had so long been unfairly accused.

CHAPTER FIVE

Uprising

A FOG OF DESPAIR SETTLED over eastern Alabama. The regular sight of Native American bodies dangling above the forest floor, the self-tied grapevines grinding into their buckled necks, was among the more traumatic signs of the hopelessness of 1835. Along with the suicide epidemic came a wave of alcoholism. Across all nine of the counties of the former Creek Nation, the towns were filled with grog shops awash with drunk and desperate souls, sacrificing whatever of material value they had left in order to blind themselves to their certain fate. Others hid out and starved. Reports of emaciated Indians were commonplace as people moved deep into the forest to try to survive on the boiled insides of tree bark—their rights to hunt and fish had been stripped by the state of Alabama. Federal agent John Hogan reported that by 1835 just about every scrap of land of any value in Barbour County had been stolen. The project of Euro-American domination was near complete. After Key's compromise, the hope of federal intervention on the Creek people's behalf had all but evaporated. Whites had won their fight for free access to land, and the Creeks were left with the anguish. For the Indigenous people of Alabama, it seemed the end of the world.[1]

Some Creeks chose to move away, as Jackson and Cass hoped, but they proved very few in number. Severing connections to the home of their ancestors and facing fears—and actual reports—of life in the West proved worse than facing the land theft, the suicide epidemic, the starvation, and the alcoholic despair engulfing the region. Yoholo Micco, a Eufaula chief, was one of the few who selected to leave. He laid out his position to Jackson in the summer of 1835. "Our privileges as a nation in this country [are] forever lost and we as a people in great trouble," he explained. Between a country filled with "bad white men and bad Indians," they dared not call their property their own. Stolen before they could even sell it as the government planned, their only path for survival was to move west of the Mississippi. Reports from the West certainly had not been encouraging. Headmen wrote to Washington to report the "unhealthiness of the country, the many deaths that have taken place among them.... From all accounts that we have received, [the western land] is a grave yard." White officials continued to regard the Native Americans' unwillingness to move with bewilderment. "The Creeks regarded their eternal separation from the county of their nativity with a kind of superstitious horror," reported one befuddled official. Several hundred Creeks had agreed to emigrate voluntarily by 1835, but that still left over twenty thousand people committed to remaining in the area.[2]

Wiser minds knew that those who moved west could expect a replay of what had just happened to the Creek Nation in Alabama. "A few years since and Alabama was, what Arkansaw now is," argued a petition signed by Opochle Yoholo and number of other chiefs: "a remote frontier country, inhabited by Indians—By Indians enjoying protection, under the government of the united States, guaranteed by solemn Treaty stipulations—Behold now their condition!!" Their future in the West was Alabama's present. "The government cannot keep out intruders—This is proved by all past experience—and if their white brethren are permitted to have access to them, it is at once fatal to their happiness—their government, nay, even to their existence."[3]

Knowing that white intruders would dog them again soon enough, they proposed a more drastic option: to get out of the United States altogether. "In short, we believe that country promises nothing better than the final extinction of our race.... The sad results of by-gone years, have taught us, that the fundamental principles of a republican society are, utterly at variance with the separate national existence of the red-men within the chartered limits of the United States." Their hope was to move to Texas (then an independent republic) or Mexico. "*Our talk is done*." But Secretary of War Cass could not grant permission to move to another country as he had no right or jurisdiction to do so.[4]

That left one option. Federal agent John Hogan began to sense the telltale signs of a new belligerent posture, even though he felt that rumors of war were being cooked up by the speculators not the Indians. At first, the changes were subtle and easily misread. He noticed that "*Not an Indian came* to the council fire but was armed with his rifle, *knife, pouch, horn*, &c., ready for battle." An 1835 observer of the ceremonial Green Corn Dance noted particularly high levels of simulated violence: ceremonial puppets being subjected to kidnapping, attacks, stabbings, scalping, and tomahawking. Boys carried cornstalks, mimicking the arms carried by the adult men. Reports came of apocalyptic signs that foretold of battle or doom: eclipses of the sun and moon, strange stars, and earthquakes. For many Creeks, the tragic world foretold by Tecumseh at the start of the Red Stick uprising appeared to be coming true. At the same time, the intruders sensed their moment of power. Jeremiah Austill had been having a "serious time" for several days with them. The whites also held a meeting to raise military forces "sufficient to drive me and the troops off." Both intruder and Native sensed the weakness of federal capacity. The day of reckoning seemed at hand.[5]

Years later, an investigator who was charged with determining the causes of the coming conflict determined that an uprising should have been no surprise given the broken treaties, settlers pushing into their lands, and constant harassment by speculators and intruders. "Circumscribed as the Creeks were, within comparatively restricted limits; harassed by intruders often without principle; pressed upon by a heavy population," the report argued, "the collisions between them and the whites were perpetual, bitter, and often times bloody." With the promises of the Treaty of Cusseta, the president placed himself in "a position of great delicacy and difficulty." The response of the Creek people was foregone. "It is impossible," it continued, "to doubt that there lies in the hearts of a vast majority of the Creeks a lurking, festering, enduring, and treacherous malice towards the race against whom they have been struggling and warring for more than a century." By the winter of 1835, the *Columbus Enquirer* reported "marauding Indians" had "committed depredations on the property of the whites" with killings and injuries on both sides. Others, like Opochle Yoholo, saw the end. Signs everywhere "portended the gradual declension and final extinction of the Creeks." Events foretold both whites and Creeks were "doomed to destruction."[6]

Residents of Barbour County noted "numbers of from two to three hundred, marching and countermarching, and going through all the manoeuveres incident to savage warfare." The residents reported the Indians "collected in bodies, with fire-arms, and painted, and when asked their motive, they were silent and would give no answer." In the face of organized drills and random violence, the intruders requested military assistance from the state of Alabama. Forwarding the petition to Secretary of War Cass, the governor wrote, "I am conclusively satisfied that the Indians are meditating and preparing for hostilities against the whites, and that unless their designs are frustrated by the exhibition of a military force sufficient to inspire them with some fear of consequences, like murderers and conflagrations will soon be enacted in Alabama." Fears turned real. The Creeks began stealing corn, shooting livestock, tearing down fences, threatening white people, and forcing them out of their houses, "avowing a determination, if they remain, to murder them." Some settlers, seeking "to avoid the tomahawk and scalping knife, have abandoned their homes, and left their all to the savage devastation and plunder."[7]

In May 1836, the episodic burning of buildings, scalpings, robberies, and killings shifted to an organized uprising against the Euro-American land thieves. The Creeks' very act of rebellion, however, meant they would forfeit any claim to any legal rights or federal protections—however meager they were in the first place. Like rolling thunder clouds of fate meeting on the horizon, the Creeks attacked the European Americans in what would be their last horrible, tragic war over their ancestral lands. The starving, subdued, begging, drunken wretches stunned the region's white population with their sudden capacity to muster widespread, organized—and violent—resistance.

This time, the states'-rights, freedom-loving intruders turned desperately to the federal government to protect them from the problem that they themselves had created. Yet it was the very racialized anti-statist values of white freedom that had cornered the Creeks into a war they had hoped their federal treaty and alliances would avoid.

In the spring of 1836, the percolating Creek violence erupted in the Second Creek War. Fighting began in Barbour County. There the blood-curdling war whoop announced the offensive outside of Glennville near the Russell County border. The original plan hatched by the chiefs called for a direct attack on Fort Mitchell and Columbus, Georgia, but those plans were delayed. Impatient warriors in the south, where land theft was near absolute, decided to take matters into their own hands. They killed one man in Glennville, then two more, and then burst into another house two days later and shot the owner as he lay in bed. As they moved from plantation to plantation, they let the slaves live, informing them that "they intended to kill all the white people." In a matter of weeks, the Creek rampage placed them in control of all the plantations in several towns in the Lower Creek nation. They then attacked stagecoaches, cut off the mail, and "sacked" the town of Roanoke across the river. Farmers and plantation owners fled for the cities or drew together for safety, leaving the Creeks in even further control of the countryside. With the takeovers, they obtained "corn cribs, houses full of meat, all the stock in their possession, plenty of clothing in their possession, and some money," reported John Hogan. The chiefs believed, confidently, "we can whip the white people." Intruders pleaded with the government, seeking "energetic action in securing its citizens from violence, plunder, and massacre."[8]

The Creek warriors poured north, up the Chattahoochee, wiping out more farms and plantations, burning bridges, stealing or leaving behind (but explicitly not killing) slaves, taking or killing livestock, and attracting the attention of other warriors in the region, who swelled their ranks. Through their pillaging, they gathered guns, munitions, and food that they hid in the swamps for further battle. As one witness reported to the governor, every point in eastern Alabama from Columbus on down "exhibits a mournful spectacle of devastation [and] waste—Every mansion is burn't the cattle driven off—Cribs of corn plundered [and] the whole country deserted." Other attacks included slaughters with no intent other than revenge or sending messages, such as the attack on the Davis family, in which all seven members of the family were murdered, their heads cut off, and one child allegedly thrown into the yard, where hogs ate the body.[9]

When the inevitable demand for federal intervention against the hostile Creeks came, it was none other than Eli S. Shorter, the antifederal speculator who had reaped the benefits of Francis Scott Key's compromise, who sounded the trumpet. His demands to the secretary of war belied his previously militant states'-rights position as little more than an instrumental idea of freedom. The federal government, he argued, ought not be "misled" nor should it "underrate" the strength of the enemy. "In making your arrangements for the protection and defence of the country, I beg and implore you to believe that we *must*, we are *fated* to have a severe and sanguinary war with these people." He exaggerated that four-fifths of the Creeks were "actively hostile and the force to put them down must be fully adequate to the purpose, and conducted by efficient officers." He asked the secretary of war to remove not just hostile Creeks but all Creeks from the area, claiming that none could be trusted. Nothing would serve the speculators' interests more at this point than a large number of troops. With the federal troops on the speculators' side, all evidence and therefore potential future claims against the speculators—many of which were still under investigation—would be wiped out.[10]

When news of the Creek uprising made it to Washington by the middle of May, the secretary of war and the president put an end to their sympathetic posturing with the Creeks and declared all-out war. Cass requisitioned $500,000 to subjugate the rebellion among the Creeks—and the parallel fight among the Seminoles in Florida, which the government feared could become a conjoined regional war. Fourteen companies of troops, including five hundred marines, were sent to Fort Mitchell. Cass asked for an additional ten thousand volunteer troops. Congress swiftly approved his requests, and a combined force of twelve thousand men—regulars, marines, volunteers, and state militia—descended onto eastern Alabama under the command of Brevet Brigadier General Thomas S. Jesup and General Winfield Scott. Jackson's orders were simple: to seek the unconditional submission of the Creeks, who "must be disarmed and sent immediately to their country west of the Mississippi." Five navy steamers chugged up the Chattahoochee to deliver supplies and troops for the coming war. All certifications of contracts and investigations of fraud were terminated. All pretense of Creek land rights dissolved on the spot. The land crises became one military operation, and federal authority worked when it had to.[11]

The Second Creek War lasted for a year, but major defeats for the Native Americans came quickly in the face of overwhelming force. Soon, soldiers rounded up Creeks and forced them to emigrate west on what became known as the Creek Trail of Tears. In July 1836, an army surgeon happened to be on hand and took lengthy notes on the "melancholy spectacle" of the final answer to the question of the Creek people in Alabama. He watched a party of five hundred marched from Fort Mitchell, manacled together, "a long chain passing between the double file connected them all together." The "stoical disposition" of the "forest philosophers" elicited almost nothing other than the occasional noise when one member pulled against the manacles on the wrists of another. The "proud monarchs of the soil," he wrote as he watched the procession, had little to anticipate beyond the "horrors of the infernal regions" where they were sent. There were more suicides. The surgeon claimed to observe one prisoner, who, failing to cut his throat with a dull knife, "forced it into his chest over the breast-bone, and by successive violent thrusts succeeded in dividing the main artery, when he bled to death." The army surgeon found such desperation not uncommon. The prisoners' silent despair contrasted with the women who followed "drowned in tears." The double-file chain gang marched for ninety miles from Fort Mitchell to Montgomery. "It was a deplorable sight," he reported, as "chains are worse to them than death." Still, the surgeon found none among them repentant for their armed resistance.[12]

The horrors continued as the prisoners were floated down the Alabama River to the Gulf, then up the Mississippi to Arkansas, then marched by land to their final destination, Fort Gibson, Oklahoma. Reports of "bilious and congestive fevers, dysentery, diarrhea, and cholera infantum" plagued the voyage. In that particular journey of 2,498 prisoners, the government reported that 339 died or had gone missing at the hands of the subcontractors hired to deliver the Creeks to the new lands. Wave after wave of prisoners were delivered west, some in chained groups known as "coffles," some by boat, some in forced marches overland. Outsiders could not help but note the "awful silence" that hung across the marches and the camps. One witness saw the December arrival of "thousands" of Creeks into Oklahoma "entirely destitute of shoes or covering of any kind for the feet; many of them are almost naked.... In this destitute condition, they are wading the cold mud, or are hurried on over the frozen road." Their feet were frostbitten, and large numbers were stumbling and falling behind the pack. "Many of them, not being able to endure this unexampled state of human suffering, die, and it is said are thrown by the side of the road, and are covered only with brush, &c. where they remain, until devoured by the wolves."[13]

Despite quick victories that led to many forced emigrations, the war dragged on for almost a full year until April 1837, when the final official battle concluded the war in the same place where it began: Barbour County. In the western part of the county, the Barbour Rangers had located a band of three hundred holdouts. The soldiers were quickly joined by an early Eufaula intruder, and US brigadier general, named William Wellborn, and a company of soldiers at the fateful site on the Pea River. The attack upon the Creeks there launched four relentless hours of up-close combat in the swamps in which, Wellborn reported, "the slaughter became unparalleled." The troops mowed down all people they could without regard to age or gender, and mercilessly chased those who fled through the swamps and killed them. By the time it was over, bodies floated facedown in the murky waters, and others lay draped and motionless over snags of timber. The militia emerged from the water battlefield described as looking like hog butchers covered with blood from the gruesome hand-to-hand combat. Although the Battle of Pea River ended the fighting in the former Creek Nation, Wellborn continued to command six companies to make sure that the Creeks who had managed to melt into west Florida did not find their way back to their homeland.[14]

By the middle of 1837, more than 15,000 Native Americans had been gathered in camps at places like Fort Mitchell and then driven mercilessly to Fort Gibson in Oklahoma. They arrived with few or no possessions. An estimated 3,500 people died on the route. The Creek people, abandoned to the new land, were not even left with enough US Army blankets to fulfill the promised supply of one for each emigrant. The contracted emigration company had to send to New York for more. The Creeks were left with nothing else.

There was still more, and worse, to come. In the autumn of 1837, one of the last major relocations became the most notorious. The story is still passed down in Creek lore as emblematic of their epic plight across the southern United States. To deliver the Creeks up the Mississippi, the contracted emigration firm hired a cheap fleet of steamboats and piled each of them with hundreds of Creek people. One in particular, the *Monmouth*, had over six hundred Native Americans on board when, caught in the dark drizzling rain and accidently in the wrong channel for northbound traffic, it crashed into another steamship. The rickety boat was immediately sliced in two. Half the Indians on board (311 Creeks, plus 2 whites) suddenly plunged into the darkness of the muddy Mississippi and drowned.[15]

Despite the brutal hardships, each group attempted to carry the town ceremonial fire with them—against the odds of weather, mud, rivers, and time—in order to ignite again the communal flames central to Creek identity. Fourteen thousand Creeks made the journey in 1836 alone. Some of the Creeks who survived the long voyage to their new lives in Indian Territory named their new community the Eufaula District of the Creek Nation. At some point we can imagine that someone charged with the grave responsibility of carrying the communal fire was able to light the new communal hearth. Eufaula, Oklahoma, is still there today.

But rather than a victory celebration, the European Americans along the Chattahoochee were consumed by a sour mix of shame and recrimination. For one, the men of Irwinton would now have to wrestle with a reputation as cowards. During the Second Creek War, they were found cowering in barrels when the noise of their own militia approaching scared them into hiding. The townspeople had also fled to the woods rather than fight the Creeks for their land, where they depended upon federal forces to protect them. One critic of the Intruders' War mockingly toasted the victory in Russell and Barbour Counties by raising his glass to "the seat of the late war with the Creek Indians: May its rich soil, now owned and settled by men too cowardly to defend it, be speedily owned and settled by a braver and more honorable set of men." Locals, angry at the speculators for leading them into the mess, demanded a federal investigation into what happened. The federal agents sent to investigate the swindles were stonewalled systematically by the speculators. In Barbour County, the indefatigable John Hogan reported complete hostility to his work: "I have had much opposition to this investigation since I came into this district, and opposition to the investigation seems to be systematized."[16]

One exasperated volunteer soldier toasted the man who had helped trigger the war. "Maj. Eli S. Shorter," he said, "together with all those who have been participants in the late Indian frauds, be forever damned in the estimation of every honest and intelligent citizen."[17]

Not everyone damned Shorter. The cotton-hungry intruders, anxious to march Indians westward out of the region, swiftly marched coffles of slaves in from the east. An orgy of slave-based capitalism filled the region. The importation of slaves from beyond American borders had ended in 1808, but the relocation of enslaved people from the states of the old slave economy to the rough and expanding cotton frontier boomed with extraordinary force. By 1840, 5,548 enslaved people tilled the land and worked in the houses of Barbour County. By 1858 the figure had more than doubled to 12,000 slaves, transforming the Creek area of Barbour County into a place made up of a numerical majority of people of African descent until 1960. An estimated $8 million worth of human chattel lived and worked in Barbour County on the eve of the Civil War, all engaged in growing the white gold that built the modern economy. As Alabama's first historian wrote in 1839, the region was "wrought and consecrated through a bitter sacrament of blood."[18]

One wonders if the speculators who initially seized the Creek village could see, in some dreamy fashion, the streets of the tiny hamlet as they would one day become, lined with enormous columned mansions built from cotton wealth derived from land stolen from the Creeks and labor stolen from Africa.

What of freedom? More than half of a century after the Second Creek War, at the 1892 meeting of the American Historical Association in Chicago, the historian Frederick Jackson Turner delivered his infamous "Frontier Thesis." That scholarly talk cemented the most famous combination of myth, theory, and history to ever permeate American ideology. He argued that the freedom-and-democracy-loving American character was forged on the line between "civilization and savagery" that we call the American frontier. As the frontier moved across the new nation, American freedom and individualism were born and born again in an epic sweep across the West.

The cultural and political interactions in the Creek nation, however, show the opposite: no such line existed and little admirable about American freedom developed in the interaction. A raw and elemental white freedom did surface as the central expression of expansion and conquest. What Turner understood as the ways that the "continuous touch with the simplicity of primitive society, furnish the forces dominating American character" may be partially right. The result was not a democratic freedom but a freedom to dominate.[19]

Walter L. Fleming, an early historian of Alabama with more than a little sympathy for white supremacy, encapsulated the outcome of the

Creek crisis in terms of a victory for states' rights—well before slavery became the center of the bitter politics of federalism. "The United States wanted the Indians to remain as states within states," he argued in 1905; "the Georgia and Alabama settlers felt that the Indians must go." As a result, "the attitude of the Federal government drove the settlers into extreme assertions of state rights." It was not an unreasonable assessment. The Owens killing in particular remained a hot subject, Fleming argued. "There was great excitement in the state, and public meetings were everywhere held to organize resistance" to federal power, he claimed. But as a result of democratic struggle and organizing, "the United States government yielded, the whites remained on the Indian lands, the state authority was upheld in the Indian counties, the soldiers were tried before state courts, and the Indians were removed to the West. The governor proclaimed a victory for the state, and the 30,000 angry Alabamians rejoiced over what they considered the defeat of the unjust Federal government." It was, he proclaimed, unlike South Carolina, nullification "successfully carried out."[20]

States' rights doctrine emerged as a result of land swindles, and the federal government became the villain because it "could, but would not, satisfy the settlers' land hunger." The inhumanity of slavery and Jim Crow, however appropriate, tends to figure most centrally in questions of states' rights and local sovereignty. Overlooked, however, is the appropriation of Indigenous lands, where the federal government always lurked menacingly and arguments about states' rights and white freedom were first worked out. Perhaps the greatest irony is that the virulence of that ideological creed among European Americans was such that an Indian hater, Secretary of War Cass, gained a reputation as an Indian lover, and the old Indian fighter Andrew Jackson failed to live up to the people's expectations and was reduced to playing the "bogeyman" of freedom.[21]

There is a lost alternative to this story. Digging deeper into Euro-American history, we find a lost model for Creek relations from before Jackson and before Jefferson promised a property-based idea of freedom to white people. In the Federal era, defined by presidents Washington and Adams, a more aggressive vision of state power dominated the political stage—including Native American affairs. The strategy was to police the Anglo-Creek border effectively in order to prevent encroachment, protect borders, and avoid war. The federal government's goal was not simple expansion but, as the historian Kevin Kokomoor explains, to impose "a restrictive policy of coexistence on state officials in the Southeast, guaranteeing Creek lands and protecting them from settlers by force if necessary, and they succeeded." Prior to the carnage of dispossession that began under Jefferson and reached its full force under Jackson, "the Federalist efforts provide an intriguing counternarrative that highlights the possibility of Native American and Euro-American coexistence."[22]

George Washington's secretary of war, Henry Knox, remained suspicious of white people below the Ohio River, who disregarded "civil power" and indulged in "angry passions." He saw their freedom as zero sum, a Hobbesian freedom of one against all: "There can be neither Justice or observance of treaties, where every man claims to the be the sole Judge in his own cause, and the avenger of his own supposed wrongs." Knox knew that Americans "cannot expect to live in peace" with the Creeks "if individuals are at liberty to invade their lands." He called for control over the states and their populations when it came to Indian affairs. It would take federal power to control the destructive consequences of the free populations' actions. As Knox argued, "The sword of the Republic only, is adequate to guard a due administration of justice, and the preservation of the peace."[23]

Instead of the Federalist vision, the notion of a Jeffersonian and Jacksonian idea of republican freedom bound the connections among self-rule, economic independence, and state sovereignty directly to domination—political, ideological, and military—of the Indigenous peoples. Freedom shaped by exclusion, freedom combined with power, freedom tied to states' rights, freedom based on theft: these factors became so unconsciously intertwined as to be synonymous with the central aspect of the American creed. The freedom ideal proved so powerful in Barbour County that it helped lead the cause of Alabama seceding from the union altogether.[24]

BOOK TWO

Citizenship

CHAPTER SIX

Igniting a Wall of Fire

EUFAULA REMAINED REMOTE AND silent during the Civil War, never touched by the battles that scarred so much of the region. Economically and socially cut off from the rest of the South by strategic war fronts, there was no Shiloh, Battle of the Wilderness, or Manassas here. Yankee muskets that fired with such intensity as to raze other, distant forests did not scar this land. Yet the violence remained, against Indigenous peoples driven from this land, against people marched here by force, against those who grew, chopped, and loaded Eufaula's cotton to sate the hungers of distant industrial harbors. And along the swampy rivers and dusty byways a drumbeat of white recalcitrance throbbed: the "old" ways—few mentioned they were barely a generation and a half old—must be restored and defended.

Eerie laceworks of Spanish moss hung over the streets and homes like theater curtains not quite ready to part. Untouched by war were the oak, sweet gum, hickory, and short leaf pine that ignored the human struggle that had raged beneath them for decades. Distant yellow jasmine, red bud, dogwood, and rhododendron continued to compete with the spring pear and plum blossoms. Wildflowers and bursts of cotton bolls remained the only break with hazy sky and green, green land. The river of "painted rocks," as Chattahoochee translates, and its many tributaries rolled on into inescapable marshy steam that hovered low above the region. The web of rivers with names given by people now purged from the countryside—Cowikee, Chewalla, Okenee, Oketee, Ufala—still flowed into the silvery Chattahoochee. In graveyards and churches for Blacks and graveyards and churches for whites rested those who had trespassed, whether by shackle or free will, on the fitful bones of the Creeks. The ghosts of all are swaddled together in the thick green coat of the very land that brought the land-hungry Europeans here. Battles dominated theaters all over the South, but not here, among the people who had done so much to start the war.[1]

In the remarkably brief twenty-five years between the Second Creek War and the outbreak of the Civil War, the version of freedom that had grown up in Eufaula had become worth dying for. Eufaula mushroomed from a ramshackle riverbank settlement under assault by Creeks and federals to a bustling commercial center surrounded by luminous homes spreading inland from the river. In that brief quarter century, the white romance of the antebellum age hardened into an ideology that would define the region indefinitely. In the short time it took for a person to be born and grow to adulthood, cotton had imprinted itself on the minds, culture, and economy of Barbour County to the point that local leaders would become militant secessionists to preserve their splendor. The cotton riches of Barbour County rapidly had bent the minds of locals around an overpowering drive to preserve their freedom and autonomy from the tyrannical plans of the North—threats both real and imagined. Having beat back the feds to secure Creek lands, they would have to do it again to ensure their freedom to enslave. The plantation economy in Barbour County and the entrepôt of Eufaula may have been little more than a generation old, but to those who lived there and profited from the system, it was a cradle of American freedom.

Unbeknown to the militant "fire eating" secessionists of Barbour County, the riches they defended were already damned by what sober economists call a "resource curse." Some 150 million years ago, the warm primordial seas lapped through the middle of what is now the Deep South. An ancient shoreline curved westward from what is today the state of South Carolina, moving southwest as it bisected Georgia and then cutting across the lower part of the state of Alabama—drawing a line right through Barbour County. Everything below that line was under water. During the Cretaceous period, this ancient expanse of the Gulf of Mexico served as an incubator for marine plankton with carbon-based skeletons. The accumulated mass of that dead plankton slowly built into a dense layer of chalk. When the waters receded, the shoreline formed the foundation for a crescent of fertile, well-drained land that would one day be known as the Black Belt for the dark, rich color of its soil. The Black Belt line could not be clearer than in Barbour County, where rich plantations dominate the north end of the county, and the lower half is surrendered to the ungenerous clay of the wiregrass region below the fall line. There, hardscrabble subsistence farms and lumber camps contrasted with the opulence of plantation life, the "penny coated clay" would become globally competitive only when forced to do so by the injection of modern fertilizers of the postbellum era.[2]

For planters and speculators in the cotton economy, the dead plankton gave shape to one of the great economic opportunities in world history—and augured trouble for human history. When European Americans drove Native people off their land, they feverishly followed that ribbon of soil with dreams of cotton riches burning in their minds. "The message was always the same: move and make your fortune, further west and further south," as the historian James Oakes portrays the process, and look "to a future of unbounded expansion, unprecedented abundance, and white supremacy." In their wake, the planters left depleted soil and the need to push farther on to new planting frontiers. Highly capitalized "pioneers with means," as another historian called them, or at least those with access to large amounts of credit, bought and consolidated land on an industrial scale.[3]

Clearly for the slaves purchased in the East, torn away from their families and driven west in chained "coffles," the line of black soil arching across the South was little more than a cursed crescent of oppression. As lands were depleted in the East, the drive westward became imperative, a tortuous path one historian calls the "second middle passage." Eufaula was not New Orleans or Charleston, but it had its open-air slave market on the meridian dividing the primary boulevard through downtown, Broad Street, just a block from the community's main intersection. Violence, slavery, and the freedom to dominate land and labor filled Jefferson's "Empire of Liberty." Rather than slavery diluting and thinning out as it moved west, as Jefferson prophesized, it became denser, more exploitative, more wrapped around the resource curse. As the planters pushed into frontier places like southern Alabama, the celebrated paternalism of the old Southeast dissolved into some of the most naked and vicious dimensions of the American slave regime.[4]

Immense resource endowments like the productive soils of the Black Belt seem like nothing but a boon to regional development—at least at first. The problem begins with the desire to exploit natural resource endowments—whether growing sugar, digging diamonds, pumping oil, mining precious metal, or planting staples like cotton. As resources produce commodities, the surrounding institutional, economic, racial, and political developments fuse with their fate. Regional politics and ideology monomaniacally twist around the specifics of resource exploitation at the cost of a more diverse set of economic endeavors. The factors of production—land, labor, capital, and the entrepreneurial energies that unite them—bend in a single, self-reinforcing direction. In the Black Belt came slave labor rather than wage labor. Monoculture rather than economic diversity. Trade based on the importation of manufactured goods rather than industrial innovation. Plantations rather than family farms. Elite power rather than town hall politics. Centralization of economic power rather than shared wealth. Slave labor rather than a sturdy and demanding working class.[5]

Upon the Black Belt grew staggering amounts of wealth, advanced technology, cutting-edge credit mechanisms, and horrifically sophisticated labor management systems. Despite creating large fortunes, cotton delivered less economic diversity, more inequality of all kinds, and much weaker democratic traditions than found in regions with less sizable resource endowments. Elites shunned manufacturing, preferring low tariffs that allowed them to buy industrial goods with money made by growing more cotton. They made foodstuffs for local consumption, but that was always secondary to filling the hungry maws of textile mills from Lowell to Manchester. They sought more credit, more money, and more slaves—which they could buy, sell, and even mortgage. The resource curse of the Black Belt was such that after cotton wealth faded, it left magnificent mansions standing among some of the poorest counties in the United States. Such single-minded economic dependency, as the historian James Oakes put it, meant that "New World slavery was itself the servant of the driving force of capitalism."[6]

The resource curse also meant that upon Black slaves working black soil grew the ideology of white freedom. Cotton defined how labor was done and race was seen. It defined what ideas were discussed and which were forbidden. It shaped institutions, and it shaped cultures. It also dictated what freedom meant. As the economic historian Peter Coclanis framed it in his study of rice in the South Carolina Low Country, the pursuit of commodity-based development created "a society whose *liberty derived from repression* and whose fragile prosperity was based almost entirely on obsequence to the dictates of Europe and procrustean labor controls."[7]

The curse drew non-slaveholders into its spell, as kinship, renting out, overseeing, sales of goods and services, legal services, and politics were also directly dependent upon cotton capitalism. The system was so powerful that it even drew the less productive areas of southeastern Alabama, including the southern half of Barbour County, into its logic. There the soil was not rich and the slaves few, but the economic and social impact of cotton proved powerful. Even the hardscrabble farmers had incentives to move into cotton and buy slaves since "cotton farming and the institution of slavery touched nearly every community in the piney woods either directly or indirectly." What that meant for the sectional divisions to come was that "in the minds of most whites," argues a regional historian, even for those outside the plantation system, "it was a system worth preserving, no matter what."[8]

For all of its long-term developmental problems, cotton delivered staggering wealth. Since the Eufaula Creeks were forced west, leaving their wetlands to inhabit the "rivers of sand" in Oklahoma, the cotton dollars transformed the wooden facades of Irwinton into stately and permanent brick buildings containing scores of commercial establishments with a wide array of goods and services. With the Indigenous people driven out, the citizens reclaimed the name "Eufaula" in 1843, a quaint point of antiquarian reference for what was becoming a minor commercial hub. A stout and elegant covered bridge, spanning over five hundred feet, connected Eufaula to Georgia in 1839. Designed by the famous enslaved engineer and builder Horace King, the structural marvel lasted until it was replaced in 1924. The Eufaula wharf did a steady business as ambitious traders sent cotton and other commodities down the river and imported fine luxuries and manufactured goods from Europe—all advertised as "tariff free." "The business of Eufaula," commented a passing journalist, "is large."[9]

The town's affluence grew to be a thing of legend. Even today, a stroll through Eufaula, past the luxurious mansions on either side of the tree-lined boulevard, confirms the faded opulence of days gone by (even if most of those extant mansions were built after the Civil War to reestablish a specific, glorified history). Their tremendous windows, dramatic white columns, ornate parlors, and tall-ceilinged bedrooms shaped the architecture of "the fabulous period." Carved walnut furniture, glass-paneled cupolas, white marble mantel pieces, intricate pilasters, graceful mahogany staircases, breezy verandas, and gardens, gardens, and more gardens ostentatiously weighed down antebellum mansions. Inside, "monumental beds of rosewood, gold cornices and long mirrors, set in gilded mounters, were taken for granted in the general design for living." The degree of Eufaula's global connections is suggested by a Eufaula banker who was remembered as donning Irish linens and Scottish tweeds, enjoying Chinese tea, and traveling in his silver-trimmed carriage in between his annual vacations abroad. John Horry Dent recorded purchasing his carriage for $500, two and half times the salary of his finest overseer. Before the Civil War, the town had the largest population, the wealthiest estates, the most cotton production, and the largest number of slaves in the Lower Chattahoochee Valley.[10]

Horace King, an enslaved architect and engineer, designed and supervised the building of the Chattahoochee Bridge. Constructed by slave labor in the late 1830s, the bridge dominated the view of the river from high atop the Eufaula bluff. It remained the primary route to Georgia from Eufaula until it was torn down and replaced in 1924.

The curse of cotton not only limited the breadth of political minds and narrowed economic logic; it also restrained agricultural diversity down to its inexorable limits. No matter the question, the answer was more cotton and more slaves. The editor of the *Eufaula Democrat*, for instance, believed that planters ought to balance out their cotton production with other commodities, including grain, livestock, food, and timber. Such caution lost out to the magnetic allure of white gold. "But our planters, instead of following these plain dictates of common sense, strain every nerve to add to the number of bales of cotton. Not only so, they invest every dollar of surplus capital they can scrape up, in purchasing negroes from Maryland, Virginia, and N. Carolina." Half a decade after the end of the Creek War, the newspaper complained of the costs of this sense of urgency. "One of the most baneful consequences of unsettledness is seen in the abuse of the soil," the paper pointed out. "All that can be made must be made immediately, without regard to an almost waste of the energies of the land. The most exhausting modes of cultures are resorted to—the fixed intention of the planter being to emigrate as soon as the soil losses its fruitfulness." The slave population doubled between 1840 and 1850. By the eve of the Civil War, there were 16,150 enslaved people working for 1,143 masters.[11]

Fear ruled the county. The town of Eufaula enforced a one-dollar fine on plantations that failed to contribute to the notorious slave patrols that combed the county every night in search of runaways—or just people out past their allotted hour. Any slave found past 10 p.m. or found to be participating in disorderly activities at any hour received thirty-nine lashes by the town marshal. Should an enslaved person religiously "exhort" another without being in possession of a license by white Christians, they also received the wrath of thirty-nine lashes—fifty for the second offense. Even slaves who had the permission of their masters to be hired out were required to be in possession of a permit issued by the town council, a process that included a rather sizable five-dollar fee. No Black person could do business of any kind without being under the watchful responsibility of a "good white man." State law prevented anyone from teaching any African American person, free or enslaved, to read or write, a crime that would result in a penalty of $250 to $500. The law was redundant given the fact that there were no free Blacks allowed in the state at all. If free Blacks were uncovered and they did not leave, they were subject to being sold at auction.[12]

Whether Democrats in favor of bootstrap autonomy or pro-business, pro-infrastructure Whigs who dominated the politics of the town, all steered their thinking toward freedom. J. Mills Thornton III, the dean of Alabama historians, concludes that "the goal of antebellum society, in sum, was individual liberty"—liberty, of course, defined in very specific ways. The foundation of the entire ideological edifice, he argues, was "that freedom was the greatest of all possessions; that it was maintained through economic action; that power could be destructive of it; and that the function of the state was to preserve it." Any "action which appeared to the citizenry to threaten individual autonomy" of whites, continues Thornton, especially the autonomy of elites, was regarded as "a challenge to democracy and a portent of thralldom." Questioning slavery, or, more commonly, the westward expansion of slavery, was the most common trigger for that fear of thralldom—and a means to consolidate political power from clamorous Democratic forces of the county, the state, and the region.[13]

A minor but revealing example of how community standards bent under the weight of the curse of the cotton imperative took place down at the Eufaula post office in 1850. Captain Elisha Betts, a citizen of Eufaula and a hero of the Second Creek War, made the mistake of developing an open-ended interest in the question of slavery. Opposed to the extremism of North and South in a time of sectional tensions, he was a self-professed Whig who felt that "every patriot and lover of this Union should feel profoundly grateful" for the voices of compromise in national politics. Hardly an abolitionist, Betts became concerned about the corrosive impact of slavery on the morals and culture of white people.[14]

To learn more, the good captain slipped two dollars into an envelope in July 1850 and mailed it off to Washington to request a one-year subscription to the *National Era*, an abolitionist newspaper. When the first issue arrived, the postmaster of Eufaula returned it to Washington without hesitation, refusing to deliver it or any paper like it. Upon learning of this, the *National Era* called it "an act of censorship to which no independent man could submit without degradation, and which, if tolerated, was a precedent for the exercise of similar tyranny in other cases." Clearly, abolitionists' definition of freedom had little in common with the kind of freedom that reigned in Barbour County.[15]

In a Eufaula town meeting, the citizenry voted to run Captain Betts out of town for the apostasy of his political curiosity. Even though Betts had saved the life of the father of the chairman of the town meeting "from the vengeance of the savages" in the Creek War, no mercy was shown. Captain Betts appears never to have returned to Barbour County. In a second large and angry town meeting, the assembled throngs supported Eufaula's "highly esteemed" postmaster, J. H. Danforth, against federal removal. The assembly resolved to refuse any other postmaster that Washington, DC, might dare send in his place. In a clamorous vote for the aye position, "every man instantly rose to his feet amid universal cheering." The call for nays delivered only silence.[16]

When word got back to Washington, the US postmaster realized he would not be able to find anyone to take the office if he removed Danforth for failing his duties, so he allowed the "the petty censor" to continue in the office despite having "defied the authority of the Federal Government." "This is freedom in a Slave State," the *National Era* editorialized; "to be at the mercy of every village postmaster, who may dictate to you, at his own sovereign will and pleasure, what you shall, and shall not, read."[17]

The Eufaula Regency, a group of states' rights militants, made the city a notorious hotbed of political agitation and influence. As a center for "fire eaters," those deeply militant leaders anxious for secession, they adopted a near conspiratorial fear of the degradation of their freedom at the hands of federal authority. Yet they were not hotheads ready to jump the ship of state. Eufaula's finest citizens committed themselves instead to a long effort to convince their Southern brethren, as local Jefferson Buford put it, to let secession "sink into our very bones and marrow and become a part of our being before they develop the fruit of action." The group's work made them "as important in Alabama state politics as the Democratic Party political machine Tammany Hall was in New York." A poem published in the local paper explained the town's commitment to states' rights liberty:

Ye patriot whigs of old Barbour
Ye patriot democrats too,
Your bright sunny south is in danger,
She calls on her sons to be true.

The union's a band of oppression.
'Tis oppression we ask you to meet;
Plant your feet on the old constitution
And strike, ere your ruin's complete

Our fathers' resisted oppression—
Fell bleeding for freedom and right,

Let their sons resist northern aggression
Have 36, 30, or fight.[18]

The reference to "36, 30" was the specific latitude set in the Missouri Compromise of 1820 between free and slave states west of Missouri. Sectional politics in the nineteenth century functioned to maintain a political balance of power in Congress, a stalemate of sorts that would help minimize political conflict—and prevent war—while allowing slavery room to expand into new lands. For the federal government to deny slavery in the West meant, as the *Montgomery Advertiser* claimed, that "a free citizen of Massachusetts was a better man and entitled to more privileges than a free citizen of Alabama." The Eufaula Regency would have none of that. The introduction of California as a free state after the territorial expansion of the Mexican-American War destabilized the old balancing act with what became known as the Compromise of 1850. The compromise gave the free states a two-seat advantage in the Senate, but in exchange the slave states got the Fugitive Slave Act. Future states, the compromise established, would be admitted by the messy and unruly process of popular sovereignty. As a result of the anxieties produced by the Compromise of 1850, the *Eufaula Democrat* changed its name to *Spirit of the South* and put on its masthead "Equality in the Union, or Independence out of it." One hundred and fifty people in Barbour County asked the governor to call the state legislature into session to discuss leaving the union. No popular vote on secession ever came of this, but the door to the question opened widely.[19]

The Kansas-Nebraska Act of 1854 ended the balancing act by throwing open to popular sovereignty the possibility of slavery in Kansas. If more people supported slavery in the new state of Kansas, then it would enter the union as a slave state. If more supported free soil, then it would be free soil. Nebraska, it was widely recognized, would come into the union free. Bands of free-soil guerrillas, known as Jayhawkers, battled with militant bands of border ruffians interested in making Kansas a slave state by whatever means they could. The open clash between free and slave forces turned the territory into "Bleeding Kansas."

Eufaulans were there too. "Who will go to Kansas?" Eufaulan Jefferson Buford asked in the *Spirit of the South.* Recognizing that the fate of slavery lay in access to the West, the Eufaulan declared, "I wish to raise three hundred industrious, sober, discreet, reliable men capable of bearing arms, not prone to use them wickedly or unnecessarily, but willing to protect their sections in every real emergency." As one of the most prominent citizens and lawyers in the town, and a hero in the Creek Wars, Buford had both the money and the social standing to raise troops for his march on Kansas. Guaranteeing volunteers forty acres, free passage to Kansas, and financial support for a full year, he claimed to be putting twenty thousand of his own dollars into the project—money raised by selling some of his slaves. "If we cannot find many who are willing to incur great individual loss in the common cause," Buford proclaimed, "if we cannot find some crazy enough to peril even life in the deadly breach, then it is not because individuals have grown more prudent and wise, but because public virtue has decayed and we have thereby already become unequal to the successful defense of our rights."[20]

In March 1856, the Eufaulans marched west toward Kansas, trying to collect additional fighters as they traveled. The event, full of patriotic fanfare, was largely a bungled disaster. Buford's men engaged in a number of skirmishes around Lawrence and other areas but were accused of maliciously destroying private property. Then in the confusion of "Bleeding Kansas," the militia fell apart and ultimately disbanded. Buford traveled back to Alabama, heavyhearted that his efforts to save Kansas from being a free state had failed.[21]

In 1860, slavery divided the national Democratic Party into three factions, three conventions, and three candidates. The crisis opened up the presidency to the new Republican Party and its candidate, Abraham Lincoln, who seemed to embody all of white Barbour County's fears about Northern aggression. Although Lincoln conceded that the federal government had no power "to disturb slavery in the states where it exists," he was clear that, as a matter of national policy, slavery would not be allowed in the western territories and new states. This was seen as an act of tyranny by the South. By hemming slavery in territorially, they were also restricting it both economically and politically.[22]

On the day the news of the 1860 election arrived, the burning effigy of Abraham Lincoln swung from mock gallows in the center of town. The election of someone like Lincoln meant the end of freedom and constitutional democracy as they understood it. "While we may be called upon to weep a little over the dead body of the old Union, we shall rejoice that the South is free," declared Eufaulan and congressman James Pugh on the election of the Illinois Republican. Militia groups organized, drilled, and marched. Some mentioned the defense of slavery, most spoke of freedom. They continually referred to Lincoln as that "black Republican." Forty-eight prominent residents of Barbour County signed a circular, making clear the stakes of Lincoln's election:

> To the People of Barbour County
>
> The abolitionists have triumphed. Shall we submit? Will Alabamians permit abolitionists to rule them? Shall we yield like slaves or resist like freemen? The great question we must now decide…

They decided to "resist like freemen." Less than a week after Lincoln's election, South Carolina called for a convention on secession. Before Christmas the state left the union, the first to do so. The news arrived in Eufaula by telegraph, and the citizens erupted in celebration as the fate of Alabama seemed to be on an inevitable path to join South Carolina. The town bells clanged, and by the time the sun was going down, the chimes of freedom were accompanied by the organization of a one-hundred-gun salute. Cannon fire blasted throughout the county. White people put candles in their windows, bonfires burned, and a torchlight procession all illuminated the Alabama night sky. After rousing speeches in favor of a Confederacy free of the yoke of federal oppression, "the ladies on the porch sang the Southern Marseillaise in splendid style." Hundreds joined in with each round of the chorus:

To arms! Then, one and all;
Let this our watchword be;
March on! March on! No faction shall
Enslave our Liberty!

The few and fearful Unionists bit their tongues.[23]

A few weeks after South Carolina, Alabama declared for secession. The town went mad with excitement. Elizabeth Rhodes noted in her diary, "There was never such a time in Eufaula as that night, a gala night, with the booming of canon in our ears. Flags were floating the breeze in all directions.... The most gloriously magnificent sight I ever beheld. Almost every home appeared as if studded with diamonds in a glorious sunlight, so brilliant were the bonfires... the cannons fired sixty salutes. The bells rang forth many peals."[24]

Men lined up to join in the fight, believing that they had to scramble to the front lines as quickly as possible to see action before the brief war would be over. "Every true Southerner is for resistance," Elizabeth Rhodes wrote. Barbour County's outpouring of men and materiel proved enormous. Infantry units from the county included the Louisville Blues, Clayton Guards, Pioneer Guards, Eufaula Rifles, Barbour Greys, Glennville Guards, Midway Guards, Fort Browder Roughs, Eufaula City Guards, the Eufaula Light Artillery, Dent's Battery, and Kolb's Battery. Three Barbour County elites, with no prior military experience, rose to the rank of general in the Confederate army. When the fighting men of Eufaula marched off to war to teach the Yankees and "black Republicans" a lesson about the Southern commitment to freedom, that cursed black soil clung to their boots.[25]

The political zealotry surrounding the freedom to enslave grew ever more frenzied. "The slavery system was now 'working like madness in the brain,'" Eufaula historian Anne Kendrick Walker noted. The *Clayton Banner* called for "the immediate outlawry" of all who "may come among us from the land where they educate and send forth emissaries to incite insurrections, secret poisonings, murders and house burnings at the South." From out at Fort Browder in

Barbour County, came reports that "some of our citizens have almost become maniacs on the subject of politics." Fears about slave revolts combined with the growing militancy as the "vigilant committee" kept watch over any congregation of African Americans. Eufaulan Parthenia Hague claimed that the Republicans believed that "the people of the South were fit only for the pikes hidden at Harper's Ferry."[26]

Alabama honored the Eufaula Regency by electing one of its members as the first governor in the entire Confederacy. He would be the first in a long line of Barbour County locals to hold the office. John Gill Shorter, a Jacksonian Democrat and nephew of the rabid land speculator, had been elected to state offices and appointed as a circuit judge prior to taking the governor's seat. His interest in economic development shifted him away from the Jacksonians, but he allied with the Regency and emphasized the defense of Southern economic development, the territorial expansion of slavery, and the political defense of the South. In his December 1861 inaugural address, the governor declared, "We may well congratulate ourselves and return thanks that a timely action on our part has saved our liberties, preserved our independence, and given us, it is hoped, a perpetual separation" from the federal government. "May we in all coming time stand separate from it, as if a wall of fire intervened."[27]

Governor John Gill Shorter struggled to maintain his political principles, but the war destroyed them all. His limited government ideals transformed into an enormous expansion of state power in every aspect of people's lives—not the least of which was the draft. He appropriated slaves from their masters to build defense infrastructure, which betrayed his fundamental beliefs about the nature of property—and which the plantation owners despised. The wartime poverty and suffering of the white population was such that he even supported an 1863 bill to offer relief to suffering white Alabamians. Moreover, he could not prevent the Union blockade of Mobile or the enemy's control of the northern part of the state. Shorter's no-win situation fueled opposition among those who believed he had betrayed his small government promises as well as those who believed he had failed to do enough to help his people. The war dragged voters from wild-eyed optimism to deprivation and despair. When he stood for reelection in 1863, he did not even win Barbour County. In his place, the state elected a Whig who had been much more hesitant about secession.[28]

As the war progressed, unity and high hopes dissolved into division and despair. Conscription was immensely unpopular, desertion high, and hardship inescapable. The wealthy could buy their way out of military service or contract to deliver supplies in lieu of fighting. The most notorious of the class dimensions of the draft, however, was the unpopular Twenty Slave Law that exempted one white man for every twenty slaves on a plantation. While supposedly designed to avoid slave insurrections as Lincoln's proposed Emancipation Proclamation was in the works, it insulated many of the most clamorous elites from marching to war. A mechanic across the river in Columbus, Georgia, said they could barely feed themselves, but "their condition is much better than the poor soldiers, who are fighting the rich men's fight, for they suffer all the privations and hardships incident to the life of a soldier, with a perfect knowledge of the sufferings of their families at home." Military mobilization in the Black Belt was "a rich man's war, and a poor man's fight," and by 1863 the plain folk knew it.[29]

Amid the confusion of war, Abraham Lincoln maintained a crystal clear idea about the ideas of freedom at stake. In 1864, he spoke to the people of Baltimore, explaining, "The world has never had a good definition of the word liberty." A nation at war with itself over slavery was in need of one. "We all declare for liberty," he puzzled, "but in using the same *word* we do not all mean the same *thing*." He saw the nation divided into two perspectives. "With some the word liberty may mean for each man to do as he pleases with himself, and the product of his labor; while with others the same word may mean for some men to do as they please with other men, and the product of other men's labor." Two different parties can see the same thing and call it "by two different and incompatible names—liberty and tyranny."[30]

Lincoln developed his thinking, as he did so very often, by way of parable. "The shepherd drives the wolf from the sheep's throat, for which the sheep thanks the shepherd as a *liberator*, while the wolf denounces him for the same act as the destroyer of liberty, especially as the sheep was a black one," argued the old Rail Splitter. "Plainly the sheep and the wolf are not agreed upon a definition of the word liberty; and precisely the same difference prevails to-day among us human creatures, even in the North, and all professing to love liberty. Hence we behold the processes by which thousands are daily passing from under the yoke of bondage, hailed by some as the advance of liberty, and bewailed by others as the destruction of all liberty." Yet there's another layer to the problem in that those who rallied to the defense of the Union were less motivated by liberation than they were their own version of freedom: not to free the slaves but merely to exclude their bondage from the free soil of western lands.[31]

Three summers of bloody conflict passed without the dogs of war visiting Barbour County. The only major campaign outside of the northern part of Alabama was at the end of the war during General Wilson's rapid-fire advance across the weakened state, taking all major industrial centers, burning the University of Alabama, and seizing the capital in Montgomery on April 12, 1865—three days after the Confederate surrender at Appomattox Courthouse. As the Confederacy melted southward, preparations were made to relocate the state capitol from Montgomery to Eufaula, but the end of the war came first. Major General Benjamin H. Grierson entered Barbour County over Hobdy's Bridge on the Pea River—the site of the final blood-soaked battle in the Second Creek War.[32]

The situation in Barbour County was volatile, Grierson noted, since the land had "been in the undisturbed possession of the rebels for several years." By the time he reached Clayton, in the center of the county, he was entirely cut off from communication with other federal forces. From captured rebel mail, he learned of the assassination of Abraham Lincoln, an act he regarded as "a despicable and savage thrust at the heart of the nation." He had to control his rage, and that of his troops, from being dispensed upon the citizens of Barbour County. Reminiscent of Marshal Crawford's impulse during the Intruders' War, his impulse had been to raze the place. "The least expression of a revengeful spirit upon my part, of indication that retaliation would be tolerated, would have gone throughout the command like a flash of lightning and resulted, no doubt, in the complete desolation of the surrounding country and death of many comparatively innocent people."[33]

Grierson and his four thousand troops found the streets of Eufaula deserted, and shutters, blinds, and curtains all closed in a combination of fear and denial of the coming of the "barbarous Yankee soldiers." As the Yankees settled in, however, they found themselves "much pleased with Eufaula"—a picturesque setting that "might well fill with emotion the heart of an artist." The people of Barbour County were simply relieved that the federals had not come to destroy what was left of their communities. "Grierson was a gentleman," noted one Eufaulan. "His men deported themselves without committing any depredation." He liberated Confederate supplies hidden in people's homes and distributed them to deprived poor people of the community, "many of whom," Grierson wrote, "were suffering and entirely destitute."[34]

By the time the war was over, the chaos and demoralization of Eufaula were unmistakable. "We could now see along the roadway, hundreds of paroled and discharged ex-Confederate soldiers, each going to their own destinations," one Union trooper wrote. "Ragged, unshaven, thin and haggard, now anxious to get home. May our God bless them and their families. They are going to need the Almighty's help if they are to exist." Local diarist Parthenia Hague also felt the despair. "They were coming home with nothing; and we could almost say, coming home to nothing." With the war over and the slaves free, Governor Shorter's successor, Thomas Watts, wondered who would govern Alabama next. His sarcastic answer: "Some flat-nosed, thick-lipped sons of Africa, appointed by your conquerors," he seethed.[35]

The sixteen thousand enslaved people of Barbour County saw it quite differently. As the Union army approached the Garland plantation, the slaves turned out en masse to great them. People "large and small" left the slave quarters of one Barbour plantation to greet the arriving troops in a "surging mass of black humanity." As one recently freed Chattahoochee Valley man believed, the Yankees were not some part of an abstract struggle over political economy, but agents of the Lord himself. "God was using the Yankees to scourge the slaveholders just as He had, centuries before, used the heathens and outcasts to chastise His chosen people—the Children of Israel."[36]

Major General Benjamin Grierson feared that the Barbour County elites were not ready to play by the new occupier's rules. "The country was filled with armed marauders," he noted, "composed mostly of deserters from the late rebel armies, who have returned to find their families suffering from the neglect and persecution of the wealthy leaders, at whose instigation they joint the rebel ranks." The plain folk, both returning soldiers and those surviving behind the lines, he found, "as a general thing, now loyal." The problem was the city's leaders. "The far greater portion of the wealthy classes are still very bitter in their sentiments against the Government," he wrote, "and clutch onto slavery with a lingering hope to save at least a relic of their favorite yet barbarous institution for the future."[37]

Grierson was right, as the surrender at Appomattox Courthouse ended only the open battles, not the ongoing political war. A ten-year struggle followed Robert E. Lee's proffering of his sword to Ulysses S. Grant. The terms of the war would be to reclaim that which Eufaulans had lost: the riches offered by dominion over land and labor. At the same time, the federal government launched an unprecedented level of political and military intervention to protect and promote the rights of freed people. The world that had been won against the Creeks and then lost against the Union army would ultimately be recaptured in the politics and violence to come. White Southerners liked to call the project to win back the freedom of home rule from the federal powers of the Reconstruction era "redemption."

CHAPTER SEVEN

"*Destroying Freedom and Liberty*"

AFTER THE WAR, FREEDOM for formerly enslaved people was not about cotton. It was about being able to leave the plantations or stay under terms of their choosing, to reunite their families, to build schools and churches, and, above all, to gain independence from the violence and control of the master class. African American freedom was about security, justice, and even equality. The hopeful terms were captured well by a Northern white observer touring the South. "The sole ambition for the freedman at the present time appears to be to become the owner of a little piece of land," he noted, "there to erect a humble home, and to dwell in peace and security at his own free will and pleasure." Perhaps he might grow some cotton, but the freedmen wished to do so "without anyone to dictate to him hours or systems of labor" and, "if he wishes instead to plant corn or sorghum or sweet potatoes—to be able do *that* free from any outside control, in one word to be *free*, to control his own time and efforts without anything than can remind him of past sufferings in bondage. This is their idea, their desire and their hope."[1]

Newly freed people tramped the road, sought to reunite families shattered by the internal slave trade, and experimented with moves to the cities. Yet most ended up staying or returning to the land they knew and worked. There they were pushed into labor gangs, often covered by labor contracts that lacked any clear rules about pay. Freedmen did not want to work for wages and certainly not without money up front, and they bristled at mysterious labor contracts being waved in front of their faces by planters and representatives of the Freedmen's Bureau. What the contracts meant when over 90 percent of the Black population was illiterate remained with the goodwill of the Union soldiers working for the Freedmen's Bureau. Whipping remained prevalent. As one Alabama bureau agent explained, his problem was "the persistency of the planters in continuing their old habits of punishing or shooting those who in any way offend them." Productivity tumbled as freedmen balked at working under the planters' coercive conditions, and planters reeled at their loss of control over their labor supply.[2]

"A gentleman had occasion to visit Eufaula, a small town in Alabama," reported the *National Freedman* after the war. Inquiring about the newly freed population, he was told, "They were quiet and orderly, and the reason given for their good conduct was, that if any of them were impertinent they were immediately shot, two were shot on a neighboring planation the night before." Peace only prevailed for freed people when federal troops were in town. After the troops moved on, several African Americans were reportedly killed under mysterious circumstances. As for cotton production, the *Eufaula News* explained that due to the "liberation of the negro, a certain degree of confusion, embarrassment and derangement" engulfed Barbour County. The contest over whites' freedom to control versus the Blacks' freedom of emancipation had begun.[3]

In the postbellum struggle for power and autonomy, Black people defined their freedom by proximity to federal power; white people, by their distance from it. Emancipation from the tyranny of white freedom could only come and could only be sustained by the force of federal bayonets operating in "boldly extraconstitutional" ways. Rarely in American history was such a stark contrast revealed between federal power as democracy for one group and as usurpation of freedom for another.[4]

Among the dizzying transformations after 1865, the freedmen had two great resources. First was the tight-knit solidarity rooted in the slave quarters, which grew rapidly into a robust citizenship that poured into the political crucibles of the Loyal Leagues and Union Leagues. In those organizations, many semi-clandestine, freedmen learned and debated and mobilized to pursue their political interests. The leagues became organizing institutions for building schools and churches, as well as the pursuit of their economic interests come harvest time. There a combination of political leadership and hope grew. Looking to the Declaration of Independence, an Alabama convention declared, "We claim exactly *the same rights, privileges and immunities as are enjoyed by white men*—we ask nothing more and will be content with nothing less." While the urban version of the leagues tended to be more educated and sophisticated, the rural areas like Barbour County oriented themselves on a simple guiding premise. As the Loyal League "catechism" stated, they had to "shun the Democratic party as they would the overseer's lash and the auction block."[5]

The other resource was the Freedmen's Bureau and the military force that stood behind it, unevenly but stubbornly standing up for the rights of freedmen. An office created by Congress and placed in the hands of the military, the bureau helped to distribute humanitarian aid and rations, assisted with contracts and arbitration of disputes, and established banks, hospitals, and schools. It is telling of the immensity and danger of the task of Reconstruction that, just as in the battle against the intruders on Creek land, the defense and humanitarian treatment of nonwhite people in 1865 fell upon the Department of *War*. More than the sum of its parts, the bureau's presence in the South provided order and hope for freed people. Unlike the federal marshals' fight with the intruders in the 1830s, the Freedmen's Bureau had a powerful mandate, serious legal mechanisms and resources, and large numbers of officers and troops at its disposal. Yet given the immensity of the challenge and the staggering geographic scale of the project, the office still lacked the manpower and financial capacity to reach and enforce postbellum civil and economic rights in the South to the extent necessary.

Echoing the Creeks' plea to Jackson for federal intervention, the freedmen saw federal power—especially the military—as the key source of leverage against the rebuilding of unrestrained white power. An August 1865 "Petition of Colored Citizens" in Mobile expressed a "deep sense of gratitude to the Government of the United Sates and understanding that is the Military Arm and not the Civil who has been the instrumentality of giving to us and to our children the blessed boon of pure freedom." Listing many needs and grievances that remained, they were nonetheless interested in "working hand in hand with the Government" to build an emancipated South. "Next to our Heavenly Father," the petition continued, "we revere the good old Constitution of the United States, and now that it acknowledges our existence[,] we are unanimous as a people to die in 'its' defence." The obstacles, however, were immense. The petition reported news "from all sources that our people are cruelly maltreated in the interior of this state of Alabama, that the planters will not yet let our people go but cruelly scourges them and shoots them if they remonstrate or plead for their freedom, that numerous . . . tales of terrible and heart rending atrocities which are related not to a civilized and Christian community but to the beasts of the forest, to the rocks & trees and stone, that at the recital of such wrongs those mute and inanimate things would be thrown into confusion."[6]

When General John D. Pope took over the military occupation of the Third Military District, which included Alabama, he saw the problem clearly. The war was won, but the struggle was still ahead, and the stakes were high. The issue hinged upon the boldness of federal intervention. "It's easy under existing circumstances to win the first victory and reconstruct these States under the acts of Congress," he prophesized in 1867. "But this victory is only the beginning of the contest and unless it be a victory openly and fairly won and very decisive in its results, it may prove not only fruitless but absolutely destructive. If hastily or partially done, reconstruction will drag with it a train of evil to this country which can never be remedied."[7]

As Reconstruction played out, freedom proved to be zero-sum: any increase in Black freedom meant a decrease in white freedom. Anything that challenged white prerogatives was understood as the path to Black domination. To speak of emancipation today without historicizing and understanding efforts by whites to recapture their freedom to dominate, without seeing how emancipation of African Americans was made into the oppression of whites, is to fail to understand a central problem of American history.

The unprecedented use of federal force during Reconstruction nurtured a belief among whites that they were victims of federal military and political overreach. By the terms of their world, they were right. As counterintuitive as it may seem, to understand Reconstruction is to understand how the white elite envisioned themselves in a struggle to regain their freedom from their federal "oppressors." Only by making freedom not a local or state question but a national one, by continuing the military campaign into the broadest protections of freed people, could former enslaved peoples hope to thrive. After all, as the Radical Republican congressman Thaddeus Stevens put it, they were not just ending slavery, but attacking a core American value. Slavery, he said, was "the most tyrannical [thing] that ever man imposed in the name of freedom."[8]

Would federal authority prove strong enough to subdue the sovereignty of white freedom? "Heaven itself had made a distinction [between Black and white]," threatened the *Montgomery Advertiser and Register*, "and the Federal bayonet and Federal authority could not break down that distinction." White critics of Republican intervention would become ever more strident and ultimately more violent. The Eufaula Democratic Club, for instance, railed against the Republican Party and Reconstruction as "the wicked working of a depraved and corrupt party, destroying freedom and liberty of the person... and in open defiance of the Constitution of the United States... [full of] the most infamous, degrading and tyrannical legislation." Their "wicked disregard of the fundamental principles of American republicanism" meant the "almost total destruction of individual rights" by their "tyrannical usurpation of ill gotten power." Locals claimed, "No people who spoke the English language had ever had such servitude," and "the whole population of ten States reduced to abject and degrading slavery." Barbour County was under "a dictatorship and a despotism!"[9]

Nothing embodied the conjoined power of the African American communities and the Freedmen's Bureau more than the education of freedmen: what W. E .B. Du Bois called "the greatest success" of the bureau's many undertakings. Local Black people were committed to financing and organizing schools, and only federal authority could assist and protect them from mob violence. "Too much cannot be said of the desire to learn among this people," explained Major General Wager Swayne, head of the Freedmen's Bureau in Alabama, to Congress. "Everywhere, to open a school has been to have it filled." Such was the case in Barbour County, as across the South, where the federally backed freedmen's schools worked in exciting and hopeful ways.[10]

In Eufaula, the Freedmen's Bureau described the transformation brought on by federal presence as "a greater revelation in public opinion than the most sanguine imaginations could have anticipated." Freedmen could demand schools "in almost every neighborhood, while a year ago in many places in this district it would not have been safe to . . . establish them." Yet reports were mixed and contradictory. While Eufaula could be listed variously as a "flourishing" system with a local white population that was "very tolerant" to the presence of freedmen's schools, other Barbour County agents read the local scene as "generally opposed to col'd schools and indifferent as to schools for Poor Whites." The bureau recorded the burning of at least two county schoolhouses "occupied by the colored people." Burnings were part of at least eighty-one confirmed destructions of Alabama freedmen's schools, although that number may be low given how difficult the numbers are to pinpoint. Of course, when harvest time came, all interests bent toward King Cotton as Barbour's freedmen's schools were emptied by the "great demand for colored children to pick out cotton."[11]

Changes on the local level depended upon a revolution in constitutional authority. Since the original Bill of Rights, there had been only two previous amendments, neither of which presented core changes to the constitutional order. In contrast, the Reconstruction amendments—the Thirteenth (emancipation), Fourteenth (equal protection), and Fifteenth (voting rights)—promised to reconfigure the relationships among individuals, the states, and the federal government. White Southerners were not incorrect to see Reconstruction politics as radically stretching the bounds of politics and constitutional theory well beyond their historic limits. They unquestionably challenged what the vice president of the Confederacy, Alexander Stephens, called the "sublime moral principle" of states' rights, a clinical term designed to hide the internal workings of state governance. It amounted to a constitutional revolution, a "second founding" in Eric Foner's terms—a transformation in federal authority as necessary as it was incomplete, as dramatic as it was difficult to sustain.[12]

The Thirteenth Amendment (1865) may not have been the "tyrannical usurpation" of Eufaulans' fears, but it was certainly a product of aggressive and pragmatic politics. The flood of enslaved people from the Southern plantations into Union territories and eventually into Union regiments pushed the president beyond his earlier positions that this was a war to save the union, not to free the slaves. Emancipation in rebel states began to make tactical sense, and Lincoln's war-time emergency order, the Emancipation Proclamation (1863), launched the beginning of the end of slavery. The great irony of the Civil War was that without the Southern rebellion to *save* slavery, there would not have been the federal opportunity to *end* slavery. As a military fiat delivered by the commander in chief of the Union forces, the Emancipation Proclamation was hardly created under democratic conditions. The Emancipation Proclamation liberated "property" in states of rebellion, providing neither complete emancipation nor constitutional legitimacy for the end of slavery. Without the Thirteenth Amendment, remaining enslaved in many places remained a real possibility.[13]

Once the Thirteenth Amendment made it to the floor of the House of Representatives, it barely met the required two-thirds majority to pass. It squeaked by on two votes—*even without the presence of the representatives from the states in rebellion*. The 119–56 vote, in other words, passed when the Confederate states could not vote and did not matter politically, a rather unique and enormous moment of political advantage for federal intervention. Suggesting the national dimensions of the problem, roughly a third of those who remained in the union refused to vote for a constitutional amendment to end slavery. When the amendment moved to the states for approval, most of the South was still under military occupation. The Confederate states had little option since the "forced ratification" would be a requirement to rejoin the union. The political event that the *New York Herald* called "one of the most remarkable, important, desirable, decisive and momentous events in the record of this or any other nation of modern or ancient times" came of postwar federal power wielded aggressively against the entire history of states' rights. Lincoln, a person who wielded words with razor-like precision, sensed the unique moment of federal and executive authority and called the amendment "a King's cure for all the evils."[14]

In the autumn of 1865, expectations among freedmen were high as the rays of summer sunshine began to grow thin. Talk about the confiscation of the planters' land was nearly ubiquitous among former slaves in the Black Belt. The belief became a fevered conviction throughout the Deep South: the Freedmen's Bureau would soon reveal the final orders of the Civil War, announcing that the federals would liberate the land on behalf of those who had worked it. The "general opinion" among the freedmen, as an Alabama justice of the peace put it in a letter to the governor, was "that there will be a division of lands and other property about Christmas." It seemed just, an Alabama Colored Convention put it, since "the property which they hold was nearly all earned by the sweat of *our* brows." The toughest lesson of Reconstruction, however, was that no land would ever be redistributed.[15]

Yet whites prepared to fight back. In 1865 Alabama convened a state constitutional convention dominated by former Confederates to rebuild the old power structure. There, the state of Alabama officially abolished slavery, repealed secession, and repudiated the state's wartime debt. But they did little else. Freedmen would be offered solely their emancipation and, eventually, whatever they might be able to fight for through the political system—though the immediate hopes for that were not good. In the first election since Appomattox, three-quarters of those elected to the new legislature consisted of former Confederate soldiers. The legislature got to work passing restrictive "Black Codes" that tried to place African American people under harsh controls that echoed slavery itself. But unlike many Southern states where the codes passed, the governor of Alabama vetoed them. He did so not out of any sense of racial justice—his attitude ran quite the opposite—but for a practical desire to avoid further tangles with federal authority. Meantime, the thirty-five thousand exhausted Union troops occupying the state had their hands full enforcing emancipation and keeping racial violence to a minimum—often serving as the only civil authority in large parts of the state.[16]

The freedom-loving Alabamians felt victimized and enraged. "We are a conquered people," explained Charles Carter Langdon of Mobile during the 1865 state constitutional convention. The loss of white freedom at the hands of the Union meant that "there is not a right that we can exercise but by consent of our conquerers." Ably capturing the sense of the white majority, Langdon continued, "Our streets are full of military, our civil government is provided for us without our choosing—and by the tinkling of a little bell in Washington, we may be dispersed in a moment and marched out of this hall at the head of a file of soldiers." As he noted with contempt, "And we are here as free—as the representatives of free men. I wish I could think so. There are no free men in this southern land. We are all slaves, all manacled."[17]

In the clutch of confusion, planters grasped wildly at other straws. "We've got to change our whole system of labor," one Alabama planter declared. "Why, I was talking, down to Selma, the other day, with Jim Branson, up from Haynesville. We figured it up. I don't know how many millions of coolies there are in China, that you can bring over for a song. It will take three of 'em to do the work of two niggers; but they'll live on next to nothing and clothe themselves, and you've only got to pay 'em four dollars a month. That's our game now. And if it comes to voting, I reckon we can manage that pretty well." Others, not so sanguine about their capacity to control freedmen, panicked over what would become of the superfluous Black people in their midst if they could not be driven back to plantation labor. "The Negro will soon have to be disposed of in some way, perhaps as the Indians were. They will soon become quite as savage, useless, and *more troublesome*."[18]

Recognizing the danger of staying in Barbour County as unprotected free people, some African Americans looked abroad. Since 1816, the American Colonization Society (ACS) did not advocate an end to slavery as much as ending free Black people in the United States by sending them "back" to Africa. The society received funding from Congress in 1819, and by 1822 had set up a colony for African Americans that later became the nation of Liberia. The slave-owning South endorsed the ACS as well, since free and politically active Black people damaged the slavery cause and impinged on the idea of white freedom. After emancipation, some African Americans embraced colonization on the grounds that they would never be accepted in white America even after the Civil War. Given the despair over the economic destitution and political oppression of the immediate postbellum period, escaping from the limited terms and material deprivation of their "freedom" seemed like a worthy gamble.[19]

Hundreds of African American people from Barbour County applied to flee to Liberia on the *Golconda*, a ship financed by the ACS. Despite attempts by the local press to retain their labor supply with warnings of the death, starvation, and disease that would befall those who went to Liberia, many saw that the only way to build the society they wanted was with a fresh start in a new land. A. E. Williams, a Eufaula freedman, wrote to the ACS on Christmas Day 1867:

> We, the undersigned, colored people, take this method to inform you that we would like to embark in May, 1868, for Liberia, if we can be accommodated. We request that you furnish us with free transportation from this place to Liberia. We are all poor, and have not any money.
>
> A.E. Williams
>
> and two hundred others, with their families

They got their wish. In May 1868, the Eufaulans combined with a much larger group from Columbus. They took the train to Savannah, Georgia, and boarded the *Golconda*. They totaled 451 emigrants, though only 39 of the original Eufaula party of three hundred or so ultimately joined the expedition headed for Bexley, Liberia.[20]

The Liberian project ended mostly in disappointment. Many did not survive in Liberia; others found a rough life, limited opportunity for farming, and the difficulties of being outsiders in a rigid social hierarchy. The ravages of the "African sickness," malaria, took the lives of many émigrés. A very few prospered. Many others soon returned to the Chattahoochee Valley. The ACS sponsored over four thousand passages to Liberia, and roughly 12 percent of them came from the Chattahoochee Valley.[21]

The reason most would-be emigrants decided not to go to Liberia was probably tied directly to new exertions from Washington. If the federal authorities did what they seemed to be saying they would do in 1868, better times might be ahead in Barbour County. The days when "the only time the Northern people ever helped the Nigger was when they freed him," as a former slave in neighboring Russell County put it, might just be coming to an end. A. E. Williams, the Eufaula leader who wrote the letter to the ACS, himself chose to take his stand in Barbour County. As Reconstruction began to work, his gamble seemed to pay off as he was elected to the state House of Representatives.[22]

By the time the Liberia expedition departed, "Presidential Reconstruction" had drawn to a close and "Congressional" (or "Radical" or "Military") Reconstruction was underway. The first phase, in which President Andrew Johnson largely allowed the old Confederate power structure to rebuild itself in the rebel states, had meant something more like restoration of the old race-based regime. That phase ended in 1867 when a dramatically more activist federal government delivered the Reconstruction Acts, the impeachment of Andrew Johnson, and finally the election of Civil War hero Ulysses S. Grant to the White House in 1868. The second phase was a magnificent, if grossly incomplete, revolution in the use of federal power on behalf of African Americans.

During the first phase, the planters, expecting a more punitive postwar settlement, gained the upper hand throughout 1866, with President Andrew Johnson assisting them in reestablishing their power. While Johnson hoped for a little contrition in exchange for his assistance to his kindred white Southerners, the Deep South states brazenly elected ex-Confederate leaders, who required his presidential pardons to take office. Some states refused to pass the Thirteenth Amendment or attached provisos of different kinds. The end of the three-fifths compromise, which meant freedmen were finally counted as entire people, promised to bolster Southern numbers in the House, even though Black people still lacked voting rights. That, combined with the Southern alliance with Northern Copperheads—Northerners who opposed the war, were sympathetic to the South, and feared the tyranny of the growing federal establishment—could mean a permanent rehabilitation of ex-Confederate power. If so, the war would have been for formal emancipation and very little else.

As a result, Radical Republicans feared that they were losing the peace during Presidential Reconstruction. They opposed the easy reentry of the Confederate states to the union. The disagreements came to a head in the spring of 1866 when Johnson vetoed both the expansion of the Freedmen's Bureau and the 1866 Civil Rights Act, which outlawed Black Codes and championed equality before the law. Andrew Johnson rejected the bills on the grounds that such federal protections exceeded federal authority and gave special privileges to Black people—arguments that would echo on into the twenty-first century. As President Johnson framed the the issue:

> In all our history, in all our experience as a people living under Federal and State law, no such system as that contemplated by the details of this bill has ever before been proposed or adopted. They establish for the security of the colored race safeguards which go infinitely beyond any that the General Government has ever provided for the white race. In fact, the distinction of race and color is by the bill made to operate in favor of the colored and against the white race. They interfere with the municipal legislation of the

> States, with the relations existing exclusively between a State and its citizens, or between inhabitants of the same State—an absorption and assumption of power by the General Government which, if acquiesced in, must sap and destroy our federative system of limited powers, and break down the barriers which preserve the rights of the States.

While Johnson's racialized anti-statism would live a long and fruitful life in American political discourse, the national elections in the fall of 1866 went strongly in the Republicans' favor. Both the white South and President Johnson were politically cornered. Congress stood ready to expand the reach of federal authority and to nationalize the structures of democracy. Congressional Reconstruction would lead to a staggering fifteen overrides of Johnson's many vetoes—including all four Reconstruction Acts—which all but destroyed his political power and led to his impeachment.[23]

The Republicans had been working on another constitutional amendment since the end of the war, this one designed to create a platform of federal protections for all Americans. The Fourteenth Amendment was a radical departure in constitutional logic—if an oddly worded, belabored, compromised, and ambiguous one. It sought to bring federal authority to bear on questions of equal protection for all citizens before the law, while strategically avoiding the tangled and volatile questions of enfranchisement and social equality—a very difficult balancing act. While it failed to create voters, the idea went, it would protect citizens. No more Black Codes, denial of freedmen's rights, legal discrimination, repression, or taking of life, liberty, or property without due process. The war and the Freedmen's Bureau had already brought the federal government into unprecedented levels of intervention in state affairs, but the Fourteenth Amendment made such intervention constitutionally permanent. It also created "birthright" citizenship (something not extended to Native Americans, ironically, until 1924), as well as a series of immediate political issues: plotting a route back to the union for the rebel states, limiting the power of Confederate leaders, plus a bit of good old-fashion politicking that helped to preserve Republican political power. It was a hash of a constitutional amendment, but among the most important ever passed.[24]

Prior to the Fourteenth Amendment, state governments were exempt from the Bill of Rights—they applied only to limiting the power of federal authority. The Bill of Rights, for instance, begins with a negative freedom, "Congress shall make no law"; while the Fourteenth Amendment declares a new affirmative capacity, "Congress shall have the power." Before long, the Fourteenth would be curtailed by the Supreme Court, misinterpretation, political ill will, and neglect, but its ratification was one of the most important events in the development of federal power. Despite the "equal protection" clause, it would require another century of state building and African American resistance to achieve the needed federal protections for minorities (and even then, they would continue to remain vulnerable to many constitutional dilemmas created by states' rights). The Fourteenth Amendment passed the House on a strict partisan vote in May. Then every Southern state other than the Republican-ruled Tennessee rejected it—partially due to President Johnson's encouragement.[25]

Exasperated, the Republicans decided that bold military rule of the South would be the only option, and they passed the Military Reconstruction Acts over Johnson's veto the following year. Exhausted by the president's wholesale pardons of former Confederates, his opposition to Black suffrage, his turning a blind eye to murder and violence, and his many vetoes, Congress set upon a policy of martial law. To defend the Black vote, they mobilized twenty thousand troops and divided the former Confederacy into five military districts. For rebel states to get back into the union, each would have to pass a constitution that guaranteed equal suffrage for African American men, disqualify Confederate elites from office, and pass the Fourteenth Amendment. The deal basically enfranchised African Americans and disenfranchised those who had led the rebellion to preserve slavery. And it happened under what approached martial law—freedom for African Americans enforced by federal guns.

Just because the federal government demanded action and backed those demands with troops, however, did not make white people willing participants. Alabama governor Robert M. Patton, who pragmatically believed that Reconstruction was both real and inevitable despite his wishes to the contrary, was discouraged by resistance to the required state constitutional convention. "I am really surprised that so many good citizens are refusing to Register," he noted, "and many others Resister (as they say) to vote against a convention." As military Reconstruction took hold, talk of violent resistance among whites swelled in the fall of 1867. Many white Alabamians simply refused to believe anything good could come of a new convention in which African Americans had the vote. Such a process, noted the Selma paper, "can make no Constitution under which any white man can live."[26]

The Alabama State Constitutional Convention of 1867, required by federal law, featured seventeen African American delegates out of ninety-six people in attendance. The convention carried the significance of being the first official political body charged with lawmaking that was biracial in both "origin and practice." The white delegates consisted of Unionists, men from north Alabama, and carpetbaggers down from the North, many of whom were less interested in Black equality than controlling politics and punishing Confederates. The convention failed to deliver on its promise of full citizenship rights for freedmen. Still, equality of franchise—the disenfranchisement of Confederate elites excepted—would finally become the law of the state of Alabama.[27]

White voters looked on the document with horror, seeing it as a step toward the Africanization of Alabama and an assault on the white man's free institutions of government. They also recognized a catch in the language of the Reconstruction Acts about the rules for ratifying the new constitution, which they organized to exploit. The new state constitution had to be passed by a majority of voters in an election *in which the majority of voters participated*. A well-staged boycott could prevent a majority from turning out and therefore sabotage the entire state constitutional process. The boycott plan was not without risk. To resist the new constitution was to risk further enraging the Radical Republicans in Congress. If the boycott failed and the constitution managed to pass, then all the offices would go to Republicans.[28]

The February 1868 vote failed to generate the required 50 percent participation to pass. A combination of the demoralization of the African American vote, because of the constitution's lack of a guarantee of full equality, and a massive boycott by white voters, because of the existence of African American voting rights, dramatically depressed voter participation. In Barbour County, there were 5,184 participating voters, of whom 1,811 were white and 3,373 were "colored," even though the population was close to a fifty-fifty Black-white split. In a crushing defeat, even though the Alabama freedmen voted in an enormous majority for the constitution (70,815 to 1,005), the white boycott denied the chance for majority participation. Again, federal authority, finding it necessary to toy with the boundaries of fair play to ensure African American rights, came to the rescue. Congress simply reversed the requirement of majority participation—but did so after the fact. Several months after the constitutional vote failed, the very same results were accepted as a post hoc victory. The pattern of equality and democracy achieved through coercive means continued.[29]

In June 1868, Alabama joined the union as a state with a new constitution—and with the full enfranchisement of African Americans. Alabama stumbled toward a semifunctional democracy, with a strong Republican Party albeit a weak governor, a number of African Americans successfully holding office in the state, and, most importantly, the federal government enforcing enfranchisement.

While the revolution was incomplete and largely still controlled by Northerners rather than African Americans themselves, the Republican Party was now in charge of Alabama and the nation. In the summer of 1868, as Barbour County whites lay under what was popularly believed to be "the bondage of military authority," Alabama passed the Fourteenth Amendment. In the fall, the most popular man in the country, indeed, perhaps the world, Republican war hero

Ulysses S. Grant, was elected to the presidency. He not only carried the home of the fire eaters, Barbour County (where 3,168 Grant votes swamped the 2,210 cast for the Democrat, Horatio Seymour), but also the entire Black Belt and the state of Alabama. The state had been completely flipped through the federal enforcement of enfranchisement. Grant won the national Electoral College in a landslide.

Few, even today, understand, however, that the popular vote margin remained narrow. The math was harrowingly close. Grant received 3 million votes to Democratic candidate Horatio Seymour's 2.7 million votes. Without the 400,000 enfranchised freedmen, Grant probably would have lost the popular vote. Under military authority, African American political life began to grow and transform the politics of the state—and the nation.[30]

Judging by the jubilant national celebrations in the North, the passage of the Fifteenth Amendment, granting federal protection of the right to vote, meant the end of the national questions about slavery and the legacy of the Civil War. It was, by far, the most lauded of the postbellum amendments. Grant, who had once believed that Black people should go through some sort of probationary period before being granted citizenship, came to believe in universal male voting rights largely because of the fuss kicked up by Andrew Johnson and the Southern resistance. African Americans were not only the most faithful Unionists, they were also good Republicans. As everyone would learn and many knew, however, the Fifteenth was the weakest of the Reconstruction amendments. By banning a denial of the right to vote on the grounds of "race, color, or previous condition of servitude," it left out the fact that a state could deny the right to vote for just about any other reason it selected.

Military occupation, the Reconstruction amendments, and the election of Grant set the stage for a semifunctional, multiracial democracy in Barbour County. "The continuation of wartime" activities in the South, explains the historian Gregory P. Downs, "gave the national government the necessary authority to suppress the rebellion, consolidate its forces, and fashion effective civil rights." Success depended upon the "military's authority to override state laws, displace judges and sheriffs, arrest outlaws, proclaim emancipation," and "run an occupation of the South that would have been illegal in peacetime." The brief but not-always-effective use of federal force meant there were "rights born in the face of bayonets, and a Constitution remade through the subservience of civil law."[31]

Eufaula locals never accepted the imposition of the new federal order, and they decided to fight back. First, they would try straight politics. Then they would stoop to dirty politics. Then they would resort to violence. The dirty politics would end with two different and competing state legislatures vying for power, and federal troops camped on the state house grounds to ensure the peace. The entire fate of Reconstruction in the state of Alabama ended up resting on one single contested ballot box from the town of Eufaula.

CHAPTER EIGHT

The Greeley Gamble and the Dueling Dual Legislatures of 1872

IT WAS AMONG THE more bizarre political meetings in American history. The Eufaula planter, former slave master, lawyer, and politician Eli Shorter traveled from Barbour County to Chappaqua, New York, to meet with one of the nation's most famous abolitionists and intellectuals, newspaper editor Horace Greeley. It was a study of opposites: the fire eater and the vegetarian, the secessionist and the Unionist, the patriarch and the feminist, the states' rights champion and the occasional socialist. Nevertheless, in the summer of 1872, the oil and water of American politics gathered in Westchester County on the belief that each needed his enemy to topple one of the most popular men in the country, President Ulysses S. Grant. The meeting was just the beginning of a series of wild and improbable plans to defeat "Grantism" and Black political power in Barbour County in the 1872 election.

Eli Shorter, nephew of the rapacious land speculator from the 1830s, had impeccable Confederate credentials. One of Barbour County's most powerful elites, he was among the most militant members of the secession-driven Eufaula Regency, a fire eater among fire eaters. He served as a state congressman, a delegate to the Alabama secession convention, and a member of both the US and Confederate congresses. He brooked no compromise on the question of slavery or states' rights. When the Civil War came, Shorter did not flinch in taking his politics to the battlefields, serving as a colonel in the Confederate army and one of the leaders of the early charge at the Battle of Shiloh—one of the grisliest bloodbaths in American history. Approaching fifty years old, and with a long and storied political career as a militant states' rights man, he was ready to rid his hometown of the influence of federal power once and for all.

When Shorter served as a member of the House Indian Affairs Committee while a US congressman, he revealed a shameless sense of the role of the federal government in local affairs. He demanded federal payment of $1.25 million to the white people of the Chattahoochee Valley for property taken by the United States Army for "public use without just compensation" during the Second Creek War. To do so required that he disregard the fact that the intruders created the war, and the federal government saved the white people of the region from their own predations against the Creeks. His impassioned speech brought shouts of disapproval in the House, and Congressman Cadwallader Washburn of Wisconsin sarcastically noted that the people of Alabama had fled their homes in fear of the Indians. By doing so, he argued, they had lost their property. "They now come before Congress to 'ask pay for their bravery!'" Washburn mocked. Like many who fought against federal power, he was unrepentantly aggressive in pursuing it for his own purposes.[1]

Shorter was utterly consistent in his defense of local rights, but Horace Greeley, one of the most important shapers of opinions in the nation, had experimented with just about every idea and fad from phrenology to Fourierism. The brilliant, eccentric editor of the most widely circulated paper in the nation, the *New York Tribune*, was "a one-man switch-board for the international cause of 'Reform,'" in the words of one historian. For a short time, he even hired Karl Marx to write for his paper. Greeley believed strongly in the ability to experiment. For him, freedom meant an intrepid search for the best and most fulfilling route forward—even if that led to some unstable and unexplored terrain. He was also famous in political cartoons for his oft-caricaturized neck beard, a forest of hair tufting out from his notoriously dense layers of clothing, which made his head look like the round blossom of a bespectacled flower. Above all, Greeley believed in westward free state expansion—"Go West, Young Man" was his most remembered phrase—and went from Whig to Republican and supporter of Lincoln. Where this leading, if mercurial, intellectual would go next was anybody's guess.[2]

Greeley's position on the Civil War swung erratically as events unfolded. First he had flirted with the idea that letting the Confederacy go peacefully would be the best plan. Then he attacked Lincoln for not moving fast enough to liberate slaves. He sought to find another nominee for the presidency in 1864 in the belief that Lincoln could not win a second term, but when the war turned in the Union's favor, he returned to backing the president enthusiastically. After Reconstruction he sought leniency for the Confederates, then accused freedmen of being lazy and coddled, then supported the impeachment of Johnson for his failures to enfranchise freedmen, and ultimately backed Ulysses S. Grant's successful 1868 run for president.

But Greeley had become suspicious of African Americans' use of their freedom. His thinking ultimately settled on one of the most toxic ideas in American political history: that Black people just wanted to get something for nothing. His paper editorialized that freedom may not have been a complete failure, but Black people "might and should have done much better." They were picky and overly assertive, he believed, demanding that land be given to them. Greeley argued that if former slaves had more pluck, they could have bought land with their own money—had they not foolishly squandered it "in drink, tobacco, balls, gaming, and other dissipation." What money he had in mind is a mystery. Freedmen, the *Tribune* continued, "might have bought therewith at least Ten Millions acres of the soil of their respective States which would have given each family an average of ten acres of mother earth; and the free and clear owner of ten acres need never stand idle or accept half wages."

Greeley and his allies were not just scornful of African Americans' use of their freedom, but wary of the entire dysfunctional state leviathan created to support them. They viewed it as an unseemly brew of corrupt patronage that had to be stopped. It threatened not only to create dependent Black people but also to undo the faith in individualism and free wage-labor values of Northern whites just as the churn of industrial protest began to rock the Gilded Age. Greeley framed a problem that would plague the nation for generations to come: the correlation between "special needs" of African Americans and any use of federal power, a connection that immediately racialized any and all federal regulatory interventions. The alliance between the Democrats and the Liberal Republicans would prove folly in the short run, but in the long run foreshadow the future of American politics. En route, the Democrats demonstrated a commitment to winning through fair means. After that, they would have to play dirty.

The opposites, the rigid Confederate planter and the fickle Yankee intellectual, united when the capricious Greeley decided to oppose the head of his own party, President Ulysses S. Grant, for the presidency in 1872. Disaffected Republicans, Northern Democrats, and Southern Democrats united under a new banner, the Liberal Republicans, to bring an end to Reconstruction. "There are thousands of men in the country who have been totally opposed to us on slavery and reconstruction," editorialized *The Nation*, "but who agree with us heartily on administrative reform." Cleaning up government and moving beyond the legacy of the Civil War was their project. "Reconstruction and slavery we have done with," he continued, "for administrative and revenue reform we are eager." After a series of runs for political office, mostly failed, Greeley managed to beat a large number of hungry rivals at the St. Louis convention to lead the Liberal Republican charge against General Grant. The Democratic South decided to throw their lot in with their former enemy and united under the Liberal Republican ticket. Enemies crawled into bed together to defeat their shared foe, General Grant.[3]

The new party's first major decision, choosing Greeley to top the ticket, was a ludicrous failure. Many Liberal Republicans were demoralized to see their lofty agenda undermined by a man who supported "quacks, charlatans, ignoramuses, and sentimentalists"—all of whom were prepared to use state power for their own ends. Given his storied career, Greeley had a past position—often contradictory—on just about everything, and almost all of them could be used against him. As Charles Francis Adams Jr. sardonically noted, the Liberals returned from St. Louis with "the great apostle of unlimited legislation on all conceivable subjects for our chosen candidate." In lieu of the unifying figure needed by the fractious party, they ended up with Horace Greeley. Grant, having formerly thought of him as an "honest, firm, untiring supporter of the republican party," had turned to calling him "a genius without common sense."[4]

For Eufaula's Eli Shorter, his audience at Greeley's sturdy farmhouse north of New York City was a dizzying experience. "If anyone had told me ten years ago when I was in the Confederate Congress standing there as a representative of a secession district in Alabama, that in 1872 I'd be here, at the home of Horace Greeley, advocating his election to the Presidency, I would have said he was a mad man." He was in the heart of not just enemy territory but the home of the architect of enemy ideology. "A war has swept over the country, slavery has been abolished, and Horace Greeley did more than anybody else to accomplish that result." Even though Grant had won the war, Shorter argued, he continued its military occupation. "But this old leader whom we are visiting here at his country home—against whom we have warred all our lives—he promises peace and he will give it to us." Shorter's interest in Greeley was simple: he promised to get the federals off the back of his people.[5]

Shorter knew that the Democrats could not possibly defeat Grant on their own. A fusion ticket was the only way to get federal troops out of Alabama and the rest of the Deep South, and so the Democrats backed Greeley too. It was the only time in American history in which one major party nominated the candidate of another party for president. The Liberal Republicans hoped to win over a coalition built of disaffected Republicans, Democrats hungry to get rid of carpetbaggers and federal power, and, hopefully, some African American votes based on Greeley's reputation for abolition. The latter was a fool's errand.

African Americans knew little of Greeley's former reputation as an abolitionist, but they knew a lot about how the Democrats behaved toward them. And they believed, above all, in the role that General Grant had played in transforming Southern African American life.

Contrary to the phrase "black rule" being bandied about widely, African Americans had not come anywhere close to seizing power in the state of Alabama. Quite the opposite, Black leadership and the rank-and-file remained circumspect, pragmatic, and keen to compromise. Fearing that overreach would lead to violent backlash and alienate white Republicans in the north of the state, moderation was their theme. As of 1872, organized violence appeared to be on the wane, Black voting was strong, and the postwar economy improving. Fear of federal intervention kept the Democrats in line and racial terrorism under control. The Democrats were in power, but they were so distracted by their own railroad schemes and hemmed in by the federals that the Republicans still had room to maneuver. By the early 1870s, the historian Michael Fitzgerald argues, "Alabama gave real signs that society might move toward a lasting form of racial coexistence, on some modest level of civil equality." Even so, the prospect that Barbour County might approximate a functional biracial democracy was unacceptable for people like Eli Shorter.[6]

Federal involvement in local and state affairs continued to grow as the federal fight against the white terrorism of the Ku Klux Klan moved to center stage. Three anti-Klan "Enforcement Acts," passed between 1870 and 1872, gave new and expanded federal powers to the Justice Department. They brought the Secret Service into the Justice Department and granted it dramatic new surveillance powers for pioneering efforts in domestic antiterrorism. The Enforcement Acts also provided unprecedent authority to protect voting rights, including the use of military power when necessary. The US Marshals were relocated to the Justice Department, and troops placed at their disposal when necessary. The possibility of ending white violence and repression of freedmen's politics became quite real. For his part, President Grant promised to "exhaust the powers thus vested in the Executive" to stop the violent suppression of Black voting rights.[7]

Grant's attorney general, reformed Confederate Amos T. Akerman, believed the time had come for the government to be "more national in theory." His vigorous federal prosecution of the Klan was part of this thinking. Thousands of pages of investigations, totaling thirteen volumes, three of which are devoted to Alabama alone, revealed the extent of Klan organizing and violence. He convicted six hundred Klansmen in the state and sent scores of men to federal prison. The federal government was now taking on an extraordinary role, eclipsing state and local governments in the oversight of voting and racial violence. As one Alabama official exaggerated, it got to the point that white people were "more afraid of arrest by troops and trial by federal judges, than the negroes are of the supposed kuklux."[8]

In Barbour County, the Ku Kluxers were out there, but less as a tangible presence than as ghostly enforcers of racial boundaries. The Invisible Empire ran rampant in the northern part of the state and the western Black Belt, but not as strongly along the southern banks of the Chattahoochee. Still, as one memoirist recalled, "in Barbour county, the best men took in the Ku Klux Klan activities—even mystic as they were—and to these activities is due much of the clearing out of the County of the obnoxious and criminal invader." The white romance with violence may have been greater than the reality in Barbour County, even if local memories focused on a people "exasperated to blood boiling resentment" who were forced "like a great wave" through the South "against the rise and assault of misguided and inflamed negroes, and infamous white trouble makers." Barbour County's Mary Buford, daughter of Jefferson Buford, who led the drive into Bleeding Kansas, sensed a light breeze of optimism for the old planter class in the Klan. As she wrote to her brother, who had immigrated to Brazil, where slavery was still legal, "Cotton has advanced, the democrats are increasing north, and there is a Godsend known as the Ku Klux Klan. It is reported to be doing a great deal of good[,] there is no doubt about it[,] keeping in check the audacious proceedings of white + black radicals." She reported the Klan's appearances around Barbour, including their threats to the scalawag Judge Elias Keils, whose support for African American voting would make him the focal point of the town's wrath in the 1874 election.[9]

Many whites in Alabama believed that the Black vote did not yet need to be destroyed, but that an alliance remained possible based on the old model of plantation paternalism. "My colored friends, we are Southern men, born upon the same soil, live in the same country, and will sleep in the same graveyard," argued James Clanton, leader of the Alabama Democratic Party in 1867. The old planter class, which claimed that Northern carpetbaggers were manipulating the Black vote, believed that Black votes were theirs to control. Planters called the softer cooptation strategy the "New Direction," though it tended to be based more on the old paternalism. "You have misplaced your gratitude, you have misplaced your trust," Eufaula's Alpheus Baker exclaimed in an appeal to African American voters. "You owe to the Republican Party, which owes you much, nothing. They have made you promises that they have 'kept to the ear, and broken to the sense.' They have used you and abused you." Northerners, he argued, enfranchised Southern Blacks solely to feed the Republican ballot box and manufacture spoils for carpetbaggers. Baker claimed that under Republican rule, party elites got to wield all the patronage while freedmen got only the "the crusts that fell from the Republican table."[10]

Baker's argument about the limits of Black Eufaulans' loyalty to the Republican Party was not wholly without merit, but it convinced few. The white elite overestimated the power of their paternalism. African American voters were hardly ready to flip to the Democrats based on the nostalgic "superb loyalty" they had shown their old masters in slavery days. The planter elite appealed: "We—to whom you were bound—we—who are now bound to you, for the wisest development of our mutual interest and prosperity—ask you to trust us as a party—as you have always trusted us as men." The former slaves had a long struggle on their hands, but they weren't fools. From their grassroots experience, Barbour County's African American voters readily grasped the truth of Frederick Douglass's belief in the Republican Party as the only instrument of Black political power.[11]

At the federal hearings about the Klan, Eufaula's James L. Pugh served as a witness called by the Democratic minority. He, of course, denied the existence of any voter suppression in Barbour County, with the exception of a widespread myth: Black voters had been beating and intimidating other Black voters interested in voting for the Democratic ticket (victims who, in the oft-told narrative, tended to be saved by the heroics of white people). Echoing Alpheus Baker, he argued that the problem was not the vote itself, but its manipulation by Northern Republicans. "I have become satisfied that the white people have made a great mistake in not accepting universal suffrage; and I believe that they would have done so if it had not been for the offensive use that was made of negro suffrage by a class of persons who were sent down there to control it in the work of reconstruction." In Pugh's imagination, the mindless freedmen were "marched up like so many cattle" and "thrown under the control of the Union Leagues and the Freedmen's Bureau, aided by the military power" to do the work of the carpetbaggers. White Eufaulans saw it as a political machine: Republicans advocated for troops, which reinforced Reconstruction, which bolstered the African American vote, which supported the Republicans, which gave them unlimited access to political spoils. They weren't wrong in how the system worked, but they were wholly incorrect to think the freedmen were going to join the party of the master class.[12]

Destroying Grant's run for reelection was the only hope to defeat the entire system of federal intervention. The discomfort of a temporary alliance of convenience with Greeley meant the possibility of achieving what the Democrats could not achieve on their own: ending the yoke of federal oppression. The Eufaula paper argued that the "the first object of patriotic desire" was to destroy the "usurpation, misrule, theft, and demonism" of Grant Republicanism. Eli Shorter championed the Liberal Republicans' platform as the "common ground upon which all parties opposed to the present Radical administration may honorably unite and battle together." Only by getting rid of federal authority could the carpetbaggers, who "deceived and plundered" Barbour County freedmen for their nefarious purposes, be driven out.[13]

It didn't work. The November vote was a landslide for Grant. The general won Barbour County, the entire state of Alabama, and the nation by solid majorities. The attempt to unite around Greeley proved to be an unmitigated disaster for the Liberal Republicans and their Democratic allies. Hopes of a new coalition rapidly melted into a coronation of Ulysses S. Grant and national approval of Reconstruction. Some Democrats, unwilling to vote for Greeley, remained home on Election Day, while African Americans turned out in strong numbers. Support among Northern Republicans for the Liberal cause also fell apart. E. L. Godkin, whose *The Nation* originally backed the St. Louis Liberal Republican convention, had since turned to calling Greeley "a conceited, ignorant, half-cracked, obstinate old creature." In defeat, poor old Horace Greeley remarked, "I was the worst beaten man that ever ran for that high office. And I have been assailed so bitterly that I hardly know whether I was running for President or the penitentiary." Despondent, he died before the Electoral College met to declare his defeat official.[14]

THE POLL.
WHAT ARE YOU GOING TO DO ABOUT IT?
H. G. "LET US CLASP HANDS OVER THE BLOODY CHASM."—[See Page 803.]
24373.31
"A Great Victory has been won in Georgia. . . . The verdict in Georgia is certainly conclusive."—New York Tribune, October 8, 1872.

"Let us clasp hands over the bloody chasm," pleaded the Liberal Republican presidential candidate Horace Greeley. Here his buffoonish efforts are mocked for encouraging white Southerners not simply to organize on his behalf, but also to murderously seize control of local politics from newly enfranchised Black voters. Although the chasm Greeley spoke of was the Civil War, a new "bloody chasm" would emerge as federal troops departed and surrendered Black voters to the riotous violence of white locals.

Calling the results of the election federal "despotism," the *Eufaula Weekly Times* saw the new despotism as a departure from constitutional tradition. The people, claimed the paper, "are willing to leave the landmarks set up by the founders of the Republic, and accept in its stead a consolidated government, with all power centered at Washington, and all State sovereignty and State rights utterly abolished." Democrats saw a declension narrative that threw into question the nation's commitment to freedom. "The patriotic spirit, the intense love of liberty, the veneration for the constitution of other and better days, and the intense pride in our model form of Government has died out," the editors lamented, and the process can "only terminate in a centralized despotism." The old freedom-loving days had passed, and where the citizenry might have once fought back it now sat idly by as the Republican Party "lays its sacraligious hand on the great charter of American liberty" in ways, they claimed, recognizable to Napoleon's march across Europe. "If we are to have an absolute master [in Grant], it does seem to us, that the country might have made a better selection."[15]

Not only were Democrats defeated on the presidential level, Radical Republican majorities had proven so strong in Barbour County that they elected an African American named James T. Rapier to the United States Congress. That a Black man would receive a majority of all of the votes in Barbour County, and go on to represent the people of southeastern Alabama just seven years after emancipation, was a stunning thing. So stunning, in fact, it was the first and, to date, last time Barbour County would ever be represented in the United States Congress by an African American.[16]

Rapier had lived a storied life. In late 1864, the Alabama-born leader returned from Canada, where he had gone for his education in exile, having decided to devote his life to the cause of the uplift of the newly freed people. As a politician, he mirrored his white counterparts' suspicion of the federal government, except his reasoning was that federal authorities had not done enough. "I shed no tears at the breaking up of the Federal government," he explained on another occasion. "For so far as the negro was concerned, it had been a cheat and a sham, and its flag, the sacred emblem of liberty, was 'a flauntin' lie.'" Now there was opportunity. After the war, he dodged a Klan lynch mob, but barely; began the first African American newspaper in Alabama; served as a delegate to the 1867 state constitutional convention; was elected vice president of the new National Negro Labor Union in Washington; and managed to win the nomination for secretary of state of Alabama in 1870. His very presence on the 1870 state ticket scared white Republican voters away, and he and the party lost that year. He then enjoyed a patronage position as the internal revenue assessor for Alabama's Second District, using his time as assessor to meet and organize throughout the Second District, solidifying his position as one of the most important African American leaders in Alabama, if not the most. He proved to be one of the strongest, most knowledgeable, and tactically wise Republicans in the state. At a speech in Barbour County, while campaigning for Congress, he proudly "buried Horace Greeley."[17]

Rapier's rhetoric often soared, but his politics remained mired in moderation and compromise, with an eye toward the long-term struggle for full, integrated citizenship for African Americans in Alabama and the nation. In the 1872 race, Rapier won a seat in the United States House of Representatives by "seeking to harmonize race relations without sacrificing principle"—an improbable feat. With the Republican Party more unified than before in Alabama, the Greeley cause dividing the Democrats, and the Klan on the run, Rapier swept Barbour County and the other three Black Belt counties of the Second District by a 2:1 margin. He siphoned off support in the white counties as well and defeated a perfect foil, Democrat William C. Oates, who had lost an arm at Gettysburg, brought out the "Lost Cause" at every chance, and enjoyed the backing of every relevant Democratic paper. James T. Rapier joined six other African Americans elected to the House of Representatives in 1872—four from South Carolina, one from Mississippi, and one from Florida.[18]

The November triumph was a heady moment for African American politics in Barbour County, not just because Grant soundly defeated Greeley and the Second District elected Rapier, but because

Barbour County also elected three African American candidates to the state legislature. A. E. Williams, who originally appealed to the American Colonization Society to send him and hundreds of other Eufaulans to Liberia, won a seat to the state House of Representatives. Thomas J. Clark, a small property owner, also won a seat to the state house. Samuel Fantroy, a propertyless minister, also took a seat in the house. Those three were joined by a white Republican, Jacob Black, who won a seat in the state senate. Black Republicans were able to parlay their slim majority in the county into a formidable political bloc of representatives.[19]

White Eufaulans undoubtedly hated the idea of being represented by a powerful African American slate, but for them, there was something even worse lurking in Washington. When those Black state representatives got to Montgomery, they would lend their support to the hated Radical Republican senator George E. Spencer. In an age before the direct election of senators, local elections had higher stakes. Spencer was, in white opinion, among the worst examples of the *species Yankee*—the carpetbagger. American lore contains few more reprehensible characters than the fiendish carpetbagger, the lowlife Northerner who slithered down to the American South, trademark satchel in tow, to make his fortune by taking advantage of a prostrate region. For white Alabamians, Senator George E. Spencer epitomized the stereotype perfectly.

Spencer, a New York native, came to postbellum Alabama for the sole purpose of taking advantage of its people for personal gain—or so the story went. He did end up wielding control of the Republican Party through bribery, perjury, extortion, manipulation, and, above all, patronage, patronage, and more patronage. In 1870, he schemed against the fate of his own party in order to become the sole person in control of distributing federal jobs in the state. He manipulated the freedmen's vote for his own purposes, often caring neither for former slaves nor native-born whites. He was also close to President Grant, who gave him tremendous political leverage, access to troops, and reason to exaggerate whatever needed to be exaggerated in order to have more federal troops at his disposal. Whites believed that

Grant liked Spencer for one reason: he could deliver Alabama to the Republican column.[20]

Yet if Spencer was a model of the Grant-era corruption that whites on either side of the aisle like Greeley and Shorter reviled, it must also be asked: What, exactly, was the alternative? Every single element of the carpetbagger stereotype was true, though never as true as Democrats claimed. But the nation was rife with patronage and graft, and it was hardly limited to the Republican Party's Southern incursion (Boss Tweed's New York Democratic machine at the time would have made Alabama Republicans blush). In Alabama, patronage happened to be one of the largest vehicles for Black economic and political aspirations, which Spencer took quite seriously. Among those profiting was James T. Rapier, a person of undoubtedly noble intentions, whose job as tax assessor for the Second District allowed him to build political support throughout the region. Spencer certainly saw the chance for riches after the war and admitted, "If we can't [get rich] any other way we can by 'Negro Suffrage.'" He had a vision for the role of race relations in the South that included a militant approach to Reconstruction by the federal government: "I am in favor of Negro Suffrage or reducing all these states to the position of territories & keeping them so for years to come until the leaders are all dead or have left the country. This is the only safe course of procedure." Like most Radical Republicans, he knew that without the strong and direct action of the federal government, the freedmen would not be free. And he would not be the first politician to get rich and build a lot of power in the interim.[21]

When the white South protested the carpetbagger Spencer, they were attacking other targets: the federal government and Black political power—or at least any type of Black political power beyond their control. Like political machines everywhere, the Republican system did not foster men of fine character or advance sophisticated models of democratic deliberation, but they did provide means for political outsiders to gain power. Whatever the many flaws of Spencer and other carpetbaggers, and they were legion, the patronage system provided jobs and encouraged the political and economic rights of former enslaved peoples, even if in circumscribed ways. They did so not with vision or republican values, but in a messy, compromised, but real way. The fact that the Democrats stooped to their own versions of corruption and vicious violence hardly made the alternative to Republican corruption any more pure.[22]

Before any of the newly elected Republicans in Alabama could be seated in 1873, however, Alabama Democrats would wage a political and legal war to overturn the actual results of the 1872 election. Even though it was based on a criminal act, it would be the white elite's last effort at anything that might be called "moderation."

The Democrats settled on a scheme that hinged on eliminating *one single box* of Barbour County Black Republican votes. If they could do this, the result would tip the balance and eliminate the county's Republican slate in the Alabama state house, giving Democrats a slim majority in the state legislature. If they could do that, then they could vote George Spencer out of office, a goal that united the entire state party. The tactic was to accuse the election supervisors in Eufaula of failing to comply with the technical requirements for the proper supervision of a ballot box with a majority of African American votes. The ballots in the box contained the future of state politics. If they were found invalid, that would be enough to win the day and rid the Democrats of their thieving carpetbagger of a senator.[23]

The Democrats swiftly obtained an injunction prohibiting the counting of the single 1872 Eufaula box. Just a few days after the election, the Republicans appeared locked out of their own victory. By enjoining the ballots of what became known as Barbour "Box One," the Democrats were able to certify official results that did not include the contested box. The quick certification meant that the Democrats technically "won" the seats that belonged to the four Republicans in Barbour County. If they moved quickly enough, they could then organize a Democratic government, which would make certain that there would be no further consideration of the excluded box. The Democrats immediately sent the certified results to Montgomery. The outgoing secretary of state was a Democrat, and he approved the now official, but corrupt, Eufaula count. Even a temporary seating of the Democratic "winners" would allow them to vote on a new senator to replace George Spencer.[24]

The Republicans came up with a countermaneuver. Rather than participate in a legislature that would preclude any hope of rescuing the legitimate Barbour County votes, some clever reader of the state constitution found that the legislature only had to meet "at" the capitol and not "in" it. The Republicans fought the Democrats' tactics by setting up a second, competing legislature in the nearby federal courthouse. While the Democrats opened for business in the state house, the Republicans went to work at the courthouse. The contest over Barbour Ballot "Box One" meant that there were then competing legislatures, each claiming to be the legitimate government of the state of Alabama.[25]

Recently elected governor David P. Lewis, a moderate Unionist turned Republican, recognized the Republican-led Courthouse Legislature and asked that federal troops be deployed to Montgomery to keep the peace while the two legislatures struggled for supremacy. Consistent with his political approach, Spencer maintained his party morale at a nearby saloon where Republicans from the Courthouse Legislature could enjoy high-end drinks and fare for free.[26]

The Republicans, whose federal connections gave them significant leverage, tried several tactics to save the election. First, they had federal warrants issued for the arrest of the certified Democratic "winners" of the Barbour County seats. They charged them with violation of the federal Enforcement Acts. As an assistant US marshal testified, the idea was "that under the Enforcement Act we could get affidavits and have Democratic members arrested and detained until the legislature was organized by the Republicans." The legislators ultimately eluded or managed bail on the warrants, and the Democrats rallied to elect their own senator, Unionist Democrat Francis W. Sykes. He was a racial liberal whom the Democrats thought might be acceptable to the Republicans if they could get away with excluding the Barbour ballot box. Both bodies, the Courthouse Legislature and the Capitol Legislature, then claimed their own quorum, their own senator, and the ability to do the people's business. Not only did the state have two legislatures, it now had two senators elected to the same seat.[27]

Matters escalated as Governor Lewis called for federal troops. This changed the tenor of the crisis, tilting the political playing field toward the ultimately victorious Republicans. As Governor Lewis put it, only federal troops "prevented the effusion of blood, or perhaps the destruction of the city." Greeley's *New York Tribune* claimed to smell a rat in the Republican's use of troops. Grant and Senator Spencer, it charged, had engaged in a corrupt bargain to "deliver poor Alabama like so much political baggage—as a common carrier might a bale of cotton," to the president and the Republican cause.[28]

By December, the nation was watching. The *New York Herald* headlines blared "Alabama Anarchy." The Republicans traveled to Washington to explain to Grant that the whole thing was "an unblushing Ku Klux plot to take possession of State government," "a desire of the old rebel element to secure control of the State Government," and "an impudent effort to steal a Republican Legislature." The *New York Times* correspondent believed the Alabama Republicans had to draw a line or lose the battle for democracy altogether. "They realized," the *Times* correspondent wrote, "that to submit to such rascality now, and fail to reap the fruits of their victory, they would be disgraced, and never deserve success hereafter."[29]

President Grant put the responsibility of solving "democratic rascality and fraud," as the *New York Times* called events in Alabama, in the hands of his attorney general, George H. Williams. On December 11, in what he labeled a "compromise," Williams removed the certified Barbour County Democrats from the Courthouse Legislature, and had the winners, the three Black and one white Republican slate, seated in their stead. The US attorney general tilted the majority in the state house back to Republican, making Spencer's seat secure. On December 17, a single legislature was formed.[30]

The *Selma Times* captured the Democrats outrage over federal intervention well. Such overreach, made "with cool impudence and sublime effrontery," was "without a precedent." "Compromise?" the paper demanded. "With who? For what? With a combination of revolutionists, and at the suggestion of Gen. Grant and his Attorney General? We say, never." It was time to pick up the old rifles and fight back. "Resist every encroachment upon the rights of the people and the constitution of the state, and only yield...when federal bayonets take charge of the capitol and disperse you." Although such outrage ran hot, no such military mobilization took place. A sense of quiet settled on the question, with Democrats feeling overwhelmed—or perhaps merely corrected—by the power of the federal government. "I decline to begin a revolution in Alabama," one Democrat finally concluded.

The chicanery, threats, and subterfuge about a similar ploy in Marengo County, and the fate of the state senate, continued until March. The Republicans won that too. Despite the immense conflict, the Republican victory, even if it was largely over who got to wield the spoils system, suggested a fundamental political transformation in the state of Alabama.[31]

The three African American representatives, the white Republican state senator, Congressman Rapier, and Ulysses S. Grant had won a stunning victory for Reconstruction and voting rights. The lessons of the election of 1872, however, were messier than they first appear. Although a distinct win for the Republicans, the Liberal challenge blunted the sword of the national Radical Republican movement. They would never again lead the Reconstruction charge with the force of the first Grant administration. For the Democrats, what looked like a possible death rattle turned out to be a refiguring of strategy. The election, both nationally and in Barbour County, stripped the Democrats of the illusion that they could get rid of federal power by fusing with the Liberals or by launching incorporation strategies like the New Direction. If they were going to defeat a majority African American electorate, they would have to move to more extreme tactics than stealing a single ballot box.

From 1872 on, the struggle to regain freedom from federal incursion and Black political power would be a much more raw, naked appeal to local self-rule and white supremacy. Compromise and formal politics were over. In the future, they would take up arms against democracy in the name of their own freedom.

CHAPTER NINE

The White Line

Afternoon, Election Day 1874

On the night before Election Day 1874, Henry Fraser walked six miles south of Eufaula on the old Dale Road. He lay his body down in the middle of the rural passageway, and there he slept. His resting body marked the meeting point for Black voters migrating in from the countryside. As morning dawned, he gathered the loose coteries of pilgrims and prepared them to head to the polling place in town. Along with his compatriot A. E. Williams, an African American state senator who had originally led the community's plans to leave for Liberia, Fraser organized the ragtag bands of sharecroppers into a political movement of many hundreds. Together they marched, rank and file, down the backroad into town as fife and drum kept their cadence. To many white Eufaulans, the amassed African American voters looked exactly like what the ginned-up rumors warned of: an invading army threatening a despotic assault on white autonomy.

Fraser and the other leaders warned their people not to bring arms of any kind into town. Fearful of provoking the violence of the Klan or the White League, the voters asked the women and children to stay home. Some reports had them carrying sticks, perhaps to be used as walking sticks, perhaps also for possible self-defense. Others recalled being told "not to fetch as much as a stick" for fear of provoking a fuss. A couple of Black voters may have even shown up with "old muskets." Everyone stopped about two and a half miles from town and left even the very limited weapons they had been carrying on the side of the road. Even after that, white authorities searched everyone as they entered town. No weapons were found.[1]

Similarly disciplined formations of Black voters, led by a shoemaker in town named Edward Odom, and a man of the cloth and state representative, Rev. Samuel Fantroy, marched in from their gathering spot at the McTyer plantation. Arriving from the north, they entered Eufaula on the Columbus Road, meeting Fraser's men coming in from the south. They converged at three polling stations set up downtown. The Black voters swelled into a group of about eight hundred, some estimated one thousand, souls in Eufaula.

Discipline was important as politics stood at the precipice. As African American voter Larkin Brown recalled, their white ally, the Republican judge Elias Keils, warned them: "I tell you, come in peace. If a man insults you, take it; do not try to resist him; bear with him." Their latitude to act was severely limited. They could not afford to retaliate no matter how they were provoked. Any hint of resistance, let alone violence, would serve as an excuse for a massive, ruthless white retaliation. They could only show up en masse, follow what rules existed, and hope that if anything went wrong, the federals would be there to intervene on their behalf.[2]

Election Day 1874 was only the ninth autumn since the shackles of slavery had been unlocked, and the fourth since the passage of the Fifteenth Amendment promised the right to vote. The path from slavery to citizenship and organized political participation seems a staggering accomplishment in such a short time. Most of the voters that Henry Fraser organized were spread thinly across large swaths of land, working their individual shares of the old plantations, sharing the crop, and facing a seemingly inescapable cycle of debt. Getting people educated and to the polls required unprecedented levels of coordination and mobilization. The historian Steven Hahn argues that across the region, Reconstruction marked "the most impressive political mobilization of any section of the working class in the entire nineteenth century."[3]

Insights into the mysteries of rural Republican organization that would lead to such turnouts are hard to come by, but a report from a preelection rally in a different county—but the same congressional district—suggests what may have gone into organizing Barbour County voters. As darkness fell, men and women arrived at the designated spot by foot, mule, and the occasional horse. Word of the particular time and location must have passed across many fences, at the numerous "deadfalls"—the late night shops that sprang up at any number of crossroads, as well as the markets and visits among fellow workers and kin. A few locals had the resources to show up "comfortably clothed" but the vast majority arrived in "ingeniously-contrived garment of rags" consisting of "neither coat, vest, nor trousers, but a combination of the three." Some were without shoes. Cotton lint clung to those who came straight from the fields. As the evening crowd gathered, their number reaching about two hundred, a wagon with speakers and musicians pulled into place under a live oak. The wagon platform served as a stage, and the musicians warmed up the crowd. Many danced. Whiskey was passed, and the speechifying began.[4]

White and Black Republican candidates argued for racial justice and Republican unity. "You are the bone and sinew of this county, this State, the entire Southern country," proclaimed one candidate. "You have rights which were given to you by the heavenly hosts. You is your own masters, and don't need to take no 'impertinencen' from no man." One speaker approved that those gathered "esteemed the blessings of liberty" but emphasized that they could not "think that they could remain free without exertions." A Democratic vote, so the common argument went, was a vote for reenslavement. "God had raised up the Republican Party to break their chains, and to the Republican Party all their gratitude was due." Black folks were still "entirely at the mercy of the planters" and the plantation owners were swindling the sharecroppers out of their share. A cloud of suspicion hung over the few white Republicans present, as they could be carpetbaggers there just for the vote harvesting. The crowd at the rally threatened to beat, even kill, the few Black Democrats who dared to speak up. The music, dancing, and speechmaking lasted until two in the morning, when the gathered sharecroppers finally made their way home across the fields in the darkness, the message of Republican unity still ringing in their ears.[5]

The problem was not convincing the Black men of Eufaula to choose the Republican ticket, the organizers knew; it was getting voters to the polls, getting them to resist intimidation once there, and then making sure that officials counted their ballots. A smattering of Black Democrats could be found in the county, but not many. Planters did threaten and cajole Black voters, vowing to bar them from employment and starve their families if they didn't vote Democratic, but they failed to make significant inroads into the voting numbers or behavior of the freedmen. Henry Fraser had his own interpretation: a Black person, he said, "cannot feel himself a democrat except by intimidation, or except he is influenced by the power of the white man." Having failed to cajole Black voters into supporting the Democrats, having failed at cheating them, the planter and intruder interests had secretly launched a plan to wield power in their own way, knowing that the will of the federal government to back Black rights with force was faltering.[6]

The discipline of the African American voters marching on Eufaula contrasted mightily with the chaos of the state Republican Party leadership that claimed to speak on their interests. Hardly the juggernaut of the white Southern imagination, the Montgomery Republican leaders had grown "embittered against each other" and the rank and file "torn and distracted." The party bent in the face of growing white militancy. Republicans had timidly nominated an all-white state ticket and voted not to endorse the civil rights bill, long pending in the US Congress. The bill heightened the ever-present fear of social equality, mobilizing Democratic fears and splitting the white vote from northern Alabama, which was historically hostile to the powerful white elite of the Black Belt. Civil rights legislation, Black Republicans well knew, left them prone to the ever-lurking extortion of white terror.[7]

Meantime, the Democrats appeared to be organizing for a race war. At their July 1874 convention in Montgomery, the Democrats labeled the "so-called civil rights bill" a "flagrant and dangerous invasion of the ancient conservative principles of personal liberty and free government." By seeking to integrate public spaces, the bill, they argued, would require "the Federal Government to take control of schools, colleges, churches, hotels, railroads, steamboats, theaters, and graveyards for the purpose of establishing negro equality and enforcing it under numerous penalties of fines, damages, and imprisonment." Local resolutions reported in the Eufaula newspaper noted how the bill "loosed the flood-gates of passion here, and made the campaign bitter beyond all precedent." What was then called the "Democratic and Conservative Party" charged the Republicans with having "inflamed the passions and prejudices of the Negroes as a race against the white people, and have thereby made it necessary for the white people to unite and act together in self-defense and for the preservation of white civilization."[8]

White editors and speechmakers showed a determination to "redeem" the state from Republican folly at any cost. The *Montgomery Ledger*, a conservative voice for white supremacy, saw 1874 as the year that would decide the question of equality forever. "We will ACCEPT NO RESULT BUT THAT OF BLOOD," they wrote. Eufaula's Eli Shorter, long outspoken about his unrelenting hostility to African American rights of any kind, had tried since emancipation to convince the freedmen to give themselves over, politically, to the leadership of their former masters. He had no success. Finally, in the summer of 1874, Shorter turned to the small number of African Americans who showed up at a Democratic meeting and declared he was through trying to win them over. "We are not going to ask you any more to go with us." Pointing at the Black voters, he declared, "If you don't come with us we will exterminate you as we did the poor Indians." Violence was not merely rhetorical. A politically active Black man was killed, unarmed, seven miles from Eufaula that summer. Two Black men were lynched in the Barbour County seat of Clayton. Eufaula judge Elias Keils could sense the beginning of "a perfect reign of terror" in Barbour County in 1874.[9]

The president of the Alabama state Democratic convention, James L. Pugh of Eufaula, set the tone for what was to come. "We hear the roar of the black wave that had its formation in the overflowing bounty of the federal government," he exclaimed in a tortured political metaphor, "but the glorious white cliffs of Caucasian supremacy, illuminated by eternal sunshine, will roll back this black sea and sink it forever from the face of this lovely land it threatens to desolate and destroy." The platform adopted by the convention argued that the situation required "white people to unite and act, together, in self-defense, and for the preservation of white civilization." As an Alabama historian put it, events of 1874, including the fevered talk of the civil rights bill, enabled "Democrats to depict racial extremism as a defensive reaction."[10]

By the time the march of Black rural voters made it to downtown Eufaula on Election Day, rumors swirled throughout the white population of Barbour County. There were rumors of Black people violently suppressing the mythologically large numbers of Black Democrats. Rumors of Black subjugation of white people. Rumors of Black violence in general. Rumors of weapons. None of these rumors were remotely true, but they were nevertheless powerful. One US Army officer, who sensed the "danger of trouble" in Eufaula, reported on fears that he did not himself believe to be true, but that he heard in the streets that day: "We are afraid that the negroes are going to mass upon us and drive us from the polls and take possession, and we intend to be prepared, and to act in self-defense, and act with a will. We do not intend that a single negro who votes *the democratic ticket* shall be driven from the polls, but shall protect him to the bitter end."[11]

While white voters concerned themselves with baseless stories about African Americans taking up arms, the threats of armed violence against Black voters were very real. In order to regain power, White League paramilitary groups shed the sheets and night riding of the Klan in favor of an open political movement that combined aggressive racial polarization strategies with open terrorist campaigns. The White Leagues were usually able to dress up their activities as respectable self-defense efforts, but their new project was a paramilitary effort, even an all-out race war, they called "the White Line." What the white Republican Judge Keils called "blood speeches" were in the air, and it was clear that battle preparations were being made. Keils wrote state officials in Montgomery one month before the election that "within the last few days we hear of more outrages being planned in the county, and we know there are *infamous schemes on foot*." He noted "the most vicious of the 'White League' are carrying into the various portions of the county, new breach-loading, double-barreled shot-guns, with ammunition, plenty of which has been shipped here." He begged for a detachment of thirty or forty troops to keep the peace on Election Day.[12]

A collapsing economy catalyzed the atmosphere of desperation. The 1874 election year became filled with bitterness and hatred across the country. The collapse of cotton prices ended the peak of bipartisanship in the summer of 1873 and instantly dissolved whatever goodwill there was in areas where an interracial democracy may have once seemed at least remotely possible. On Wall Street, a railroad credit bubble had burst, triggering a national and international financial panic. Prior to 1929, in fact, the Panic of 1873 was known as the "Great Depression." The economic cataclysm delivered chaos to Northern industrial class relations and reoriented politics away from the Civil War and its legacies, placing a horrible fiscal squeeze on local and state governments. The crisis made a lot of people poor and desperate. In Alabama, banks closed and railroad projects shut down. In the words of Eufaulan James McLure Buford, local newspaper editor: "Everybody is broke and insolvent, or nearly so; and taxes amount to confiscation. We are all barely able to live."[13]

On Election Day, when the polls failed to open on time, nervousness spread among the columns of African Americans gathered in downtown Eufaula. Many African American voters questioned if holding their ground was worth it, whether their votes would be counted anyway, if trouble was going to erupt. Fraser and his colleagues patrolled the rural throngs, trying to keep their spirits up and their minds concentrated. At 9:00 a.m. the polls finally opened. Voting proceeded, and everything seemed to be going smoothly.

Just after noon, confusion erupted over a young African American who had queued up to vote. The Black voters said he wasn't old enough, which his father confirmed to be true. Democrats offered him a vote if he chose their ticket. People, white and Black, began to crowd around them, hollering, jeering, and taunting. They ushered the youth into an alleyway. A white poll observer, Charley Goodwin, took him aside and explained that he was prepared to allow the youngster to vote if he selected the Democratic ticket. One of the Black Republicans present, Milas Lawrence, exclaimed to the young man, "God damn you, are you going to vote the democratic ticket?" The Democratic poll observer countered, "God damn you, do you take it up?" "You are taking it up for your people," replied Milas Lawrence, "and I will take it up for mine." Then a white Democrat in the crowd yelled, "Shoot the damned son of a bitch!" and drew out his bowie knife, stabbing Lawrence in the shoulder. Unarmed, Lawrence "broke and ran" as the white mob yelled that he should be shot.[14]

A single pistol shot cracked the air. Someone, probably Alpheus Baker, shouted, "Fall in Company A," "Fall in Company B." Rifles materialized. Guns came from the back rooms of stores. They suddenly appeared on porches. The town's best citizens pulled firearms from sheds. White men on the street produced as many as four pistols each and opened fire. Smith & Wesson army pistols fired, shotguns blasted, while rifle muzzles fired down out of second-story windows. Shots came from both sides of the street "like hail from the clouds." Bodies began to fall. People "stampeded and gone in every direction." The white people in the streets seemed to have disappeared, but a few stayed low and out of the way. "In a twinkling of an eye," recalled Henry Fraser, "the street was foggy with powder-smoke." Black voters ran for their lives.[15]

Amidst the cacophony of gunfire, Fraser was trampled. He pulled himself up and managed to make it to cover under the corner of a house. Bullets whizzed overhead, and glass shattered as indiscriminate firing hit storefront windows. There he hid under the steps and witnessed how "the colored people all broke and ran" in every direction. "Some were shot from the upper part of the city, and some from the lower part," he explained. "They shot both ways, and the black people commenced running in opposite directions. [Shooters] followed them as long as they had anything to fire with."[16]

Alpheus Baker called his men back into line, and the shooting stopped. The federal marshal on the ground estimated that at least six hundred shots had been fired by whites; an infantry officer guessed four to five hundred; Fraser figured more like sixteen hundred. One witness claimed that an African American person *may* have emptied the six barrels of a single revolver at the white attackers, but even *if* that happened, it appears to be the only armed action by any Black voter. United States Deputy Marshal J. A. Adams said, "I saw no negroes shoot that day."[17]

The dead and wounded lay in the area around the polls. Corpses had to be hauled off in carts. They eventually found the body of one missing person by following the circling buzzards to where he had fled, bleeding, into the woods. When congressional investigators later asked US Marshal James D. Williford about what he witnessed at the Eufaula election "riot," he responded, "My opinion of that Eufaula riot is that it was simply a massacre." Estimates by federal officials figured that about 80 voters were shot that afternoon, and about eight or nine of them killed. Fraser believed there were 160 casualties. The Republicans estimated that 500 African American voters fled for their lives before getting the chance to exercise their voting rights. Whatever the exact numbers, the Democrats made good on their promise to hold the White Line and carry the 1874 election "by powder and lead."[18]

Talk of a violent attack on Reconstruction had been stirring throughout the county prior to the election of 1874, but the idea, the model, for the Eufaula coup originated in Colfax, Louisiana. The practice known as the "White Line" emerged there on Easter Sunday 1873 when uncontested white power was violently resurrected. A heated race battle ended at the local courthouse with African Americans surrendering, only to face a mass execution of at least

60, perhaps as many as 150. Most of the executed were shot in the back of the head. Colfax ended as more than a single massacre. It proved to be a contagion. "The drama of it was so powerful that killing defenseless people registered in their minds as acts of bravery," argues Nicholas Lemann about Colfax, "and refusal to obey laws that protect other people's right registered as acts of high principle." The idea that white people courageously drew a line resonated widely, and the model was emulated and expanded throughout the South. Later, in 1876, the Supreme Court would further embolden unrestrained white freedom in the *Cruikshank* decision. The Colfax murderers, the high court decided, could not be prosecuted under the Fourteenth Amendment since the federal government could police state, but not individual, behavior.[19]

As the shooting in Eufaula stopped and calm returned to the streets, Alpheus Baker jumped up on a box and led the crowd in a victory cheer. One Black voter recalled that the victorious whites "shouted and whooped and yelled like a lot of Indians." "Throwing up their beavers," they hollered, taunted, and yelled. "Let the Yankees come. We are ready for them."[20]

By "Yankees," Baker meant the federal authorities stationed in Eufaula—both US Marshals and a federal troop detachment stationed to maintain order during the election. Deputy Federal Marshal Williford, having watched locals fire "indiscriminately into the mass of negroes," a crowd he estimated to number about one thousand, rushed over to the local troop headquarters to ask for assistance in keeping the peace. Williford's only support was one other marshal, and he would need a great deal of armed support from US infantry stationed there if the election violence was to be suppressed.[21]

Anticipating the violence that was brewing in town ahead of the election, Captain A. S. Daggett had previously written his commander, General Irvin McDowell, at headquarters for the Military Division of the South located in Louisville, Kentucky. He had asked for clarification about his latitude to intervene in what he feared was a deteriorating situation in Eufaula well before the massacre. Daggett wrote that he assumed that he could act as *posse comitatus*—martial support for the preservation of civil authority. The rules of engagement had been established in 1871 with General Order No. 54, which required officers to mobilize as requested by US marshals or other civil authorities in order to maintain civil order.[22]

Two weeks before the election, word came back from General McDowell that Daggett was mistaken. General Order No. 54 had been superseded by McDowell's own General Order No. 75 of October 1874, which severely limited the use of federal troops. "No; you are not right" about the role his troops should play, McDowell snapped. "General Order No. 75 fully sets forth your duty. You are stationed at Eufaula to aid United States civil officers to execute processes of the United States courts." The order clearly read: "Commanding officers of posts or camps will hold themselves in readiness to move on any requisition made on them by the United States civil officers, to enforce the writs of the United States courts." As a result, when the shooting of Black voters began, Daggett claimed that he had no choice but to order his lieutenants to stand down. Daggett watched the bodies fall in the street from the safety of his hotel window.[23]

Marshal Williford, outraged by Daggett's unwillingness to act, had another option in reserve. General Healey, head of the United States Marshals Service, had given him about twenty subpoenas to serve. Williford realized he could interrupt the violence by demanding to serve the subpoenas immediately. The general's orders did not allow much, but they allowed the troops to protect the serving of writs. Williford explained the situation and requested troops to assist him on the premise that it was unsafe to serve the papers without federal troops. "Very well; I have writs," he said, and they were right in his hand. "I have fifteen or twenty subpoenas. Are they not writs?"[24]

In an exercise of extreme pedantry, Daggett pulled out an enormous dictionary to distinguish between "writs" and "subpoenas." Growing impatient, Williford exclaimed, "Colonel, they will burn the town and kill everybody else." Daggett closed his dictionary. "Very well," came his response. "I cannot help it if they do; I cannot give any assistance under my orders." He refused to even support the serving of subpoenas against the perpetrators of the violence, but he did tell Deputy Marshal Williford that he was free to make a list of those he wished to serve. Later, Daggett claimed, he would locate the men and have them meet him at a certain point to be served. He was part of a long line of officious characters, like Francis Scott Key, who chose a narrow reading of the rules over taking a stand on behalf of the people they were charged with protecting. Stunned by Daggett's insistence in following orders so superciliously in the heat of a violent emergency, Williford retorted, "Well, captain, that is a queer way for me to do business," and left the office.[25]

General Irvin McDowell was the source of Daggett's order to stand down. McDowell had a reputation as, at best, "a hard luck general for whom nothing went right." At worst, he was plagued by rumors of undermining the Union cause. His performance as the commander of the first major encounter of the Civil War, the Battle of Bull Run, got people talking. The battle ended in a notorious rout, a retreat Sherman called "an ugly stampede." McDowell claimed his men and, it would seem, his officers, were not prepared. McDowell was demoted. Then it happened again at another major Union loss at the Second Battle of Bull Run. He took a great deal of blame for both defeats and faced a court-martial. While he maintained the support of General Grant, his soldiers seemed to hate him; rumors of his traitorous Southern sympathies mushroomed among his beleaguered troops.[26]

In contrast to Daggett's orders to stand down, Williford's orders from the US Marshals Service were to hold the line. The marshal's office of the Southern District of Alabama included specific commands to "preserve order and protect and support the supervisors appointed by the circuit court of the United States." The marshals were to arrest anyone tampering with the votes, falsifying votes, illegally voting, preventing legal voting, tampering with ballots or boxes, preventing free ingress to and egress from stations for registration, election, or canvas, miscounting votes, interfering with a marshal, or "if any election officer makes any distinction founded upon the color of the applicant or voter." Marshals were to pursue these issues "prudently but energetically." They were also directed to arrest violators of the edicts without a warrant. Should a deputy marshal fail in his duty in these regards, the marshal himself was liable to be arrested for violations of his official duty. As impressive as those orders were, they meant nothing without the power of federal guns, which remained holstered under military order that election day in Eufaula, Alabama.[27]

The day hinged on what the federal troops would do, and everyone knew it. A secret battle over troop deployment in Eufaula had been going on well before Election Day. In addition to white Republican judge Elias Keils seeking troops through the governor's office, Republican congressmen Alexander White and James Rapier had telegraphed the US attorney general for military protection of the vote. Alpheus Baker, leader of the Election Day violence, knew the fate of his plans to redeem Barbour County from "negro rule" hinged on whether the federals would intervene. Baker sent a telegraph to President Grant, trying to figure out if the president would protect Black voters. "Will you permit our troops to be so employed"? he asked, clearly probing to see if his rebellion would face federal opposition. There is no evidence that Grant bothered to reply. It is reasonable to believe, given the boldness of the White League's actions, that they knew that General Order No. 75 would be interpreted narrowly and strictly. Perhaps a leak at the telegraph office allowed the information to circulate as it did in nearby Spring Hill.[28]

"Big riot to-day," reported the Eufaula newspaper with glee after the election. "Several killed and many others hurt—some badly—but none of our friends among them. The white man's goose hangs high. Three cheers from Eufaula." The Republican vote in Barbour County collapsed. Despite a large Republican majority, the district's African American congressman, James T. Rapier, was replaced with a white supremacist. Democrats "won" a majority in a county that was said to have a 2:1 majority of Republican membership. All of the vocal Republican leaders were soon driven from the county. If any remained, they did so in fear and silence. As a result of the massacre, a federal Senate investigation concluded, "the colored people of the county have been taught that they cannot vote without protection,

OFFICE OF U.S. MARSHAL.
KKK
CALL HOME YOUR TROOPS
SHALL WE CALL HOME OUR TROOPS?
"We intend to beat the Negro in the battle of life, and defeat means one thing—EXTERMINATION."—Birmingham (Alabama) News.

A federal marshal idly protects a Black voter from a white mob in this 1875 cartoon from *Harper's Weekly*. Printed just months after the violent coup in Eufaula, it suggests the thin line between protection and violent oppression in the Reconstruction era, as well as the passive but crucial nature of federal support for voting rights.

and they have seen no evidence that any power exists which can prevent or punish the crimes of democrats when committed for political purposes."[29]

Two versions of freedom were at stake in November 1874. One was an African American civic version that required strong federal intervention to protect. In contradistinction, the second was a form of white sovereignty that allowed an unbridled minority to do what they wanted. At stake was something more troubling than a simple defense of white supremacy. Tested and affirmed in the violence of 1874 was a core piece of the white American idea of freedom. Despite its promises to the contrary, the federal government's inaction sustained a freedom defined by race, rather than a civic freedom defined by law and democratic ideals.[30]

An acrid taste of failure, betrayal, and injustice drifts across the centuries and clouds our perception of federal authority, white freedom, and African American agency. The 1874 Eufaula election massacre was only one of scores of similarly violent episodes across the federally occupied South. For many, the political fires of the period continue to burn bright as lasting symbols of federal overreach from an era of direct assault on white freedom. To them, as for much of the United States, Reconstruction was remembered for the better part of a century as an unnecessary, misguided, and ultimately failed federal effort to establish "negro rule" and foment a "blackout of honest government." Yet the truth was that federal troops, while unprecedented in peacetime presence, were never anywhere near what would be remembered as the myth and trauma of an overwhelming federal takeover.

The violent retaking of white freedom in the fall of 1874 has a name: *redemption*. Those who made it their political project were called *redeemers*. The concept perfectly captures the evangelical sense of righteousness involved in saving a people from wayward error and evil. The redemption mythology—built on hyperbolic tales of white victimization, Black incapacity, and federal corruption—permeated American political and intellectual life for generations. Even after the immediate political crises of Reconstruction passed, an inescapable suspicion endured that federal intervention served the interest of an untamable and unruly Black society, while simultaneously threatening to crush the freedom of white people. The power of the word "redemption" is such that even well-trained historians continue to use language of the planter elite unconsciously and reflexively even to this day. Rather than "election riot," the label commonly used, the more accurate term would be that of US Marshal Williford: *massacre*. Rather than "redemption" to describe the 1874 events in Barbour County, the more accurate term would be *coup d'état*.[31]

In the redeemers' eyes, the day's most important victory was ridding District 2 of its African American congressman, James T. Rapier. He lost by 1,056 votes out of a total of 39,000 cast in Alabama's Second District. In some counties, he only got a few votes. In others, none. In Barbour, where Black Republicanism was strong, he lost by only 108 votes despite the shootings. Without violent intervention in polling at both Eufaula and Spring Hill, it is reasonable to believe that voters would have once again delivered an African American to represent the Black Belt in Washington, DC. Instead, Barbour County sent Jeremiah Williams to replace Rapier in office. His gentlemanly demeanor and Confederate military valor did nothing to hide the baseness of his appeals. "Shoulder to shoulder, white men! Beat back the mongrel foe!" he campaigned. "Your wives, your children, your country call upon you. Forward in solid column.... Ring out the charging cheer all along the Caucasian line."[32]

As victors are wont to do, white Eufaulans began to write and promote the story of their redemption almost immediately. Their accounts differ sharply from the preponderance of evidence. They claimed that rural Blacks marched in from the countryside looking for trouble. Those present claimed to see "the devil in many of the negroes" who were armed with "pistols, heavy clubs, and [wagon] wheel spokes," demonstrating "clearly that they meant to carry such weapons for no other purposes than to fight." City leader Eli Shorter described a peaceful white citizenry neatly deputized with badges on their lapels in anticipation of "threats made by the negroes." Fortunately, as a result of the forward thinking of the city's fathers, so the fable goes, "good order was preserved."[33]

The fine white people of Eufaula were able to maintain order until midday, the redemption narrative goes, when "colored republicans, with jeers and personal violence" interfered with the election. White people testified that the Black voters were "violent and turbulent," many "armed with clubs" and with "pistols strapped around their bodies." The riot began when a person they variously described as "a very bad negro" and a "turbulent negro" with "an oath against the whites" drew his pistol and fired at a white man who was trying to keep the peace. This was almost certainly a reference to Milas Lawrence, who was stabbed with a Bowie knife and fled for his life. "Instantly," the story goes, "the blacks drew their weapons and commenced a general attack upon the whites." The confusion that followed was so great that no accounting of "particular individuals" could ever be made, except to say that the shooting was clearly "chargeable to the colored people."[34]

Had the white residents of Eufaula not armed for self-protection, so the mythology tells it, "nearly all of them would have been killed who went into the street during that riot." A local grand jury concluded that "the whites provoked no difficulty, and only fought on the defensive, and the proof failed to show that any white man did any act or used any weapon, except under a reasonable apprehension that it was necessary to save his own life or the life of others, to prevent body harm to himself or others and to suppress the outbreak." The presence of the federal authorities emboldened an otherwise docile Black population. "If these United States troops had not been located here that day in this county," Eli Shorter claimed, "there would not have been the slightest disturbance at the polls; that the negroes were encouraged under the belief that these troops were here to protect them, and they were more violent than they would otherwise have been; and if those troops had not been in this county, I do not think that there would have been any bloodshed in Barbour County that day."[35]

The redeemer myth became central to white Americans' sense of history. Walter Fleming, an important historian of Alabama's Reconstruction, gave the fairy tale the weight of scholarship. In his 1905 book on Reconstruction in Alabama, he explained how African Americans in Eufaula took part in the "fairest" elections since freedmen got the vote. Fleming followed others in cementing in dubious fact and willfully wrong interpretation the popular idea that Reconstruction was both a terrible thing and a complete failure that ought never be repeated. South Carolina's redeemer mythology found a wide audience in celluloid form in one of the most technically brilliant, but fundamentally racist, films in cinema history, *Birth of a Nation* (1915). In 1941, a local Eufaula historian writing during the New Deal, Anne Kendrick Walker, claimed that redemption meant the end of an era marked by the "curse of political corruption" that had been "hung like a millstone around the neck of the people" by "unscrupulous and contemptible scalawags and carpet-baggers." One hundred years after the Civil War, George Wallace, for one, could still smell the "vulturous carpetbagger and federal troops" who stripped his people of their freedom.[36]

As African American people patched the wounded and prepared to bury the dead that November afternoon, the White League set their plans in motion for even more electoral violence. Though they felt the need to shoot Black voters, they were equally—perhaps more—concerned with the misguided white people who supported them. They called them "scalawags." And in Barbour County, the person who embodied that role more than anyone was Judge Elias M. Keils. In the fall of 1874, all angry white fingers pointed to the white Eufaulan who encouraged and abetted the twisted ideas of political equality among African American people.

On the evening of Election Day, following the noonday massacre in Eufaula, they would deliver Judge Elias Keils his comeuppance.

CHAPTER TEN

The Fate of the Scalawag

Evening, Election Day 1874

As the rare white organizer and politician who believed that African Americans deserved protection in the practice of their democratic rights, Judge Elias Keils earned the title, according to a local historian, of the "most bitterly hated man" in Barbour County. He wielded a certain charm and charisma—"slight of build, good looking, and of brilliant mind," they said—but he provoked the ceaseless ire of the town's white leadership. His reputation as a race traitor cut "like a red scar" across the historical record of Eufaula, Alabama. White Eufaulans ostracized him, ridiculed him, threatened him, tried to eliminate his job, and finally, they decided to kill him.[1]

Keils was the town "scalawag," a pejorative term for any white Southerner who cooperated with Republicans and African Americans after the war. The label assumed near mythological proportions, surpassing mere "traitor" to one's race or region. Rogue, scoundrel, thief, parasite, good-for-nothing, backstabber, opportunist—the connotations were limitless. An unmerciful caricature published in 1868 captured the popular hatred of "the local leper of the community." Federal power had twisted the scalawag's mind away from his local community to an opportunistic alliance with outsiders. "Now, possessed of the itch of office and the salt rheum of Radicalism," one Alabama paper editorialized, "he is a mangy dog, slinking through the alleys, haunting the governor's office, defiling with tobacco juice the steps of the Capitol, stretching his lazy carcass in the sun on the square, or the benches of the Mayor's Court." Many, like Keils, had actually been Southern Unionists before the war, but the stereotype clung to a myth of opportunistic betrayal: these once stable Southern allies had abandoned their white brethren when they spied a route to political power provided by federal intervention during Reconstruction.[2]

The scalawag and the Black voter were inseparable in this mythology. African Americans could be framed as a docile and happy lower order that took leadership cues from the paternalism of white elites. Or they could be a feared source of violence, insurrection, and latent political power set to rob whites of their freedom. According to the Reconstruction melodrama, it was the scalawag who made the difference.

Not only were scalawags opportunists, they were saboteurs, manipulating Black voters away from their alleged docile affinity to their former masters and toward the radical Republican Party. As Eufaula's Eli Shorter summarized Keils's role in local politics: "One bad man's influence with a mass of negroes, numbering thousands, can do a great deal of harm, and has done it." Equal rights, men like Shorter believed, meant incursions into, even the destruction of, the liberty of white people. "Every white man in the South *feels* and *knows*" that the scalawag "is aiding and assisting the black man to be become ruler and master of the white," claimed the Montgomery paper. Thrusting so ill-equipped a person onto the political stage was "an outrage upon him, for which there is no parallel in the history of any age." Manipulated by resident scalawags, the freedman had to be regarded as innocent. "We do not much blame him that he is a voter...and shall altogether forgive him, but never his white coadjutors." It was only by destroying the vehicle of empowerment of African Americans, the white agitator, that the "long, bloody, and fierce struggle for his decimation" could be avoided.[3]

Scalawags like Keils joined a shifting set of alliances that included Black Belt freedmen, other scalawags, and Northern carpetbaggers under the banner of the Republican Party in order to launch a direct, if often quite cautious, attack on the economic power and labor system of the Barbour County planters. This unwieldy alliance courted another piece of the Reconstruction political puzzle: north Alabama whites who despised the power of the planter class but remained fearful of social equality for African Americans. If these voters threw their support to the Republicans, they could pose a real threat to the power structure of the Black Belt. The coalition rested on either the reality or at least the threat of federal intervention to back up the right to vote.

Well before the fall coup, a violent confrontation at the polls in February 1874 provided the pretext for a reckoning that Eufaula's Democrats had been waiting for a long time. A town meeting was called in March to try to figure what to do with the agitator whites blamed for riling up the local Black population. The city fathers drew up a long list of accusations: Judge Keils had characterized the white leadership as a "mob" and as a group of "law breakers"; he equated their fraternal organization, the Order of Patrons of Husbandry, as a "second edition of the Ku Klux"; he claimed that white Democrats sympathized with white criminals; he believed some of the most respected lawyers in town ought to be disbarred; and he had gone so far as to say that members of the city council were "enemies of public order" and "abettors and apologists of murder."[4]

Keils may have been busy "slandering" the white elite, but the real accusations were that he promoted, protected, and coddled African Americans. He hired Black men as court officers and supposedly filled the local Republican ticket with incompetent people who would be supported "mainly by ignorant and irresponsible negroes." As judge, he let people free who had been charged with minor crimes or on trumped-up charges, including, according to white accusers, a list of "fugitives, vagrants, thieves, perjurers, [and] burglars." He filled grand juries with Black majorities. Because of Keils, "the gallows have gone out of fashion here; the penitentiary is but little used—the chain-gang has become a sort of myth." The judge believed that the sharecroppers were being cheated by the planter class, and he went so far as to claim that field hands were underpaid and often starving. An epidemic of theft during hard times he dared to connect to the fact that planters were not paying their workers. "Gentlemen," Keils directed a grand jury on the problem of thievery, "you ought to examine and find out whether such persons had been paid by their employers and if they had not been—why then you ought find bills against the employers also."[5]

To be a Republican was to face social exclusion, political coercion, and employment blacklisting, but to be a *white* Republican meant a near complete ostracism from white society, especially as Eufaula built up to the 1874 campaign. The ostracization of white Republicans like Keils became so complete that it got a name: "Barbour County fever." The moniker included any tool at the white majority's disposal for making life unbearable for white radicals—from snubs in the community, school, churches, and political life to the pure terror of the Klan and the White League. Dr. Daniel, a Eufaula native, watched his medical practice shrink to the point he had to leave town because his father merely assisted Republicans on occasion—neither he nor his father were actual members of the party. Public alienation, Daniel explained, "operates in depriving a man of his business, in keeping him out of society; it makes his life disagreeable in nearly every respect." Ostracism meant receiving "the contumely of the intelligent and the jeers of the ignorant."[6]

Keils was such a pariah that Eufaulans immortalized him in a popular local 1874 campaign song, written in a minstrel dialect:

Keils he sits on de City bench,
His nigger juries raise a stench,
He puts white men in the calaboose,
And turns black thieves and rascals loose.

M[inerv]a, born from the brain of thunder,
A full grown gal that was a wonder;

But the way Keils burst from an ignoramus
Into a judge, was much more famous.

One Jackass wore a Lion's skin,
Another, a Judge's gown got in;
But the first wus a decent Royal beast,
Compared wid de countrified Judge, at least.

Oh, de good nigger works and de bad one steals,
But he's got a mighty good friend in Keils;
For what cares de Judge, for de stealing a shoat,
If turning de thief loose gains him his vote?

De day of nigger rule is past,
De white man's day is come at last...[7]

Constant but sporadic political violence plagued the county throughout the spring of 1874, but by August it had been refined into something resembling a systematic attack on Black voters, the Republican Party, and Keils's leadership. At a meeting of thirty-seven delegates of the Barbour County Republican nominating convention in Clayton, the White League launched its latest campaign. As the delegates attempted to go about their business, they reported hearing "throats in the streets" threatening to break the door down and end the radical interracial convention. A white man outside the building, Keils recalled, "pretended to command some sort of a militia company, brought out his company in force with their guns, and paraded the streets." When Keils emerged from the convention, he faced protesting Democrats who "chased men across the square with guns, pistols, and clubs," followed by "shooting, striking with sticks, and running down colored men through the streets." Some of the Black Republicans took cover in the only safe place in the area: the United States Post Office. The meeting had to be relocated to the outskirts of town.[8]

Keils worked his appeals for safety and security of the vote up the ladder of the compound republic. "Mob law has prevailed long enough," Keils declared to the state attorney general, detailing the growing violence in Barbour County by election season. "I have made up my mind to take the Bull by the horns—The law *shall* punish the guilty—The law *shall* protect the innocent." To implement his resolve, Keils asked Governor Lewis to declare martial law. A former slave-holding Alabama Unionist turned Republican, the governor denied Keils's request, calling him "an incendiary, or a fool," and advising his attorney general to tell the impertinent Keils "to shut his mouth about my course" of action. Lewis was a moderate, and by backing civil and voting rights for Black people he and his fellow moderates stood to lose the white vote—especially in the northern part of the state where there were solid numbers of white Republicans. Opposing civil rights meant betraying African Americans, the core of the party in the state, but openly supporting a militant scalawag with state troops was simply too risky in the volatility of the economic crisis and a national debate about the civil rights bill.[9]

The governor had a better idea: federal troops and spies might do the trick, while keeping the moderate Republicans' hands clean. In September, federal authorities penetrated Klan meetings and showed up at Democratic Party "meetings" (often mobs) that had a tendency to turn violent against African Americans. When local politicians threw Judge Keils in jail for releasing prisoners that the white citizenry felt needed to remain imprisoned, the federal authorities retaliated by arresting the mayor and seven other local officials for a short time. The local papers may have publicly threatened him, but as long as federal troops stood by his side Keils's enemies were held at bay.[10]

As the fall election season heated up, a dual movement was afoot: plans for violent Democratic white resistance combined with Republicans' crises of funding, faith, and competence. As the *New York Tribune* put it, the overexposure of freedmen's oppression meant that the "outrage business" had "already been overdone" to the point of political exhaustion in the North. The once powerful intervention of Reconstruction was drifting toward the same weak federal response to the needs of the Creek people four decades earlier. Radical Republicans on the national level were losing their backbone, and the threat of social equality continued to undermine their political power in the border states. As the *Mobile Register* registered its hope about the national change of heart: "The white people of the North have awakened from their nightmare. The negro is no longer the fashion. . . . The North have found that they could not make a silk purse out of a sow's ear, and have cast Sambo overboard." With Republican "budgetary starvation and bureaucratic inertia," the time for the Democratic Party to seize power in Alabama seemed right.[11]

Black voters in Clayton reported open discussions of violence. Locals reported to Keils that leading Democrats were strategizing about "how to raise a row" in order to "kill republican voters" on Election Day. As voting approached, Keils wrote to the US marshal that they needed soldiers at the polling places in Barbour County. He requested particular officers he knew were not part of the White League for the assignment. "If you could give us these," Keils pleaded, "we will carry this county largely." While the request for particular officers later smacked of corruption to those who hated him, his words expressed sincere confidence that the Republicans could hold their majority in a fair election. Yet he feared that weapons were being stockpiled to take the election by force. "With references to the campaign," Keils explained, "we hear of threats by the White League, but as long as the company of soldiers are here, under the present officers, we think we will have peace. But if they should be removed, or most of them before election, it would lose us the county." Others agreed. The federal marshal for Eufaula, P. W. Henly, telegrammed the attorney general of the United States requesting a company of troops for the protection of Republican voters in Eufaula. African American congressman James Rapier similarly demanded detachments of soldiers to the polling place of Alabama's Second District.[12]

On Election Day, as smoke and bullets filled downtown Eufaula, Judge Keils was busy serving as an election supervisor appointed by the United States Circuit Court at a polling station eighteen miles away, deep in the Black Belt region of Spring Hill. Things were calm until around 11:00 a.m. on Election Day, when "signs of rowdyism" were followed by gunfire. That appears to have been the signal, as a crowd of perhaps seventy-five men ran to a nearby vacant store, where their weapons were stored. Emerging armed, the White League Democrats paraded around with their weapons and taunted voters until nightfall. Many brandished breech-loading shotguns, and some carried a gun in each arm. People had been coming in raising trouble with "all sorts of insolent remarks," Keils noted, but he managed to remain calm and do his job as a poll watcher. He recalled that the mob was prepared to shoot anyone who "did not exactly suit them." The essence of their marching chants, he explained, was: "'We are going to make these damned negroes behave themselves. If they don't we will kill out the last one of them.' That was about the amount of it."[13]

As the pressure mounted from the armed mob, Keils's sixteen-year-old son, Willie, pleaded with his father, "You had better let me go after Lieutenant Turner and his men to come here." The judge agreed with his boy. Willie dashed just three hundred yards from the Spring Hill polling place to discuss matters with Lieutenant Turner, who stood by with his detachment of ten US soldiers. Willie urgently explained that the poll workers were going to need help protecting the ballots and possibly themselves from the swelling number of White Leaguers outside the polling place.[14]

Lieutenant Turner explained to Willie "how impossible" it was for him to assist and how much he regretted it. He laid out the same problem that stopped a military defense of voting rights in Eufaula earlier that same day: General Order No. 75. The order bound the troops from assisting in local affairs, he explained to Willie. "I sympathized very much with him," the lieutenant later explained, "and begged that he would induce his father to come down and stay with my troops where I would protect him, but I could not go near the polls or interfere with the election in any way." Upon hearing the news from Willie, Keils still refused to abandon his post.[15]

A message arrived at the new telegraph office in Spring Hill—possibly the first message ever to come over those wires. "Keep your troops away from crowd," it read, signed by Captain Daggett in Eufaula.

Turner later confessed that he believed that the Democrats probably intercepted the telegram telling him to stand down. It was delivered, handwritten and without an envelope, exposed to anyone who wanted to see it. Lieutenant Turner figured "a large number of people" had seen the telegraph, and he noticed "a considerable change in the tone of the crowd about the polls" after the telegraph arrived in the afternoon. The Democrats, it would seem, had learned they could act with impunity.[16]

Meanwhile, J.W. Comer, a member of one of the largest, most powerful, and most affluent planter families in Barbour County, walked in just as the Spring Hill polls closed. He was pretending to be drunk. He sat down with Keils, claiming to have "drunk a barrel of whisky." Keils believed him to be pretending. An argument ensued about whether the ballot box that Keils stood watch over would be pivotal to the Barbour County total. Comer, believing that it would, offered the judge one thousand dollars in exchange for possession of the ballot box. "Don't talk to me about $1,000," Keils replied. "The inspectors have this ballot-box under charge. I am here to watch it." Comer repeated his offer. Keils once again refused the bribe. In so doing, he declined Comer's paltry attempt to avoid bloodshed.[17]

Darkness settled in, the doors to the polls were carefully barred, and lamps were lit to begin the count. Fearing the mob outside, Keils got up and made sure the door was barred "good and strong." Keils recalled that a total of 732 votes had been cast, of which he figured about five-sixths were Republican. The judge noticed, however, that one of the Democratic poll watchers had been slow to get his vote count prepared. Then that same Democratic poll watcher simply got up and unbarred the door.[18]

The White Leaguers burst in, guns blazing. They immediately shot the lantern out. The flash of firearms provided the only illumination in the darkness. Bullets began flying—"promiscuous shooting all around"—in the general direction of Judge Keils and the ballot box. Everyone who could get out did, except for Keils and his son. Pinned down by bullet fire, they dove behind a counter for protection. All Keils remembered hearing, "may be a hundred times," was "Kill him, damn him, kill him" as the bullets flew.[19]

How or why the firing stopped remains shrouded in confusion, but Judge Keils survived the onslaught. When he got up from behind the counter where he had been curled up next to his son, the boy's hand slumped off of his shoulder. Willie's weak voice in the darkness said that he had been "shot to pieces." A growing crowd of Black people shielded Elias and Willie from further attack, and they took him up to see the local doctor.[20]

The next day, Keils returned to the polling station to find the ballot box destroyed. Ashes and burned fragments of ballots lay scattered about the room, "riddled all around with bullets." The strong Republican vote evaporated in the heat of mob violence. The following day, his son succumbed to the four bullet wounds he received in the attack—the fatal shot was in his abdomen. Many whites claimed that Keils had used his son as a shield during the attack in a most cowardly manner. The *Eufaula Times* offered an apology—of sorts. Everyone knew the judge was the real target, the paper explained, "the shot that struck him was intended for his father, and that no one intended to harm little Willie." Keils was brokenhearted.[21]

That the federal troops never budged or offered assistance came as a complete shock to Keils, who believed that the Spring Hill poll operated safely under their protection. The fact that they had been ordered to stay away from the polling station was "something I had never suspected before," he recalled. Still, he couldn't imagine acting otherwise, even if he had known. "If I could have gotten out of that door and got away I should have gone," he reflected. "But it would have been certain death to have undertaken to have gone. I knew that, and therefore thought the safest way would be to stay in there, which I did."[22]

When Captain Daggett visited to express his condolences for the loss of Keils's son, the judge sternly informed the federal officer that his dispatch ordering Lieutenant Turner to stand down "caused the destruction of the ballot-box and the murder of my son; I told him that I considered him guilty of the murder of my son." Daggett showed him the order from the controversial General McDowell at headquarters in Kentucky. Keils remained unmoved. "I thought

[it] never was intended to be understood as he understood it," Keils later explain to the investigators. "I know, in fact, that it was not." In the western part of the Black Belt, where federal monitors and soldiers were prepared to keep the peace, or in nearby counties where the order was interpreted more liberally, polling took place without violence.[23]

The local paper interpreted the Election Day shootings in Spring Hill and Eufaula with galling, detailed, and unrestrained mendacity. "We hope the negroes will learn a lesson from this and understand that they cannot run 'ruffshod' over white men and go unpunished," the paper crowed. "It was by the teachings of such men as Keils and his ilk, that caused the negroes to step beyond that bound which has no limit." Turning to the role of federal authorities, the paper upended and twisted the sense of causation: "We were present and noticed particularly that United States Marshal Williford made every effort to stop these Radical negroes from abusing negroes who desired to vote with the Democrats, but all was of no avail, they kept it up until it culminated in the trouble which these leading Radicals have all along desired." The problem all along, of course, was that of the fiendish scalawag Keils, who pushed and prodded the freedmen beyond their natural station in life:

> We now state it as our solemn conviction, that every drop of blood shed on Tuesday was the natural, the inevitable result of the murderous midnight teachings of that archfiend of darkness E.M. Keils. Time and again he has told these hordes of ignorant barbarous negroes to come to the polls *en masse* and 'not fear the Democrats that they would not shoot a frog!' By every effort on his part has he incited the negroes to bloodshed! And in the name of justice and humanity E.M. Keils is solely and entirely responsible for the blood of these poor deluded, ignorant negroes, and for the blood of those white men poured out on Tuesday. In the name of God and justice is there no way to reach the conscience of this fiend in human shape? Will not the ghastly dead faces of these wretched negroes fill his soul with bitter remorse when he well

> knows that they met their fate solely on account of his bad advice? If this will not reach him let the blood of his poor boy whom he placed before him, to protect his own coward carcass at Spring Hill—let this sad lesson sink deep in his soul if he has one.[24]

To Senate investigators, Keils later summed up the event far more succinctly and persuasively. "The whole democratic party, with perhaps one or two exceptions, turned themselves into a mob and came into the room and destroyed the ballot box where there were 450 or 500 republican majority, and murdered my little son who was with me."[25]

The violence in Eufaula proved to be pivotal in liberating the state from what whites believed to be "negro Republican" domination. After the election, the Montgomery paper wanted to "congratulate" its readers "on a happy release from local misrule." Where once there had been violent division, the paper envisioned North and South joining together, united not by federal authority but by what they believed to be "freedom." "The bonds of union are no longer the bayonet," editorialized the *Advertiser*, "but the subtle, indissoluble ligaments of mutual, fraternal regard which stretch from heart to heart all over this great, glorious and free country." With federal power in retreat, North and South could now rebuild a shared platform of white supremacy or, at least, a willingness to ignore it and the violence it entailed. "By this generous token the South will now strike hands with the north and re-echo the words of the immortal Webster, 'Liberty and Union, now and forever, one and inseparable.'"[26]

The state Colored Citizens Convention that assembled in Montgomery after the election saw it differently. Writing to President Grant, they pleaded for increased federal protection. "But for the presence of the United States troops, and civil officers of the United States, hundreds of the active and earnest republicans of this State would have been assassinated." Even then, "many of our race were shot down and killed at the polls." They wondered if Black people had a "future destiny" in the state or whether they needed to escape the unchecked power of white people. As they explained to the president, they felt they were being driven from the state on a biblical scale. "The solemn question with us is," they appealed to the president, "shall we be compelled to repeat the history of the Israelites and go into exile from the land of our nativity and our homes, to seek new homes and fields of enterprise, beyond the reign and rule of Pharaoh?" Enumerating the "evils" they faced, they turned to the federal government. "We present these facts for the consideration of the Government of the United States, and ask its immediate interference in the terrible situation that it has left us after solemnly promising to guard us in the enjoyment of the privileges that it has given to us—namely, all the rights of citizenship." The 1874 elections had been so disastrous for the Republican Party nationwide, however, that the prospect of federal protection had become politically impossible.[27]

Depleted personally and politically, Ulysses S. Grant had little to offer the Black South in the fall of 1874. He had sent troops into Louisiana after the Colfax massacre, but had no stomach for triggering a comparable political backlash. He was hemmed in by a year of economic crisis, looking on in despair as his party and his presidency were consumed in a swamp of corruption scandals. As for Reconstruction policies, the nation was abuzz with a scandalous indictment written by former Radical Republican James S. Pike: *The Prostrate State: South Carolina Under Negro Government.* Supposedly a neutral eyewitness account since he was once outspoken in his antislavery position, it described the "mass of black barbarism" that South Carolina had become with African American voting. Pike's polemic further weakened the nation's resolve to support freedmen's rights. As early as January 1874, the president declared his fatigue with Reconstruction publicly. "I begin to think that it is time for the republican party to unload," he declared. "I am tired of this nonsense. Let Louisiana take care of herself, as Texas will have to do. I don't want any quarrel about Mississippi State matters to be referred to me. This nursing of monstrosities has nearly exhausted the life of the party. I am done with them, and they will have to take care of themselves."[28]

Meantime, Keils had been hauled off to "a little filthy" jail cell for resisting an officer and carrying a concealed weapon—if there was any truth to them at all, both infractions were probably related to his efforts to stay alive. Given the real fear that he could be lynched in the night, his wife set up camp on a mattress outside the doorway to the jail and kept vigil. "She knew I was in danger of being murdered," he recalled. The white Eufaulans would not let anyone bail him out—and threatened to arrest anyone who offered. He was only released when the United States Court in Montgomery issued a subpoena for him to appear as a witness. After that, he officially resigned his judgeship and fled to Washington to assist with investigations into White League activities in Barbour County. On Christmas Eve, he served as the first witness in the congressional committee appointed to investigate the "murders or assassinations, or other acts of violence" committed around the election of 1874 in Alabama. From there, he continued to work for justice in Barbour County and the rest of the Deep South.[29]

Nationally, Reconstruction faded inconclusively over the years that followed, but in Alabama, especially in Barbour County, November 3, 1874, marked the bitter end. Hope lingered that the Republican Party might be able to rebuild, that the federals might return, but in retrospect, the change in politics was swift and dramatic. George S. Houston, a classic Bourbon Democrat, became governor. He set to work building a convict lease system and enforcing the power of the planters. In Eufaula, the governor appointed Alpheus Baker, the leader of the Eufaula election massacre, to replace Elias Keils as judge. J.W. Comer, the man at the head of the Spring Hill mob (but who whites claimed was the one who saved Keils's life), took a seat in the state senate. The next year, 1875, Alabama's "redeemers" passed their constitution. It decreased the size of the government, limited taxation, and restrained African American political power. White Democrats probably wanted to disenfranchise African American voters constitutionally right there and then, but lingering fears of federal intervention should they be found in violation of the Fifteenth Amendment prevented them. Formal disenfranchisement and Jim Crow would have to wait until the 1901 constitutional convention.

While Keils drew white anger as the most hated man in Barbour County, the story of freedman A. E. Williams best illustrates the arc of possibilities during Reconstruction. His first impulse was to flee as the primary signatory on the appeal to the American Colonization Society to move to Liberia. He then appears to have selected to stay in Barbour County under the hope of the new day promised by Radical Reconstruction. Politically active, he won a seat as director of schools in 1871, then won election to the state legislature in 1872, representing the people of Barbour County at the height of interracial democracy. In 1874, he ran again, and helped Henry Fraser organize the sharecroppers for their march to Eufaula to vote in the 1874 election. Despite the massacre that ended that effort, Williams still managed to get reelected to the state legislature. With the Democrats' uncontested power on the state level after November 1874, however, A. E. Williams was unceremoniously expelled from the state house without reason, "a revolutionary proceeding" he called it, simply "no contest at all." His story comes full circle as he, like all other Black Republican leaders, had to flee from Barbour County. Rather than choosing the elusive freedom of Liberia, he fled for his life, as trumped-up charges of perjury and threats of murder ensured that he would not be able to return without ending up in the penitentiary or the chain gang—or worse.[30]

Williams's experience was hardly unique as democracy in Barbour County and other counties in the state was completely, violently, mercilessly crushed. Reports of shootings of Black Eufaulans "without the shadow of an excuse," elections carried by "fraud and force," stuffing of ballot boxes, and Democrats—openly threatening Black voters "with death, jail, or the penitentiary"—swearing "to anything to convict us." Occasionally even a law-abiding Democrat would confess that "my political friends" in Eufaula "are bringing ruin, I fear, upon the country and upon me. I would prevent lawlessness if I could, but the odds in my own party are too strong against me." It took nothing to indict and convict a Black Republican of just about anything. Voting by 1876 went from strong Republican majorities to victories of Democrats by thousands of votes. "Killing republican negroes is only a frolic now," wrote a white Republican from Barbour County.[31]

The freedom to subjugate, steal, and subdue had returned to Eufaula once again. "Every republican that had taken any prominent part in politics or had anything to say previous to the election," explained African American Henry King, "why he was always pointed out and was indicted." People lost their jobs, got blackballed from business pursuits, were thrown in jail, placed into convict labor camps, threatened, and killed. Republican votes had been reduced to a few token votes in each beat. As one Black man from Eufaula claimed before the 1876 race, despite the African American majority, "the White League say they will carry this county by 3,000 majority next month, and I think they will. . . . They won't give me any work to do because they think they can't use my vote as they please. I have no money to get away from here. . . . We are not allowed to have any colored men on the juries now; it takes no time to indict and convict republicans; if he is a colored republican, that is enough to convict him." As an older white Republican from Eufaula explained, "No man can be free here except the democrats, and they must be good at shooting or knocking down 'niggers' to prevent being suspected of not being sound on democratic principles."[32]

An exodus followed. "Some have left because they were tired of the lawlessness there," Keils reported from his collection of correspondence. "Some of them left because there were trumped-up indictments against them, and others left on account of their families, because they had been ostracized and proscribed, and their children had been ostracized in the schools, and their families in the churches." They left Alabama and spread out across the country. "Some of them are in Mississippi; some of them are in Texas; some of them are in Florida; some of them are here [in Washington]; some of them are in Tennessee, and some of them are in South Carolina; they are pretty well scattered, you see." Among the biggest losses was African American congressman John T. Rapier, who lost his historic seat as the representative of Alabama's Second District due to the suppression and murder of Barbour County voters.[33]

The administration may have lost its nerve to back up Southern democracy with federal force, but there were still politicians in

Washington with an interest in shining a light on the coup in Barbour County. Congressman Charles Albright, a stout, teetotalling Union officer who served one term in Congress from his district in the Pennsylvania coal country, took part in a fact-finding mission to Alabama to unearth the truth of what happened on Election Day 1874. His experience there drove him to write a blistering attack on the decline of postbellum hope, which he sent to President Grant.

Democracy in Alabama, Congressman Albright began, was a "mockery and a sham" for both whites and Blacks, dragged down by a "spirit of intolerance, proscription and intimidation" such that white Union men "will feel compelled to leave or surrender their manhood and give up their political convictions." Blacks he found to be "at the mercy of the landowners and their old masters." Even though Black people had been deserted by federal authority, "Their faith in God and confidence in the Republican party are evidences of moral heroism grandly sublime." His temper reaching a feverish pitch, he continued: "To commit the colored people to the care of the men who tried to destroy the government and who are assuming their old arrogance and race superiority is to turn the index finger on the dial plate of Christian civilization backwards—and to allow to be perpetrated a crime and stupendous infamy that will darken and pale the fading years of the 19th Century and that will almost make the celebration of our centennial, a day of lamentation and sorrow."

What Congressman Albright saw was the failure of the compound republic. "My dear sir, I use strong words—but I remember that the evil is great and the remedy to overcome it must be proportionately strong. I believe therefore in stretching the Constitution to the utmost limit to bring relief to the Southern states in protecting the rights of all." He closed his note to Speaker of the House James Blaine and President Grant with word that he was off to investigate events in Eufaula, where "the testimony will present a chapter of barbarism that will shock the world." Nobody listened.[34]

The failure of Reconstruction and the descent into terror and, eventually, Jim Crow has been laid at the feet of a number of events. Unexpected, of course, was the economic crisis that heightened racial animosity and redirected political energies. But also playing a role were the rejection of land redistribution, factionalism and corruption among the Republicans, the inability to make strong political connections with white voters in the South, the postwar exhaustion of the North, the interminable mess and complexity of state politics, and the aggressive drive for redemption in the South. Weighing all of these factors, it is clear that above all, it was the temerity of armed, local violence that transformed Southern politics.[35]

The surrender of the South to one-party rule through "powder and lead" set a pattern that would not change for the better part of a century. After 1874, the African American people of Barbour County were left without any hope of federal allies. Not having troops to defend the rules of democracy, Judge Elias Keils explained, meant a holiday of white freedom: "license to the armed mob . . . to murder at will." When White League Democrats, including many of the city's finest citizens, were brought up on federal charges for the crimes of November 1874, all witnesses against the accused disappeared or were thrown in jail. Nobody was convicted except Black Republicans who dared to speak out against the atrocities. "The State courts," Keils explained to the attorney general of the United States in the summer of 1875, "as conducted in Barbour county for the last six months are simply engines of oppression." Keils grasped what the Creeks understood and the civil rights workers would come to understand almost a century later. "To sum up the whole facts," he continued, "we have no law or justice in Alabama, and we never can have any peace there unless the United States Government secures it to us, as we think there is full and complete authority for doing."[36]

In the vacuum left behind by federal retreat, new innovations in the freedom to harm would arise. Soon would come the neoslavery of convict leasing, the vigilante justice of lynching, the degradation and debt of sharecropping, and the official disenfranchisement of Blacks under a new state constitution. "And then," Keils detailed about pushing freedmen into convict leasing, "they have been put upon the block and hired out, *sold*, publicly, at $2.00 per month, to pay the fine and costs." As if being thrown into the convict leasing system was not bad enough, those bidding on the new imprisoned labor force cajoled and intimidated people to make sure nobody bid more than $2.00 on any of the convicted.[37]

With the power of white freedom reestablished, the dominant class again stood on top. A decade of rich postbellum democratic possibility was foreclosed. With the federal government moving toward repose on questions of intervention in the South, a host of new forms of white freedom rushed in, beginning almost immediately with the profits of the new convict leasing system. There to engineer the new form of slavery was J.W. Comer, one of Barbour's finest planters.

BOOK THREE

Federal Power in Repose

CHAPTER ELEVEN

The Prison Mines

PRISONERS STUMBLED AND CLANKED through the predawn light, making their way from the stockades where they slept to the mines where they labored in darkness. Prodded by guards and hobbled by ankle irons, they trudged every morning but Sundays through the heat, the rain, and even the occasional Alabama snow. Upon arriving at the pits, they descended into the miles of underground blackness that laced the earth just outside Birmingham. Armed men stood watch over the entrances for the duration of their labors as the prisoners mined coal. They drilled holes for explosives, ignited them, and released avalanches of rock, which they then sorted and loaded by hand. Often on their knees, sometimes in water up to their chests, each convict dug and moved eight to twelve thousand pounds of slate and coal per day over the course of their sentences. Fueled by meager rations, they managed to pile incredible tonnage into coal cars to be pulled up to the daylight by mules.

The convict lease system is starkly emblematic of the terror that filled the void left by the retreat of federal authority. After the collapse of Reconstruction in 1874, convict leasing took off rapidly to become a system of labor, a mode of social control, a shortcut to industrialization, and a stream of private and political revenue—a panacea, really, for all that ailed white Alabama in the last quarter of the nineteenth century. The African American prisoners hailed mostly from the Black Belt, convicted of a variety of crimes—some small, a few real, most trumped up. Labor contractors bought up their sentences and fines from county jails and the state prison and then leased them to the mine operators at a tidy profit. The prisoners had no choice but to sign the contract placed in front of them by the labor contractors. Although the prison miners, unlike chattel slaves, had hopes of regaining their freedom one day, unlike with slavery their overseers had no investment in keeping them healthy or even alive. Convicts were disposable, cheap, and in near infinite supply. The convict labor system reestablished the terms of the old regime but looked to the future, balancing the slavery past and the industrial future.[1]

The prisoners resurfaced after dark and dragged themselves back to the stockade in their leg irons. For months they did not shower and changed clothes only rarely. The convicts ate their meager grub and lay their bodies down on vermin-infested bedding packed into windowless rooms and surrounded by overflowing buckets of human waste filled by men not infrequently dying of dysentery. The only fresh air available filtered through the slim cracks in the walls. One state official described the "damp sleeping clothes, damp bedding, deficient cubic space and ventilation, want of sunlight in the cells, and, for the men, cold water for bathing purposes, and general overcrowding." It was "unfit in every particular for the habitation of animal beings." The threat of the lash, a heinous symbol of the slave system, returned. According to one report, every single miner had either been whipped or witnessed a whipping. Even the most basic health care was lacking, and many were maimed in the various tortures designed to enforce discipline.[2]

Convict leasing, as well as other horrors such as lynching and constitutional disenfranchisement, flourished in the void left by the retreat of federal power after the 1870s. Whereas the Black vote and the Republican Party—and the federal authorities that assisted them—all lost political legitimacy, the locking up of prisoners to use as convict miners had the full sanction of the county, the state, and much of the region.

The stunning thing about convict leasing was the rapidity with which it grew after the coup of 1874. Back when African American "crime" had been the responsibility of masters and plantation managers, Black people represented zero percent of the prison population. As Reconstruction collapsed, however, the Black conviction rate rapidly rose. African Americans made up 8 percent of the total convict population in 1871, leaping to 88 percent in 1874, and then 91 percent in 1877. And the mines boomed. The state commissioner of industrial resources noted that mining was in the "merest dawn of its infancy," with just 40,000 tons mined in 1873. Just over ten years later, the state mined 2.2 million tons of coal, of which 401,000 tons were mined by prisoners. When Tennessee Coal and Iron, typically known simply as TCI, came to town, they consolidated "the largest coal company in the South." Half of TCI's output was dug by prisoners. In 1886, the firm alone contracted for six hundred miners for ten years.[3]

One convict who did time in the horrors of both the Eureka and Pratt Mines had the audacity to write to the reform-oriented prison inspector about conditions. "Have worked hungry thirsty," Ezekiel Archey complained, "half clothed & Sore." Sentenced to ten years for burglary and larceny, crimes which he may or may not have committed, he managed to survive long enough to be released—though they kept him longer than his original ten-year sentence. "All These years oh how we Sufered. No Humane being can tell." Throughout Ezekiel Archey's sentence, death haunted him. "Some one of us. were carried to our last Resting. The grave. Day after Day we looked Death in The face & was afraid to speak." After grueling days of digging coal, their cells filled with filth and disease and the stink of human waste, he said. They went to bed wet and woke up wet: "our Agony & pain seams to have no End." Even in the stockade, where he slept, ankles chained to the bed, the smell of excrement in the air, they still had to listen to "Every Guard Knocking beating yelling." He concluded: "Fate Seems To curse a convict Death Seems To Summon us hence."[4]

The convict mines were located far from Barbour County, some 180 miles northwest of Eufaula, in the north-central part of the state near Birmingham. Many convicts, however, were from Barbour County.

Ezekiel Archey was not. But one of the primary individuals who masterminded the convict lease system and profited from Archey's fate and that of hundreds of other prison miners was one of Barbour County's most prosperous and powerful citizens, J.W. Comer.

The Comers were among the county's most prosperous families and owned one of the biggest plantations up at Spring Hill, the location of the shooting of Judge Keils's son. Comer was, as one Republican put it, "the head and front of that Spring Hill mob" that ambushed the polling station in 1874. He tried to bribe Judge Keils prior to the destruction of the ballot box and the shooting of Willie Keils. Having fought in the Civil War and done all he could as a local Barbour County "hero," as they called him for his efforts to undermine Reconstruction, J.W. Comer had found his way to a bold and profitable business. With the void in federal and Republican power after 1874, he could pay the county jails and state penitentiary for their prisoners and then lease them to the mines. From his remote corner of southeastern Alabama, and later, from the mines themselves, he became a kingpin in a complex interlocking system of convict leasing. Funneling free people into jail, and then convicted African American men into the mines, Comer helped create some of the most brutal labor conditions ever devised on "free" American soil. Along the way, the system fed the empty state coffers and enriched J.W. Comer.[5]

Local prison logbooks are filled with mysteries. Most convicts were young men, some were old, a few were women. Their sentences ranged from a single year to the rest of their lives. Their crimes allegedly included everything from murder to arson to gambling to burglary to "not stated." J.W. Comer owned the contract on one Barbour County local, John Baxter, for instance, who, at the tender age of thirteen, had been taken into custody on November 22, 1878, for the crime of "aiding prisoner to escape." Perhaps he was trying to liberate a father or brother from the convict mines, but we'll never know. His sentence was two years, and Comer leased him into the mines. Another fifteen-year-old boy from Barbour County, Mose Granville, got five years for "grand larceny." They listed his conduct in the mine as "bad." Ned Jones was contracted to Comer for four years for "adultery," perhaps suggestive of the obsession with using sex to reinforce the race line. They got Jim Morris for "grand larceny." Comer paid top price, $18 per year, for one Henry Caruthers, who was enslaved to him for five years; Spencer Caruthers, probably his brother, got two years. Whether the two young men were engaged in some criminal enterprise or whether some white man wanted their family land and needed them gone, we'll never know. In Barbour County, almost seven hundred convicts were leased out just between 1891 and 1903 alone. Most of them were destined for one of two big Birmingham firms, either Tennessee Coal and Iron or Sloss-Sheffield Steel and Iron. The going rate for leasing out was about $6 per month.[6]

No matter how they got into the mines, prisoners had a way of getting lost in the system. As the state board of prisons complained of the county system in 1886, there was not "anything like a record kept until a few years ago and we have had application made to us to ascertain what has become of persons sentenced to hard labor prior to 1883, of whom there is absolutely no trace; they have disappeared as completely as if the earth had opened and swallowed them." The earth had, indeed, swallowed them, lost as they were in some mine tunnel someplace, remembered only "by the few at the humble home, who still wait and look in vain for him who does not come."[7]

Officials advertised their prisoners or received solicitations from private lease operators like Comer, who had men posted at the county courts to take advantage of the policies on court costs. County convicts faced responsibility for their own court costs, sheriff fees, jurors' fees, and costs of trial, which Comer's men paid off and then took the prisoners into indentured servitude. Later they would be charged for food, medical treatment, and upkeep, which amounted to even more substantial and unpayable costs. Under the lease system, the convicts could then work off their growing debt by adding additional time onto the sentence they received for their alleged crimes. Misdemeanors in the Black Belt were translated into significant profits.

The county convicts often functioned free of the limited regulatory oversight of the state, and this created substantial financial incentive to increase the number of local prisoners in the system. For the county, it was not just the chance to outsource the care and feeding of prisoners, it was a chance to make real revenues in lease fees. Draconian laws served economic as well as political power. They were designed, claimed one critic, "to place the liberty and equal rights of the poor man, and especially of the poor colored man, who is generally a republican in politics, in the power and control of the dominant race, who are, with few exceptions, the landholders, and democratic in politics."[8]

Republican critics recognized that incarceration and convict leasing provided means not just of generating profits but of reestablishing antebellum race and labor relations. "The accused is little better than a slave," explained the Republicans remaining in the General Assembly of Alabama about the changes to the state penal code. "We need not remind you how such a policy [of convict leasing] is at variance with all the results intended to be wrought out by the war for the preservation of the Union. That was a conflict of ideas as well as of armies," the report argued, "while the slave-labor system did not triumph at Appomattox, they are thus seen to be practically triumphant in Alabama." Should such a convict regime prove successful and durable, they continued, "it would practically reverse the verdict wrought out at the point of the bayonet, reverse the policy of reconstruction, and strike out of existence not only our free-State constitutions, but the laws made in pursuance thereof, thus violating the fundamental conditions of the admission of Alabama into the Union. If this is allowed to be done, it is not difficult to perceive that the war for the Union was a grand mistake, and the blood and treasure of the people spent in vain."[9]

The Thirteenth Amendment abolished slavery. The amendment contained a complicated clause, however, that allowed for considerable maneuvering. Slavery would no longer exist "except as a punishment for crime whereof the party shall have been duly convicted." This became known as the "exception clause." While the clause lends readily to a sense of conspiracy, its language had been in use for decades in a variety of statutes that banned slavery. Northern prisons included labor, and few believed they should be emptied out. Still, alternatives had been presented at the time. Senator Charles Sumner of Massachusetts and Representative Thaddeus Stevens of Pennsylvania, the lions of Radical Republicanism, believed that the difference between race slavery and the penal system required more clear and aggressive separation. Republicans tried to make clear that this was not supposed to encourage convict leasing or for-profit penal systems. Their ideas were not adopted. Instead, the reinstatement of slavery-like conditions required only the excuse of a crime in need of punishment.[10]

That was J.W. Comer's hope: to turn back the clock on the federal aggression that delivered the South to civil war in Barbour County and the rest of the Deep South. His local reputation among white elites was one of "charm and magnetism" backed up by "matchless courage," yet to the convict laborers of the Eureka Mine the gentleman planter from Spring Hill was notorious for his unrestrained brutality. "You know that comer is a hard man," Archey wrote in the winter of 1884. "I have seen men come to him with their shirts a solid scab on their back and beg him to help them and he would say let the hide grow back and take it off again. I have seen him hit men 100 and 160 [times] with a ten prong strap the say they was not whiped he would go off after a escape man come one day with him and dig his grave the same day." Such brutality transcended workplace discipline and spoke of something darker. "The need to control labor cannot explain such sadistic cruelty," argues one historian about Comer; "it sprang from a deeper source."[11]

One witness reported that after Comer caught an escaped prisoner, he turned his hunting dogs on him to tear at the prisoner's flesh without mercy. He forced the prisoner to lie "on the ground and the dogs were biting him. He begged piteously to have the dogs taken off him, but Comer refused to allow it." Then he personally "took a stirrup strap, doubled it and wet it, stripped him naked, bucked him, and whipped him—unmercifully whipped him, over half an hour." Comer must have exhausted himself lashing the prisoner over and over and over; one can imagine beads of sweat pouring down upon his victim as he freed his anger and fear on him. "The Negro begged them to take a gun and kill him," the witness said. "They left him in a Negro cabin where . . . he died within a few hours." Others in Eureka faced the water torture, what would later be known as "water boarding," in which water was "poured in his face on the upper lip, and effectually stops his breathing as long as there is a constant stream." This simulated drowning had the advantage over whipping in that the victim could recover faster and get back to work.[12]

To the degree that freedom meant the capacity to dominate others, J.W. Comer was a remarkably free man. Orlando Patterson described such people in his *Freedom in the Making of Western Culture.* "Men with unrestrained freedom of power in both personal and political life were free to change their fellow men, to organize as never before, to create and transform their worlds, to define the good, and to impose the means by which those over whom they exercised their absolute freedom lived," he argues. Although Patterson saw this brand of freedom as "unrestrained by the inertial weight of tradition," Comer's was all about the will to power to reestablish tradition, to fight federal power, and declare his independent capacity to treat others as he wished. He retrofitted a dying past to an unstable future. In words that spoke of J.W.'s unique brand of cruelty, Patterson argues, such free men "were also free to brutalize, to plunder and lay waste and call it peace, to rape and humiliate, to invade, conquer, uproot, and degrade." When Nietzsche equated the "will to power" to the "instinct for freedom," he touched on the type of freedom Comer wielded. Nietzsche saw something of what Comer saw in himself: "the same active force" in power and freedom displayed "on a grand scale in those artists of violence and organizers and that builds states."[13]

Comer's particularly vicious brand of white freedom undoubtedly came from the cotton fields, but it may have also been made more virulent by his upbringing. He lost his father, the extraordinarily powerful Barbour County planter John Fletcher Comer, just as he began his struggle toward young adulthood at the age of thirteen. In the absence of the patriarch, perhaps he felt some primal need to defend the labor systems and racial ideology of his family's planting empire in Barbour County—a thirty-thousand-acre spread—just as the world split open on those very subjects. Or it could have been his enlistment in the Fifty-Seventh Alabama Infantry Regiment as a young man in 1863. Participation in the brutal savagery of the Civil War itself scarred many other older and more worldly men. Entering the war late, perhaps he simply had something to prove. Whatever it was, something gnawed at J.W. Comer to make him atavistically, physically, torturously cruel to Black people.

In J.W. Comer's Civil War portrait, one can see his arrogance marbled with more than a hint of insecurity. In it, young J.W. sits confidently, left hand propped casually on his sword, hat cocked just enough, his legs casually crossed. He is only eighteen years old, but he poses like a figure in command of his world—yet with an awareness that he is not yet that figure. His smooth face readily betrays his youth, but his body exudes his privilege. His eyes leak a bit of fear, belie a certain fragility. By far the most striking aspect of his portrait, however, is the need to include another person in his portrait: his body servant, a young man named Burrell. The person enslaved to do J.W.'s bidding stands beside but just behind him, hat in hand, arms limply by his side. His posture makes him seem vulnerable, ready to do whatever is asked of him. Perhaps there is genuine loyalty in the photo. More likely there is fear of someone's freedom from restraint on their visceral capacity for violence.

The fact that Burrell saved J.W.'s life during the war makes his former master's trafficking in neoslavery after Reconstruction more galling. Burrell accompanied Comer into battle, feeding and clothing the young patriarch and his ambitions. In 1864, at the Battle of Atlanta, J.W. took a bullet, and Burrell managed to get his wounded master off the battlefield and to the banks of the Chattahoochee, which cuts southwest from Atlanta down to the Alabama state line. In ways lost to the record, he somehow procured a flat-bottomed boat, a "bateau," got J.W. into it, and rowed over one hundred miles through war-torn Georgia to the Alabama border at the city of Columbus. There Comer's mother met him and transported young Comer back to the family plantation in Barbour County. J.W. eventually returned to the war. Afterward, having been saved by his slave, he went on to establish the fiendish system of sending freed people into the hellish world of the convict mines. Perhaps his lashing out was an effort to prove his superiority over the "inferior" who had once held his life in his hands, rowing him back to Alabama.[14]

It wasn't just about coal: J.W. Comer, like other Alabama plantation owners, also leased convicts to pick his cotton. At the massive family plantation, Comer kept as many as forty-five souls "unnecessarily chained and shackled" when they were not working his fields. The prison inspector who exposed J.W.'s use of prison labors for his fields found his treatment of them unacceptable even within the horrific logic of the convict labor system. "Things in bad order," he reported. "No fireplace in cell. No arrangements for washing... no hospital. Everything filthy—privy terrible—convicts ragged—many barefooted—very heavily ironed." It was, as Douglas Blackmon called it, "slavery by another name."[15]

The young Barbour County patriarch and Confederate soldier John Wallace Comer poses confidently with his enslaved body servant, Burrell, who saved Comer's life at the Battle of Atlanta. Burrell rowed his injured master over one hundred miles down the Chattahoochee to deliver him to his mother's care at Spring Hill. Comer went on to further his fortune by trafficking convict labor into Alabama's coal mines.

Men like J.W. had set about reestablishing not just control of labor but the entire range of social power they had lost since the Civil War and Reconstruction. Under the "redeemers," the once vanquished Black Code laws returned. Petty thefts became felonies. Stealing corn or cotton, in the middle of the global depression of the 1870s, became a felony punishable by between two and five years; breaking into a house, garden, or smokehouse could mean as much as twenty years. Sunrise and sunset laws prohibited the sale of livestock or agricultural goods at night, which not only increased the convict numbers but also forced sharecroppers to only trade through their plantation owners. As a result, the convict population not only swelled into a useful army of convict laborers, but African Americans outside of prison remained vulnerable to being thrown into jail for the slightest pretense. Not only could whites solve their problems with alleged "crime" and "vagrancy," they could funnel questions of law and order toward the courts—at a profit—rather than leaving them for vigilante groups like the Klan or the White League.[16]

The convict labor system also helped guard against those Black people who still had the franchise from voting Republican. In the election of 1876, the first national voting since "redemption," J.W. and his brothers made clear that the cost of crossing the political white line would be immense. "They told me if I worked against them, the White Leage [*sic*], I should go on the chain-gang," explained one potential voter in Barbour County. "I know they meant what they said, so I am just leaving. . . . I have not violated any law, but that don't matter; if I am brought to trial, though I am innocent, I will be convicted, because I am a republican. How long will the United States government allow such things?" It was similar for Hilliard Miles, who made the mistake of fingering J.W. and his brother, the future governor, Braxton Comer, as the people involved in perpetuating the election violence of 1874. For accusing a Comer, they found him guilty of perjury and sent him to the penitentiary. Vocal Barbour County Republicans, shrinking in number, complained of threats of "death, jail, or the penitential, and they swear to do anything to convict us."[17]

Not only did the convict labor system get the coal mined, the cotton picked, and the racial hierarchy restored, but it increasingly became central to government functioning. The freedom of a low-tax state rested to a surprising degree on the revenues of convict leasing. The Panic of 1873, which played no small role in the political dynamics leading to the attack on Reconstruction, also fomented enormous fiscal crises on the local and state levels. The 1874 "redeemer" gubernatorial campaign highlighted the high taxes, fiscal irresponsibility, and penitentiary "mismanagement" of the Republicans and their Black constituents. The state was in debt—especially the debt incurred by once ambitious railroad plans—and it starved everything else to service it. The state and county governments stripped down the public sector, outsourced what remained of public works, paid off the debt, sliced salaries, stopped internal improvements, cut taxes, and wrote budgets of austerity.

Alabama was already one of the lowest-tax states in the union, so the money to run the state and county governments had to come from somewhere. Men like J.W. Comer and his colleagues had the answer: fill the state coffers with money from imprisoned and leased Black convicts. As John Bass, the new Alabama state warden, put it in 1877, "We have cause to congratulate ourselves as to our financial success, as well as the sound and prosperous condition so evidently attending the management of this institution—a position that forbids it ever again burdening the tax payers of the state." He not only made the penal system pay for itself, he looked forward to "putting money into the state treasury instead of drawing therefrom."[18]

The leasing system depended upon contracts, which depended upon a nonexistent liberty for African Americans. After the war, the Freedmen's Bureau agents sought out written agreements between free workers and plantation owners, stressing to the freedmen the "solemn obligation of contracts" and believing that if former bondsmen "can be induced to enter into contracts, they are taught that there are duties as well as privileges of freedom." Yet early contracts may have included neither negotiation nor even compensation. Instead, "the negro promises to work for an indefinite time for nothing but his board and clothes," explained Captain J. W. Cogswell of the bureau, "and the white man agrees to do nothing." Former slaves associated the white idea of white freedom with the contract and recognized themselves as victims of it when they were forced to work on plantations in perpetual debt. Back on the masters' land, they were, as the historian Pete Daniel put it, "defrauded of their wages and deprived of mobility either by threats that they could not legally move until their debts were paid or by actual force" in a world in which 80 percent of the sharecroppers in Alabama owed debts totaling a full year's labors. Could it be a fair and free contract when African Americans "were denied access to land, coerced by troops and Bureau agents if they refused to sign, and fined or imprisoned if they struck for higher wages?"[19]

Convict leasing also kept the mines free of unions, serving as what one union organizer called the "Damocles Sword of the Alabama Miners." Prison labor could be a forceful deterrent to labor organizing by replacing free workers with convict labor and by dividing the solidarity of the workforce between Black and white, free and unfree. Interracial solidarity during strikes and organizing drives was often stronger than the operators expected, and there were many skilled free Black miners who had learned their trade as convicts. Yet even well-organized miners remained susceptible to division—especially when up against the combined forces of the operators and the state government. In the massive Alabama mining strikes of the first decade of the twentieth century, when eighteen thousand miners walked out, employers could readily play the race card against the miners. One of Birmingham's most successful coal operators, Henry DeBardeleben, testified before a state legislative committee that "if all were free miners they could combine and strike, and thereby put up the price of coal, but where convict labor exists the mine owner can sell coal cheaper."[20]

Wage-earning miners were at the forefront of protests against the use of convict labor, less out of solidarity than of self-interest. Their leverage, however, was limited. In 1879, a skilled miner could earn a dollar per ton of coal, but three years later it had dropped to less than half that. Five hundred miners plus several hundred day laborers walked off the job in protest of the lower wages and their cause, the lease system. The company refused to negotiate. They could mine coal at 45 cents per ton, the miners were told, or get their tools and leave. The workers called the bosses' bluff and took their tools and marched off the job, believing they could find work in the district. But no other coal operator would hire them. The mine sat still. Rather than starting up again with new replacement workers, the owner leased the mine to J.W. Comer, who staffed the operation with convicts.[21]

Although reformers pushed against the convict lease system for decades, there was no real threat to the system until the turn of the twentieth century when an unlikely group of allies emerged. The great African American leader, educator, and intellectual, Alabama's Booker T. Washington, had developed an unlikely, and somewhat clandestine, political collaborator in the fight against convict labor, one Thomas Goode Jones. After the Civil War, Jones looked toward reconciliation with the North rather than resistance. In 1883, when Jones was head of the Alabama state militia, he saved an African American from the wrath of a Birmingham lynch mob. As Jones's politics matured, several other things became clear: he was not out to destroy the Republican Party, he believed in the rule of law, and he opposed funding white and Black schools based on the amount each race paid in taxes. Even though Jones was a redeemer, white supremacist, segregationist Democrat, and former Confederate, he showed enough daylight between his thinking and the rest of the white oligarchy that Booker T. Washington believed he might be of value. Most importantly, Washington saw that Thomas Goode Jones was a severe critic of the convict labor system.[22]

When a federal judgeship opened in Alabama, President Theodore Roosevelt asked his acquaintance Booker T. Washington whom he would recommend for the position. He recommended Jones for the seat. The whole thing played as a measured act of bipartisanship and moderation—a Republican choosing a Southern Democrat for the federal bench. The Southern congressional delegation was "unanimously delighted" that a Democratic leader had been picked. African

Americans, however, held out hope that he would continue to reign in the worst abuses of white power. Then the president shocked the white establishment by inviting Booker T. Washington to dine with him and his family at the White House. It shattered a once impregnable racial barrier. Among the most notorious responses to the dinner was that of South Carolina's Benjamin "Pitchfork Ben" Tillman. "Now that Roosevelt has eaten with the nigger Washington," Tillman declared, "we shall have to kill a thousand niggers to get them back to their place." The white South then rebuffed Roosevelt, and the president's hopes to foster a two-party system in the South "began and ended" with the appointment of Judge Jones.[23]

Two years after Jones took his seat on the federal bench, however, he launched his fight against the convict labor system. In 1903, Jones wrote to the attorney general of the United States, Philander C. Knox, informing him of the need to investigate "a systematic scheme of depriving negroes of their civil liberty, and hiring them out" to the mercy of a contractor. The system that they deployed, he explained, "is to accuse the negro of some petty offense" and then entrap him in the hands of a white contractor who will pay his fine and fees and then send him into the mines. "Men and women are arrested on the flimsiest charges," he detailed, and "they are brutally whipped, worked and locked up without let or hindrance. The tortures inflected," he said, "are severe and sometimes result in total disability or death."[24]

Through Judge Jones, the practice of convict labor entered the federal courts. The first major case turned on John Pace and Fletcher Turner, landowners in Tallapoosa County who had used convict labor to work their land. In an unexpected turn of events at the first trial, Pace pleaded guilty in hopes of leniency. Jones sentenced him to five years in federal prison for each of the eleven counts he faced. The judge, allowing for Pace's rather miserable health, allowed the sentences to be served concurrently. It was nonetheless an enormous victory for opponents of the convict lease system. A month after the first testimony, over thirty indictments were made. This caused the next two cases, consisting of forty-five charges against George and Barancas Cosby, to end in confessions as well. Yet Jones wanted to expose the system to the public more than he wanted to punish the convict labor traffickers. He gave the accused only a year and a day in federal prison.[25]

Meantime, the *Montgomery Advertiser* shot back at Judge Jones with yet another rehearsal of the redemption mythology and lessons of the venal nature of federal authority crushing Southern freedom and independence. "Several millions of ex-slaves, suddenly exalted to citizenship, was the heritage we received from the Federal government," editorialized the paper. Given all the rights they were "neither prepared nor fitted" to use, they chose to "despoil, degrade, and humiliate the real citizens of the almost helpless South." The federal government and Northern agitators may "assail" Southerners' methods, argued the paper, but "we intend to settle this race question in our own way."[26]

Judge Jones's quick string of victories against convict labor did not last. In the summer of 1903, the third case came up, and it was against prominent citizens Fletcher Turner and his son Allen. Their case went to trial—with an all-white jury. Trying to get the case tried on the facts and not simply race, Jones delivered a long and emotional charge to the jury. His voice rose and fell, his fist pounded the bench, his gaze remained fierce. The judge cited everything from federal to biblical law, but he knew that the question of race was probably his obstacle to conviction. Finally, he stopped, lowered his voice, and said, "But there is one issue and that is between us and our God, to which, in view of some of the appeals which have been made to you, I must allude. There are twelve white men on that jury, there is one white man on this bench. Every officer of this court is a white man. The question between us and God and our consciences is, can we rise above our prejudices, if we have them, so far that we as white men are able and willing to do a negro justice? God forbid that your verdict should be other than just." His speech was to no avail. The case ended in a hung jury.[27]

With that trial, Jones's will to challenge peonage seemed to collapse. From then on, nothing but pardons and suspended sentences made up what the historian Pete Daniel called the judge's "experiment in leniency." Accounting for Jones's new indulgence and timidity is difficult. It might have stemmed from a general sense of futility. It may have been a way to avoid violence—toward both witnesses and convicts. It may have been because African Americans in Alabama, facing tremendous threats of retaliation, asked him to end it. He may have actually believed that he had fundamentally altered the system—that by exposing it and finding people guilty, his work was done. He may have just had a hard time finding his fellow white elites guilty of such a heinous system of brutality. Jones certainly took cover, perhaps satisfaction, in the belief that his action on the federal bench had exposed the peonage system. In the fall of 1903, he even pardoned guilty traffickers, explaining to Booker T. Washington that it would "smooth the pathway for the races" in Alabama. An examiner for the federal government, Stanley W. Frisch, told the attorney general that Jones's cases "have attracted general attention, and accomplished extensive results in breaking up the peonage system in this district."[28]

Nothing could have been further from the truth. The tally of punishments indicated a failure. Of the ninety-nine indictments, four people went to jail for a total of five months, and fines totaled five hundred dollars. The myth that the system had been exposed and destroyed essentially allowed it to continue unabated. Alabama's place at the top of the wicked list of states complicit in convict leasing remained unchallenged. Like federal marshal Crawford in the Intruders' War, Judge Jones's goodwill may have simply been destroyed by the enormity of the obstacles he faced.[29]

As Judge Jones withdrew from confrontation, the state of Alabama redoubled its commitment to the prison labor system, making a convict's failure to complete his contract or pay his creditor prima facie evidence of intent to defraud his employer. In *Bailey v. Alabama* (1911), the United States Supreme Court ultimately found the law unconstitutional. A state, argued Justice Charles Evans Hughes, "may not compel one man to labor for another in payment of a debt, by punishing him as a criminal if he does not perform the service or pay the debt." Seemingly enlightened justices like Oliver Wendell Holmes dissented, claiming that laborers needed to honor their promises and that only "impulsive people with little intelligence or foresight" would get caught in this system in the first place. While many saw in the *Bailey* decision the "knock out blow" to convict labor, thousands remained in the convict mines. Like with protecting Indigenous lands or Reconstruction voting rights, the story was the same. "To succeed," writes one student of the system, "federal officials likely needed to sentence hundreds, if not thousands, of peon masters to years in federal penitentiaries." Federal authority possessed no such will nor wielded such power.[30]

B.B. Comer, J.W.'s brother, became another of the many governors from Barbour County as well as a defender of the convict lease system. Known as a progressive with regard to his personal hobby horse, railroad regulation, he also embodied the Southern "progressive" position on race and labor relations. In 1911, in Comer's farewell address to the General Assembly, he warned the people of Alabama against ending the convict lease system as the cost would be too high. The prisoners, he argued, "funded the schools, pensioneers, and judiciary." His remarks were directed at state senator Robert Moulthrop, a fellow Barbour County resident and convict labor reformer. Moulthrop opposed the private use of convicts in operations like the mine leasing system, not because the system was cruel beyond measure, but because he believed the convicts should focus on public works and internal improvements that improved the health of the state—not be used just to line the pockets of the coal operators. His efforts at even such mild reforms ended in naught. Even after Alabama's Banner Mine exploded in 1911, killing 128 miners, the vast majority of whom were convict miners, little happened. Unlike New York City's Triangle Shirtwaist factory fire the same year, in which the death of 146 young, female garment workers launched an enormous push for regulatory reform in the factories, the Banner explosion ended in little by way of progressive reform other than further commitments to further disenfranchisement and the growing Jim Crow order.[31]

Eventually the national exposés, federal court challenges, mine disasters, and progressive politics caught up with the convict lease system. In 1927, Governor Bibb Graves, whose racist bona fides were clear from his solid-gold KKK "passport," ended up being one of Alabama's most progressive governors. He moved dramatically on a host of issues, including, finally, the end of the convict labor in the mines. He shifted prisoners out of the coal pits and into prisons and road work. The last men to leave an Alabama convict mine did so in June 1928, singing "Swing Low, Sweet Chariot" as they left the underground darkness for the last time.[32]

Even though the state stopped trafficking in slave labor for the mines, the issue was not over. The year that Graves outlawed the practice, county sheriffs threw 37,701 prisoners in jail and leased them to chain gangs or local owners. One out of every nineteen Black men over the age of twelve remained in involuntary servitude of some form. The final blows would not really come until the New Deal and World War II. Meantime, for well over half a century, convict labor afforded whites the freedom that would resonate with antigovernment policies of the twenty-first century: low taxes, a cheap and disposable workforce, and union-free workplaces. It also freed men like J.W. Comer to take out their unrestrained rage on their African American neighbors, for profit and politics alike.

CHAPTER TWELVE

White Oligarchy as Jeffersonian Democracy

THEY CAME BY TRAIN, wagon, horse, boat, and foot. Ten thousand visitors flooded the picturesque streets of downtown Eufaula on Thanksgiving Day 1904. At the intersection of the prosperous two-laned Broad Street and Eufaula Avenue, they crammed together to listen to the speeches, cheer marching veterans, applaud the colorful parade, and pump their arms in unison to a brass band. One fantastic float featured eleven women waving to the crowd, each dressed as one of the original eleven states that seceded from the union. The name of every Barbour County Civil War veteran was read, and the Eufaula Rifles fired their weapons skyward. The main event, and the official reason for the gathering, was the United Daughters of the Confederacy's unveiling of a thirty-five-foot shaft of Georgia granite topped by a confederate soldier carved out of Italian marble. The crowd roared. The celebration of the people's "love and reverence" for the sacrifice of Barbour County's fighting men was the biggest celebration the town had ever seen.[1]

Similar shrines to the lost cause, all sponsored by the United Daughters of the Confederacy (UDC), sprouted up in towns throughout the South in the early twentieth century. Montgomery already had one, Huntsville got theirs the following year. Sebastian County, Arkansas, got theirs the year before, featuring the ever-popular slogan "Lest we forget." Ocala, Florida, chose "The South Reveres" as her founders. Over in Rome, Georgia, they expressed their appreciation for Confederate officer, war criminal, and first Grand Wizard of the Ku Klux Klan Nathan Bedford Forrest for saving their town from Yankee destruction. While many simply honored the dead, also common were maudlin inscriptions of "sublime self-sacrifice and undying devotion to duty in the service of their country," like the one in Monticello, Georgia. On the monument over on the Georgia side of the Chattahoochee in Columbus, stone masons carved, "No truth is lost for which the true are weeping nor dead for which they died." Hattiesburg, Mississippi, declared in no uncertain terms their townsmen "cheerfully gave their property and their lives" for the Confederate cause. Graham, North Carolina, got theirs just months before Eufaula. It declared, "Conquered they can never be, whose souls and spirits are free."[2]

The inscriptions dotting the region made clear that all who served in the defeat were noble, all sacrificed willingly, all were united to protect the Confederacy. The ladies of the UDC reshaped military defeat in a war for slavery into a victory for honor, nation, and tradition. The monuments anchored a unified memory, they buried trauma, and they silenced the complexities of history, promising an ongoing vigil against any further federal power that threatened alternative stories. Carved in marble were monuments to a victory in the never-ending struggle over distribution of power in the compound republic. The people of Alabama struggled to renew "the spirt and forms of American liberty" only to be "punished by the Congress of a fraction of the Union" and the "despotic rule of the sword."[3]

The sense of solidarity in the face of persecution allowed for the growth of an irascible culture in constant fear over the loss of their freedom. As the venerated political scientist V. O. Key put it, the South emerged from the sectional conflict in "a sort of sublimated foreign war," engulfed in a "continuous state of siege." In 1923, the Alabama state motto was changed from the Reconstruction-era

"Here we rest" to a more truculent "We dare defend our rights." At its most optimistic, this battle footing was not simply a defensive posture. It contained not just the memory of redeeming the South, but also the hope of winning back the entire nation to the vision of Southern freedom.[4]

If the unveiling of the Eufaula monument seemed like a victory rally, it's because it was. No longer referred to as redeemers, the white elite in the Black Belt had become known by the adjective "Bourbon." In an echo of the restoration of the royal house of Bourbon after Napoleon's defeat, the Southern oligarchy had reversed much of the revolution of the 1860s and 1870s and managed a full restoration of the old racial aristocracy. Surpassing the crude violence of the voting massacres of 1874, the Bourbon victory included the mobilization of an entire ideological and political system—means of violence, law, culture, and history. White supremacy as a practice may have emerged "from the holds of a slave ship," but the rise of the phrase and the specific set of practices of "white supremacy" rose after Reconstruction, helping to solve the contradiction of the presence of a free Black people who were no longer regulated by the brutal legalities of the slave regime.[5]

When the monument went up, the prosperous white Eufaulans could celebrate a trio of victories that guaranteed the protection and retrenchment of their post-Reconstruction world. The first was the defeat of the federal elections (or "force") bill, which would have provided for federal supervision of local election procedures. The bill, in essence, raised the specter of Reconstruction and was remarkably close to the Voting Rights Act that passed seventy-five years later under Lyndon Johnson. The second element in this era of triumph was the defeat, through enormous fraud, of the Populist political uprising of the 1890s. Centered on Eufaulan Reuben F. Kolb's three insurgent campaigns for governor, the Populists challenged the very economic—and at times racial—foundations of the Southern Democratic Party. Third and finally, those celebrants in the streets of Eufaula could cheer confidently of the Lost Cause, knowing that African American and poor white voters had been disfranchised in the state constitution of 1901. Combined, these three developments ensured that neither the federal government, nor Black people, nor poor whites—let alone all three together—would threaten the elite of the Black Belt again. By 1904, the people of Eufaula honored their past and their dead, but they also looked forward to enjoying the power and freedoms, free of federal involvement, for which the Confederacy had originally left the union.

The Barbour County elite and commoner alike saw themselves as the heirs of Jefferson and Jackson, men in favor of the people of the land and opposed to political domination by federal power. While Jeffersonian commitments to an anti-statist brand of freedom had long been mobilized against Indians and enslaved people, by the turn of the twentieth century, Democratic politics turned against the putative hero of its own story: the poor white farmer. By crushing the political interests of poor whites in the early twentieth century, the Black Belt elite showed that, as much as they hated people of color, they loved power far more. In smashing both the Black and white poor of Barbour County, as well as the tentative links between them, the Black Belt Bourbons ultimately achieved that which was unimaginable to Jefferson himself: the building of an oligarchy based on his principles of freedom from centralized government. The specter of popular democracy had been vanquished, and the self-styled partisans of the Jeffersonian and Jacksonian tradition could rule and ruin as they saw fit.

The potential of federal power, largely run out of Barbour County since 1874, had reappeared when Massachusetts congressman Henry Cabot Lodge introduced the federal elections bill in June 1890. The bill authorized federal courts to appoint supervisors for federal elections, who were in turn granted the power to oversee registration, verify information to voters, administers oaths, prevent illegal immigrants from voting, and certify the election results. The bill also gave federal officials the ultimate power to overturn elections results—even those certified by state officials. The House even included the provision for military force to guarantee the proper conduct of elections.[6]

Lodge's bill generated more fear, excitement, hyperbole, and concern than any federal endeavor since the Grant administration. Eufaula's paper found the bill yet another federal attempt to trammel on their rights and freedoms—"a scheme to rob the people of the States of the dearest right of American citizenship." Most decried the bill as a tactic designed to inflate Republican voting numbers and further infect the bad blood of race, region, and partisanship. The Republican platform did include the argument that the Democrats "owe their existence to the suppression of the ballot by a criminal nullification of the Constitution and laws of the United States." Yet the correspondence behind the bill confirms that it was mostly a genuine attempt to make the Fifteenth Amendment a living thing. As Congressman Lodge argued, "The Government which made the black man a citizen is bound to protect him in his rights as a citizen of the United States, and it is a cowardly Government if it does not do it!" The House of Representatives took time from Washington's usual obsessions that year—the tariff and the coinage of silver—and passed the force bill on a near partisan vote.[7]

The Senate floor manager of the elections bill was Senator George Frisbie Hoar of Massachusetts. At first, Hoar planned on keeping his defensive remarks to a minimum on the Senate floor, but it soon became clear that he would need every single Republican to vote for the bill to pass. The attacks on the bill and his party's motivations ultimately inspired him to deliver a speech in favor of federal voting rights that lasted for two straight *days*.

Looming large in Hoar's mind were the values of Charles Sumner and Thaddeus Stevens that had driven Reconstruction years before. "The struggle for this bill," Hoar argued, "is a struggle for the last step toward establishing a doctrine to which the American people are pledged by their history, their Constitution, their opinions, and their interests." He laid out what he believed to be "incontestable proof" of the constitutionality of the bill, before waxing more philosophical. People claim, he argued, "that these two races can not live together except on the terms that one shall command and the other shall obey. That proposition I deny." He asserted the "error" of the white South was "their assumption that race hatred is the dominant passion of the human soul; that it is stronger than love of country, stronger than the principle of equality, stronger than Christianity, stronger than justice." If the Southern Democracy had put a fraction of effort into citizenship and uplift that it had into disenfranchisement and subjugation, "the two races would to-day be dwelling together under the flag in freedom and in honor, in peace, prosperity, and in mutual regard." As Senator Hoar concluded to his opponents, "You have tried everything else, try justice."[8]

By the Gilded Age, the Republican Party had drifted far from its moorings in the egalitarian vision of free soil and free men, and toward an obsession with the politics and legality of the protection and expansion of property in the new age of corporate capitalism. Lincoln once explained that the leaders of his party "are for both the man and the dollar; but in cases of conflict, the man before the dollar." By 1890, the logic of Lincoln's party had been radically reversed in favor of the dollar. A group of "Silver Republicans" wanted free coinage of silver. Eastern Republicans wanted the holy grail of economic policy, the protectionist McKinley Tariff. Southern Democrats wanted the bill destroyed, and they launched a massive filibuster to do so. In a not-so-grand compromise, the silver bill passed, the tariff passed, and voting rights died in the Senate.[9]

The Lodge bill was the last federal attempt to regulate voting until the late 1950s. Any state that wanted to ignore or undermine the Fifteenth Amendment could do so with impunity. And they did. The Republicans all but completely abdicated their once vibrant role in protecting voting rights, a project that would slowly be picked up by the Democratic Party in the post–World War II era.

For Eufaulans, the shutting of Lodge's "Pandora's box of evils" was cause for celebration. The failure of the bill was "altogether the grandest and most important achievement in the Senate for years," the local paper declared, ignoring that the legislation died in the Senate as a result of political dealings not principle. Scoring a "great victory over wrong" by killing an "effort to destroy the autonomy of the States" meant "the whole country will rejoice." No effort "embraced more danger to the theory and principles of the government under which we live than the so-called Lodge election bill," they claimed; "No measure ever more seriously threatened the peace, happiness and prosperity of the American people." The bill sought to loosen the grip of race-based one-party rule in the South, but the Eufaula paper editorialized that the defeat of the Lodge bill was actually the defeat of a reassertion of Republican domination. "Any measure in a republic that tends to perpetuate the power of any particular party," the paper claimed with unintended irony, "is extremely dangerous to that republic and is a stepping stone to its subversion."[10]

Even after the elections bill failed to make it out of the Senate, locals remained on edge. Up in Union Springs, when two "honorable and respected citizens" were taken away by United States marshals on the order of federal judges for violating United States elections laws in 1892, it triggered fears that the bill might return. "If the democratic and liberty loving people of Alabama needed any spur to rouse them into feverish and determined activity," the Eufaula paper returned to editorializing, they merely had to think about how the "old carpet-bag days have come again when our people are to be arrested on frivolous charges, trumped up for politics purposes, and dragged before republican tribunals to answer for the administration of our local government." Barbour County "understands and the democracy of the state understands that it is the re-introduction of the force bill period of 1874 and it won't work!"[11]

The next challenge to the Black Belt elite was Southern populism. Eufaula's hometown hero—or rascal, depending on one's politics—was Reuben F. Kolb. In the spring of 1892, special trains delivered hundreds of visitors, bands performed, and "many other attractions" were available for a "Great Political jubilee" held in Eufaula. With the current governor, the likely future governor, and local Populist challenger Kolb taking the stage, the paper promised "NO BITTERNESS, no ugly tempered people" just a "jolly crowd." Although from Barbour County, Kolb's brand of politics tended to be aimed against the Black Belt Bourbon elite and tended to generate a hostile response. "Here I live," Kolb declared to thousands of hostile Eufaulans, suspicious of his attacks on the local elite, "here I expect to live, and here I wish to die and be buried." But it had been a brutal two years in Alabama politics. Kolb had been bamboozled out of the previous gubernatorial race, he was about to have one completely stolen from him, and he would have another stolen the following campaign cycle. "Never before have we had a such a campaign as is going on in our state at present," Kolb declared to the crowd. "God forbid that we shall ever have another like it."[12]

Although known as the "best handshaker in Alabama," Reuben Kolb was an unlikely Populist. Born in Eufaula, he was a man of comfort. He trained at the University of North Carolina, marched when Jefferson Davis was inaugurated, led Kolb's Battery to honor in the Civil War, and married a noted Alabama beauty. He inherited the sprawling Woodlane Plantation a few miles south of Eufaula, where he was set to enjoy life as another wealthy Barbour County patrician.[13]

The curse of Southern cotton became obvious to Kolb after the war. Once the wartime inflation subsided, cotton prices plummeted, spiraling from a high of 17.9 cents per pound in 1871 down to 5.73 cents per pound by the end of the century—a price significantly less than the actual cost of production, especially as soil exhaustion began to take hold. Kolb turned to becoming a committed scientific agriculturalist. He experimented and diversified crops every year, planting sugar, potatoes, collard greens, onions, oats, corn, cantaloupe, pear, peaches, and above all, the commodity that brought him considerable fame and significant fortune: a melon he called "Kolb's Gem." He made money from his melons, boasting he could make more in 150 acres of melons than 500 acres of cotton on the best land. He began showing his agricultural successes at fairs, where he won numerous prizes and increased his fame. His experiments confirmed that the region had to escape the curse of cotton. "There is, nor can be but one outcome to the all cotton idea," he concluded: "disaster not only to the pocket book, but to the land as well."[14]

His success as an innovative farmer led him to serve as the state's commissioner of agriculture from 1886 to 1890. He began to travel the state, ask questions, and discuss matters with locals. Handsome, quick with a story, and with an exceptional oratory ability, he was a natural on the circuit. They called him "genial Reuben." Doing the state's work, he hosted daylong seminars to school farmers on new methods, events that often ended in a festive barbecue. Although Kolb's mission and practice remained educational, critics in Montgomery began to suspect he was using state resources to build political support for a race for the governor's office. Meeting with farmers of the insurgent Alliance movement as he traveled, he began to see the problems were not just with agriculture, but with the entire political system.[15]

Despite his patrician background, Kolb's stout shoulders, frock coat, thin hair, and long drooping mustache gave him the look of the late nineteenth-century Populist that he became. Frustrated with falling crop prices, rising railroad rates, inadequate access to credit, and the very existence of the crop-lien system, people who worked the land, both white and Black, began to organize. They started in the cooperative enterprises of the Grange, then built the politics of the Greenback-Labor Party, followed by an organization known as the Agricultural Wheel. These efforts laid the foundation for what would become the swelling membership of the Farmers' Alliance, a national grassroots movement that began in Texas and swept east. Alabama built one of the largest Alliance movements in the country, second only to Texas's itself. The Alabama Alliance included some 120,000 white people, and the Colored Alliance had another 50,000 people. The Alliance then transformed into the People's Party in 1891—an organization known more commonly as the Populist Party, a great egalitarian thrust against the growing economic inequalities in the industrial age. Their slogan, "Equal rights to all and special privileges to none," created ideological and political unity for the collective rights of agricultural, and often, industrial, labor in a political culture that had long thrived on individualism.[16]

Although the Populists saw themselves as the heirs of Jefferson, the shibboleths of economic and political independence no longer worked in an age of corporate economic and political power. They pushed the old ideas of anti-statism to the side of the road and marched forth with calls for collective organization and distribution of their commodities, regulation of the middlemen who kept them from seeing the fruits of their labors, and federal intervention for a more just economy. The agrarian uprising had many visionary aspects, but the core of their agenda was the subtreasury plan—a scheme for depositing grain in federal warehouses in exchange for certificates of deposit that could be redeemed when markets were more favorable to the farmer. Above all, the Alliance movement fomented a culture of deep study and analysis, passionate rhetoric, and mass political mobilizations. While some elements were nostalgic and racist, the Alliance was the last great challenge to American industrial capitalism by a small-holder democratic culture.[17]

The Alabama Populist movement faced a number of thorny issues. Given that the vast majority of the movement was among the small holders in the northern part of the state, could they escape the Black Belt's stranglehold on the state's politics? How could connections be made with industrial workers—in the case of Alabama, the coal miners? What relationship could the Alliance, and later the Populist Party, have with formal politics: As an independent party or as part of the Democratic Party? And what about the great divide, that of race? Would their movement be segregated or initiate an attack on not just the economics of farming but its racial caste system as well? A historian of African American populism called it "the largest mass movement for political and economic change in the history of the American South until the civil rights movement of the 1950s and 1960s." But that did not mean it was successful.[18]

In 1890, Kolb first attempted to serve the Alliance movement by bringing them into the regular Democratic Party in his first run for governor. Raucous county-level Democratic politics, always a vibrant and at times violent sport, turned on the Populist question that election year. Even in Barbour County, where local elites would never allow an Alliance victory, the debates were resolved with whatever weapons happened to be within reach, including "knives, stove wood, and umbrellas." Many of Barbour County's finest citizens engaged in an orchestrated attack on his character, which produced an enormous full-page exposé on his alleged character flaws. They even dredged up questionable assertions about his supposed support for the Republican scalawag Judge Keils from Reconstruction days. "Help me and the delegates you have elected," he wrote to the Alliance, "to defeat the unholy cliques and combinations now forming of plutocrats against the people."[19]

At the state Democratic convention, Kolb held a sizable lead over the other four leading Democrats, but he fell just shy of the votes necessary to surpass the threshold for the nomination. After three tense days of canvassing and balloting, the other candidates pooled their supporters and united behind one candidate. Strategically, they chose the one who came in last—by far—head of the state militia and party insider Thomas Goode Jones. Choosing the candidate with the fewest votes was a strategic choice: the weakest person on the roster would not be able to control the delegates of the other candidates. As a result, Jones—later to be put on the federal bench, where he would fight the convict labor cases—won the Democratic nomination, and therefore the governorship, by default. Had he withdrawn as the weaker candidate, his votes would have most likely gone to Kolb. It was a peculiar but successful piece of electoral sacrifice and engineering that suggested much about the importance of defeating the agrarian insurgent. Jones won on the first round of balloting as the unifier of the various anti-Kolb candidates.[20]

The next year, Kolb announced for the governor's office only to face a campaign that one historian called the "most scurrilous on record in Alabama." With Jones backed by the "monied interests"—railroad, bank, lumber, coal, iron, and Black Belt money—as well as the party machinery, Kolb fought back with the votes of farmer and labor organizations. The Alliance movement was growing more popular, more aggressive, and more to the left, but Kolb's limited support in the Black Belt was on the wane in 1892. And the fix was in: there was little hope that he could win the Democratic primary since it was an open secret that the election would be stolen from him. As the Democrats met to nominate Jones, Kolb joined up with a dissident faction known as the Jeffersonian Democrats—a near complete move toward the People's Party since the Jeffersonians and the People's Party nominated joint tickets. The bitterness, name calling, and endless accusations of being a sellout, Judas, demagogue, silk stocking, socialist, or plutocrat all ran wild and rampant in the press and on the soapboxes. "Which side are you on?" was the demand of the Kolb supporters. An attack on Kolb, the man from Barbour County was always quick to declare, was an attack on the Alliance.[21]

The Black vote, squeezed between the Democratic Bourbon oligarchy, the Jeffersonians, and their own Republican preferences, became a "priceless commodity" in the contest. The twelfth plank of the Jeffersonian Democrats declared in vague, but radical for the time, terms: "We favor the protection of the colored race in their political rights and should afford them encouragement and aid in the attainment of a higher civilization and citizenship, so that through the means of kindness, fair treatment, and just regard for them, a better understanding and more satisfactory condition may exist between the races." The regular Democrats drowned out the Jeffersonians' moderation on race with a torrent of vicious attacks on the "nigger rights section" of the Jeffersonian platform. The fractured Republican Party did not even offer a state ticket. It instead backed Kolb, but urged Black Belt African American voters to neither register nor to vote so the Democratic machinery could not steal their ballots. Staying home, in the hopes of not having their votes stolen, was the best hope for African American voters. Whites connected Kolb to fears of Reconstruction. "Never forget that this is a White Man's Government, and can never be anything else," editorialized the *Alabama Sentinel*; "It is merely a matter of anything to beat Kolb . . . just as twenty-five years ago it used to be anything to beat [Ulysses S.] Grant."[22]

Had the election been fair there is little doubt that Kolb and the Jeffersonians would have won in 1892. But Jones officially took the contest, winning on votes that were never cast. The ballot stuffing and fraud were blatant to all. Kolb won handily outside of the Black Belt and the cities. Had African Americans had the right to vote in fair elections in the Black Belt, he would have won that region too. African Americans in the Black Belt had organized *not* to vote, however, on the theory that votes not cast could not be corrupted or stolen. They were wrong. As one author improbably conjugates what happened, "blacks were voted" by the Democrats. "The voice of the people—both white and black—has been stifled," exclaimed one Populist. Kolb and the Jeffersonians were left with a rearguard struggle to ensure a fair count—hardly the reimagining of the farm-labor economy they had hoped for. "A hard rain and the votes of those who know him best, drowned Kolb yesterday in Eufaula," crowed his hometown paper.[23]

By 1894, the economic panic of 1893 made the farmers' and workers' demands all the more urgent, but the electoral problems remained the same. Joseph C. Manning, the founder of the People's Party in Alabama and a man far more radical than the compromising Kolb, dug deep, declaring, "Like hired hounds, we cling at the feet of plutocracy and democracy. Shall we do it any longer? ... In the language of Patrick Henry, 'let us have Liberty or death.' Kolb is our Patrick Henry." Despite support from striking coal miners, African American Republicans, Populists, and Jeffersonian Democrats, Kolb was swindled out of his votes by the Bourbon elite for the third and final run of his career. Alabama politics became engulfed in talk of violence, establishing a rival state government (again), and even revolution. When Kolb's campaign manager, Peyton Bowman, showed up at the Eufaula courthouse to do some politicking, he received a horrifying reception. As someone known for speaking before integrated audiences, "he faced a hostile crowd with calmness, when he knew that right behind him was a man armed with a large knife, ready to plunge it into his back, and with pistols drawn all around him and pointing at him." In the ensuing violence, white supporters fled for their lives, and Black men were leaping from second-story windows. Despite the mayhem, it was reported, "he did not take back a word he had said, and he denounced some Eufaula men unsparingly." As one Eufaulan put it, "I hate him, but his is the bravest man I ever saw."[24]

There were no constitutional provisions for contesting elections—if the votes could be stolen, in essence, the election was won. "In the Black Belt there was a magical process," explains the historian Francis Sheldon Hackney, "by which Negroes who walked into the polling place to vote Republican, plus those who stayed at home, and even a few who were dead, were all counted in the Democratic column." It was said that they voted "live negroes, dead negroes and dogs" to put Jones in office. Kolb had been swindled again.[25]

The Eufaula paper was elated that hometown traitor Reuben Kolb had been defeated. "We are elected, Good People! Kolb Loses Everywhere! A land Slide for Democracy!" They celebrated their majority by claiming that "Revolution and Anarchy Spewed Out. Prepare to Shout. The State Safe." Kolb appeared finished, but he was determined to take his rightful seat as governor even if the official results were against him. "You, fellow citizens, have twice elected me governor of this state," Kolb wrote in the *People's Weekly Tribune*. "And this time, by the grace of God and the help of the good people of Alabama, I will be governor. December 1 is the day fixed by the law for the inauguration of the governor. On that date I shall be in Montgomery for the purpose of taking the oath of office and my seat as governor." The *Mobile Register* rejoined with the headline, "Kolb to be Seated If It Is to be Done by Slaughtering the State Militia." The Populists countered by calling the Democrats the "Fraudocrats," and some demanded to "MEET FRAUD WITH FORCE."[26]

Despite the heated rhetoric, the Populist revolution ended in a whimper. As Jones took the oath of office on the hallowed steps where Jefferson Davis swore allegiance to the Confederacy, Kolb took the oath of office before a justice of the peace in downtown Montgomery. Afterward, he walked up the hill and onto the capitol grounds, only to be stopped by twenty companies of state troops. Dodging the soldiers, he and his band of Populists made it up the stairs to where Jones was taking the oath. Trying to speak, Kolb was rebuffed by the governor. Kolb turned to one of his associates for advice. "Go ahead, Captain," he urged. "They may kill you, but you will go down in history as a martyr to the Populist cause." The Eufaulan declined and descended capitol hill. He eventually climbed aboard a wagon across the street from the capitol building and delivered an impassioned message, arguing that he was the rightful governor to the few hundred committed Populists who had shown up for the inaugural—a tiny fraction of those who voted for him that felt compelled to show up. By then, his voice was in the wind.[27]

The Populists fought for a genuine alternative to the growing industrial order. The subtreasury plan, an Alliance scheme to store and monetize commodities, was visionary; their ideas about race did not tend toward equality but they were way ahead of most of white Alabama; and their demands for government intervention in economics were unprecedented. They were defeated in Alabama by a Bourbon elite that only believed in an anti-statist democracy for themselves. This elite Jeffersonianism, a narrowly democratic anti-statism that served the Bourbon class, proved devastating to the future of Alabama. "Populism failed," explains one historian, "and because it failed the same poverty continued and an 'elite' still ruled, and the blacks sank even further into the dead end of segregation and disfranchisement."[28]

One thing was for certain about the Kolb insurgency: such class-based politics could never be allowed to rear its head in Alabama again. The 1900 state Democratic convention was the third and final element in the creation of an oligarchy under the banner of Jeffersonian values. United as a "white man's convention," the dissent and acrimony—and reform—were over. "I love to look in your white faces, and to see your straight hair," Eufaula's Congressman Henry De Lamar Clayton exclaimed at the opening of the convention. "I have wished for ten years to see the white people of Alabama united as they are to-day. I got tired of hearing of Alliances, tired of hearing about Populists" but now we "have gotten together" and "buried our differences." They were united by a common cause, Clayton proclaimed: "the momentous proposition that the white men of Alabama must stand together now and forever."[29]

Progressivism, the largely middle-class movement of reform and good government in the first decades of the twentieth century, is often seen as a continuation of many of the themes of populism. For much of the industrial North, progressivism was an attempt to right the balance of power between the people and the corporations through an enlarged role for the state, municipal reform, and good government. But in Alabama as in much of the South, it was often all that plus enshrining white supremacy. The signature piece of Alabama "progressivism" was the 1901 state constitution, which all but eliminated the Black vote and eviscerated the poor white vote. In the progressive mold, the new constitution did much to eliminate fraud, but did so by also eliminating large parts of the franchise altogether. The essence of the 1901 constitution was: elections would no longer have to be stolen if the franchise were only in the hands of the right people.

In Barbour County, hometown newspaper editor William Dorsey Jelks became the main voice for disenfranchisement. Jelks believed in a strict racial hierarchy, and he made it his mission to throw whatever fuel he could on the racial fires in the town of Eufaula, the state of Alabama, and the nation as a whole. Jelks captured the nastiest, least accommodating, most vicious version of New South politics. In an 1882 editorial titled "Mr. Nigger," he described the Black man as an "ignorant devil," "a foul blot," and "a blight upon the land." Should Black Southerners transgress white women, he threatened, "his neck will be broken without the benefit of judge, jury, or clergy." He advocated a long-term "cleansing" of the entire region of Black people. Dismissing the Southern moralists and Yankee intruders who opposed vigilante justice, he argued that lynching was "a cure and an effective one, too for the guilty brutes, and it does suppress the evil as far as they are concerned." Even in the twentieth century, after he backed away from lynching as the solution to the South's problems, he maintained in the *North American Review* that the "law of separation is written in the blood of the whites and is ineradicable."[30]

Jelks's position as editor of the *Eufaula Daily Times* allowed him to gain political contacts and power, which he parlayed into a seat as a state senator and then as the second in a long line of Alabama governors elected from Barbour County. As much as he liked the idea of lynching as a way to control Black men, his mission was political: to support calls for a constitutional convention to disfranchise African American voters for good. The mechanisms of disenfranchisement were well underway in the last years of the nineteenth century, but when Governor William J. Samford died in 1900, the new governor would be the president of the Alabama Senate. That individual was Eufaula's William Jelks, who had already served as chair of the Committee on Constitution, Constitutional Revision, and Amendment. He served as governor of Alabama until 1907—a longer span than anyone else up to that time.

Such disenfranchisement conventions swept the South in the late nineteenth and early twentieth centuries. From Mississippi (1890), to South Carolina (1895), Louisiana (1898), and North Carolina (1900), each convention replaced informal systems and a patchwork of laws with specific, direct constitutional means of disenfranchisement. The new proposed Alabama constitution would accomplish what the constitutional writers of 1875 could only hope. If passed, it would no longer require the types of violence like the massacres of 1874 or the fraud of the Populist period. The Alabama constitutional convention debates reveal a fascinating legal wrestling match not about *whether* to block Black voting but *how*. What was the best way to thwart the Fifteenth Amendment and prevent the federal courts from interfering in whatever method they selected? They may have still been fighting the remnants of Reconstruction, but the question went all the way back to Thomas Jefferson, who championed ward-level political power structures rather than federal power, and John C. Calhoun, who argued for states' rights to nullify federal law. Could a state nullify a federal law, in this case the Fifteenth Amendment's constitutional guarantee of the right to vote? If not a frontal assault on federal power as Calhoun once championed, could they find some other clever work-around?

Judges, former governors, and leaders of all types met from May to September 1901 to debate the cleverest way to evade the Fifteenth Amendment. Spectators filled the galleries and newspaper editors debated every move and countermove. Many states had already opted for the "grandfather clause," which allowed only descendants of voters to vote, in addition to the usual poll taxes and literacy tests that would curb poor and illiterate farmers from political participation. The Alabama Democratic elite, fearing that possible opposition to the grandfather clause was brewing in federal courts, began to consider different options. Their short-term solution was a patriotic version of the grandfather clause with connections to the Lost Cause: a temporary plan that became known as the "soldiers' clause" or the "fighting grandfather clause." If a potential voter's grandfather had fought in a war on any side, then that individual could vote—even if they could not meet the other requirements such as literacy. While that guaranteed an all-white registration, it also meant that should the regular grandfather clause of other states be challenged in the US Supreme Court, Alabama's constitution would live to fight another day. The tactic also fulfilled a promise not to disfranchise poor whites.[31]

The fighting grandfather clause served its purpose for a year before the permanent voter registration system went into effect in 1903. Then there were several paths to registration: one could prove the ability to read and write a section of the United States Constitution, prove ownership of $500 or more in property, or simply be of good character to the satisfaction of the board of registrars. To vote under the new constitution, one had to pass a literacy test, be employed for a year, not have been convicted of a crime, and not demonstrate moral or mental failings. Few Blacks could meet the requirements to register or vote, but then, taking aim at poor whites, there was also an annual poll tax of $1.50, no small sum for dirt farmers, required to be paid to vote even after one cleared the registration hurdles. The Alabama state constitution was an authoritarian document cloaked in the mystical goals, as the document begins, to "secure the blessings of liberty to ourselves and our posterity." While the right to vote was not being "denied or abridged by the United States or by any State on account of race, color, or previous condition of servitude," it was being denied by a host of other means.[32]

Of all the disfranchising state constitutions of the period, only Alabama's went to a popular vote. Governor Jelks returned to Eufaula to drum up votes. The meeting at the town's Opera House was a "red letter day for Eufaula" as "all hearts throb with pride and patriotism at this hour," panted the local paper. Jelks declared with a straight face, "I am tired of fraud and rascality in high places—tired of the obsolete and ancient old state constitution under which we have existed for so many years—tired of its erroneous machinery made during the bitter days of so-called reconstruction and scalawag carpet bag rule," which, he argued, left the state with staggering annual debts. The new constitution, he told Eufaulans, was "very much better than the old—a constitution every white man ought to support and vote for." As if the old constitution were hundreds of years old, not twenty-six, he claimed, "The old constitution does not fit the times."[33]

For all that the actual votes mattered, Jelks could have stayed home. The ratification election ended up as the worst case in a long history of "Alabama's history of 'stolen' elections, fabricated returns, and a perjured black vote." African American leaders in the Black Belt returned to the strange but not unwise tactic of urging their constituents not to vote at all so that it would be impossible for the swindlers to count their votes in favor of the new constitution. Better to not be counted at all than have the Black vote twisted in favor of their enemies. Unfortunately, the logic did not hold, as once again Blacks "were voted," even when they stayed home. The totals alleged enormous support among African Americans for their own disenfranchisement. The victory came from the Black Belt, where "almost every eligible Negro was 'voted.'"[34]

Since the constitutional vote pitted the northern counties against the Black Belt, it has always been assumed, as the historian C. Vann Woodward put it, the poor whites turned disenfranchisement down "flatly" since constitutional voting rights depended not just on race but on class. While the Black Belt counted its fictious votes for the constitution, which passed in a landslide of fraud, the new constitution was *defeated* in the cumulative votes of the other fifty-four counties in a close tie. While the divided vote meant that many poor whites sided with the white elite and against Black voters, essentially embracing their own political demise, it was clear that the fraud in Barbour County and the rest of the Black Belt alone was responsible for the passing of the disfranchising state constitution.[35]

This sharecropper's cabin outside of Eufaula had been in use since the slavery era. The documentary photo, taken in the 1930s as part of the New Deal's Federal Writers Project, suggests much of the durability of the old ways in Barbour County long after emancipation.

African American voter enrollment was still 181,315 in 1900. By 1903, it had been beaten down to a mere 2,980—a reduction of over 98 percent. Although white voting fell as well, it fell nowhere near as dramatically (from 232,821 to 191,492 in three years). By the beginning of World War II, however, the cumulative effects of curtailing the vote of a larger population meant that in the long run, in gross numbers, more poor whites were disfranchised than African Americans. In lieu of white egalitarianism, poor whites received elite domination.[36]

The old Jacksonian tension between the irreconcilable poles of political liberty and political power had found its synthesis in the enjoyment of elite white freedom as absolute power. Federal power was nowhere to be found, and the compound republic was no longer compound. The promise of Jeffersonian freedoms, however flawed they had been by slavery and the stealing of Indigenous lands, still held out the promise of small-holder independence. In their place came an elite form of Jeffersonian ideas, held together by the oft-invoked ideas of "white supremacy," "white democracy," and the "white man's party." Alone, these ideas are too thin and inelastic to encapsulate a world in which patriarchs ruled a society structured by both race and class, but now access to racial hierarchy was open to the poorest whites. Racism was democratized even if little else was. White supremacy was not simply a racial view, but also a political order, an economic system, and an ideological framework. White supremacy was a powerful force throughout modern history, but it had particular meaning, resonance, and prevalence in the late nineteenth and early twentieth centuries. Josephus Daniels, the powerful North Carolina newspaper editor, New Dealer, and champion of white supremacy, explained it clearly. White democracy was rooted in Thomas Jefferson's framework of "constitutional government and individual liberty." Yet that freedom explicitly did not include "the newly evolved theory" that "men of all races have been found to be equally capable in every respect and . . . should be merged without distinction." Disenfranchisement and segregation were not antithetical to Jeffersonian egalitarianism. They were essential.[37]

Like so many of Eufaula's ostentatious antebellum homes, the Shorter Mansion was built long after the Civil War to recapture the lost grandeur of the antebellum South. First built in 1884 to house the descendants of one of the richest families in Barbour County, it burned in 1900 and was rebuilt in 1906. Today it houses a museum and serves as an anchor for touring the famous homes of Eufaula.

The newly emerging logic of white supremacy meant that one's liberties, political claims, social standing, labor power, and property values continued to be based on an orientation toward racial hierarchy, but in a way that was more democratically distributed among whites than they had been during slavery. It was not a Jeffersonian redistribution of wealth or land but of racial status. To the extent, as Orlando Patterson writes, "one is most free when one can do as one pleases with others," it is expressed as "the exercise of power or domination over others." And losing one's place in the hierarchy was to lose one's most precious Jeffersonian value: freedom. To the degree that African American people were "denaturalized, denativized, Nataly alienated, deprived of all claims to citizenship," then that meant, by contrast, white people were natural, native, entitled citizens. By creating a difference, a contrast, an "other," the system defined not just inferiority but superiority, not just degradation and subservience but honor and strength, not just subjugation but freedom. The South, argues Patterson, "continued to hold on to the old agrarian capitalist version of possessive individualism with its emphasis on honour and on freedom as power over others."[38]

When those Eufaulans and their guests applauded the unveiling of their Confederate monument, they had much to celebrate. In the absence of federal power, in their isolated corner of Alabama, it was easy to see their new statue not as a memorial to a lost war but as a monument to a long fight they had won. Those triumphs were a twisted version of Americana: a set of aristocratic ends, pursued by authoritarian means, via Jeffersonian logic.

CHAPTER THIRTEEN

Lynching as an Act of Freedom

FROM HIS CHILDHOOD ON, David Frost Jr. lived in terror of a single brush with the flesh of a white woman. One day a mundane errand brought him far too close for comfort. While waiting outside of a roadside store with the family mule, David's mother sent the boy inside with a nickel and a stone jug to buy a gallon of kerosene. The white clerk filled the jug and handed it over to him. There and then it almost happened. When her hand got close enough that it might accidentally touch his, he panicked, jerked his body back, and watched helplessly as the jug crashed to the floor. Without incident, the clerk replaced the jug and the kerosene and sent him on his way. Frost's mother could not understand her boy's carelessness. Yet he had internalized a fact of life in Barbour County: to stay alive, he would need to steer clear of even superficial encounters with white women.

David Frost was born in 1917 and raised five miles outside of Eufaula. He learned from his parents, in very specific ways, how to negotiate being young and "colored" in the Black Belt. He remembered vividly listening to his parents tell cautionary tales of lynching. "My parents would tell it like it had just happened," he recalled.[1]

How many mobs, how many bodies, how much torture and mutilation were necessary to keep the social order? Not many. David

Frost, for one, had never seen a lynching. The writer Richard Wright knew what young Frost felt: "The penalty of death awaited me if [I] made a false move and I wondered if it was worth-while to make any move at all." It only took a small number of outsized, extralegal, and physically barbarous acts to infect an individual's heart with terror and govern the imagination of an entire people. Most of the racial violence was not about lynching at all, but about the daily grind of assaults, thefts, beatings, and violent enforcements of segregation that one could do little about. But it was lynching that seared onto the human consciousness: the nauseating fear of the devil on the edge of town or of small gangs of vigilantes scouring the countryside on the rumor of some transgression. As Richard Wright continues: "The things that influenced my conduct as a Negro did not have to happen to me directly; I needed but to hear of them to feel their full effects in the deepest layers of my consciousness. As long as it remained something terrible and yet remote, something whose horror and blood might descend upon me at any moment, I was compelled to give my entire imagination over to it, an act which blocked the springs of thought and feeling in me, creating a sense of distance between me and the world in which I lived."[2]

A person did not have to see a dead and mutilated body to know that white people relished a uniquely sinister form of liberty: the freedom to take a life with impunity. As gruesome and improbable an expression of freedom as lynching was, federal powers proved incapable of touching it.

It was the Iver Peterson story that haunted Frost's young and anxious mind. That was the one that got repeated, the one about the Peterson boy. His death at the hand of a mob took place six years before Frost's birth, but it carved itself into the psyche of his parents, and they, in turn, etched it into their son's mind as they taught him to negotiate the power relations of Barbour County. There were many stories that could be told, but that was the one he had been trained not to forget.

Every night, Iver Peterson would walk his girlfriend home from her job serving an affluent white family on Eufaula's Cherry Street.

On a February evening in 1911, Peterson waited for his gal as usual. "Here I am," he said in the dark when she came out. But he mistakenly startled Mrs. Hudson, "a prominent woman of Eufaula . . . in social and church circles" who was returning home from her neighbor's house. At the sound of her screams, Peterson fled. The hosts leapt up from fine tables covered in linen, rattling the imported china, and rushed into the street. Who, they wondered, was that Black man waiting in the darkness to prey on innocent white women? They aggressively questioned everyone. Iver Peterson's girlfriend finally, most likely tearfully, explained that she met Iver nightly for their evening stroll home. She had undoubtedly heard stories about what this might mean. Perhaps she hoped that these fine and reasonable people she worked for would not descend into barbarity. Maybe this would be different. With neither crime nor victim, white hearts started to race, people and weapons gathered, and any pretense of white civilization evaporated. The hunt was on.[3]

"Eufaula's finest citizens," as the local paper put it—led by the city's most prominent physician, Dr. Walter Britt—scoured the countryside for Iver. They searched all night until, around eight in the morning, Deputy William Beverly found him in town behind the house of Congressman Henry De Lamar Clayton Jr. Hoping to thwart the lynch mob, the deputy planned to stash his prisoner quietly at the county jailhouse in Clayton for his own protection. Local police could go either way in these situations, but it was not uncommon for them to at least try to do their duty to protect prisoners from mob violence. At about the eight-mile post on the Clayton-Eufaula highway, however, the lynch mob, driving hard, caught up with the deputy and his prisoner. They dragged Iver Peterson away. The deputy may have seen himself outnumbered or felt himself to be outranked by the town leaders, or simply not been convinced that a Negro's life was worth it. He chose not to make a stand.

Just past the Cottonhill Road intersection, on some large rocks in front of the Pleasant Grove Church, the vigilantes held Iver Peterson down. Everyone knew what came next. In a sexualized ritual of horror common to so many lynchings, Dr. Britt cut Iver Peterson's testicles from his body. No record of the details exists, but James Baldwin described a similar scene in his short story "Going to Meet the Man." "In the cradle of the one white hand, the nigger's privates seemed as remote as meat being weighed in the scales; but seemed heavier, too, much heavier." Baldwin imagined, "The white hand stretched them, cradled them, caressed them" before the victim "screamed and the crowd screamed as the knife flashed, first up, then down, cutting the dreadful thing away, and the blood came roaring down."[4]

The mob then threw a rope around the thick branch of an oak tree and lowered a noose around Iver Peterson's neck as blood poured from his groin. They heaved his body off the ground to break his neck. Dr. Britt was said to be the first to pick up his gun and shoot Iver Peterson's swinging body, and the rest of the mob then followed his lead. So many news reports used the words "riddled with bullets" that it had become a cliché of newspaper reporting about lynchings. Their job complete, the mob returned to town and left Iver Petersen's body twisting in the cold air of the leafless winter morning.[5]

"Listening to my parents tell about the lynching of the Peterson boy made me very afraid of white people," recalled Frost. "My mother taught me never to touch a white woman." By his account, he grew up "one of the most frightened persons in the world."[6]

Two things took the edge off the horror of the Iver Peterson story for young David Frost. First, he knew that Iver's brothers immediately got to work oiling up their guns. The story he heard was that the brothers exacted their revenge on one of the members of the lynch mob after they cornered him down by the Chattahoochee River. The one they really wanted to kill was Dr. Britt—the leader, the one who castrated their brother, the one who fired the first shot. He eluded their revenge. By killing one of the vigilantes they paid their own price by having to flee Eufaula—and their family and lives—in order to avoid the same fate as Iver. They were never heard from again.

The second thing that young David Frost knew was that things could have been even worse. What happened to Iver was not as bad as what happened to that other poor boy he heard about up in Union Springs in neighboring Bullock County. That story got told too.

There, rumors of sexual predation again pumped oxygen into the fires of hate. When the mob found the boy, they strung the youngster upside down by his heels. Folks heard his screaming and went to get his mother, who rushed to the scene to plead desperately for her son's life. They had probably already castrated him when she arrived. She started fighting with the mob to free her son, but they tied her up to a nearby tree and forced her to watch. With the boy still screaming, they cut out his tongue and tried to present it to his mother. Before they finalized their bloodlust, the mob shoved sticks into his eyes while his mother watched, her body either helplessly writhing against her bonds or simply frozen in horror.[7]

Many white people would have seen Frost's fears as clear evidence that the system worked: lynching restrained the predatory nature of otherwise uncontrollable Black men. The myth of having to protect white womanhood against Black bestiality became the central tale of white supremacy in the "lynching era"—that period between Reconstruction and World War II. The relationship between whites and Blacks during slavery, so the white fable went, had once been rooted in a paternalistic relationship in which loyal and docile slaves enjoyed the fruits of an economically and socially benevolent plantation system. That mythological bulwark dissolved with the end of chattel slavery to reveal a different and equally flawed ideology: that of raping and thieving Blacks, disconnected from the control and discipline of the plantation, roaming an unprotected landscape in search of their favorite prey, white women. Any transgression of the gendered norms or racial practices, however accidental or fictitious—as David Frost was raised to know—could result in a brutal, torturous death.

Lynching policed the boundaries of white supremacy, to be sure, but it also patrolled the lines of gender. The great champion of antilynching, Ida B. Wells, explained, "White men used their ownership of the body of the white female as a terrain on which to lynch the black male." To the extent that Southern society was a hierarchical puzzle, lynching clarified where each piece belonged. Vigilante violence served as a sort of "folk pornography of the Bible Belt," as the historian Jacquelyn Dowd Hall argues, dramatizing everyone's role in the social system. The violent spectacles made clear not only that Black people were vulnerable to the power and whims of whites, but also that white women required the protection of white men who played the hero in the bloody melodramas. Men who were natural and unconstrained, the logic went, were inherently violent and powerful, dominating others with violent abandon—be it rape or lynching or the connection between the two. Other scholars have explored different dimensions of lynching, such as the psychoanalytical dynamics—which the ritual castration makes all but obvious. Historians also point to a variety of other triggers: panics over the price of cotton, the anxieties produced by industrialization and modernization, the deep-seated traditions of Southern honor, and the savage ritual dimensions of Christian sacrifice. If there is one thing we know, however, it is that racial violence—from the subtle to the vicious—was widespread and various in means, intentions, time, and place.[8]

Largely unexplored in the varying explanations of American lynching is something fundamental: the continuity of the underlying idea of *freedom*. Reframing the most heinous aspects of American violence as part of the most cherished set of principles in American life is neither obvious nor easy to accept. It requires seeing lynching as what one historian of the South called "something akin to a prerogative"—a right one could have for the taking. In Ashraf H. A. Rushdy's intellectual archaeology *American Lynching*, he points out how the power of racial terror "arose precisely out of an ideology of the sense of what rights accrued to someone possessing democratic freedom" in a slave society. For people of European descent, the capacity for violence was their "birthright, their heritage, the final statement of their freedom." A Virginia statute declares that a master killing a slave "shall be free of all punishment... as if such accident never happened." *As if nothing happened.* White freedom grew out of the actions of those who had "the right to maim, torture, and kill with impunity." To understand lynching is to root it in slavery, which fostered "the sensibility of freedom, first for the colonial generations, and then for all white people in the generations after the Revolutionary War."[9]

After slavery, the project of white-domination-as-freedom continued—but as the right to dominate even on a whim. Whites enjoyed that most perfect form of freedom with regard to Black people, a "world without restraint."[10]

Lynching in Barbour County and the rest of the nation must be understood less as a stand-alone problem than as another permutation in the expression of the "sovereignty of the people." As Aristotle feared and Jefferson celebrated, a powerful democracy had the capacity to overrun the rule of law. Or put another way, justice can be embedded in a kind of folk law rather than legal formalism. The extreme version of the Jeffersonian-Jacksonian idea is that the real constitution is not the one on paper, but the one embedded in local whites' freedom and capacity to decide what was right and wrong in their communities. This is what one historian calls "popular constitutionalism." The people, the argument goes, *are* the law or are even superior to the law. And "the people" are white and they are local and they are free. In the 1880s Frederick Douglass recognized that white people worked within a twisted constitutional logic, and that his people might be better off if the entire veneer of legalism were simply stripped away into a war of one against all. He believed Black people

> should be about as well situated for the purposes of justice if there were no Constitution of the United States at all; as well off if there were no law or law-makers, no constables, no jails, no courts of justice, and we were left entirely without the pretence of legal protection, for we are now at the mercy of midnight raiders, assassins, and murderers, and we should only be in the same condition if these pretended safeguards were abandoned. They now only mock us.

Lynching and political violence are tied to a long history of *herrenvolk* democratic anti-statism—if in a particular masculinist form. The system was self-reinforcing: the less state involvement there was, the more that white sovereignty flourished.[11]

Much of the promise of white democratic life was premised upon the devaluation of Black bodies. Beyond a simple "freedom" versus "state power" lies a dialectal tension funneled through the survival and empowerment of African American people. To defeat the federal government was to express freedom in exactly this context. The murder and dismemberment of Black bodies bordered on the dismemberment of the nation-state—the source of the original wound of the white Southerner.

The lynching of Iver Peterson was part of a series of lynchings in Barbour County. In 1879, just five years after the election massacre, a posse killed two "sullen, indifferent and defiant" African Americans for possibly having something to do with two traveling salesmen who had gone missing. The salesmen may have left a rather tempting $180 in the local bank, and if someone had taken the money then the two Black men may have made useful scapegoats for someone else's crime. Two years later, Josh Shorter, a Black teenager, was hanged for the standard accusation of an "atrocious assault on a respectable white girl," aged twelve. A mob shot and burned Edgar Onlu at the stake in 1893 when he supposedly confessed to murdering a white shopkeeper. Confessions were often ritualistic extractions that justified the death of the accused—most of which were delivered in desperate panic as a rope tightened around the victim's neck. The act of confession was almost always reported in the papers.[12]

The 1901 state constitution, for all of its legal contortions to disfranchise Black voters, actually included some potential for change: a section stipulating that if a prisoner was killed or badly harmed due to the "the neglect, connivance, cowardice, or other grave fault of the sheriff," he could be impeached. It was the type of statute that could readily be ignored or enforced. Places like Eufaula that once had the law unto themselves now faced the possibility of discipline by the state of Alabama. The sheriffs of both Bullock and Mobile Counties were actually impeached by Barbour County's own, Governor B.B. Comer, for failing to stop lynching.[13]

The intervention of the state of Alabama made the case of Laurence Davis quite different than that of Iver Peterson. In 1909, Laurence Davis was accused of raping Lizzie Thomas, a young white telephone operator in Eufaula. The sheriff had him locked safely in jail on an otherwise sleepy Sunday afternoon. Little did Davis or the man in charge, Deputy Sheriff Virgil Crawford, know, but plans for a lynching were spreading throughout town. When they did hear word of the growing Eufaula mob, which included the mayor himself, the deputy double-locked all the jail's doors. Crawford tried to deputize other citizens but could only get two men. The deputy called for the National Guard company, most of whom were in church on Sunday afternoon. The leaders scrambled through the churches to muster the men. Governor Comer demanded that the sheriff "protect the prisoner—shoot if you must, but protect the prisoner." By then, a "drunken mob of about 180 men" with sledgehammers and a large timber to use as a battering ram had gathered in front of the building. They began beating down the door.[14]

As those at the front of the crowd crushed the door, there stood the guardsmen, rifles and bayonets at the ready, staring back down at the vigilantes. One famously short guardsman, Eufaulan Junius B. Couric, stiffened up. In the midst of a "cussin' match," they taunted him about both his height and his protection of a Black prisoner. "That's all right, you big stiff, I'm here doing my duty and if you put your foot on this landing—if even you touch it I'll drill you through with a bullet," Couric responded. A shot rang out and hit the ceiling—perhaps as a warning, perhaps as an accident while clearing out a jammed cartridge. The mob then came to a sudden standstill. One of the leaders of the lynch mob, "a well known man in whom the mob had confidence," saw the obvious. "Boys, they have got all of the military here—plenty of them. They are too many for you. You had better go home." The vigilantes dispersed, leaving their hanging rope on the threshold of the jail, a taunting reminder of the prisoner's narrow escape. The soldiers held vigil at the jail with their prisoner throughout the night.[15]

The next morning, the sheriffs and the troops hustled prisoner Laurence Davis onto a train bound for Montgomery. Before they arrived at the next stop at nearby Union Springs, however, the train stopped on a deserted stretch of track. From there, the prisoner was whisked to a horse-drawn carriage that carried him "on a fast drive" to the jail in Clayton for safe keeping. When a reporter asked the sheriff if he would really shoot a friend and fellow Eufaulan in defense of a prisoner, he responded, "The man who would join a mob to lynch my prisoner is no friend of mine. I'd fire on any man who would go into a mob to do me that wrong." As local historian David E. Alsobrook put it, a comparison of the Peterson and Davis incidents "clearly showed only a well-coordinated, armed force—preferably troops—could defeat a large, frenzied mob."[16]

The only cure, short of changing the hearts of white people or the armed resistance of Black people, was the power of the federal government. Combatting the freedom to dominate in its most visceral forms, as Native Americans trying to enforce treaty rights and African Americans struggling for the freedom of political participation during Reconstruction learned, required a social contract in which the federal government worked aggressively to restrain the freedom of the dominant caste. In the case of lynching, the federal government could never manage to make lynching illegal despite the introduction of literally hundreds of anti-lynching bills in the twentieth century. Unlike many of the other cases explored here, it fell to the limited commitment of state governments to control lynching. And the state of Alabama demonstrated an incomplete interest in this, mostly as a way to shore up its national reputation, attract Northern investment, *prevent* federal intervention, and stake a claim to membership in the vibrant New South.

Even if Congress never budged on lynching, Republicans often manipulated the cause against the Democrats. Newly elected Republican president Warren G. Harding announced that "Congress ought to wipe the stain of barbaric lynching from the banners of a free and orderly representative democracy." He then visited Birmingham in 1921 to celebrate the fiftieth anniversary of the industrial miracle of the "Magic City." Racial equality had long slipped from the Republicans' agenda, but he took the moment to suggest that there was work to do on race relations, especially after African Americans had proven their citizenship and patriotism in the Great War. Harding saw a regional convergence at work: the South, especially places like Birmingham, was industrializing; the North was receiving migrations of African Americans; and the Great War had unified the nation. "The race problem is national rather than merely sectional," he declared. He called out, ambivalently, for Black political rights. While he believed the vote was important, he maintained the line on social equality. "I would accent that a black man can not be a white man, and that he does not need and should not aspire to be as much like a white man as possible in order to accomplish the best that is possible for him. He should seek to be, and he should be encouraged to be, the best possible black man, and not the best possible imitation of a white man." Despite the condescending dimensions of his speech, Warren Harding received rousing support from African Americans and silent scowls from whites.[17]

President Harding spoke at a very particular moment. After the Great War, with lynchings up to more than one per week in the United States, African Americans looked to federal legislation for assistance. Harding's support revived the hopes of a floundering bill that had been introduced in 1918 by Leonidas Dyer of St. Louis. The bill would make lynching a federal crime, allowing for prosecutions of perpetrators, those failing to protect life, or those failing to prosecute the crime. It also included county-level compensation for victims' families. The NAACP had been hesitant to get behind the bill given the questions of its constitutionality, but the civil rights organization signed on in 1919 as postwar racial violence rocked the nation, with scores lynched and countless more killed in race riots in one of the most riot-torn years in US history. With mass protests, letter writing, petitions, and public pressure of all kinds, the bill cleared the House in early 1922 due to what the *New York Times* called "an insistent countrywide demand." To help get it past the recalcitrant Southern opposition in the Senate, the NAACP took out a dramatic full-page ad in eleven national newspapers titled "The Shame of America." It largely rebuked the rape myth with hard facts, explaining that "the United Sates is the only land on earth where human beings are burned at the stake."[18]

The Southern Democrats had sharpened an old tool, the filibuster, which they mobilized to destroy the Dyer bill. The filibuster had been a longstanding parliamentary maneuver, but World War I ushered in a more aggressive version of the tactic, a rule requiring a two-thirds majority vote for cloture to end debate on a bill. The Southern Democrats wielded it with tremendous parliamentary skill. The Dyer bill was merely the practice run, as they would continue to filibuster any challenge to the racial order throughout the twentieth century. The filibuster turned an undemocratic system, one stacked against African Americans from the start, into a political brick wall that allowed a minority of Southern senators to block anything they did not want from getting a vote. Like other anti-lynching bills to come, had the Dyer bill been given a simple majority vote, it would have certainly passed.[19]

The Dyer bill ended up another echo in the cavernous void between 1875 and 1957 in which no federal civil rights bill of any kind became law. Still, in its campaign for the Dyer bill, the NAACP had found its voice. The organization "made the United States Congress a trumpet through which the facts of lynching [were] broadcast to the country." A concerted Republican effort might have made the difference, but Warren Harding, despite his endorsement, never pushed the bill. It had never been clear to the NAACP leadership that the Republicans believed in stopping lynching or whether they just wanted a way to berate Democrats and shore up the Black vote. The results made the leadership realize that the civil rights struggle was now in the lurch between two parties: on the one hand, tepid and ineffective support from the Republicans, and, on the other, supportive progressive Democrats hamstrung by their party's Southern segregationist wing. W. E. B. Du Bois, reflecting back on Frederick Douglass's famous dictum about the Republican Party being their ship, was ready to give up on the party of Lincoln. "For God's sake," he sharply remarked, "give us the sea."[20]

The killer of Eufaula's Willie Jenks (or Jenkins, depending on the source) did not care about debates in Washington. A decorated Black World War I vet, in 1922 Jenks was accused of "insulting a white woman" up in Batesville, a spot on the road between Eufaula and Comer. Having become tangled up with a white moonshining mob, he found himself blocked from being able to see his wife. Details are unclear, but one of the leaders of the gang may have decided he wanted her for himself. Realizing he was in trouble with the gang, Jenks fled on a train to the Georgia side of the Chattahoochee. The mob on horseback, pistols holstered on their sides, caught up with him and drove him back to Batesville like a cow—dragging him forth with a rope fixed around his neck. There they forced him to drink a coke bottle full of urine and then cut one of his tendons to prevent his escape. Willie Jenks knew his fate, so when he saw his chance, however small, he tried to make a run for it. He was last seen "riddled with bullets," his body strapped on a mule. He was later found in the bottom of an abandoned well. David Frost recalled, "Willie Jenkins had fought in World War I in France and came home without a scratch. He had escaped all the German bombing and all the German shootings but he could not escape this mob here in Barbour County."[21]

Despite the failure of the Dyer anti-lynching bill in 1922, and at least partially because of the threat of federal intervention it represented, state authorities continued the occasional fight against lynching on the local level. In July 1929, a plot worthy of a film noir tested the Alabama state government's commitment to control white freedom, but whether it suppressed, deflected, or institutionalized racial violence depended upon a very long view of the political struggle against lynching.

Late at night on July 10, 1929, an eighteen-year-old white woman named Beatrice Clarke was found stumbling down the railroad tracks in the dark toward Eufaula. She was bleeding from a shotgun blast to her arm. Clarke reported that she had been raped, shot, and left for dead just four miles north of town. At the scene of the crime, where railroad tracks cut near a country road, the authorities found the body of Jack Hines, a white twenty-eight-year old automobile mechanic, dead from a short-range shotgun shot to the chest. Hines's Chevrolet was gone. Beatrice Clarke claimed that she and Jack Hines had been riding in the car that night when they were held up at gunpoint by an unknown Black man. He demanded, at gunpoint, that they drive down the deserted road for a quarter of a mile. There he stopped the car, got out and killed Hines, raped and shot her, and then made his getaway in Hines's Chevy. Beatrice Clarke then dragged herself back down the railroad tracks to Eufaula to report the crime. There were rumors around town that she was not telling the truth.[22]

An African American gas station attendant named Bob Turner tipped off the police that the man they were looking for was allegedly one Lester Bouyer, aka Charlie Harris, a Black sawmill worker. Turner's incarcerated father also played a role in identifying Bouyer. In exchange, Turner appears to have received part or all of the $600 reward offered, and his father got parole for the information leading to the identification of the assailant. After a sustained manhunt, the authorities picked Bouyer up not far from the prison where he had already served time for other offenses. The day after they arrested Bouyer, the police announced he verified "every detail" that they had already pieced together. Beatrice Clarke, still in the hospital, identified him from his photo. A grand jury quickly indicted him for murder. Bouyer was never charged with the rape, assault, or attempted murder of Beatrice Clarke—only the murder of Jack Hines.[23]

Knowing that the authorities would bring Bouyer back to Eufaula for trial, masked mobs began searching cars entering town to seize the prisoner for a round of vigilante justice before the courts had their say. Governor Bibb Graves decided to make this a test of state authority. One of the most progressive governors in the South, he sought to end convict leasing, increase the quality of education, and build highways. Even though he counted the Klan in his political coalition (and was rumored to be the Exalted Cyclops of the Montgomery chapter), he was just a bit progressive on race. "There will not be a lynching in Alabama if I can help it," Graves announced. It would not be easy. The national press reported "a highly inflated public mind" with regard to vigilante justice throughout the entire region.[24]

To keep the prisoner alive, Governor Graves sent two National Guard infantry companies and twenty state police officers to Barbour County. General Walter E. Bare, commanding officer of the

National Guard, told the press, "We have been called upon by the government to protect this negro during his trial; that protection will be given." The prisoner arrived by train, and a swelling crowd of fifteen hundred people was there to greet him. With bayonets fixed, the soldiers marched the prisoner three blocks to the courthouse. A detachment stood watch at the entrance to the Chattahoochee bridge, on the expectation of an organized vigilante attack from the Georgia side. The press reported that the "entire countryside was in a lynching fever." Fifty soldiers remained in the courthouse during the trial, with another one hundred and fifty outside to keep the crowd, now closer to three thousand in number, under control.[25]

As the National Guard stood watch, the trial inside the Eufaula Courthouse only lasted two hours. For reasons unknown, Bouyer pleaded guilty and received no defense. The stories presented were patchy, the evidence thin, and the motivation seemed to be based on little more than the irrational violence of Black men. Jury deliberations lasted ten minutes. In no time, the prisoner had his sentence: death by electrocution. After he was found guilty, Bouyer went back on his testimony that he had ever assaulted Beatrice Clark, though he continued to admit to the murder of Jack Hines. Letters flooded into the governor's office requesting a seat at the electrocution.[26]

The African American press praised the governor's protections as a breakthrough in justice, while condemning the entire trial. Saved from a mob, the Black papers argued, Lester Bouyer still received a legal lynching. "The fact that this had to be done to avoid a lynching is a sad commentary on American civilization," editorialized the *New Amsterdam News*, "but it is more than had been done in other cases. There is still the question as to whether Bouyer had a fair trial, but the fact that he had a trial shows an improvement." It was a success, argued another, because it "proved to the world that lynching can be avoided." The defense was nonexistent and the jury all white, "but there was no illegal lynching and a step forward has been made."[27]

The governor, in turn, received national praise for having stopped a lynching. This was hardly because of his commitment to civil rights, explained one historian: "He was primarily concerned about the adverse publicity that would befall the state if Bouyer died at the hands of a mob." *Time* magazine put it in uncomplex terms, made palatable for an audience that preferred the new mass journalism: "Judge Lynch foiled."[28]

Just months after the drama of the Hines murder, the stock market collapsed, and the entire world economy followed. The three pro-business Republican presidents of the 1920s, Harding, Coolidge, and Hoover, were replaced with Franklin Delano Roosevelt, a dramatically different Democrat who was not interested in restoring the Jeffersonian dream, but in launching a massive growth in the role of the state in people's lives to combat the global economic calamity. With the biggest reorganization of the peacetime political economy, the NAACP and other civil rights advocates hoped that perhaps Roosevelt might also use federal authority against the epidemic of vigilante violence. Reform was everywhere. Why not federal control of lynching as well?

In 1935, the NAACP drew up another bill, much like the Dyer bill, in the hopes that the new climate of expanding federal authority might prevail upon the most heinous aspects of the Jim Crow system. The organization got the progressive Colorado senator Edward Costigan and New York reform stalwart Robert Wagner to introduce it as the Costigan-Wagner anti-lynching bill. For Roosevelt, there was too much at stake—social security, collective bargaining, fair labor standards, housing, the Works Progress Administration, rural electrification, banking reform, and a host of other new government programs—to get behind race relations with any vigor. Much of the New Deal labor legislation already excluded domestic and agricultural workers as a sop to the labor regime of the South. Despite Eleanor Roosevelt's rock-solid commitment to the bill, it would fail without FDR's support. "If I come out for the anti-lynching bill now," Roosevelt calculated, "they will block every bill I ask Congress to pass to keep America from collapsing. I just can't take the risk." The lynching bill sat "like a poised avalanche" over the president's reforms, reported the *New York Times*, ready to sweep the president's reform agenda away. When the anti-lynching bill was reintroduced in 1937, it passed the House only to face the longest filibuster in half a century by Southern senators over fears that the party of Jefferson was becoming the "Afro-Democratic Party."[29]

The Civil War and Reconstruction haunted the lynching debate. Hugo Black, then an Alabama senator but soon to begin a career as one of the towering liberal Supreme Court justices of the twentieth century (and, like Graves, a former Klan leader), helped filibuster the anti-lynching bill. He compared it to the federal suppression of Southern freedoms under Reconstruction. "We all know the history of that period; and I mention it only because the bill under discussion today is a lineal descendant of the type of thought that placed the heel of the military oppressor upon the people until they could tolerate it no longer." A champion of the bill, in contrast, called the successful blocking of the bill "Appomattox in reverse." Of the many ghosts haunting the Southern Democrats' fight to preserve the libidinal rush to destroy other people's lives was an old friend advocating nullification. "A careful listener" of the lynching debates, argues one historian, "might well have heard echoes of John C. Calhoun instructing his colleagues on sound constitutional doctrine."[30]

After an eight-day standoff in the Senate, the anti-lynching bill was adjourned. Across the Chattahoochee in Columbus, a worker penned his political worldview to the president, declaring his desire for boosting wages and limiting hours but not a challenge to his place in the racial order. "I wish to thank you for the straght from the sholder speech you made in gansvell and to let you know I wosent suprised for I knew you wosent a quiter and I wish to let you know I am hartly in favor of your brave fight for the wage and houir bill for we working people know who it is that is fighting you and why." He ended: "I wonto tell you I faver every peace of laslatin you have askfor exsept the antilinchen bil." The president had read the politics with horrific clarity.[31]

As for David Frost Jr., he eventually turned around to face down the fears that chased him as a boy. An imagination once compelled by fears of violence turned to resistance. "Somewhere down the line, after I stopped being afraid of white people," David Frost Jr. recalled about his early fear of lynching, "I began to hate most white people." After World War II, he would be among the first to join the NAACP in Eufaula, and among a handful who surmounted the ridiculous obstacles white people and the constitution of Alabama put in the way of his right to vote.[32]

In the case of Dr. Britt, the ghost of Iver Peterson would not let him go. As he later confessed to David Frost's mother, he couldn't escape the horror of what he had done. Sometimes when the good doctor put his head down to sleep at night, he could hear Iver Peterson begging for his life. On other nights, when he rode in his buggy back from taking care of his patients in Barbour County, he sensed Iver's presence sitting silently on the back of his carriage. As they rode together through Eufaula, he felt the ghost of his victim rocking the carriage back and forth as it traveled through the sweat of the Eufaula night. Legal impunity might be a form of freedom, but even the law could not provide freedom from the conscience.[33]

CHAPTER FOURTEEN

A New Deal for Southside?

Mr. Nolan, a white tenant farmer in Dale County just south of Barbour, passed away sometime around 1900. His wife, Nancy Nolan, a young mother of three with nowhere else to go, took over her husband's labors and combined them with her own into the formidable combination of planting cotton, tending a household, mothering children, harvesting the crop, and paying the interminable debt. Her nine-year-old son had to pick up his father's plow and carve his own furrows through the barren wiregrass soil. The widow Nolan tried for five years to make a go of working her plot before finally giving up on tenant farming. She and her kids packed up what little they had and abandoned the land, making their way over the northern county line. They finally settled in Eufaula. There she took up with the new textile mill, an option available to only whites throughout the South. At the Eufaula mill, she worked all night and had two of her young boys working in the mill during the day. "It was bad," she recalled.[1]

The mill was a grimy place. A layer of tobacco spit coated the Eufaula mill room floor. Machine oil, grease, and a thick fog of humidity from belching steam covered everything else. No decent toilets were to be found, just a single, wretched outhouse that served all the mill workers. There was no running water, and ill-nourished and ill-rested workers shared water buckets, dippers, and disease. Chronic bronchitis, tonsilitis, asthma, and a host of other respiratory ailments were rampant. As in all mills, the exposed belts, grinding gears, and machine blades threatened life and limb—and were known to take both. "It is a fearful sight to see one of the belts on these high-speed machines break or come off and whip and curl like a snake," remarked one textile worker, or to see a pulley "jump off a shaft and come across the floor like a cannonball." White men, white women, and white children all worked in dreadful conditions. At the end of twelve hours of drudgery, repeated six days per week, the steam whistle finally released the operatives into the outside world, where they breathed the Eufaula air choked with coal dust from the mill's power plant. Early the next morning, they returned to do it again.[2]

The Great Depression and the New Deal challenged the structure, practice, wages, and power relations in American industry. By 1934, spurred on by the official recognition of unions in the National Industrial Recovery Act, workers walked out in an enormous region-wide strike that swept through textile mills across the South. The Eufaula mill, however, never went on strike, and in fact, even the workers defined themselves in opposition to the New Deal. From the grimy turn-of-the-century mill sprang a remarkably robust brand of paternalism, one that workers came to regard as a marvel and a wonder in employment relations. It also created a unique version of racialized anti-statism that kept the federal powers at bay.

Prior to the Civil War, poor whites remained on the margins of the slave-based cotton production system. But with slavery gone, race was no longer the sole driver of the labor market. Whites slipped from independent subsistence farming and fell further under the tyrannical yoke of King Cotton. The dream of the independent Jeffersonian yeoman, to the extent it ever existed, drifted further into a medieval nightmare as more people lost their land, worked for large landowners, and came under the sway of distant cotton markets. Some tenant farmers, known as sharecroppers, labored in exchange for a share of the crop; others paid a combination of rent and a share of the crop, known as share-cash; some fortunate few managed to pay the entire rent in "cash tenancy." No matter the system, debt was the never-ending burden.

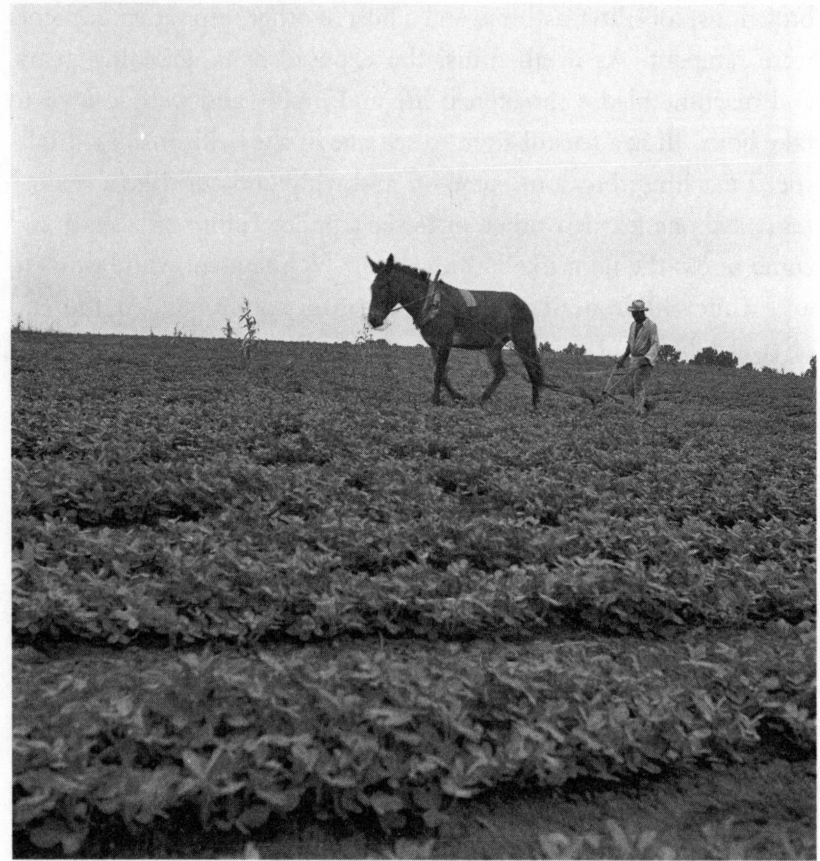

Well into the mid-twentieth century, springtime still meant long days of plowing behind a mule. With technology that predated the birth of Barbour County, this scene has a modern update: the farmer is working a peanut field after the fall of the cotton economy.

The grinding poverty of tenant life was as predictable as the seasons. As the historian Wayne Flynt evocatively describes the anxious cycle of tenant farming:

> The appearance of spring brought the need for a mule to plow the earth and for seed to plant. The owner of the land provided these essentials for a fixed rent or a share of the crop. The optimism of planting time turned to the anxiety of summer, when the searing

heat could wilt plants and people, when too much rain could rot cotton, when there were never enough hands to hoe weeds from the rows, when not even the open passageway of a dogtrot cabin or its flimsy construction provided enough ventilation for comfort. Then came fall and the back-breaking labor of pulling the puffy wad from the boll, fingers cut and split by burrs, back aching with fatigue, no sundown or thunderstorm unwelcome that promised an end to the day's toil. "Settling up" time followed, with the occasional good years outweighed by the bad ones. Winter arrived with growing debts at the nearest crossroads store, debts that almost always equaled or exceeded the cropper's share of what was left in the fall. And so it went, year after year, decade after decade.

Alabama was one of the leading states in the disreputable business of tenant farming, and it just kept getting worse. In 1880, the ownership-to-tenancy ratio was roughly 1:1. By 1910, over 60 percent of farmers were tenant farmers, and that grew to 65 percent by the 1930s. Whites continued to expand their share of tenancy, especially as African Americans, blocked from decent work in the mills and other occupations, fled to opportunities in the industrial North during the wartime Great Migration. By the Great Depression, two-thirds of Alabama tenant farmers were white, many of whom, like the widow Nolan, were more than ready for the steady paycheck of textile mill life.[3]

In contrast to the whites moving into the mills, few African American sharecroppers would ever rise above their fate if they remained in the Black Belt. All the diligent labor in the world could barely make a dent in one's circumstances. "I have sowed my labor into the earth and lived to reap only a part of it, not all that was mine by human right," explained the ambitious Black sharecropper Ned Cobb just up the road from Barbour in Tallapoosa County. "That's the way colored people met their lives in this country, livin on a white person's place. White man's money been comin from the colored race—this state, the bosses of it and the moneyed cats, as long as I ever knowed, has been taking the nigger's labor."[4]

Land was never distributed to freed people after emancipation. Instead, sharecropping, and its attendant cycles of debt and subservience, provided something short of true independence. After the Great Migration of Black farmers to the North, increasing numbers of poor whites slipped into sharecropping. New Deal agricultural resources went to landowners, rarely making it to the truly needy tenant farmers.

Many whites, in contrast, believed cropping to be more of a short-term move to stay afloat in hard times. It typically ended, however, in slipping into a long-term cycle of debt and a life of transience in search of a better deal. Landlords pushed tenants away from subsistence crops and strangled them with a vicious and inescapable debt finance system. Market relations were controlled by the landowner, the soil was exhausted, and faraway lands were rapidly creating a global surplus of cotton. As one observer put it, tenancy amounted to a "miserable panorama of unpainted shacks, rain-gullied fields, straggling fences, rattle-trap Fords, dirt, poverty, disease, drudgery, and monotony that stretches for a thousand miles across the cotton belt." Sharecropping proved that commodity capitalism didn't care about race as much as it cared about labor, and it cared about race only when it helped divide workers and make labor cheap.[5]

Being a millhand, on just about any terms, was therefore a liberation, delivering consistent wages, minimum debt, and modest security. In Eufaula the mill workers lived and worked in an area known as Southside, a town within a town, an isolated factory district within the isolation of Eufaula itself. The enclave of white working-class "lintheads" served as a "fortress" that protected mill workers from the opprobrium of elite Eufaula, the residents of which rarely crossed the tracks. Forever separate from the famous opulence, style, architecture, and opinions, the Southsiders had managed to leave behind the despair of the land owned by someone else, escaping the cyclical misery of tenancy and debt, and to take up residence, as it was said, "below the tracks." By simple virtue of pigmentation, the lowest cotton mill operative also stood well above the majority of the people of Barbour County. As one resident put it, there were three Eufaulas: "One was white, one was black and one was Southsiders."[6]

Every Eufaula mill worker in the early twentieth century marked local history by the time before and after the arrival of the man everyone called "Mr. Donald." The mill, started in the 1890s, shuttered in the national economic panic of 1907, and then reopened under new ownership in 1909, evolved from the dark satanic mill of William Blake's fears into a shining example of mill paternalism at the hands of Donald Comer. The old machinery was smashed and dragged out of the building, and new, more efficient technology was brought in to make finer, more upmarket textiles. Before long, as weaver Mrs. Lee Snipes recalled, there was "a fountain of running ice water, marble toilets, marble floor, five commodes, all cleaned every day." Management went from indifferent to caring. "We have first class bosses, too," she added. The length of the workday was shortened. Electricity replaced coal and steam. Workers found themselves with smart uniforms—a different color for each department. They moved into trim cottages, some that grew to have finely kempt gardens, all financed with company-sponsored home loans at reasonable rates. Mill operatives enjoyed their own regionally famous band, a baseball team, a variety of social clubs, life insurance programs, college scholarships, and above all, a spacious community house staffed by social workers and educators that even included a kindergarten for the little ones. Eventually, Mr. Donald even bought a summer camp on the Florida coast for his workers' vacations. As Mrs. Snipes concluded, "It used to be that we were just factory folks or 'lint heads.' Now we are 'Mill operatives' and we hold our heads high." After thirty years at the mill, she reported, "my work is such happiness."[7]

Historians have long debated the type of noblesse oblige on display at Eufaula's Cowikee Mill no. 1. Was it rooted in the alleged paternalism of the master-slave relationship? A reflection of how "yeoman and cracker turn to the planter," as W. J. Cash, the opinionated author of *The Mind of the South*, put it, waiting "eagerly upon his signal as to what to think and do"? Perhaps it was a form of complete control of workers' lives or a fatherly relation to an infantilized working class? Maybe even a source of genuine Christian care? It was all these. Paternalism was all-encompassing in its social reach, having "evolved into a blend of consent and force, accommodation and intimidation." While living under the sovereignty of Mr. Donald proved much more inviting than the other workplace alternatives available to poor whites, paternalism was also a form of unfreedom. It displaced the politics of the state with local sovereignty, it stunted the flow of the compound republic to the boundary of the plant gate, and it placed workers at the whims of the employer, even if in the case of the Eufaula mill, those whims were often good.[8]

The man whom Southsiders affectionately called "Mr. Donald" was Donald Comer, son of Governor B.B. Comer and a member of one of the wealthiest and most powerful families in Barbour County, indeed, one of the wealthiest families in all of Alabama. He was also the nephew of the sadistic J.W. Comer—overthrower of Reconstruction and runner of convict laborers. B.B. Comer, a vaguely "progressive"—if viciously anti-labor and unrelentingly pro-segregation—Southerner, believed that mill villages were essentially corrupting in nature and were to be avoided. He wanted to see poor whites remain on the land as much as possible, urging them to work in mills primarily as a supplement to "farming." Mill-owned housing was to be avoided. As for African American croppers on his sprawling Barbour County acreage, B.B. was a Southern paternalist but showed little mercy for anyone outside of his control. He chided one servant to the point of kicking her off the plantation for stealing table scraps for herself rather than feeding them to his dog. As he wrote his overseer about his sharecroppers: "Any negro who violates his contract with you, make him pay up before he leaves or beat him to death. I mean that literally."[9]

In 1907, B.B. Comer bought up the old Eufaula Mill, folded it into his economic empire that included several other mills across the state known as the Avondale Mills, and placed Donald in charge. In 1927, B.B. passed away and Donald inherited a large share of his father's wealth and his enormous properties, including the largest plantation in Barbour County, valued in excess of $10 million. Thin, bespectacled, a bit sickly, soft-spoken, and earnest, Donald Comer looked more like a stern, no-nonsense preacher than a barrel-chested Comer. He became one of the largest textile executives in the state, and certainly one of the more famous and beloved of industrial paternalists in the South. Like many progressive Southerners he advocated prohibition, education, industrialization, crop diversification, road building, public heath, and literacy. He continually championed the modest idea that women and children should not work at night, though he had to be pushed toward the abolition of child labor.[10]

Donald Comer's idea of the social compact in Eufaula was rooted in white Christian uplift, resting on a vague, nondoctrinaire sense of the social gospel. "Live and let live is not enough," he explained; "live and help live is what a Christian America wants to do and what we are trying to do with the help we are extending." While some believers in the social gospel embraced organized labor or Christian socialism—some even supporting the racially integrated struggles of the Southern Tenant Farmers' Union or the rise of industrial labor under the Congress of Industrial Organizations in the 1930s—that was not the case for Donald Comer. For his entire life he hated two things: booze and labor unions, which he managed to conflate into a single conspiracy. "I think all of us will agree that selfish corporate interests linked with whiskey and then added to that Union Labor can come near controlling the political situation in any section." The honest, sober, anti-union worker, dedicated to his employer, was Comer's model. Large corporations and unions did not care for workers but only for themselves, he believed. He had little to say on questions of race except to support the segregationist status quo, providing separate and radically unequal access to the lily-white largesse of his mills.[11]

The Depression began in cotton and textiles in the 1920s, well before it did for the rest of the country. Times were tough. Like the rest of the South, Comer greeted the election of Democrat Franklin Roosevelt and his idea of a New Deal with unchecked enthusiasm. He gave his vigorous support to the deluge of long-overdue federal programs—many of which he had championed well before the Great Depression. Comer embraced not only FDR's Tennessee Valley Authority, but the whole alphabet soup of New Deal programs. The Agricultural Adjustment Act (AAA) he believed would end the cycle of debt and overproduction of tenant farmers, while the Rural Electrification Authority (REA) would bring inexpensive electricity to rural areas. The Farm Security Administration (FSA) would provide resettlement, relief, and rehabilitation to destitute farmers. The Federal Emergency Relief Administration (FERA) would provide federal jobs in publicly useful arenas. He also believed it was time for a wages and hours bill, one that would provide a minimum-wage rate and maximum hours, though this had to come with an absolute commitment to keeping wages lower in the South—a differential that would allow the Southern cheap-labor developmental model to continue. "I want our employees to feel that it is their Government that has been strong enough to accomplish this beginning of a new era for them," Donald Comer remarked, "and that it will be that same Government who will protect them." Protect them, that is, but not necessarily empower them.[12]

Many Southern elites differed with Donald Comer, fearing the New Deal's break with the anti-statist tradition of the Democratic

Party. Jeffersonian independence suddenly seemed to be drowning in a sea of federal programs, as the Democrats took over the Hamiltonian philosophy of state-guided economic planning. The pastor of Eufaula's First Presbyterian Church wrote to FDR, laying out his concerns about the "experiments which the administration is trying out." Were they a permanent reorientation or a temporary move to confront the economic emergency? "The people here will gladly welcome a swift return to the old constitutional, conservative type of democracy," he explained in 1935. "I am a democrat of the deepest dye, but we cannot afford to depart from the faith of your fathers." A turning point in the elite's relationship to the Democratic Party might be at hand. "The New Deal does not appeal to the better, more conservative class of business men the impression seems to be that any kind of Federal interference or compulsory control of private affairs will soon disrupt the South."[13]

Eufaula's pastor had the same ideas as W. J. Cash. "The basic Rooseveltian ideas," he argued, "with their emphasis on the social values as against the individual, and on the necessity of revising all values in the light of the conditions created by the machine and the disappearance of the frontier, ran directly contrary to the basic Southern attitudes." The subtext of all elite critiques of federal intervention was a twofold fear: raising wages and ending segregation. The first would deprive the South of its comparative advantage in cheap labor by equalizing the North-South wage differential, and the second would undermine the not unrelated belief in white supremacy. If federal power was allowed to do anything by way of intruding in state and local ways, many feared, it would also be capable of intruding in these two pillars of Southern life.[14]

Secretary of Labor Frances Perkins, who visited the Avondale Mills and met with Donald Comer, recalled that the Barbour County executive "had a humane if not trade union conception of the rights of the worker and of the employers' duty in relations to them." She wrote to him, that "it is a great comfort to me to know that there is an employer in this country like yourself who is conscious of his social obligation to his workers as well as the economic one. I have on a previous occasion indicated to the President my knowledge of your interest in your workers, and shall take the first occasion to refresh his memory concerning your social-mindedness." As Perkins understood, Comer's belief in the New Deal package stopped at any legislation that gave workers the right to organize, at which point he demonstrated outward, even aggressive, hostility. For Comer, the lines of power ran between federal authority and industry, which may then paternalistically be deployed to assist workers. The lines of power were never to bypass industry and run directly between government and labor.[15]

FDR believed the centerpiece of the early New Deal—the National Industrial Recovery Act, and its bureaucratic expression, the National Recovery Administration (NRA)—to be "the most important and far-reaching legislation ever enacted by the American Congress." The NRA's initial popularity was undeniable, as celebrations were organized in towns across America. The official government parade in New York City drew a quarter of a million marchers, two hundred bands, and another nearly two million people watching from the sidewalks. Compliance with the NRA principles allowed businesses to display the famous Blue Eagle, an image that cropped up everywhere as a symbol of hope and solidarity in the summer of 1933, the fourth miserable year of the Great Depression. For most people, the NRA meant that the federal government had finally arrived to help. It was the boldest, most radical economic policy in American history, but it was also among the most untenable, confusing, contradictory, and constitutionally questionable.[16]

The NRA promised a vision of economic regulation to rationalize cutthroat competition and stabilize prices. Yet much of it was the opposite of what the country needed: in a period in which people had very little, it proposed to give more power to corporations so that they could create a scarcity of goods in order to drive up prices. Re-inflating prices, even when people had no money, was believed to be a viable strategy for producing a recovery. The NRA allowed business leaders in specific sectors to set prices, wages, production, hours, and "fair practices" in their industry. It was a model of business self-regulation under government oversight. Partially because it was a Democratic initiative and partially because of the dire nature of the Great Depression, the South lined up for the NRA.

Southern nostrums of independence from federal power curdled in the heat of the Depression, but that was partially because the Solid South proved able to protect what mattered. Nothing could pass without the support of Southern Democrats, and the Southern Democrats killed anything that might upset the racial status quo. For the most part, the NRA promised to organize capitalism, but not disorganize white supremacy. Agricultural subsidies went to landowners not tenants, leaving tenants with absolutely nothing unless landowners felt like sharing, and later New Deal programs would exclude agricultural and domestic workers all together as a sop to Southern politicians interested in keeping the region low-wage and segregated. To maintain the paternalistic system and prove the value of bosses' benevolence to the workers, the meddlesome federal government had to be kept somewhat at bay—even if it was needed in the dire circumstances of the Great Depression.[17]

Donald Comer, like most men of his region and his class, lined up almost fully behind the NRA. He joined the Cotton Textile Code Authority in "good faith" and with "wonderful results," he exclaimed, to set wages, prices, and codes of fair competition in the industry. Yet there was a problem—a big problem—for Donald Comer. The act contained a provision, known as Section 7a, that guaranteed the rights of workers to form unions and bargain collectively with management. "I still continue to be one of those who feel that paragraph 7 A of the N.I.R.A. had no place there," he argued. He believed that the code authority process was enough, and that any independent voice for workers that might come of Section 7a violated his paternalist vision. "This is not a time to teach that the employer and the employee are natural enemies," he proffered. While Section 7a rekindled the hopes of moribund trade unions, Comer asked his workers "not to be in a hurry to follow strange leaders who were coming with promises of wonderful things."[18]

Comer had little trouble squelching solidarity in his isolated mill in Eufaula, but up in Birmingham, where the coals miners had created a rich union culture, he faced a different situation. Just weeks after the passage of the National Industrial Recovery Act, an organizer named Ike Robinton began speechifying against Comer's paternalism. He began with an easy target: his father, B.B. Comer, who had violently and viciously destroyed the Birmingham-area mineworkers' efforts in 1908. Donald, he argued, was "just a chip off the old block." He has paid "you starvation wages and most of you have borned and raised here and he is a God." But "I know he has stretched you all out, cut your wages, then tell you he was not making anything." His paternalistic ways were "so the children would think he was a God and he could raise them up and work them to death before they were grown." Donald Comer drew the line. That fall he told his stockholders that if the union drive succeeded, "I am ready to liquidate."[19]

While Comer continued to believe all regulations could and should be made through code process, not in negotiations with his employees, workers across the South decided to take advantage of the federal promise of union legitimacy under Section 7a. In the General Textile Strike of 1934, twenty-three thousand of the thirty-five thousand Alabama mill workers walked out on their employers, closing twenty-eight of the forty mills in the state. The strike swept across the South, particularly the heart of the industry in the Carolina Piedmont, drawing more than two hundred thousand mill operatives into the national strike. One participant felt it to be "the closest thing to a revolution I've seen in this country." Facing stretch-outs, dramatic pay differentials as compared to New England mills, and disappointment in the failed results of the NRA promises, they breathed life into the weak promise of Section 7a and pushed the moribund United Textile Workers of America to back the regional general strike.[20]

In the '34 walkout, the Eufaula workers chose their boss, Donald Comer, over the textile workers' union. Over five thousand workers across Alabama signed an oath pledging their loyalty to Comer. Every family at the Cowikee Mill in Eufaula signed on with "100% confidence in your leadership and our appreciation for the many kindnesses shown us." Donald Comer, they affirmed, was "dealing always with us fair and square." Such letters, which smacked of a certain breathlessness and uniformity, seemed less like grassroots support for Comer than an orchestrated campaign by the mills to discredit the textile workers union. Beyond a doubt, any missing signatures on the letter would have been noted by management. It was well known that union supporters would be fired on the spot.[21]

As rumors of "flying squadrons" of union organizers, which served to draw workers together and share news across isolated villages during the strike, spread across Barbour County, the townspeople prepared. The sheriff, the chief of police, and the American Legion organized in an armed defense committee to keep the union men out of Eufaula. Authorities at Camp Benning denied their request for a machine gun, but they posted armed guards at the major entrances to town. Farmers, too, prepared to join for the battle. "If any outsider tries to come into this community," one farmer wrote, "you just blow your whistles and ring your bells and we farmers will unhitch our mules and get up our axe and hoe handles and join the fight wherever we are needed."[22]

Neither the flying squadrons nor the strike ever reached Eufaula. As a Eufaula worker put it, "We are proud to work for Mr. Donald Comer and there has never been a strike or any trouble in any of the mills. We would fight for him, not against him." Meanwhile, the taint of Section 7a had Mr. Donald questioning his commitment to the NRA: "Whatever rights southern industry is going to get and maintain is going to come as a result of political force and power rather than through the NRA."[23]

Workers at eight of the nine Comer mills had pledged their loyalty to management, but the Birmingham workers were all in for the strike. Comer took it personally. He lashed out at the textile workers' union; he blamed the New England textile industry for a conspiracy to starve the Southern industry of production by driving up wages; and he blamed Section 7a for meddling in the private world of labor-management relations. He thanked the cities who supported him during the "threatened invasion" and decried the "professional labor agitators" who were "not the least interested in any of the things they claim to be." He punished the Birmingham workers by paring back his famous recreation and social programs, and he relocated his management offices out of the city. "Such rare public displays of Comer's retaliation for perceived disloyalty," explained a local historian, "revealed that his paternalistic velvet glove was fortified with steel." Yet there were no mass firings or outwardly vicious actions against the strikers.[24]

The strike ended in a complete and bitter defeat. After three weeks, the striking mill workers throughout the South were driven back to work by the National Guard, a lack of support from other institutions in the villages, and vague federal promises that action would be taken on their behalf. They quickly discovered they were on their own. Even Section 7a, the much-vaunted federal guarantee of unionization, was all promise with no federal enforcement mechanisms. More than seventy-five thousand mill operatives ended up on blacklists. The scars were such that it was rarely mentioned again. When the rest of the nation erupted in waves of sit-down strikes a couple of years later, the textile workers stuck by their looms. The failure of the 1934 strike played no small role in dragging down the organizing of the South for the rest of the century and beyond.[25]

The '34 Textile Strike demonstrated the contradictory nature of the early New Deal giving more power to capital and making empty promises to workers. "While the rhetoric of the New Deal mobilized the South's poor to challenge local established authority in unprecedented numbers," writes one analyst of the strike, "the New Deal's political structure worked in the opposite direction, reinforcing the power of the South's economic elites." Framed another way by historian Kari A. Frederickson: "Southern conservatives supported early New Deal programs because they could control them and because they personally benefited from them." When that balance no longer worked, Southern elites, including Mr. Donald, resisted the enhanced power of the state under the New Deal.[26]

Comer's embrace of FDR's programs all but crumbled during what is often called "the second New Deal." When the Supreme Court found the NRA unconstitutional in the spring of 1935, it was clear from the national labor unrest that industrial relations still needed a discernable federal right to organize. Senator Robert Wagner of New York had the answer: the National Labor Relations Act (often called the "Wagner Act"). The new law included a genuinely enforceable right to organize, as well as rules and regulations for business and labor, and a federal board to oversee the unionization process. Roosevelt also pushed the Fair Labor Standards Act of 1938, which created a floor for wages and a ceiling on hours. The national equalization of minimum wages—through collective bargaining or minimum wages—Comer continued to see as a plot by New England mill owners to drive Southern mills out of business by doing away with the South's all-important wage differential. It was also one of the most dramatic reaches of federal authority in American history. Comer redoubled his call for federal leadership to assist in industry-wide self-regulation, not worker empowerment. Still, Senator Robert Wagner had to admit that the Comer mills were different. "Mr. Comer," the senator remarked, "if all employers were like you, we would not need this law I am sponsoring."[27]

Cotton ruled all other concerns in Barbour County and the rest of the Black Belt. Here, bales of cotton sit outside the compressor, waiting for storage and shipping at Dean & Moore Cotton Warehouse in Eufaula in the 1930s.

The strike and the turn of the New Deal toward more tangible working-class empowerment took Comer in an unexpected direction. Rather than fight, he deepened his commitment to paternalism through a new profit-sharing program that he called "Partnership with the People." He experimented with the program in the mid-1930s before applying it to his entire textile chain in October 1941. The first 5 percent of profits went directly to the shareholders, but after that, the remaining profits were shared: half of the remaining profits went to the shareholders and the other half was divided among the workers. The profits were delivered on top of the area's "going wage" for mill work. This meant an effective increase of 12.5 percent over the decade of the forties. Though formidable, if inflation, the massive increase in national wages after the war, and gains won by rising industrial unions in the United States are all taken into account, the effective increase was less impressive than it might have seemed.[28]

Whether desperate, foolish, or bold, the unions once again targeted Comer's enlightened paternalism after the war. As part of the CIO's 1946 "Operation Dixie," an attempt to bring the success of the industrial labor movement in the North down to the South after World War II, the textile union focused on the Avondale chain. As one union representative explained workers' attitudes: "They say they're sick and tired of being born in a Comer house, going to a Comer school, working in a Comer mill, being buried in a Comer cemetery. Right now they're scared of their bosses, but they want a C.I.O. union—not Comer's paternalism." Yet the unions once again found the Avondale chain to be "impregnable." Operation Dixie was largely one long humiliating litany of defeat for labor. The unions lost on religion; they lost on the CIO's commitment to racial equality; they lost on the CIO's association with Communism; they lost on the intransigence of local power structures; they lost on paternalism; they lost on the memory of '34; and perhaps more than anything, they lost on the history of Northerners coming down to tell Southerners what to do under the guise of a military-sounding "operation." For Southern textile workers to embrace the New Deal, argues the historian

Bryant Simon, would require them "to reinterpret history"—in particular, the part about African American political power, rights, and voting of the Reconstruction era.[29]

Donald Comer, as tall as he stood for his record of treating employees well, began to track much closer to the Southerners' larger relationship to federal power as the New Deal matured. In 1936, Roosevelt was reelected by between 87 to 97 percent of voters in Deep South states. Even for a one-party region, the numbers were extraordinary. As long as Roosevelt showed a certain "pragmatic forgetfulness with regard to racial matters," the alliance between the federal interventions and the South could survive. Many Southern Democrats were enraged by the union-enabling Wagner and the minimum-wage-setting Fair Labor Standards Acts, but by successfully wrestling key exemptions for agricultural and domestic workers from federal regulation, much of the Southern racial and agricultural order remained relatively untouched by the long arm of the New Deal. During World War II and afterward, when civil rights groups and urban Democrats advocated a Fair Employment Practices Committee to integrate American workplaces, they drew the line. Black people saw glimmers of a freedom in the New Deal, but Comer called workplace integration "one more Government control," which "means one step nearer state socialism." He then bolted the Democratic presidential ticket for the Republicans.[30]

The combination of benevolence and control in mill village paternalism reveals some of the deepest and most complex layers of the problems of American freedom. In its purest form, paternalistic employment selects the freedom to control, to determine, to dominate, to be the sovereign—the freedom to be the boss over the freedom of civic and political life of the workers and the nation. Such a bargain may—or may not—be a good deal for workers depending upon the situation. Undoubtedly, few workers in the closed world of Southside were anything but grateful to Donald Comer given the alternatives of tenant farming and less-generous mill work.

Textile workers and managers both used various family metaphors to describe mill life with such frequency that the most groundbreaking history of Southern textile life was titled *Like a Family*. On Southside, a father, a single master and decision maker, was substituted for the political participation of the workers over the larger national political process. The creation of the "semi-autarkic private estate" of the textile-mill-cum-household depended upon the subordination of all members of the household—wives, children, servants, wage earners—to the paterfamilias. In industrial paternalism, substitution of private decisions, however benevolent they might have been, deprived the public sphere of democratic debate. Emmanuel Kant called a government of paternalism—in which a leader "wants to make people happy in accord with his own concept of happiness"—the "greatest despotism" because it offered no actual political rights at all. The unfreedom of paternalism checked workers' ability to engage in the politics of civic life while maximizing the benevolent freedom of Donald Comer.[31]

Donald Comer may have been able to claim by the 1950s that "there is no 'wrong side of the tracks' today" at Eufaula's Southside or any of his mill towns, but that was true because of what *he* wanted. Fortunately for Eufaula, he generally wanted good things. Mill paternalism preserved Comer's freedom and autonomy, the control and sovereignty of the master, but a mastery rooted in the history of a family's control of the largest plantation and sharecropping operation in Barbour County. In fact, Southern paternalism was not simple benevolence, but a system grounded in the boss's access to everything from the courts to the police, newspapers, personal connections, and even the federal legislature. Not only did his shining example preserve Donald Comer's latitude to act as he wished, it also provided cover for other mill operators' significantly less responsible brand of industrial independence.[32]

Because of the charity, beneficence, even decency of Donald Comer, Franklin Delano Roosevelt's New Deal never really affected Southside. Yet because of places like the Cowikee Mill in Eufaula, the federal regulatory state also never fully came to places very much in need of the New Deal. As a result, the South remained the low-wage haven Comer sought, and the regional anti-statism and anti-unionism that remained endemic there presented a glaring vulnerability in the American class struggle. By offering the nation a region of low wages, low regulations, and low unionization rates, with as much freedom from the postwar industrial settlement as it could wrangle, the South contributed to the decline of the even modest levels of working-class political and economic power achieved in the North.

CHAPTER FIFTEEN

The Bourbon from Barbour

Trampled and battered like a city that's been taken by storm"—that's how American writer John Dos Passos described the impact of wartime production on the port of Mobile in 1943. On Pinto Island, just across the river from downtown Mobile, the wartime shipbuilding boom transformed the Alabama Dry Dock and Shipbuilding Company from a small repair operation into an enormous industrial city. The behemoth rose above the once sleepy port like an ungainly giant, with enormous steel hulls towering above murky waters, dwarfing the legions of workers busy cutting and joining steel brought down from Birmingham. Over thirty thousand men and women had enrolled in the workforce to build the massive Liberty ships and oil tankers that poured into the bay and out to theaters of war. The War Manpower Commission called it "the most congested shipyard center in the country."[1]

The area teemed with new people thrust into a confusing mix of inadequate housing, unfamiliar surroundings, new forms and organization of work, food shortages, bad health care, and negligible opportunities for recreation. Residents faced one of the highest rates of inflation of any city in the United States. But the pay was unquestionably good and the hours plentiful—when workers peered out from underneath a decade of economic depression, they saw opportunity and arrived in Mobile in droves.

Two months after Dos Passos made his comments, some four thousand white workers in Mobile, armed with pipes, tools, and clubs, descended upon Black workers. Shouting "get every one of them Niggers off this island," white workers began attacking scattering Black workers; some were caught and beaten, some thrown into the river, and some simply chose to dive into the river to avoid the wrath of the white mob. It took the United States Army, stationed at Brookley Field, to restore order. Nobody was killed, though fifty people were seriously injured. Black shipbuilders, fearing for their safety, refused to return to the job for weeks. The irony of racial violence during a global war against racial supremacy escaped few African Americans, many of whom saw themselves in a "Double V" campaign: victory over fascists abroad and white supremacy at home. But that was not happening in Mobile in May 1943.[2]

Mobile Bay was hardly an isolated event among the epidemic of race riots that same year. In Los Angeles white soldiers attacked Latinos in what became known as the Zoot Suit riots; another shipyard erupted with whites attacking Blacks in Beaumont, Texas; and Harlem faced two days of violence when a white police officer shot a Black soldier. The most horrific riot was in Detroit, where pressures like those in Mobile ended in the death of twenty-five African Americans and nine whites. It took six thousand federal troops to end the turmoil in Detroit. By the time the war was over, Eufaula, Alabama, too, would be engulfed in its own race riot.

The racial violence in Mobile came in response to a federal government order to hire twelve Black workers for skilled positions at the dry docks. The promotion stemmed from the most significant, and oddly tepid, federal interventions into race relations in generations: President Franklin Roosevelt's Executive Order 8802, launching the Fair Employment Practices Committee (FEPC). The agency's mission was to end "discrimination in the employment of workers in defense industries or government because of race, creed, color, or national origin."

The executive order did not come from Roosevelt's uniquely progressive vision of race relations, however, but as a response to widespread discontent over occupational segregation—especially in defense industries. A. Philip Randolph, the president of the Brotherhood of Sleeping Car Porters, the most powerful Black union in the country, threatened to have a mass protest of Black people descend on the nation's capital during a global war against Aryan supremacy. Less than a week before the march was to take place, the Roosevelt administration agreed, in June 1941, to create the FEPC in exchange for the march being called off. As Randolph declared, Roosevelt had signed the first executive order "on behalf of Negroes since the immortal Abraham Lincoln issued the Emancipation Proclamation in 1863." The march, postponed indefinitely to the consternation of many, finally happened a generation later at the Lincoln Memorial in 1963.[3]

Prior to FDR's order, seven thousand of the thirty thousand workers on the Mobile dry docks were Black, and not one held a skilled position. Under the auspices of the FEPC, one dozen Black workers were upgraded to skilled welder positions—an act that white workers perceived as an affront to the interlocking nexus of skill, craft, tradition, and white supremacy. With those twelve workers appearing to threaten the position of the twenty-three thousand white workers at the docks, white workers fought back without mercy to keep Black workers off the job. It was not just the FEPC, but the entire cluster of New Deal federal interventions on behalf of workers that had the shipyards in turmoil, including an interracial union organizing drive on the docks. If whites wanted to stop integration, then they had to stop federal authority—from the FEPC on down. Local powers won the stalemate as the War Manpower Commission recommended a defensive retreat. Officials ordered the Alabama Dry Docks to create segregated shipways for Black and white workers. In the Black shipways, the African American workers could have any job short of foreman. It was essentially the establishment of "separate but equal," but with more equality than that idea normally included.[4]

Though the FEPC was underfunded and highly controversial, it proved reasonably effectual in integrating much of defense production in the North, but the South remained steadfast in its resistance to workplace integration despite the efforts of the commission.

Similarly, the Supreme Court decision *Smith v. Allwright* (1944), which banned the all-white primary, stirred white Southern anger against federal power. Like so many federal interventions for racial equality in the South, the FEPC and *Smith* may not have been powerful enough to create fundamental change, but their existence was enough to strike fear in the heart of white supremacy. Together they restaged scenes of hysteria over federal intervention reminiscent of the great Reconstruction melodrama.[5]

As it had been since Reconstruction, the core of racial politics was not a fear of social equality, but a fear of "Negro domination," of having white freedom stripped by the lustful power of African Americans. As a self-described "War Worker" wrote to the governor, we "will have the negroes ruling, or fighting, (or *both*) before many more years pass by!" A. P. Randolph's March on Washington Movement "is planning to 'take over' as soon as they get strong enough, and they think that will be about the time the World War is over." This is "NO joke, that they are planning to take over the top jobs, and offices in our Government, and rule the whites, or kill them!" As it is, he explained, white people are "almost hourly insulted by the negroes, pushed around by them, and often slapped, cursed and knocked down by their overbearing, superior attitudes, you would understand how serious the situation is becoming, and see that the South does not vote themselves out of *their* freedom. The negroes are not satisfied with Equality, they demand superiority, and are going to fight for it if necessary.... The next war will be the whites['] fight for their freedom from the negroes!"[6]

Trying to juggle the anxieties of the wartime state, the local interests of people like the "war worker," and taming even the limited racial vision of the New Deal fell upon the shoulders of the governor: Eufaula's own Chauncey Sparks. Not all white supremacists are snarling, cross-burning, night-riding, and robe-wearing. Some, perhaps the most threatening, are bespectacled, patrician, and business-like. For men like Sparks, transgressions of the racial order were not to be met with physical terror, which he opposed, but with a calm, firm tutelage that could aggravate, even corner, the most committed civil rights champion. The core elements of white supremacy—segregation, voting restrictions, and occupational discrimination—remained sacrosanct for Sparks, but he evinced a paternalistic vision of separate racial progress. Race relations were built mostly on local custom and law, and his job was to stop federal intervention into the sovereignty of local affairs.[7]

Nicknamed the "Barbour Bourbon" in the press and by his peers, Chauncey Sparks took office just four months prior to the white riot in Mobile. Thickly built, high-cheeked, square-jawed, and flush-faced, Sparks wore the vest of his three-piece suit tightly wrapped around his barrel-like build. A lawyer, judge, and farmer in Barbour County, he had a house on Broad Street among the other mansions of Eufaula, but his did not speak of antebellum grandeur. His home, like the man, was all business and no sentiment: modest, low-slung, yet set unambiguously among the most affluent residences. He never lost himself in the antebellum fever dreams that many of his neighbors seemed to enjoy. Patient, hardworking, and meticulous, he spent most of his political career exercising fiscal prudence by opposing sales and income taxes, limiting salaries of elected officials, and fighting for balanced budgets. Not a popular figure, he received less than a quarter of the statewide vote in the Democratic Primary during his first run for governor in 1938. When he ran again in 1942, the only thing that kept an economic liberal out of office was the sudden passing of the extraordinarily popular Bibb Graves, which opened the opportunity for Sparks to win his long-shot campaign. In 1942, Sparks's conservatism squared off against one other candidate of significance, a newcomer progressive populist named Jim Folsom. But "Big Jim" had yet to earn the name recognition he would soon achieve in the postwar era. Despite stern speeches that lacked political fire, Sparks won.[8]

The Eufaulan never fired the imagination of Alabama's masses, but he promised to "keep the federal government's nose out of Alabama business" and preserve "absolute segregation." Otherwise, he was out of step—a businessman, banker, attorney, and no-nonsense politician in an age of reform that mobilized the people against these interests. In a world of larger-than-life political characters in the New Deal era, Sparks was a defender of separate but equal—with a greater commitment to the equal side of the equation than most of his peers, including very large increases in funding of Black universities. "The Negro should be given his civil rights," he argued in his paternalist mode, "which includes the right to vote, when he is qualified, on the same basis as the white man." He believed "the interests of the two races are identical"—living side by side in separate spheres. In an era of class-based populism, however, he stood firmly on the side of the economic elite. In an era when business was under attack, he championed the economic powers of the state, the "Big Mules," as the industrial and the planter classes were called. He was so frugal, some might say miserly, that he charged rent to his niece who served as the hostess for the lifelong bachelor while living in the governor's mansion. His biggest accomplishment was taming the state debt. Despite his abiding conservatism, he could not buck the trends of the era and ended up governing as a bit of an economic liberal during his governorship.[9]

The Barbour Bourbon was part of a regional pattern of Southern Democrats who simultaneously remained the political "backbone" of the national Democratic Party while struggling against federal intervention that might threaten the Southern racial and economic hierarchy. An epoch-defining split in the Democratic Party had just begun. As Mississippi's circuit court judge Thomas Pickens Brady wrote, the "white Jeffersonian Democrat" had been abandoned by "Iscariotic" Northern liberals. The divergence began in 1936 when "the great Democratic river was beginning to split into two forks" as fears of federal encroachment on white sovereignty began to be called "nationalization." Charles Wallace Collins noted in his infamous postwar tract *Whither the Solid South?* that "the whole Negro problem is infected with the deadly virus of stateism," which he regarded as "a broad scheme for national planning which, if it became the law of the land, would nationalize all civil rights and effectively deprive the States of their republican form of government." As the head of the Southern States Industrial Council, a group interested in fighting federal wage regulations and occupational integration to keep Southern labor as cheap and pliable as possible, put it, "We, both Democrats and Republicans, are now reaping the whirlwind of our association with the

New Deal." Sparks, the ever-sober white supremacist, planted his feet against the political whirlwinds as best he could. A party man, and not a Dixiecrat, he nonetheless tried to maintain his paternalistic vision for race relations constant and far from federal power.[10]

To the degree that there was a single theme in the South's relationship to the New Deal, it was the dance of accepting federal relief while blocking federal interference in local affairs. Many militant segregationists enjoyed and encouraged the spread of the Democrats' federal largesse into the South but would then threaten to bolt from the party of their Jacksonian ancestors when things got too close to touching questions of white supremacy. Without the New Deal, the South languished in poverty; but with it the mythological threat of "black rule" loomed. Yet for Northern liberals, there could be no New Deal without the support of Southern Democrats. As the historian Richard Hofstadter put it, the World War II–era Democratic Party "thus finds itself in the anomalous position of being a party of 'liberalism,' whose achievements are subject to veto by a reactionary faction." It is no surprise then, that the FEPC was passed by executive order, not legislative process, and remained temporary as a result.[11]

The Double V campaign for African American emancipation from Jim Crow during the war thus had its opposite campaign: white supremacists' victory abroad needed to be matched with a fight against "totalitarian" incursions into their freedom at home. The wartime state generated a demand to return to the nation's mythic roots in "limited government, state sovereignty, and white supremacy." As Birmingham columnist John Temple Graves put it in some remarkably twisted logic, the war against fascism was not a war against white supremacy but actually "a war for state's rights, of the right of individual lands not to be invaded by outsiders, not to be dictated to or aggressed against." For many white Southerners, this was a fight against domestic totalitarianism, in which tyrannical federal powers would dictate how inferior races would be handled. If the New Deal was really the new tyranny of state socialism, then, as many claimed in the confused hothouse of wartime letters and speeches, the FEPC was the Gestapo. In short, this was a war for white freedom.[12]

Governor Chauncey Sparks may have been a condescending and paternalistic segregationist, but he was neither afraid nor above taking his messages directly to Black audiences, whom he believed would support his plans for segregated uplift. At the annual Founder's Day celebration at Booker T. Washington's Tuskegee Institute, Governor Sparks looked out at his audience of Black students and faculty and dismissed the question of civil rights out of hand. "There should be no race question in the sense it is often used, which would mean, I think, a political issue, or an economic combat." Alabamians needed to forget conflict and turn to the facts of "a definite, fixed and unchanging policy of relationships which would remove the so called problem forever from our political, economic and social life." Once white and Black understood that they belonged in separate spheres, they would be "freed from strife and jealousies, petty conceits and ambitions and make for the two races happy home indeed." The principles he based that happy future on were "first, absolute racial segregation; second, independent racial development."[13]

His demands for reinforcing segregation came with calls for the end of lynching and mob violence, while simultaneously firing the most aggressive shots across the bow at any "outside agitators" who would dare try to enter the realm of Alabama's racial politics. For most Southern white leaders, Jim Crow segregation was forward-thinking, allowing each race a place to flourish in the "natural" racial order. To tamper with that, especially through federal authority, was dangerous folly and an affront to Alabama's right to rule its own affairs. Publicly, Sparks tossed the word "nigger" around with impunity and believed that slavery saved the Black race. Yet he also denied that race had anything to do with the events at the dry docks in Mobile. For Governor Sparks, white supremacy was just that: calmly understanding everyone's place in the natural order. "White supremacy does not mean injustice, exploitation, unfair discrimination, but means the preservation of that influence and that guiding hand which has enabled both the white race and the Negro race to advance thus far."[14]

If the federal government would stop interfering with what Sparks called "rainbow ends and butterflies" such as desegregation, then

Alabama could readily maintain its peace and prosperity. The FEPC showed that the New Deal, and American liberalism more generally, was falling into the hands of fanatical national planners, Communists, negro organizations, labor agitators, and a motley crew of fellow travelers hell-bent on destroying "the South's color lines, segregations laws and sacred traditions," as the editor of the pro-business *Alabama* magazine put it in 1944. The politics of Reconstruction echoed on, returning this time in the form of New Dealers and wild-eyed leftists—with "Communists" increasingly standing in as a generic term for anyone who stood against white freedom in the South.[15]

Two federal incursions shaped Sparks's fight with the federal authority. The first was the Fair Employment Practices Committee's efforts to integrate production, such as those at the Alabama Dry Docks; the second was the end of the all-white primary under *Smith*. The developments—one by the regulatory state, and one by the Supreme Court—augured the start of a revolutionary future in civil rights during this, the so-called forgotten years of the civil rights movement. In both cases, Governor Sparks's basic position was: "When the government at Washington, thru its executive, or judicial branches, undertakes to force upon a State a standard which it does not and will not accept, it is a denial of freedom."[16]

Sparks had a clear understanding of how the natural order was supposed to work, and it was "influences from outside" that threatened what he imagined as the "mutual benefit" and "friendly intercourse which bespeaks better conditions for both races." It was not outside white and Black demagogues that he ultimately feared, but federal power. Few things bothered him more than the meddling of the FEPC that ignited the unrest in Mobile. "Another thing that was devised by the altruistic thinkers is the Fair Employment Practices Committee," he explained to the Kiwanis Club, "a thing as hostile to the genius of American government as anything that has been thought up and put into practice within its whole history." Then he twisted centuries of slave-based labor by claiming it was the federal government that was making race a matter in the workplace where previously it had not been an issue. "Is the color of a man's face to be the basis of his employment? Have we no right to consider fitness, character, experience, ability? Are we taking away from those who employ the right to screen their employees, the right to select the best?"[17]

The FEPC stirred the ghost of Reconstruction, rattled fears of sectional sovereignty, and made incursions into the sanctity of the right to manage. "For the Bourbons" like Sparks, writes the historian Glenn Feldman, FDR's Executive Order "was the ultimate offense" to their power, freedom, and prerogative. Most obviously, it challenged the entire idea of Black inferiority and their second-class position on the job, but it also attacked a core freedom that business people enjoyed: to manage the enterprise without regard to social harm. The federal agency had a tiny budget, little power, and not much in the way of staff, but the very idea of the FEPC led to histrionics. The Bourbon editor of the *Alabama Magazine* charged that the FEPC was the product of "fanatical New Deal 'master-planners,' Communists, negro organizations, labor agitators and a motley crew of fellow travelers" out to "stamp out the South's color lines, segregation laws and sacred traditions."[18]

When the managing editor of New York's liberal *P.M.* newspaper criticized Chauncey Sparks's response to events in Mobile, the governor fired back, "Alabama is determined to use all available force to prevent riots. We have had none of any consequence and we would not have any but for influences over which we have no control. If self-seeking politicians, misguided philanthropists and outside influences would quit trying to regulate matters which are entirely local, we would have no future difficulty. We are undertaking to forestall any new disorders by emphasizing among ou[r]selves and to the outside world that all races in Alabama shall have justice, education and a square deal." Everything "shall continue to remain so in peace and accord if we can be let alone and zoot-minded propagandists and reformers do not mislead, misguide, and misinform."[19]

For African Americans, in contrast, the "outside agitation" of the federal government was a glimmer of hope, a lever to increase their power in the fight against employers and local and state governments. This, Sparks believed, was a tragedy: "It is unfortunate that the Negro seeks relief thru the Federal government rather than his own State government." In so doing, they raised the possibility of shifting the race question beyond local white control, challenging the freedoms and power that they had long relied upon. "Such practices and habits on his part further estrange the relationship and make it difficult for the two races to get together upon any grounds of mutual understating and helpfulness. Such things engender an ill will, an underlying suspicion and jealousy, instead of a friendly, good neighborly attitude, one toward the other with a mixed determination that each shall have a rightful place in the economic and civil life of his State." He called African Americans' turn toward federal power "foolish," and he drew a line: "We are not going to be browbeaten, or highjacked into the acceptance of something we know is harmful." The threat of the FEPC, therefore, was not simply about the racial order but a challenge to the sovereignty, freedom, and economic power of the white elite.[20]

An order by the United States Army to end discrimination and segregation at recreational areas like exchanges and theaters at Montgomery's Maxwell Field shifted the struggle with the federal government. The overriding of Alabama's racial system was ready-made political theater: federal power not just demanding skilled jobs but mandating that white people work side by side with Black people as equals. The Bourbon from Barbour wasted no time telegramming President Roosevelt in protest—as well as managing to get his telegram reprinted in newspapers throughout the South. He also reached out to the Alabama congressional delegation, all of whom lined up in opposition to the integration of the air base, helping to make him the point man on resistance to federal intervention. As former Governor Frank M. Dixon, a militantly outspoken segregationist, wrote to Sparks, "Our situation as Southern Democrats is rapidly becoming absolutely intolerable," but he wanted Sparks to know "how greatly I approve of your courageous stand and how deeply I sympathize with you." The political effrontery continued without an actual plan, while FDR chose not to respond publicly. White Alabama won, however, as Maxwell Field rescinded the order.[21]

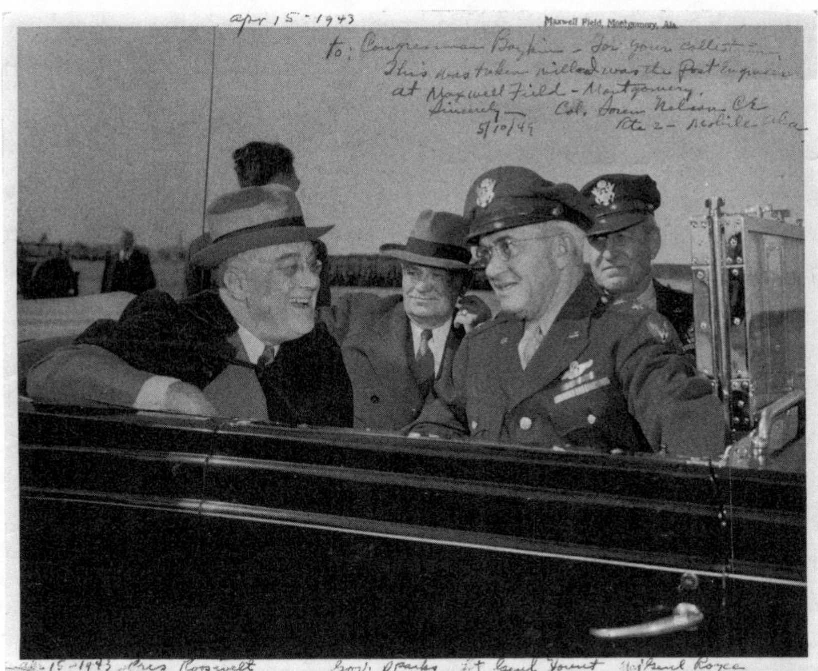

President Franklin Roosevelt visits Maxwell Field in May 1943 with Barbour County's Governor Chauncey Sparks with him in the back seat. Sparks fought workplace integration under the FEPC, including the integration of the federal airfield. Rosa Parks later cited her time working at Maxwell as an example of how integration, if allowed, could work. Roosevelt refused to move boldly on race relations, however, for fear of losing a central element in the Democratic coalition.

Like the FEPC, the landmark court decision *Smith v. Allwright* (1944), which ended the segregated primary, challenged local white control of the political process. Should all other obstacles to voting fail, the whites-only primary served as the last stop in white political control. If African Americans somehow managed to learn to read, prove they could do so to local registrars, buy property, pay poll taxes, and keep the necessary records required to vote, they then faced one last, enormous obstacle: the all-white primary.

Lonnie Smith, an African American dentist in Houston, sued his county election officials to win the right to vote in what had been a whites-only party primary process. He won the argument that his

Fifteenth and Fourteenth Amendment rights were being violated because state authority was delegated to the private affairs of a political party. The decision threw into turmoil the Southern system of keeping the nomination process restricted to white candidates—in a region in which many counties had Black majorities (Barbour County was still 55.5 percent African American)—and began what some on both sides of the struggle called the Second Reconstruction.[22]

The Bourbon from Barbour embraced the obvious workaround. *Smith v. Allwright*, he argued, "permits qualified Negro voters to participate in primary elections when conducted at public expense and out of public funds." Yet there was plenty of room left to maneuver, as, he calculated, the decision "leaves with the states the right and authority to determine [other] qualifications" for voting. Just as the Fifteenth Amendment could be subverted by a variety of the restrictions on voting other than race, they just had to come up with types of qualifications for voting other than skin color. "If it does the South can adapt itself as it will do, in my opinion, and that without directions from Washington, be giving the right to vote to all qualified, whether white or Black, and at the same time preserve party integrity. If it does not, the decision is a blow to friendly relations between the races in the South, and bodes ill." By 1948, Sparks compared the Supreme Court's civil rights rulings as acts of a Stalinist "Polit Bureau." In the face of the *Smith* decision, Sparks lost much of his cool-tempered paternalism and became what one commentator called the "angry jutting chin of regional defensiveness."[23]

The path around *Smith v. Allwright* took the shape of the Boswell Amendment, named after State Representative E. C. "Bud" Boswell. This addition to the state constitution made the capacity to "understand and explain" a selection of the Constitution the requirement for registering to vote. Key to the Boswell Amendment was placing voting rights as far away from federal authority as possible and in the subjective control of the local registrar. County-level control made it a perfect foil to the Supreme Court's intervention. After all, Jim Crow was hardly a uniform system of top-down state rule but rested upon the firm foundation of local action and belief in white supremacy.

As Governor Sparks explained to a constituent who was upset about violations of Jim Crow, "Our segregation laws are few." Jim Crow depended upon what one historian accurately calls the "radical localism of white supremacy." Boswell promised to take advantage of that localism. When Sparks explained in 1946 that the problem was "not racial intolerance" when it came to voting, it was the Supreme Court's "sectional intolerance," he meant tolerance for local forms of white freedom to decide who should and could vote.[24]

The Boswell Amendment passed both the legislature and the Alabama electorate, with nearly two-thirds of the counties voting in favor, a vote bolstered by rock-solid support in the Black Belt. Enacted in 1946, it launched another volley in the endless back-and-forth of federal power and state/local resistance. A federal judicial panel found in 1949 that the amendment violated the Fifteenth Amendment because its implementation discriminated on the basis of race. The Supreme Court upheld the decision. In 1951, the Alabama legislature countered again by adopting a voter qualification law that returned the idea that voters be able to read and write any section of the Constitution, as well as be of good character, and swear that they were not part of any group or agency devoted to overthrowing the government. This law, however, included a key inoculation against further federal encroachment: a uniform questionnaire that allegedly evened the playing field for all applicants. The law stood until the federal government again countered in 1965 with the Voting Rights Act.[25]

The federal squeeze on local and state sovereignty during the war—the FEPC and *Smith v. Allwright*—foreshadowed the future more than transformed the present. Sparks managed to navigate these obstacles, mostly by deepening a commitment to localism in order to thwart federal power and national attention. The re-creation of separate but equal on the dry docks and placing power in the hands of the county registrars in reaction to the Supreme Court's ending of the all-white primary affirmed the agility of localism to subvert the power of the federal government.

The distance left to travel, however, was revealed on the Fourth of July in Eufaula in 1945, partway between VE Day and the dropping of the atomic bombs on Japan. State pressure was building, uniformed Black soldiers began to return home, patriotic fervor was running high, and the postwar future remained unknown. In Eufaula, a mysterious riot that the *Pittsburgh Courier* called "one of the most serious racial situations in America" showed that World War II had changed everything except the "quotidian experience of white supremacy in Alabama."[26]

According to police, Ethel Luck, an eighteen-year-old white employee at the Cowikee textile mill, walked to her job at the mill on a country road and regularly passed by the home of Peter Paul Hall, an eighteen-year-old African American man (whom the press reported as being twenty-four). On the way home from her night shift at six thirty in the morning, police claimed that Peter Paul Hall attacked and raped her twice and then held her for several hours. He then allegedly forced her to walk about a mile to the Little Chewalla creek, where he drowned her at one o'clock that afternoon. The next day, they arrested Hall at four in the morning, at which point the police claimed, as they always did in such cases, that he "readily confessed the crime."[27]

The mill workers then "organized to beat all negroes" in town that night, and whites terrorized the Black population of Eufaula. The African American press reported that "gangs of whites hunted down, attacked and drove all negroes from the streets of downtown Eufaula Saturday night as an aftermath of the arrest and alleged confession of Peter Paul Hall...on charges of criminal assault and drowning of an 18-year-old white girl." The military police from Fort Benning and the state highway patrol rushed to help maintain order. The Black press reported that "as many as fifty Negroes have been leaving nightly" for fear of violence. "At the rate that colored people are leaving town," one Eufaulan reported, "there won't be any here soon." A curfew was established, and the state police remained a constant presence between July 5, when Hall was arrested, and his trial on July 17.[28]

Authorities wasted little time in arranging for Hall's trial less than two weeks after his arrest. Governor Sparks conferred with local officials, who requested adequate protection from the state for the prisoner in order to thwart a lynch mob. Hall had to be returned to Eufaula from Montgomery for indictment and arraignment. They used five cars to hide him and confuse the mobs so as to get him in and out of Eufaula. On the day of the trial, they had fifty or sixty patrolmen to protect Hall just long enough for him to receive the death sentence in a three-hour trial from an all-white jury, less than two weeks after he was arrested. "Eufaula Negro Rape Slayer Is to Die in Chair," screamed the papers. We know that the story ends with eighteen-year-old Peter Paul Hall being killed by the the state the next month, but whatever else may have happened in the summer of July 1945 remains mysterious.[29]

By the middle of the twentieth century, a version of modern conservatism had just begun to take root based on the tensions between local and federal power. Racial conservatism and economic conservatism became linked to the point of being a single laissez-faire, freedom-loving ideology known simply as conservatism. Federal intervention of any kind—whether on lynching, segregation, voting, or the regulation of the labor market—constituted a threat upon the sovereignty of a free people. And the New Deal, however necessary its dollars may have been, was an overreach of the long arm of the state to rob "the people" of their rights and freedoms. "If the Federal government would allot us what is our share, and not tie to it unacceptable requirements," argued Governor Chauncey Sparks, "it would render a better service. I am unwilling for the South, or my State, to surrender its independence for a mess of pottage. Unless Washington is willing to allot with no strings attached, I prefer that my people, thru the proverbial sweat of the brow, earn their living and achieve that character of civilization which the Lord of hosts ordained."[30]

Reconstruction memories bordered on a "syndrome," in the words of one historian, based on "an almost manic concern for states' rights, local autonomy, hyperindividualism, an unfettered—almost fetishistic—view of freedom, political conservatism, sectional pride, traditional values, religion, and gender roles (in fact, reverence for all things traditional), pride in the white race's leadership and achievements, disdain for hyphenated Americanism in favor of ethnic, racial, and cultural homogeneity." The terms of freedom and subjugation orbited not slavery, which only lasted three decades in Barbour County, but the search for cheaper labor, Northern capital, and above all, white control of the power of the franchise. As Alabama family memoirist George Packer wrote, the federal government became "something alien" and "a threat to freedom and custom."[31]

Two figures suggested that a volatile future was beyond the grasp of Sparks's moderate segregationist politics. When Ms. Recy Taylor, a twenty-four-year-old African American woman, sharecropper, and mother, was walking home from an evening service at Rock Hill Holiness Church in Abbeville, just down the road from Barbour County, she and her companions were stalked by a green Chevrolet packed with six white men carrying knives and a gun. The men proceeded to gang-rape her. The NAACP sent a young woman down to investigate the assault, and Alabama became a focus of attention from a wide array of left-progressive forces. The NAACP representative was named Rosa L. Parks, and her refusal to give up a seat in a segregated bus in Montgomery a decade later would ignite ten years of tumultuous civil rights activism that raged well beyond the paternalist ethos of Chauncey Sparks.[32]

The other figure was an anxious, gaunt, twenty-six-year-old war veteran from Barbour County whom Sparks accepted as a protégé in the business of state government. That young man, who learned to calculate the political angles of everything, ended up squaring off against the coming civil rights movement and the federal power that aligned with it. He would ride the tidal wave of resentment against the federal government to the Alabama governor's mansion. Sparks's new appointee was a young man named George Corley Wallace.

BOOK FOUR

Democracy

CHAPTER SIXTEEN

The Fightin' Judge

OTHER PEOPLE HAD FRIENDS, George Wallace liked to remark, but he had cronies. Oscar Harper was one such crony. During Wallace's 1958 run for the governor's office, he and Harper drove all around the Yellowhammer State in Harper's shiny Cadillac. Wallace had already exhausted his battered old Ford on the campaign trail, but he wasted no time making sure everyone knew that Harper's Caddy wasn't *his*. "Now what kind of car is that anyway?" he'd say, feigning a sort of populist astonishment at his arrival in such a fine automobile. "This is a nice car," he'd say, "but it isn't my car." Loaning out the Cadillac and driving George around was more than just an innocent favor between two Barbour County boys. While Wallace campaigned for governor, Harper soaked up business contacts and state contracts as they stopped at diners, crossroads, grocery store openings, and civic clubs across the state.

Shabbily dressed and nervously chewing on his cigar, Wallace chattered ceaselessly with Harper about his big plans and the many small ideas required to achieve them. His sweaty porcelain face framed by his dark oil-soaked hair was never so animated as when he was talking about his favorite subject. "George Wallace was born thinking about politics," Harper recalled. "That's the first thing that enters his mind in the morning. It's what he's thinking about at night.

And I believe he dreams about politics. He couldn't have been knee-high to a june bug when he knew he was going to spend his life as a politician."[1]

Press secretary Bill Jones, another crony, echoed the same idea. "Wallace went to bed thinking about votes," he said, "and he woke up the next morning thinking about votes." Another Alabama pol marveled at his drive. "George can out politick any man all day long. When I'm through politicking I like to go home, I like my likker, I like my woman. George just goes on politicking right through the day." Perhaps the truest thing ever said about the governor's capacity as a political animal came from his adviser John Kohn. "If George had parachuted into the Albanian countryside in the spring of 1962," he said about a man who invoked his anti-Communism regularly and reflexively, "he would have been head of a collective farm by the fall, a member of the Communist Party by mid-winter, on his way to the district party meeting as a delegate by the following year, and a member of the Comintern in two or three years."[2]

For George Wallace, the values didn't matter, the principles didn't matter, the party didn't matter. The politics and the votes—they mattered. That was the central fact of Wallace's life. Policy, program, platform, and personality all derived from the single animating fact that George Wallace's heart and veins pumped politics and little else. When anything one might call principle clashed with his hunger for votes, his drive for political power almost always won.

"Moderation," he claimed, "was political suicide." Wallace based his tactics, he explained later in life, on giving "the people something to dislike and hate." He mobilized voters by creating "a straw man for them to fight." He believed enemies were inherent in all politics. "They'd rather be against something than for something," he explained. His brand of populism was very different from that of Barbour County's Reuben Kolb in the 1890s, whose Farmers' Alliance promised a progressive populism that could unite the poor against the economic elite. In contrast, Wallace's conservative populism worked against a dyad of enemies: the African American people below and the federal government above. His real political magic was to blur the lines between those two antipathies with his shrewd capacity to redirect overt racism toward safer terrain: hostility toward the federal government that threatened white freedom. Being against the feds rather than directly against African Americans gave him more latitude, more deniability, more appeal, and more electoral power—while still capturing the vote of the most diehard racist. It was the rediscovery of an old formula, an echo of the demand for racialized sovereignty that began in Barbour County when invading Europeans stole Creek lands.[3]

George Wallace was born in 1919 just a couple of miles from the site where the blood-soaked Alabama militia emerged from the swamps of the Pea River after terminating the Creek Indians' final stand against white intrusion on their land in 1836. His anxious, unrelenting political drive began in the tiny hamlet called Clio tucked down in the southwest corner of Barbour County. The political reporter Theodore White called Clio a "seedy, mournful village," and the hardscrabble town in the wiregrass region was a long way from the mansion-studded streets of Eufaula—a town itself already beginning to look back to fading glories rather than forward to a hopeful future.[4]

George Wallace's entire youth and young adulthood were marked by the declining fortunes of Alabama's farmers and sharecroppers. Following the economic boom during and just after the Great War, cotton and other commodity prices kept falling. And falling. For much of the Deep South, the Great Depression began in the early 1920s—well before the stock market crash of 1929. Anyone trying to plant cotton then was pretty much getting robbed. Poverty, disease, and illiteracy defined their world. One survey of Barbour County revealed that 85 percent of all school children had hookworm. Others had the combination of diarrhea, dementia, and dermatitis known as pellagra, a disease caused by poor diet and vitamin deficiency. The disease had all but disappeared during the booming war years but came back with the hard times of the twenties and the thirties. The area was bleak for poor whites, and it was close to hopeless for African Americans. Although the Wallaces were much better off than many of their neighbors, their mortgages ran up while the quality of their properties ran down.[5]

Scrappy as they come, Wallace learned to fight with his fists early on. He slugged it out in makeshift boxing rings—his drunken father often pitted his boys against each other right in the living room. George C. would fight anybody, swinging at kids way above his meager weight class. As a teenager, he would fight during halftime at the Barbour County High School basketball games, and he twice won the bantamweight division of the state Golden Gloves competition. Even though he was a scrawny five feet seven inches, he also played football, leading his team as quarterback. Even in football he demonstrated an intuitive sense of how resentment motivated people. When Clio was scheduled to line up against a much more powerful team from Troy, Alabama, he huddled his boys together and read them a letter he had obtained from their opponents that made fun of the Clio team as rubes and hayseeds. He hoped by sharing the letter his team would get angry enough to deliver the underdogs to victory. After they lost, everyone found out that George Wallace had written the letter himself.[6]

He also learned about political fights. Early on he started making social connections, mercilessly pumping people's arms, and championing the cause of local politicians. "The most exciting night of my life," he recalled, was watching the mysteries of vote tallies accumulate on the chalkboard at the age of nine, when he got to stay up until midnight to watch his grandfather win his race for probate judge. At the age of sixteen, when he found out that the state senate would hire interns for the summer of 1935, he wrote every senator and then drove up to Montgomery to lobby them all in person. "Hello, my name's George Wallace," he would say, "I'm from Barbour County, and I sure would appreciate your vote for page." His relentless push won him the job. When he arrived at the state capitol, still a teenager, he stood on the historic star embedded in the marble marking the spot where Jefferson Davis once took the oath of office as president of the Confederacy. A prophet of his own ambitions, on that spot he swore to himself that he'd be governor one day.[7]

Capable of greater stamina and determination than his opponents, he could bring down more-powerful adversaries in rings both pugilistic and political. "Bigger opponents were often over-confident and lazy," he recalled about fighting; "a certain amount of pain must be expected and tolerated; opponents must be dispatched without mercy; and fighters must be prepared to do whatever is necessary to win." As much as he liked fighting, however, he didn't like World War II much. He served in the Pacific after finishing his law degree from the University of Alabama in 1942. He refused officer training because he figured there would be more voters who were enlisted men after the war than those who were officers—a tactic that eventually served him well. After nine dangerous missions flying over Japan as a flight engineer, he ultimately refused further training or flight assignments as the war came to an end. He was spent. Exhausted, anxious, and on the edge of a breakdown, Wallace convinced the air force to let him go. The military doctors noted his "anxiety attacks, anorexia and loss of weight," and in December 1945 returned him to civilian life.[8]

He rushed home to his wife, Lurleen, a working-class girl he fell for just before enlisting in the war. Marrying George at the age of sixteen, Lurleen would bear the burden of her husband's ambitions, living in an array of cramped dingy boarding houses and apartments while taking care of their four kids with very little money. While Lurleen was alone with the domestic drudgery, George spent all of his time and attention roaming the county, and later the state, building political relationships and hunting up votes. His neglect of his family, compounded by a number of extramarital affairs, made the 1950s a brutal time for young Lurleen. Things would get so bad that she—a poor girl from the Deep South—would file for divorce by the end of the decade. Wallace, probably seeing the cost of the divorce to his political career, promised to shape up—and did. Lurleen retracted her suit.[9]

Meantime, with the war over, George Wallace turned to his one true love—Alabama politics. After a stint as assistant attorney general, a patronage position he obtained compliments of former governor and Eufaulan Chauncey Sparks, he jumped at a chance to run for the Alabama House of Representatives in 1946. Lurleen typed political letters from their cramped little apartment, while George, who didn't yet have a car, hitchhiked around Barbour County in search of votes. Walking and begging rides allowed him to connect with everyone in the area face-to-face with his relentless smile and handshake. He won and proceeded to pursue his position in the legislature with the same drive, introducing dozens of bills and ignoring his family while reveling in a political world soaked in cigar smoke, bourbon, race, and the fight for the little (white) guy.[10]

"The two things that had the greatest impact in my life," Wallace remembered about the formation of his political outlook, "were Reconstruction and the Depression." In Wallace's political imagination, the global economic crisis and the myth of the Lost Cause were both periods of ruin. "My father used to tell me," Wallace recalled in the 1980s, "that poverty and illiteracy in the South resulted from the way we were treated after the war when they burned the schools down, burned the railroads, just desecrated the South. We are just now overcoming the effects of that tyranny and of the iniquitous Thaddeus Stevens, who wanted nothing but vengeance." Reconstruction had become a ghost story, a fiction haunting the freedom dreams of white people; but the Depression was a real economic calamity. To avoid these dual disasters, Wallace would try to help the people economically while fighting the federal government's intrusion in Alabama's future.[11]

After World War II, the federal ship of state began a long, wide turn toward rights-based liberalism. President Harry Truman, citing FDR's "Freedom from Fear," launched the Committee on Civil Rights. The committee's report presented a remarkably sophisticated understanding of the tension between local white freedom and federal power. Freedom did not come from the absence of government, the report explained, but through the assurance that federal authority would defend people against the freedom of others. "Bills of rights restrain government from abridging individual civil liberties," the report argued, but the time was right for the government to play an active role in restraining the freedom to dominate. It was "government itself by sound legislative policies" that "protects citizens against the aggressions of others seeking to push their freedoms too far." The title of the report derived from the Declaration of Independence's recognition of the need for central government: "To secure these rights, *governments are instituted among men*," it said, emphasizing the need for strong and forceful federal government.[12]

Truman demanded that Congress implement key parts, but hardly all, of the report's recommendations. Anti-lynching, the end of the poll tax, a permanent Fair Employment Practices Committee, and the end of segregation in interstate transport all topped his list. The Southern press attacked Truman: legislators convened committees and reports, a delegation of Southern governors met with the head of the Democratic National Committee, and Governor Strom Thurmond of South Carolina showed the press the empty spot on the wall where Truman's portrait once hung. "We have reached a turning point in the long history of this country's efforts to guarantee freedom and equality to all citizens," Truman declared before ten thousand members of the NAACP gathered at the Lincoln Memorial. "There is much that state and local governments can do in providing positive safeguards for civils rights. But we cannot, any longer, await the growth of a will to action in the slowest state of the most backward community." It was a Southern Democratic apostasy—from a Missourian no less. The national Democratic Party was thrown into question as a party of white Southerners. So, many of them decided if not to totally abandon the party of Jefferson and Jackson, then to rattle its foundation something fierce.[13]

No sooner did George Wallace join the state legislature than he also managed to become an alternate delegate to the national Democratic Convention in Philadelphia. It was there, in 1948, that he declared himself "unalterably opposed to the Nomination of Harry S. Truman and the so-called 'Civil Rights Program.'" Given that most of his career would orbit around the question of federal power and civil rights, it was a fitting launch to his fledgling national career. At the convention, Hubert H. Humphrey, the liberal mayor of

Minneapolis, rose to make an impassioned plea for the convention to back Truman's civil rights agenda. "There are those who say to you—we are rushing this issue of civil rights," Humphrey declared to the convention hall in his midwestern twang. "I say we are a hundred and seventy-two years late.... The time has arrived for the Democratic party to get out of the shadow of states' rights and walk forthrightly into the bright sunshine of human rights." The convention went mad with support for Humphrey, Truman, and civil rights. A Southern counterproposal was firmly defeated, and the civil rights plank passed by 651½ to 582½ votes.[14]

Southern resistance hardened. That evening Alabama delegate and state politician Handy Ellis announced to the convention that the people of his state directed their delegation "never to cast their vote for a Republican, never to cast their vote for Harry Truman, and never to cast their vote for any candidate with a civil rights program such as adopted by the convention." The Southern rebellion began anew as half the Alabama delegation walked out of the hall along with large numbers of delegates from the rest of the South. Some six thousand Southern rebels moved down to Birmingham, where they launched an alternative to the Democratic Party, formally called the States' Rights Democratic Party but known more casually as the Dixiecrats. There they nominated South Carolina governor Strom Thurmond for the presidency, who declared the FEPC "foreign doctrine" incompatible with "free America."[15]

The Dixiecrat revolt was only one in a series of vectors pulling the Democrats apart in 1948. The far left had lined up behind former vice president Henry Wallace and his Progressive Party; skeptical white Northern liberals were far from sure that Harry Truman was up to the job of succeeding the mighty Franklin Roosevelt; and the Progressive Democrats, a party of South Carolina African Americans, demanded to be seated in lieu of the segregationist regulars. Now, the white supremacist wing of the party was also in open revolt. The Republican Party looked like the national race was theirs for the taking. Contrary to the infamous headlines, however, Dewey did not defeat Truman.

As significant as the Dixiecrat revolt was for the destabilization of the Democratic Party, the rebels did not include in their number the man who would become the country's most famous destabilizer of the party order: George C. Wallace. Like Chauncey Sparks, he chose to struggle within the system, remain loyal to his elders, and live to fight another day. The fact was, Wallace was quite a moderate on questions of race (by Black Belt standards), preferring to talk about improving schools and roads. But like the rest of white Alabama, he had no truck with interference from the federal government. He figured that clinging to the party regulars was his best shot for the political future.

In the state legislature, Wallace became synonymous with political energy and ambition, although some preferred to call it naked opportunism. The press corps named him the "most promising young legislator" of the session, and he ran unopposed for a second term in 1950 to represent Barbour County and the other surrounding counties of his district. Then he made a surprise move: in 1952 he ran for an open position as circuit court judge for Barbour and Bullock Counties. It wasn't a sure thing, as he had to beat Preston Clayton, a wealthy, decorated World War II officer with a name so steeped in history and political power that the county seat was named after his family. Wallace managed to defeat him by returning to his indefatigable efforts in grassroots campaigning, driving maniacally across the district and buttonholing every constituent he could find in his usual single-minded determination.[16]

Wallace not only won a six-year term as judge in Barbour County against all odds at the age of thirty-two, but he now earned a decent annual salary for the first time, which enabled the family to buy a house in Clayton behind the high school. Judge Wallace became citizen Wallace, a pillar of the Clayton community. He was now rooted in a place where people came to him rather than him constantly chasing people. In addition to his judgeship, he opened a law practice, joined in an insurance company partnership with his mentor Chauncey Sparks, became a churchgoer and officer, and signed on to be Clayton's municipal attorney. In 1955, he even requested and

In Clayton, men gathered at the courthouse, in front of the shops, and around the town square to enjoy the shade, play checkers, have a cool drink, talk business, and argue politics. This spot was nicknamed "Liars' Bench" for the tall tales told on languid afternoons. It was settings such as this that George Wallace relished for the connections he could make and votes he could win.

received an appointment to the Board of Trustees for Tuskegee Institute. "You've got to have the Negro vote from now on if you expect to run for anything," he remarked, "and I'm going to lay my groundwork right now." Most of all, the stability, the income, and a decent house brought the long-suffering Lurleen a bit of relief from the poverty created by her husband's ambitions.[17]

Tuscaloosa had football, Muscle Shoals had music, and Barbour County had politics. Politics ran so deep in Barbour County, the joke went, that to absorb all the shenanigans, speechifying, and vote counting, they needed *two* county seats. One was in Eufaula, the other in Clayton, some twenty-two miles to the west. The rickety old neoclassical county courthouse had been sitting on the Clayton town square since before the Civil War. A Confederate soldier monument provided by the Daughters of the Confederacy in 1909 loomed over it. Despite the surroundings, Judge Wallace was not the snide and snarling figure he would become in the 1960s. "George Wallace was the first judge to call me 'Mr.' in a courtroom," recalled the noted African American attorney J. L. Chestnut of Selma. "Judge George Wallace was the most liberal judge that I had ever practiced law in front of." When another African American attorney came from Birmingham, Wallace knew there would be no restaurant in town that would seat him for lunch, so he arranged for sandwiches and iced tea for two in his chambers for the duration of the trial. When Fred Gray, the Black attorney who defended Rosa Parks in the busing case in Montgomery, defended clients in Clayton, he said he thanked Wallace "for treating me as a professional, being generous, and as nice as any judge in whose courtroom I had tried a case. And that was the truth."[18]

Despite being a protégé of the "Bourbon from Barbour" Chauncey Sparks, Wallace was a "Big Jim" Folsom man. At least at first. Big Jim was a New Dealer, a populist, and, truth be told, a believer in racial equality. A folksy, plainspoken tower of a human being (he was six foot eight), Folsom was one of the great characters of Alabama politics. He liked women, he enjoyed liquor, and he loved the people. He stomped around the campaign stage with a mop and bucket, claiming that he was going to clean up politics. Then he'd pass the bucket asking the people to reach into their pockets and fill his bucket with the "suds" necessary for him to get to cleaning. Renewing the old Populist vision of the 1890s, he ran for the governorship by calling for easing voting restrictions, racial harmony if not equality, the rewriting of the segregationist constitution from 1901, and even women's rights. He believed in the New Deal. On race relations, he went so far as say that, given the complexion of the people of Alabama, there was already a certain amount of "moonlight integratin'" going on. In a statewide radio address, he asked if Black people, who made up 35 percent of the state's population, were getting 35 percent of the state's "fair share of living." At campaign events, he went out of his way to shake hands with Black people. He accepted the support of the Congress of Industrial Organizations (CIO), the left wing of the labor movement known for interracial organizing. He denounced corporate interests and championed roads, schools, and pensions. As governor from 1947 to 1951, he threatened the power of the Big Mules and the Bourbons of the Black Belt, but the state legislature managed to unite to block his every move.[19]

By law, Big Jim had to sit out the next race as he could not succeed himself, but "the little man's big friend" returned for his second successful run for the governorship in 1954. George Wallace managed his campaign in the southern part of the state, well knowing that supporting Folsom in the Black Belt was a difficult job. There he learned Folsom's mastery of the theater of politics, tried to duplicate his folksy charm, and saw the power of championing a big political vision. "Make no small plans," Folsom told his young protégé, "they have no magic to stir men's blood." Wallace had a way of occasionally twisting the campaign to be more about Little George than about Big Jim, but organizing for the 1954 campaign was Wallace's apprenticeship into the political big leagues. Big Jim won big, taking the Democratic primary with sixty-one of sixty-seven counties in the state. The white people of Alabama seemed to be choosing candidates who were "soft" on the race issue. It boded well. A Black-owned newspaper, the *Birmingham World*, proclaimed, "Race issue politics is becoming losing politics in Alabama."[20]

Yet race relations quickly turned from simmer to raging boil. Fourteen days before the Democratic runoff election, the Supreme Court of the United States issued its decision in *Brown v. Board of Education*. Not even Big Jim was thinking about integrating the schools. Then in August 1955, African American citizens of seven Black Belt counties petitioned the state department of education, demanding that the state adhere to *Brown* and integrate the schools. Then a seamstress and NAACP secretary refused to step to the rear of a Montgomery bus on December 1, 1955. Following Rosa Parks's bold refusal, a twenty-six-year-old preacher with a powerful mind and a gift for oration became the moral voice of a new phase of the civil rights movement. For 381 days, with Martin Luther King Jr. as their spokesman, Montgomery's African Americans boycotted the bus system. Then, in February 1956, federal courts ordered that a woman named Autherine Lucy should be enrolled at the University of Alabama. A mob drove her off the campus. Meanwhile, the integration of public buses made its way to federal court, which found against the city's segregation laws. Finally, Montgomery ended its segregation ordinances and allowed riders to sit anywhere on the bus. By the mid-1950s, the modern, mass stage of the civil rights movement had come hard and fast to Alabama.[21]

The entire system of segregation seemed to be under assault, and white supremacists lost no time mobilizing. It only took forty-eight hours after the Montgomery busing ordinance changed before someone fired a shotgun through Martin Luther King Jr.'s window. People took wild gunshots at integrated buses as they drove by. They bombed the Reverend Ralph Abernathy's home, blowing the porch off, and then bombed his Hutchinson Street Baptist Church to bits. Then they bombed First Baptist. They bombed three other churches and another home. In 1956, the entire congressional delegation of Alabama and most of the rest of the South signed "The Declaration of Principles," more commonly known as the "Southern Manifesto." The document backed the "massive resistance" underway against integration. "We decry the Supreme Court's encroachments on rights reserved to the states and to the people," declared the manifesto, "contrary to established law and to the Constitution." It was, they claimed, an exchange of "naked power for established law." Groups known as White Citizens' Councils sprung up across the state, demanding that the line be drawn on federal intervention in local race relations. They went from a few hundred people to eighty thousand members by 1957, all demanding to hold the line against integration.[22]

The middle ground evaporated. As race relations polarized, Wallace abandoned moderation as well as his relationship with Big Jim Folsom. Seeing where the political winds were blowing, he got behind segregation hard and fast. He rushed over to the capitol building, yelling to every legislator he could find, "cussin' Folsom out so you could hear him at the other end of the building." Folsom tried to stand his ground and draw Wallace back to the fold, but he failed on both counts. One might be able to imagine a slow, erratic path toward integration under leaders like Jim Folsom, but in the mid-1950s, the glacial pace of "moderation" ended with the US Supreme Court's *Brown* decision.[23]

Down in Barbour County, the White Citizens' Council gathered at the largest rally Clayton ever hosted. The longest motorcade anyone had seen delivered Georgia governor Marvin Griffin to the high school football field—a stone's throw from Wallace's house—where a crowd of some 4,500 people assembled to declare their commitment to segregation and white supremacy. With Folsom failing to hold the line on integration, the crowd all but adopted the governor of their neighboring state. "Give them a tide of public opinion," he declared, "and yea, even 1,000 years from now, we won't have integration." The governor's opening remarks were interrupted with shouts of "Where's Big Jim?" Someone shouted back, "He's with Lucy." Tying Folsom to both his womanizing and his sympathy for the woman trying to integrate the University of Alabama was a double shot. Griffin claimed if Georgia could have seen that those nine men on the bench "would bend to minority political pressures, Georgia would not have ratified the constitution." Today, the governor continued to the Clayton crowd, "both parties are trying to see who can toady to Negro minorities and stab us in the back."[24]

When news spread that the FBI collected evidence on segregated juries in Georgia's Cobb County, George Wallace knew a political opportunity when he saw one. He decried the "unwarranted and deliberate invasion of State Sovereignty by the federal police" as a "direct insult to the people of that county and to State Sovereignty." If the FBI came to Barbour or Bullock Counties, Wallace blustered, he would have "every member of the FBI" involved "arrested and put in jail for contempt of court." There was no hint that the FBI was coming his way, but when the story went out on the wires, he was the hero of his own myth. "Unless we assert ourselves and if we continue to allow such gestapo methods in local affairs, then surely local government in America will be dead forever." At the massive White Citizens' Council rally in Clayton, Governor Griffin praised Wallace's "courage in informing the do-gooders and meddlers that he would put the [FBI] scalawags in jail." The hometown crowd erupted in applause. Wallace had them right where he wanted them—at least for the moment.[25]

That spring, Wallace had discovered a powerful political formula—or at least all the pieces required to make it work. The first step was to uncover an episode of federal intervention on race relations. This allowed him to generate outrage about federal authority, but not necessarily attack integration itself. Then he could blow it out of proportion, preferably at an opportune moment. His grandstanding on the FBI happened just as mobs of students at the University of Alabama were busy stoning Autherine Lucy's car and driving her off of campus, which made headlines in all the papers. Even when Wallace lost his confrontations, which he inevitably did, his histrionic calls to preserve sovereignty and freedom allowed him to draw together both rabid segregationists and racial moderates who still believed in states' rights and wanted to continue to fight the carpetbaggers. By generating often artificial conflict with federal authority, Wallace created a system that generated votes. By losing to the feds, he won local politics.[26]

What might be dubbed the "Wallace Formula" had not matured into a coherent system by the time Judge Wallace decided to run for governor in 1958. Despite the *Brown* decision and his repudiation of Folsom, he still had one foot in the material needs of the people of Barbour County, the New Deal, and a bit of the lingering populism of Big Jim Folsom. He ran on improved roads, luring industry to Alabama, better public education, increasing old-age pensions, building highways, clean government, and his long-standing favorite: building trade schools. In contrast, his opponent John Patterson drew a stark line on integration and mobilized the Klan. In a last ditch attempt to save his campaign, Wallace went on television and declared, "I want to tell the good people of this state... if I didn't have what it took to treat a man fair regardless of the color of his skin, then I don't have what it takes to be the governor of your great state."[27]

On moderate grounds, George Wallace lost the governorship of the state of Alabama in 1958. A few days after his defeat, Wallace paid a visit to Seymore Trammell, the district attorney of Barbour County. "Seymore," Wallace said to him in his Clayton office, "I was outniggered by John Patterson, and I'll tell you here and now, I will never be outniggered again." He had found the last piece of his formula.[28]

A more race-conscious George Wallace returned to fight for the governor's mansion in 1962. This time, he had his complete political

In 1958, George Wallace campaigned for governor in front of his hometown of Clayton before a banner promising to "Keep Alabama Southern." He ran his first campaign as a populist and a racial moderate. Defeated by the overt racism of his opponent John Patterson, he vowed never to lose on race baiting again. Following a long line of Barbour County politicians, Wallace effectively transformed a fight against civil rights into a political war on the federal government.

formula, which was now unleashed from the constraints of racial moderation. He found a new foil in the oft-forgotten Civil Rights Act of 1957, the first civil rights legislation since 1875. Despite the bill's moderation, Strom Thurmond attempted to block it with a record-breaking filibuster that clocked in at over twenty-four hours of nonstop reading of anything and everything at hand, from the Declaration of Independence to his mother's biscuit recipe. It was Senate majority leader Lyndon Johnson's brilliant if sinister parliamentary maneuvering that simultaneously made sure the act passed and that it was the weakest bill it could possibly be. This made Johnson a hero to both sides. Although the act's improbable existence was a testament to Johnson's powers to keep his party glued together amid the strain of racial politics, its fatal weaknesses meant that it ultimately engendered more white resistance and outrage over federal overreach than it did positive gains for African Americans—a perfect political setting for George Wallace.[29]

The 1957 act gave birth to the US Commission on Civil Rights, as well as the Civil Rights Division of the Department of Justice. While the division lacked subpoena power, it could, theoretically, enforce voting rights through court orders. The commission, in contrast, had the power to subpoena witnesses and hold hearings, although it completely lacked enforcement power. The Civil Rights Commission consisted of presidential, Senate, and House appointees charged with reviewing and recommending actions on the question of civil rights. As Senator Johnson put it, as if reasonableness had anything to do with it, the commission could "sift out the truth from the fancies; and it can return with recommendations which will be of assistance to reasonable men."[30]

In 1958, the commission began subpoenaing voting records of six south-central Alabama counties with African American majority populations, including Barbour and Bullock, the counties that made up Judge Wallace's circuit. In January 1959, the Justice Department gave Wallace four days to turn over the registration books in their search for voter suppression. In so doing, they handed Wallace all the tools he needed for a comeback. Some county registrars simply resigned rather than comply with the federal order. Others let the commission look at the registration books without removing them from the custody of county officials. Wallace, as always, had bigger plans. The moment had far more potential political payoff than the FBI descending on some county in Georgia. Here they were, the Yankees come to subpoena the registration records of Barbour County itself. It was perfect.[31]

Wallace held a press conference to announce that as judge of his circuit, he controlled the voting records and would not succumb to the meddling demands of the federal government. It was a masterfully staged set piece—a standoff between him as guardian of local liberties and the federal government coming to take them away. Except there was a minor problem: George Wallace did not actually want to go *to jail* for defying a federal court order—or at least not for a long period of time. So George Wallace motored up from Clayton to Montgomery to see his old college chum, the racially liberal federal judge Frank M. Johnson Jr., whom Eisenhower appointed to a US district judgeship for his support during his campaign (and for which Wallace had sent a supporting letter). Johnson began a long and courageous career of decisions in favor of civil rights cases, beginning with his ruling in favor of Rosa Parks in 1956. Judge Johnson would go on to put the full power of the federal bench behind civil rights advocates for a generation to come—including in a number of key cases in Barbour County. Wallace knew he had to do some fast talking.[32]

He arrived at Johnson's door on a particularly cold night. Invited in, he pleaded his case over several cups of late-night coffee in the kitchen. "Judge, my ass is in a crack," he begged, "I need some help." Wallace explained that he wanted Johnson to toss him in jail for a symbolic week or two for defying the commission instead of the six months in federal prison that his defiance could get him. A serious conviction, he well knew, might prevent him from reaching the governor's mansion, but a minor one would be convenient and make him a martyr. Johnson would have none of Wallace's legal theatrics. Johnson promised to throw the book at him if he refused to comply with the commission's subpoena. If Johnson had his way, he told him, Wallace's stunt would mean he would have to run for the 1962 governorship from federal prison.[33]

Wallace dodged Judge Johnson's body blow and came back with an upper cut: "What if I turn 'em over to the grand jury in each county, and let them turn 'em over to the Civil Rights Commission?" The plan allowed him to defy the Civil Rights Commission, avoid jail time, and position himself as a champion of the common man against the federal government. Wallace's plan required acquiesce to federal authorities, but he would save face and maybe get some good theater out of the deal. Translating technical losses into political wins was how George Wallace worked.[34]

Wallace then assembled grand juries out of a courthouse packed, as his trusted aide Seymore Trammell put it, with "rednecks, and nigger-haters, and footlog walkers, and possum hunters. They were the kinda folks who'd do anything we told 'em to do without thinking twice. That's what he needed; that's what we got. It would work just as he'd planned from the beginning." Having deflected responsibility for the subpoenas onto his grand juries, George Wallace then held a press conference, positioning himself as the hero of federal resistance. He pulled out his most militant anti-federal rhetoric and postures, and promised to hold the line on federal power, while his hastily assembled grand juries handed over the records.[35]

"You've got the story of your lives, fellas," Wallace exclaimed to reporters. "The most dramatic confrontation since the Civil War. A clear confrontation between a sovereign state judge and his court on one side, and the federal government and its court on the other." Trammell even performed the service of typing up the report for the grand jury, a body he called a "sacred bastion of Anglo-Saxon liberty," and made sure the rigged jury commended "the courageous action of the Honorable George C. Wallace, the hero of the hour," who risked his very freedom in carrying out the duties and oath of office as a circuit court judge. With his trademark sneer and puffed-up chest, he raised the US commission's subpoena, and damned it as "a Roman holiday investigation, held in a federal courtroom, surrounded by a circus atmosphere with television platforms and ladders, newsreel cameras and hired publicity agents." His statement projected more anger and incredulity than coherence, but then came the ol' Wallace punch. "I will stand up and defend the rights of the people of Alabama, regardless of the personal sacrifices. That is the motto on which this great state was built: We dare defend our rights."[36]

Wallace then proceeded back to federal court, where he had to appear before Judge Johnson on possible contempt charges. There, Wallace's attorney wildly raised his hands, proclaiming, "We plead guilty. We plead guilty." Johnson stared at him in complete disbelief. The grand juries had already turned over the records, and Johnson knew political theater when he saw it. Wallace still hoped for a guilty verdict and a light sentence. Johnson found Wallace not guilty by "devious methods" and "means of subterfuge." His court, determined Johnson, "refuses to allow its authority and dignity to be bent or swayed by such politically generated whirlwinds." Yet Wallace had already won without even getting the minor sentence he hoped for from Judge Johnson.[37]

The television cameras whirred as Wallace left the courtroom. It was a finely orchestrated moment. "I was willing to risk my freedom" in the battle with the "evil Civil Rights Commission," Wallace declared to the press. He claimed the commission to be a 1959 version of Sherman's March to the Sea—this time "stopped in the Cradle of the Confederacy." It instantly reignited his political career. With his confrontation with Judge Johnson and the electoral commission, Wallace cemented his ability to lose the fight but win the politics. He turned to organizing the next gubernatorial campaign as "Alabama's Fighting Judge."[38]

Meantime, the US Civil Rights Commission released its report in 1959, showing "a consistent pattern of denial of equal protection of the laws as regards voting in six Alabama counties." In turn, the Alabama state legislature passed a law, without a single dissenting vote, authorizing county registration boards to destroy their records—including the written record of the biased system of questionnaires used to maintain disenfranchisement.[39]

The 1962 gubernatorial campaign of "Alabama's Fighting Judge" had begun. Technically his opponent was none other than Big Jim Folsom back for another round, but Wallace's real opponent was Judge Frank Johnson, serving as a political proxy for all forms of federal incursion. He never even bothered to mention his real political opponent's name. The feds, Wallace claimed, would always back down in a real fight. And if they said otherwise, they were "integrating, scallawagging, carpetbagging liars!" If faced with having to integrate Alabama's schools under a federal order, he claimed, "I shall refuse to abide by any such illegal federal court order even to the point of standing at the schoolhouse door." It was one of his biggest applause lines on the campaign trail, and he later made good on the promise at the University of Alabama. "Vote Right—Vote White—Vote for the Fighting Judge," was the new slogan.[40]

Wallace's exhausting campaign schedule was such that he seemed to be everywhere. "From the red clay hills of Barbour county to the governmental whitewash of Montgomery to the pine-studded shores of Lake Guntersville," the Montgomery paper reported, "Wallace scoured the state, ensuring that no hand would go unshaken, no pair of eyes unmet, no minds unfilled with the Wallace name." His relentless barnstorm built on his intimate knowledge of the state, its communities, their needs, and their customs. Yet the core stump speech, which had grown folksier and more familiar, remained much the same. He sharpened it with each appearance until it was a finely tuned political performance. Like a mix of William Jennings Bryan, Elvis, and an old-time snake oil salesman, George Wallace had perfected his method. As one chronicler described his campaign events:

> He stood flatfooted on the back of the truck. He hollered into the microphone about the outside evils encroaching on these good peoples' everyday lives, and when he got that bait planted real good and solid, he'd jerk the old fishing pole. "First thing you know, the federal courts'll be telling you who you can invite over for Sunday dinner and who you can't," he allowed. They whistled and clapped. They liked that. They'd punch each other in the sides with their elbows and nod and grin. "Ol George'll tell 'em," they said. He would rock forward on his toes and back on his heels. "The federal government up in Washington is breathin' down our backs, and we got to fight 'em off! You elect me yo' governor and I'll fight 'em!" And they knew he would.

Nary a mention of integration or Black people was made, but it was still a speech very much about race.[41]

Judge George Wallace of Barbour County won the 1962 governor's race in a landslide. He became the fifth person from Barbour County to win the office. At his inaugural on that bitter cold January day, he announced the rallying cry for white supremacy, "Segregation now, segregation tomorrow, and segregation forever." That clarion call was nearly drowned in a sea of demands for white freedom. In his 1963 inaugural, he was ready to project his racialized anti-statism throughout the country. "And you native sons and daughters of old

At his 1963 inaugural address, Governor George Wallace famously declared "Segregation Forever," but devoted most of his speech to championing a long struggle for white freedom from federal "tyranny."

New England's rock-ribbed patriotism," he proclaimed, "and you sturdy natives of the great Mid-West, and you descendants of the far West flaming spirit of pioneer freedom, we invite you to come and be with us, for you are of the Southern mind, and the Southern spirit, and the Southern philosophy[;] you are Southerners too and brothers with us in our fight."[42]

The first inaugural of George Wallace was also the beginning of his run for president of the United States.

CHAPTER SEVENTEEN

The Albert Street Club

THE FIGHT AGAINST FEDERAL power found a perfect foil in the *Brown v. Board of Education* decision. The decision seemed to promise a new era of integration and equality for African Americans, but no tools were given for the enforcement or delivery of that promise. The ambiguous, ambivalent, and protracted federal enforcement of one of the most significant Supreme Court decisions of the twentieth century provided both hope for Black people and a continuous fountain of opportunity for white people to fight the feds. That lack of clear enforcement mechanisms also served as an endless source of frustration for civil rights champions. "In 1954 I was delirious. What a victory!" recalled the NAACP's Thurgood Marshall of his triumph in the Supreme Court. "I thought I was the smartest lawyer in the entire world," he crowed. "In 1955, I was shattered. They gave us nothing and then told us to work for it. I thought I was the dumbest Negro in the United States." It would take decades for the court's decision to work through social and legal life, generating an agonizing series of reasons and opportunities for local whites to fight against limits the decision imposed on their freedoms.[1]

The NAACP's victory in *Brown v. Board* destroyed the legal doctrine of "separate but equal," which had legitimized racial segregation in the United States since 1896. Despite the court's follow-up demand for "all deliberate speed" in integrating American schools, the result was mostly "a ringing ambiguity" that left ample space for local interpretation and lots of local resistance. Eufaula, Alabama, would be under court orders for integration until 2003—almost half a century after *Brown*.[2]

In the early 1950s, across eight Southern states, there was no known African American student who attended school with white students. None. The original strategy for school integration among civil rights champions had been to leverage "separate but equal," demanding improvements to African American schools until it became too costly to the white majority. The cost of maintaining two truly equal school systems, the theory went, would drive districts and states to integration. Yet it was hard to see progress in the postwar years.

Around 1950, the NAACP shifted its aim from improving Black schools to integrating them, and the new strategy blossomed into a direct assault on the very idea of school segregation. Spearheaded by Thurgood Marshall, the NAACP began collecting cases and data on school segregation, finally landing on the case of Linda Brown, a third grader in Topeka, Kansas, and a dozen other plaintiffs. The Brown case was really the name of five separate cases consolidated into one desegregation case. The court handed down one of the most important legal decisions of the twentieth century: ruling that segregation violated the equal protection clause of the Fourteenth Amendment. It was a unanimous decision shaped by the grit and determination of new chief justice Earl Warren. Even Alabama's own former Klan member and then Supreme Court justice, Hugo Black, voted for the plaintiffs. On its own, the decision desegregated nothing. But it opened a new phase in the struggle and began a long, concerted fight in all arenas of American social life—in polling places, schools, lunch counters, buses, Congress, and the White House—to tear down racial segregation at last.

While many in the NAACP and other groups saw school integration imminent after *Brown*, by 1960 the number of students attending integrated schools in the Deep South remained close to zero. In the face of deep local and state resistance, the decision presented less a wholesale victory over segregation than an updated picture of the limited commitment of the federal government and a new front line in the centuries-long struggle for Black freedom.

To win social change through Supreme Court action carried opportunities and risks. "The nine Justices, as has often been said, constitute the least democratic branch of the national government," explains Richard Kluger in his history of the decision. "Yet this, most likely, was one reason why the Court felt free to act: it is not compelled to nourish the collective biases of the electorate; it may act to curb those unsavory attitudes by the direct expedient of declaring them to be intolerable among a civilized people." Unfortunately, enforcing the *Brown* decision required the coercive power of the federal government, and the commitment of the legislative and executive branches remained tepid, at best.[3]

Privately, President Dwight Eisenhower did not approve of the coercive nature of the *Brown* decision. "I am convinced that the Supreme Court decision *set back* progress in the *South at least fifteen years*," he noted about the decision of the chief justice he himself had appointed. "The fellow who tries to tell me that you can do these things by *force* is just plain *nuts*." Still enjoying his reputation as the man who saved the world from fascism, Eisenhower might have done more to prevent the South, and the nation, from descending into the racial violence of white resistance that followed Brown.[4]

Supreme Court justice William O. Douglas noted the consequences of the president's ambivalence. "If he had gone to the nation on television and radio telling people to obey the law and fall into line," Douglas said, "the cause of desegregation would have accelerated." Instead, "Ike's ominous silence on our 1954 decision gave courage to the racists who decided to resist the decision, ward by ward, precinct by precinct, and county by county." Chief Justice Earl Warren believed the president could have at least mentioned that the nation was dedicated to the principle that "All Men are created equal." But Ike believed people changed their behavior because people changed their minds. Justice Douglas framed Ike's response in words that captured the entire federal posture on civil rights: "There was tragedy in Eisenhower's attitude." Ike was wrong. Law, properly enforced, changed behavior. And until the federal government enforced the law, behavior would worsen. Local control was nearly synonymous with segregation, and the absence of a voice to the contrary took its toll.[5]

Soon enough, the old racialized anti-statism mobilized. In September 1957, when white mobs prevented the enrollment of Black students at Central High School in Little Rock, Arkansas, and Governor Orval Faubus said that "blood will run in the streets" if schools were integrated, Ike sent in the 101st Airborne to escort nine African American students into Little Rock Central, despite his preference for local control. "It was my hope that this localized situation would be brought under control by city and State authorities," he explained in a special televised address. "If the use of local police powers had been sufficient, our traditional method of leaving the problems in those hands would have been pursued. But when large gatherings of obstructionists made it impossible for the decrees of the Court to be carried out, both the law and the national interest demanded that the President take action." Eisenhower may have thought this was a new and unprecedented act, but he was rehearsing an old story. Proponents and opponents alike began to call it the "Second Reconstruction." The fate of Black freedom was once again tied to the federal government, and any hope of defeating white extremism depended upon federal politicians not losing their nerves.[6]

Any serious observer in the South—or much of the rest of the country—already knew that local meant separate and separate meant unequal. When someone announced the decision at the Board of Education meeting in Eufaula, few understood it and those who did responded with stunned disbelief. They could not even conceive of the idea. The *Brown* decision began to feel real only when it was bolstered by the yearlong bus boycott up in Montgomery in 1955, and the Supreme Court's follow-up decision integrating transportation in *Browder v. Gayle* (1956). The state of Alabama, however, reacted not by integrating schools, but by instituting a statewide ban on the NAACP when the organization would not turn over its mailing lists.

State officials claimed the NAACP's actions were "causing irreparable injury to the property and civil rights of the residents and citizens of the State of Alabama." Just as it had during Creek removal, Reconstruction, and the New Deal, it became clear to white Eufaulans that something had to be done to preserve their freedom and autonomy from the long arm of federal overreach. They began to take action.[7]

While no school in Alabama lifted a finger to integrate any students, white Eufaulans came up with a clever if primitive plan to thwart *Brown*. If they could completely segregate the community geographically, then geographically defined school districts could be whites-only, even without laws to preserve segregation. Yet there was a problem: the city was not perfectly segregated by geography. One obstacle prevented a clear north-south racial divide in Eufaula: a small neighborhood of African Americans living up on Albert Street. To subvert *Brown v. Board*, the city would have to move these Black residents out of the otherwise white north side of town.

The Black residents of Albert Street were surrounded on all sides by white Eufaulans. Their little community on the northwest side of the town, known as Flake Hill, was one of the few enclaves of Black homeowners in the area—a vibrant spot of Black property ownership and neighborhood families that had managed to stay together since the end of slavery days. The Eufaula Housing Authority declared their homes to be substandard and condemned them, using eminent domain to place the land under the Eufaula Housing Authority's control. "Slum clearance," it would be called in other places, but these were middle class homes. The city would pay the Albert Street homeowners for their property, they promised, then "redevelop" the neighborhood and sell the revitalized properties—to white residents only, the Albert Street group was dead certain. Meanwhile, the former Albert Street residents would be sent to the southeastern side of town, the Black side, where they could hope to buy new homes with the money the city gave them for their places in Flake Hill.[8]

In the city's fight against the most important federal intervention in US civil rights history, it armed itself with another wing of federal power: the Housing Act of 1949. A flawed and compromised product of the late New Deal, the Housing Act was ambitiously packed with goals of eliminating slums and building quality housing, but it was enabled by few tools and resources for getting the job done. Developers and reformers, conservatives and liberals came to the idea of slum clearance from a variety of directions, leading to a muddled mission for the act. Liberals wanted to improve the lives of the poor, but conservatives deplored that public housing would compete with private housing—even if slum clearance itself was an acceptable idea. The housing bill became a rallying point for anti–New Deal Republicans, while Truman rallied behind the act and lambasted Congress for its inaction on the bill. Once the Democrats took back Congress in 1948, the act passed, promising "a decent home and suitable living environment for every American family." It was Truman's only new proposal from his Fair Deal that got enacted within the narrowing purview of progressive legislation in the immediate postwar period.[9]

Shelley v. Kraemer (1948), which ended racially restrictive covenants, suggested that housing policy might be at the forefront of the civil rights struggle. But the political restrictions on housing policy meant that the Housing Act supported, and often deepened, residential segregation rather than helped to end it. Racial tensions around housing deepened throughout the following decade, exacerbated by uneven local application of laws, meager resources for rewriting local practices, local pressures, and a pattern of local governments handing over planning to private contractors. Sometimes the political squeeze of the segregationist wing in Congress was to blame; sometimes it was an attitude of naive (even willful) colorblindness in the face of the United States' much harsher racial reality. African Americans bore the costs and received few of the benefits of New Deal and Fair Deal housing initiatives. By the end of the 1950s, nine out ten families displaced under the urban renewal were nonwhite.

The Housing Act is most often remembered as a push for "Urban Renewal," or what African Americans derided as "Negro Removal." Forcing poor urban African Americans to move was a mechanism for improving housing real estate values or enhancing commercial development. Yet the Eufaula city fathers had an additional objective: they were using the act as an end run around the requirements of *Brown v. Board of Education*. The kicker was that they were going to do it with the financial assistance of the Housing Act. With federal assistance, the city would buy and condemn the properties, then redevelop them—all as a way of subverting the federal intent of the *Brown* decision. The segregationist wing of the Democratic Party on the local and national levels continued to hold the cards in such matters. As Alabama senator John Sparkman put it, "Federally imposed requirement for racial integration would certainly result in the rejection of this form of Federal [housing] aid by many communities where the need for low rent housing, especially for minority group families, is most pressing." Since these questions were "complex and deeply rooted in local traditions, institutions and emotions," policy, according to the US Commission on Civil Rights, would need to "rely heavily on local responsibility and local wisdom."[10]

Many critics involved in housing policy saw the Eufaula-type tactics coming. Frank Horne, a former member of Roosevelt's "Black Cabinet" and an official in the Housing and Home Finance Agency, saw through the various assurances about race in federal housing. He feared what white Eufaulans figured out. The structure of federal funds, he argued, did not "preclude the possibility of Federal funds and powers being utilized by localities to clear entire neighborhoods, change the location of entire population groups and crystallize patterns of racial or nationalistic separation by allowing private developers—for whose benefit the legislation is primarily drawn—to prohibit occupancy in new developments merely on the basis of race."[11]

As the National Urban League's Lester Granger predicted right after the *Brown* decision, "strong efforts would be made to establish more rigid housing barriers against Negroes 'as a compensation' for breaking down school segregation." Frances Levenson of the National Committee Against Discrimination in Housing wrote to Urban Renewal Administration commissioner Dave M. Walker, explaining exactly the tactic Eufaula was embracing. "Some Southern communities," she wrote, "are actually using the program to insure future school segregation by moving minority families out of presently integrated neighborhoods."[12]

The residents of Albert Street, knowing they were a Black island in the middle of a white urban plan, organized themselves into the "Albert Street Club" to prevent the demolition of their homes. Their complaint was clear: "We have lived in this area for over fifty years. Now the White people want to take our community... redevelop it with White homes, an extension of the White school and a White Park." The Albert Street Club complained to Alabama Democratic senator John Sparkman about their plight. They also wrote the US Justice Department. Nobody responded. Martin Luther King Jr. would later express his sorrow at the "misfortunes that the Negroes of Eufaula, Alabama are confronting" and "commended" them "for their fearless stand." But it was the Montgomery movement's attorney that delivered hope.[13]

In December 1957, the Albert Street Club sent a delegation to meet with a young attorney of recent fame named Fred D. Gray. In 1955, Gray was a twenty-five-year-old, fresh-faced young man just out of law school when NAACP activist Rosa Parks refused to give up her seat on a segregated bus. Gray defended her, and he went on to play a crucial role in the legal wrangling of the yearlong Montgomery Bus Boycott. To the extent that Alabama was the center of the civil rights struggle, Fred Gray was the legal drive at the center of the center. The young attorney dedicated his life to, as he often put it, "destroying everything segregated I could find."[14]

The Eufaula Board of Education sweetened their idea to maintain segregation when they not only built a nice new shiny high school not far from Albert Street for the white kids, but also built a new school for the Black kids called McCoo High School, named after a respected African American doctor in Eufaula. They located the African American school on the Bluff, the southeast-side neighborhood where they wanted to relocate the Albert Street residents. If they could get all the white people on the north side, and all the Black people on the south side, then there would be, legally speaking, no segregation in the schools—just in residence. It was a perfect plan: preserve public schools, dodge the *Brown* decision, keep the Supreme Court out, maintain segregation, and use federal funds to accomplish the job.

Fred Gray reported that not "one iota" of progress had been made since *Brown* in Eufaula or anywhere else in Alabama, and the "the entire plan [to take over Albert Street] was racially motivated." Gray found himself with ten plaintiffs from the Albert Street Club. One of them, David Frost Jr.—long grown since he dropped the kerosene jug after almost touching a white woman as a boy—figured that what was happening worked this way:

> When the Supreme Court ruled that the schools had to be integrated and everybody had to go to the closest school, the white people started to figuring out how to get the black people away from around Eufaula High School. . . . The white people set out to condemn all of the black people's property around that school. They got very busy in Eufaula to buy up all the colored people's property that was close to the school so they could tear down the houses and fix it so only white people could live there. That way they could have residential segregation.

But attorney Gray also knew that the Eufaula Housing Authority had the absolute legal power to condemn the property. So he took it to federal court, arguing that his clients' constitutional rights of due process and equal protection under the Fourteenth Amendment were being violated. He requested an injunction.[15]

As did so many federal discrimination cases in Alabama, *Tate v. City of Eufaula* landed on the docket of the indomitable federal judge Frank M. Johnson Jr., who heard endless local civil rights cases in Alabama. The plaintiffs argued that the deal to buy up the Albert Street properties was not just some simple urban renewal effort: it was a segregationist plot. Gray argued that a "tacit understanding" existed among the defendants and the city's private developers to sell the redeveloped land only to white buyers. His clients, he claimed, believed that segregation defined the defendants' "policy, custom and usage" and that the future use of the property would be no different than the segregated past's. Yet there were no contracts or concrete plans to point to—only the obvious weight of tradition in Eufaula and all of the Deep South as well as the impetus of *Brown*. The plaintiffs also noted that the defendants refused to allow them to buy the redeveloped land—never mind the fact that the price of the new housing would be well beyond the capacity of the former African American owners—especially at the prices they were offering the current residents for their old properties.[16]

The City of Eufaula hammered back against the Albert Street Club's claims with no fewer than twenty-six separate reasons for dismissal of the case. Their arguments—lack of jurisdiction, failure to state a claim, lack of an existing controversy—essentially boiled down to one issue: the case was premature. The plaintiffs' case *predicted* a violation of constitutional rights based on historical pattern and precedent, but it could not prove that those violations were *going* to happen. Judge Johnson decided that the court was obligated to believe that the defendants would "recognize the law that is now so clear; this law being to the effect that there can be no governmentally enforced segregation solely because of race or color." The history of segregation was not on trial, Johnson ruled; the plans for condemnation and renewal were. Segregation might well continue, but this case did not yet rest on an actual act of discrimination.[17]

Yet the judge's decision sent a warning to the defendants by sketching a future that, to most observers, was most certainly going to happen. To rule on the case and not dismiss it, the judge both argued and prophesized,

> this Court must assume the redevelopment plan will be fully executed, the schoolboard will acquire the land from the Housing Authority and construct thereon a public school, that qualified eligible Negroes will seek admission and that the school board will deny such applications solely on account of the fact that they are Negroes; that land for a public park will be acquired and a public park developed thereon, that Negroes will desire to use such park facilities and will be denied that use solely because they are

> Negroes; that those plaintiffs and/or others similarly situated will in good faith apply for public housing and if eligible will be discriminated against solely because of their color; and that the redevelopers will violate the binding covenants.

He knew the courts could not speculate that far ahead. But his detailed decision smacked of a certain sense that he knew what the defendants were up to. Judge Johnson declared, "This Court declines to declare or enjoin upon such future contingencies." With that, he dismissed the case.[18]

Fred Gray had one more tactic in mind to help the members of the Albert Street Club. Given that the fix was in on the redevelopment scheme, he went the other direction. He embraced the plan and tried to get as much money for his clients as he could. All members of the Albert Street Club believed that the amount they were being offered was about half the actual value of their property. Gray took the Eufaula Housing Authority to court seeking higher home values in the condemnation cases. That case ended up in the Barbour County Circuit Court with Fred Gray as attorney for the plaintiffs and Judge George C. Wallace presiding. One might expect a standoff between Fred Gray, one of the great young and bold civil rights lawyers in Alabama, and George C. Wallace, the symbol of resistance and hate, to be a bitter confrontation. It was not.

Gray began the *Eufaula Housing* cases, each of which had to be adjudicated individually and serially, by attacking the heart of the matter: the problem of Black people being excluded from jury duty. Gray challenged the composition of the jury, arguing that African Americans were not being allowed to serve as jurors in Barbour County. Wallace dismissed the motions, but in retrospect, Gray took considerable pride in being thirty years ahead of the Supreme Court, which did not find that a "private litigant in a civil case may not use preemptory challenges to exclude jurors on account of race" until the 1990s. Even though his motion was denied, Gray enjoyed being in Wallace's court. This was 1958, the year Wallace was defeated for the governorship, but before he had taken on his more rabid, and race-baiting, political persona. Gray explained that he was "appreciative to him for treating me as a professional, being generous, and as nice as any judge in whose courtroom I had tried a case. And that was the truth. I enjoyed trying the case before Judge Wallace."[19]

As one of the plaintiffs, the ever-feisty David Frost Jr. remembered, because of the lawsuit, "I wound up getting five thousand three hundred dollars for my property, more money than I had ever had in my life." With the Albert Street Club receiving double or triple what they expected, they were hesitant to push the matter further. Gray thought there could be an appeal to be made, but the residents declined. Having received more than they expected for the properties being taken from them, they still told Gray, "Well, lawyer, we appreciate everything you have done and we know you want to appeal it, but we are satisfied with the awards and we think we will take our money." They took the money and moved to the Black side of town. The plaintiffs won their battle for money, but the forces of segregation won the war.[20]

As the pressure to integrate continued, schools fell back on a new iteration of white freedom or, as it became known, "freedom of choice." The idea was simple: all students, regardless of race, could choose to go to whatever school they wanted to attend, clean and simple. A surface read of the idea of "freedom of choice" might seem fair, but a closer look reveals that this was yet another attempt to block federal pressures for integration. No white kids were going to attend any of the Black schools, and the vast majority of Black kids were not going to face the wrath of white mobs at the white schools. Despite initial federal support for the plan, the concerns for African American parents were endless: "Would mixed-race schools take their children seriously? Protect them against white hostility? Give them a better education? How would their angry white neighbors react to such a revolutionary change in local custom?" Furthermore, the need to fully integrate faculty, supervision, and service workers remained elusive.[21]

Freedom of association and freedom of choice hardly offered a clear and affirmative right. It largely meant the right to choose less *with* whom one served, socialized, worked, and went to school than *without* whom you were "free" to do those things. The idea of freedom of choice and freedom of association preserved a fundamental right to discriminate, and to discriminate on a systematic basis, not simply based on individual discretion. "There is all too often no freedom in the freedom of choice plan," Ralph McGill, the anti-segregationist editor of the *Atlanta Constitution*, explained. "It too frequently is freedom in reverse. It offers a segregationist, racist-dominated community or board an opportunity to proclaim a free choice, while they covertly employ 'persuasions' to maintain segregation or meager tokenism.... The freedom of choice plan is, in fact, neither freedom nor a choice. It is discrimination."[22]

In the fall of 1965, "freedom of choice" meant massive resistance to integration in Eufaula. There were moves to have a few students move across town to desegregate grades one, seven, nine, and twelve. Between a refusal of tokenism among the local African Americans and a reluctance to have more than a few Black students at the white schools, nothing happened. The US Department of Health, Education, and Welfare threatened to withhold funding, however, and by the fall of 1966, sixteen African American students entered the sparkly new high school, named after none other than George Wallace.[23]

A group of nineteen Barbour County students were denied their "freedom of choice" to attend a white high school because the school board decided there was inadequate transportation available. Yet the reason transportation was not available was that the school board was still running buses based on the old segregated system. So, an African American student might choose to go to a white school but she would be denied admission because there was not any transportation for her. There was no transportation, of course, so that she could not attend. To get beyond token integration, the transportation system would have to be redesigned. This circular logic captured the essence of the "freedom of choice" model. In 1966, in *Franklin v. Barbour County Board of Education*, Gray filed suit on behalf of the African American kids and parents who had chosen the difficult path of integration on a freedom-of-choice basis. Again, Judge Johnson heard the case, but this time he required exact remedies be implemented, including a county-wide school bus transportation plan.[24]

Meantime, Fred Gray and associates were working on a bigger, more visionary fight to force school integration in Alabama. Gray won the case of *Lee v. Macon County Board of Education*, which sought the integration of Tuskegee High School in Macon County in 1963. Since Wallace was by then the governor, and having proclaimed himself a militant segregationist in his inaugural address, he came out swinging against the integration of Tuskegee High that fall. In his first year in office, he busily stomped the state declaring, "We will never surrender!" As the integration of Tuskegee High was imminent, he circled the campus with hundreds of state troopers to enforce his executive order postponing the start of school. Wallace then placed National Guard troops at the high school to prevent Black students from entering. President John F. Kennedy volleyed back by federalizing the Guard and having them return to their barracks. Wallace edged back from his earlier militancy. "I can't fight federal bayonets with my bare hands," he said.[25]

The answer, recalled Fred Gray, "hit me like the burning bush speaking to Moses." Wallace had handed him everything he needed. He immediately scrambled all of his associates back to work at ten thirty that night in 1963. If Wallace could close one school, then that proved that the governor had the power over all the schools in the state. Gray was no longer up against one hundred school boards scattered around the state. He could put all the cases together. Several years of complex wrangling ensued, but, as a result, in 1967, a panel of federal judges ordered every school on every level in the state to desegregate wholesale. It invalidated the "freedom of choice" plans and included very specific guidelines in order to prove compliance with federal expectations for integration.[26]

With federal victory at hand, white public school students began a long secession from the public school system by moving into the various growing private schools, known as "segregation academies." There they could continue to express their "freedom of association" outside of the public realm. Foot dragging continued, and it was not until 2003 that Eufaula was officially in compliance with the *Lee v. Macon* guidelines and taken off the federal list of noncompliant cities. At least officially, school integration was complete in Eufaula, nearly fifty years after *Brown v. Board of Education*.

Even though the white Eufaula high school had to integrate under *Lee v. Macon*, the school board canceled all official social activities indefinitely, including proms. The order lasted for decades. By 1990, student demand increased for Eufaula to hold its first integrated prom, although the board still remained reluctant. The student body president who lobbied the school board, an African American student athlete named James Samuel, who had been selected for the Air Force Academy, explained, "I think we're the only school in Alabama that does this. We're the only one in America I hope." The school board president, Billy Houston, however, continued to regard it as an issue of freedom of choice. It's "a case of individual preferences by the students" to have separate events.

The battle between local freedom and federal intervention took decades to win. It wouldn't have happened without a vibrant, local social movement in the 1960s unlike anything seen since Reconstruction. Yet the fears of Black people on the move, with the even modest support of the federal government, would stoke the national ambitions of Governor George Wallace. But for all the steadfast white resistance and threats of violence, even Barbour County finally had to give in to change. And when, in May 1991, Eufaula finally held its first integrated prom, nothing happened but dancing and celebrating.[27]

CHAPTER EIGHTEEN

From Clayton to the Nation

CLAYTON, ALABAMA, WAS CLOSED for the night. Everyone was down at the game. The Samson High School football team had traveled an hour and a half through the Alabama wiregrass in October 1963 to take on the young men of Clayton. Fans milled through the gate, pausing to buy chances at a cake raffle or picking up refreshments from high school girls selling hot dogs and Cokes beneath a canopy. Men unfolded ungainly old metal chairs and set them up along the sideline. There they could pace and discuss strategy for the evening and maybe relive a few hard-fought contests of the past. Boys played under bleachers in the shadow of the electric lights as bass drums pounded, trumpets blared, and the town chanted on the cheerleaders' cue. Black kids, barred from all-white Clayton High, peered through the chain-link fence. It was a regular Friday night in every town in the South—and much of America.

Then came the surprise. Alabama's governor bounded onto the field of his hometown high school. It was less than a year into Wallace's first term. Everyone in Clayton knew him, and he knew them. Never much for the intricacies of policy and governing, it was the campaign he loved—even when there wasn't one. "Heighdy, George!" "We're with you, little man!" "Keep fighting, Judge!" "God bless you, George!" He'd been shaking hands with people in Clio, Clayton, and much of the rest of Barbour County since he was five years old. That evening he signed the boots of cheerleaders and the sides of drums, as well as just about every scrap of paper and object people could press in his hands. Climbing up to the grandstand, he boomed through the microphone with some folksy pablum. "It sure is good to be home and see all you folks. Ya'll come up to Montgomery sometime and visit us. You're always welcome."[1]

These were not simply his constituents, they were his people. Without them, there would have been no judgeship, no governor's race, no "Segregation Forever" speech, no stand in the schoolhouse door, and no plans, real or rumored, to rattle those Kennedy boys in a longshot bid for the highest office in the land next year. Maybe, too, four Klansmen would not have been inspired to dynamite the 16th Street Baptist Church in Birmingham and kill four little girls just a few weeks prior to Wallace's appearance at the Clayton game.

The spring and summer prior to Wallace's visit to the football game had been all about Birmingham, the citadel of American segregation, and the most recent target in the Southern Christian Leadership Conference campaign to liberate the Black South. There were mass meetings, marches, sit-ins, a downtown boycott, and the mobilization of large numbers of youth to shore up the flagging movement that spring. It was all met with massive resistance and Sheriff Bull Connor's dogs and fire hoses. After it ended in a victory-cum-stalemate, Robert Kennedy even visited Wallace in the spring to try to negotiate, but he got the message when he arrived at the state capitol with the Confederate flag hoisted over the US flag, and Wallace recording their conversation. The meeting was futile. "It's like a foreign country," Bobby said. "There's no communication. What do you do? I've never been asked if I'm a communist before." Then came the bombing on September 15, 1963. And just weeks afterward, Wallace showed up in Clayton.[2]

In August the civil rights champions gathered en masse at the March on Washington. On hold since the World War II–era fight over the Fair Employment Practices Committee (FEPC), the march put the focus directly on federal power. Martin Luther King Jr. put forth a vision that singled out the people of Alabama as the test of modern civil rights. "I have a dream," he proclaimed, "that one day, down in Alabama, with its vicious racists, with its governor having his lips dripping with the words of 'interposition' and 'nullification'—one day right there in Alabama little black boys and black girls will be able to join hands with little white boys and white girls as sisters and brothers."

For the white people of Clayton, Wallace was not "vicious"; his words did not "drip." Lord knows they didn't want any interracial hand-holding. The governor was their warrior, their champion, standing firm against federal meddling in their traditions and way of life.[3]

Wallace couldn't help weighing in on school integration, the hot-button issue of the day. "This is why we can't integrate the schools in Alabama," the governor said, as if the white crowd filling the bleachers at the football game made the case obvious. The fantasia of hometowns, Friday night, football, and segregation all blended into one. "This isn't just a football game; it's a social function. It's the same in every city in Alabama. The school is the center of social life. Hell, these people just plain don't want to mix. Ask 'em. Ask 'em if they're in favor of what I'm doing." No doubt, they were in favor. The white people of Alabama delivered Wallace to Montgomery on the wings of the largest vote and the largest majority in the state's history.[4]

"Did you hear they're blaming me for that bombing in Birmingham? Isn't that a hell of a note?" He was particularly aggravated that *Time* magazine, for one, had superimposed his picture in front of the church's stained-glass window where the face of Christ had been blown out by white terrorists. He called it "defamation by photography." The governor saw the question of law and order differently than his critics. "They say my defiance of the federal law caused the climate that led to the bombings," he argued after the Clayton High game. "Hell, Martin Luther King was the one who started breaking laws in Alabama. Why don't they blame him? He broke our laws, but he says he doesn't have to obey them because they're unjust. Well, for 100 years the Supreme Court thought they were just, and we still think so. And I say the 1954 Supreme Court decision [*Brown v. Board of Education*] is the most unjust law on the books."[5]

As hearings began on President Kennedy's civil rights bill, Wallace built on the wild premise that liberals, who often blurred into communists in his rhetoric, were going to crush the freedom of white people. The bill, he claimed, was "part of the drift toward centralized socialist control and away from the free enterprise system." "I tell you," he said that evening after the football game, "them damn Kennedys are going to ruin this country." The Associated Press article covering his hometown visit was titled "St. George Wallace vs. Federal Dragon."[6]

When Wallace invoked the Kennedys, all minds darted to the previous spring, when Wallace fulfilled his campaign promise to "stand in the schoolhouse door" to block the integration of the University of Alabama. The blocking of the integration of the University of Alabama showed Wallace's mastery of political theater. On one side of the pathway that led to the university's Foster Auditorium was an enormous press gaggle, with all the television networks and major city daily reporters present, cameras at the ready. On the other side stood grim state officials and guardsmen. The groups glared at each other under the bright sun across the campus walkway. In the middle was George Wallace. Deputy Attorney General Nicholas Katzenbach recalled Attorney General Bobby Kennedy telling him, "Look, it's too dangerous a situation, and I don't know what the man'll do if he's crossed. He wants his show; you're gonna have to give him his show."[7]

As the hour arrived, the governor bounced out with his Napoleonic strut, puffed out his chest, and took his place behind a podium carefully placed in front of the schoolhouse door. With a microphone strung around his neck, he was ready. Deputy Attorney General Katzenbach then got out of his car and made his way to the defiant governor, his orders to integrate the university, signed by President John F. Kennedy, in his hand. Two students, Vivian Malone and James Hood, waited patiently in the car to shield them from the humiliation of the standoff with the governor. "Don't let him say anything to the students," Attorney General Bobby Kennedy told Katzenbach.[8]

The two opponents, Katzenbach and Wallace, made for a perfect study in contrasts. The notoriously short but cocky Wallace was dwarfed by the towering and pensive Katzenbach, but the governor made up for his stature with an ornery defiance. Wallace stood confidently in the shade. Katzenbach stood nervously in the sun, mopping his sweating, balding head. Wallace feared he might be arrested, while Katzenbach feared the whole thing would descend into violence. The governor wanted his show, while Katzenbach fumed at the theater of the whole thing. Katzenbach had been to Phillips Exeter, Princeton, and Yale Law (the Kennedys' idea of diversity—not Harvard but Yale). He was a Rhodes Scholar and had that Ivy League spirit that defined the new breed of federal officials in the Kennedy administration. Wallace, in contrast, hailed from Barbour County's tiny backwater hamlet of Clio, made it through the University of Alabama law program, and anxiously clawed his way to the governor's mansion. Both men had served on bombers in World War II, in different theaters. While Wallace teetered on the edge of a nervous breakdown, Katzenbach had been shot down over the Mediterranean and spent two years in prisoner of war camps.

Wallace's hand jutted out to halt Katzenbach as he approached the podium. Katzenbach barely got to say anything before Wallace interrupted him, saying, "Now you make your statement, because we don't need your speech." Without responding to Katzenbach's plea to allow the students to register, he said, "I have a statement to read." Wallace had a way of stretching and bending the vile dimensions of racism until they seemed like dignified, principled appeals to constitutional logic. He began what amounted to a five-minute diatribe on states' rights. "The unwelcomed, unwanted, unwarranted, and force-induced intrusion upon the campus of the University of Alabama today of the might of the Central Government offers frightful example of the oppression of the rights, privileges and sovereignty of this state by officers of the federal government." The "threat of force" from the feds lay outside of law and justice. He lectured everyone on the import of the Tenth Amendment: "The powers not delegated to the United States by the Constitution, nor prohibited by it to the States, are reserved to the states respectively, or to the people." It was only because he was there, Wallace claimed, that thousands of angry Alabamians were not there in his stead. He would not accept trampling on "the exercise of the heritage of freedom and liberty under the law."[9]

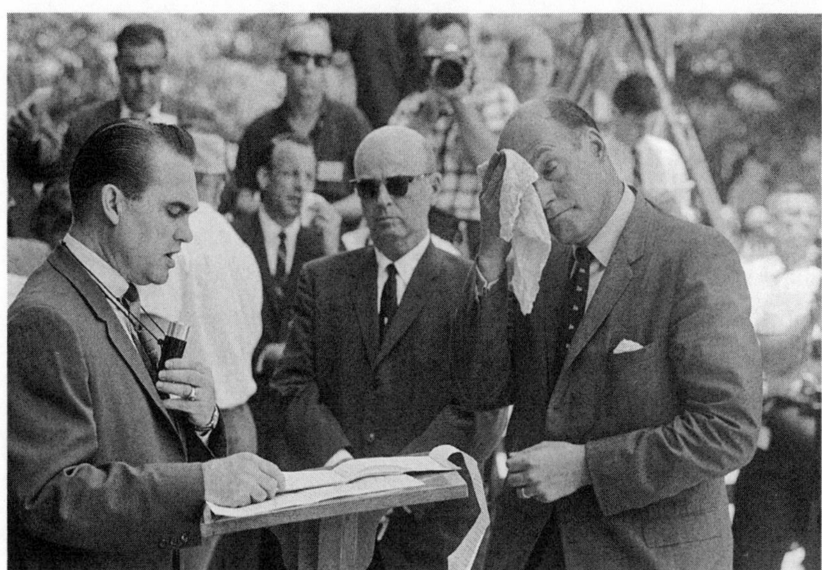

United States Deputy Attorney General Nicholas Katzenbach sweats it out in the sun as George Wallace fulfills a promise to "stand in the schoolhouse door" to prevent the integration of the University of Alabama. The political show helped prevent white violence but did not prevent African American students Vivian Malone and James A. Hood from registering for classes. Between the two men stands US Marshal Peyton Norville Jr., whose presence—along with three automobiles full of additional marshals at the standoff—harkened back to the marshals who defended Creek settlements against white intruders and protected Black voters during Reconstruction.

Katzenbach endured Wallace's face-to-face lecture before politely asking, for a fourth time, for the governor's compliance in letting the students register. Silence. An exasperated, sweaty deputy attorney general turned around and left down the path. Wallace got what he wanted—the image of him standing firm between federal authority and the University of Alabama. It became one of the most iconic images of the civil rights era.

Soldiers had rehearsed the step that might have come next—the physical removal of Wallace if necessary, but it never came to that. After Kennedy federalized the Alabama National Guard a few hours later, the general of the guard walked up the same phalanx of press and officials, saluted Wallace, and said, "It is my sad duty to ask you to step aside, on order of the President of the United States." The governor explained that "Alabama is winning this fight against Federal interferences because we are awakening the American people to [the] trend toward military dictatorship in this country." He walked away, got in the car, and headed back to Montgomery.[10]

The touch-and-go moment had passed, and the two admitted Black students, Vivian Malone and James Hood, walked in through another door without incident and finished the registration process for the summer session 1963. As he had with his standoff with Judge Johnson, Wallace lost the policy but won the political moment. He would continue to do the same throughout his career. After he stood in the schoolhouse door, he received over one hundred thousand letters and telegrams, 95 percent of them positive.

That night, John F. Kennedy had enough. He went on television to declare civil rights a "moral issue" that was "as old as the scriptures and as clear as the American constitution." It was a nice thought, but neither document was all that clear on the question. Kennedy did, however, commit his administration to the civil rights bill. Is it possible to believe, he asked in an oblique reference to Cold War values, "that this is a land of the free except for the Negroes?" It was the first time since Reconstruction that a president had so sided with justice for African American people.[11]

Wallace was rapidly becoming a national symbol of defiance that transcended the South. He certainly knew he couldn't win a presidential nomination—at least yet. "But I could sure stir things up. I could show Kennedy there's a hell of a lot of folks up North who feel the same way we do down here," he concluded. He believed in his heart that his cause was not Southern, it was American. And the South wasn't the problem—he just knew it—the North was. The South was not an anomaly that needed to be reformed or protected. It was the most American of places, where virtue and order and freedom reigned. The Deep South was not trapped in some logy, Spanish moss–draped past; it was the future of American politics. Wallace knew he was the man to deliver the rest of the nation to the Southern ways of freedom.[12]

The month following Wallace's visit to Clayton, however, Kennedy visited Dallas to shore up political support in the state. His reception was hostile; the city was mean and cold against him. The "KO Kennedy" bumper stickers revealed both a feverish belief that Kennedy was too soft on Communism and too strong on defending the rights of Black people. Some were primed to believe that there was just too strong of a connection between the two.

Then came the awful scene that seared into the American consciousness: the open-air limo moving slowly before Dealey Plaza, Jackie in pink, the president's head suddenly snapping back, the agent urgently climbing up the back of the car. Droopy Lyndon Johnson of Texas took the oath of office in the forward cabin of Air Force One on the tarmac at Dallas's Love Field. The man liberals believed to be just another Southern cracker with power, the guy the worldly Kennedy insiders liked to call "Uncle Rufus Cornpone" behind his back, the guy who slapped backs and used the word "nigger" in the Senate cloak room, the master of the Senate who got things done—or prevented them from ever happening—was in charge. Seven and a half months later, Johnson would break through a deadlock of nearly one hundred years and pass the Civil Rights Act in July 1964.[13]

Meantime, Wallace moved from Alabama to the national stage in the fall of 1963 and spring of 1964. As he barnstormed the nation, he developed an almost magical capacity to dodge specific attacks on integration with arguments about the overreach of the federal government. Who didn't enjoy a feisty jab at the lumbering federal government? People around the nation began to see what the white folks in Clayton already appreciated: by wrapping racism into questions of federal power, and then making both race and federal intervention into an assault on American freedom, Wallace had himself a winning formula and a growing national audience. The governor's reputation as a "corn-pone redneck big-man-in-Alabama but nowhere else," as television newsman Mike Wallace put it, dissolved in the face of his quick wit and belligerent charm. He had low expectations on his side. "Hi, yall. Sho good to see yall," Wallace privately goofed around, mimicking Northern assumptions about his appearance. "I'm jes an ig'rant ol' hookwormy redneck from Alabama come up to visit yall," Wallace said, mocking his audience's presuppositions. "Ain't had no education and didn't wear no shoes 'til I was thirty, but I come to ask yall for yall's vote." There were plenty of racists up North, but they rarely had a chance to hear a real firebrand. What they got instead was one of the craftiest figures in American political history.[14]

Audiences at various universities, radio shows, and television programs in 1963 and 1964 liked him—quite unexpectedly for most Northerners. When liberal Berkeley, California, voted down an open housing initiative, he noted, "They voted just like the people in Alabama." He reminded his Chicago audience that Martin Luther King Jr. found the midwestern city to be the most segregated place in the United States. He disagreed with Abraham Lincoln, he argued, because Honest Abe thought that Negroes weren't ready to vote or hold public office. Wallace thought they could be—at some point. He proved sharp, too. At Harvard, he attacked the social science methodology that had been used to defeat the separate-but-equal doctrine in the *Brown* decision. He cited the *Federalist Papers* and attacked the qualifications of the Supreme Court Justices. When the grandson of W. E. B. Du Bois tried to bait him at Harvard, Wallace countered that they work together. "Between you and me both, we might kick out that crowd down in Washington," he proclaimed. "Maybe we should run on the same ticket." Although he was plagued by protestors wherever he went, even hostile crowds often couldn't help themselves from bursting into laughter and applause despite their politics.[15]

His success suggested that much more of white America was Wallace Country than many were comfortable imagining. Governor for barely more than a year, the audacious "Fightin' Judge" decided to enter the Wisconsin Democratic presidential primary in March 1964. Lyndon Johnson undoubtedly had a lock on the Democratic nomination, but the governor was there to test his national power and, as always, to send them a message. By the time he landed his little prop plane in Wisconsin to file for the state primary, he had replaced one of two Confederate battle flags on the side of the plane with the US flag. Where it once said "Stand Up for Alabama," it now read "Stand Up for America." The South had largely been playing defense since the surrender at Appomattox Courthouse. Now George Wallace was ready to go on the offense and take the Southern cry for white freedom to the national level.

Working-class voters on the southside of Milwaukee confirmed Wallace's wildest hopes. In front of seven hundred Polish Americans at Serb Hall, his national campaign found a key piece of its base. In a world of "brats, beer, and bowling," the barrel-chested men of Serb Hall received him with the same enthusiasm as the high school football fans in Clayton. The overflowing crowds in the drab meeting hall greeted him with endless choruses of "Dixie"—*in Polish*. "Dixie sounds good in Polish," the governor later remarked. On the surface, these were not Wallace's people—Catholic, ethnic, Eastern European—the working-class heroes who flocked into Franklin Roosevelt's New Deal coalition and backed the Catholic John Kennedy. But things had been changing, and coalitions were shifting. Bronko Gruber, a local tavern owner who helped organize the rally, introduced Wallace. He called out two African Americans in attendance who failed to stand for the National Anthem, delivering a chorus of "boos" and shouts of "Send them back to Africa." Gruber descended into a horrible litany of stereotypes. "They beat up old ladies 83-years-old, rape our womenfolk. They mug people. They won't work. They are on relief. How long can we tolerate this? Did I fight at Guadalcanal and come back for this?"[16]

The room overflowed with white rage, but Wallace artfully deflected much of the overt racism toward animosity for the federal government. He attacked the godless Supreme Court for outlawing the Bible from public schools; he indicted the State Department for abandoning Poland; and he argued that the civil rights bill would "destroy the union seniority system and impose racial quotas" that would allegedly put their jobs at risk. He told his audience, already angry about open housing laws, that the bill would prevent homeowners from having the freedom to sell their home to whomever they wanted. He argued in every way he could that federal intrusions in their lives were ruining the things they needed and respected, without ever quite saying it was the fault of Black people directly. In a forty-minute address, he got thirty-four standing ovations. George Wallace owned the room. "For the man from Barbour County, Alabama," writes Wallace's biographer Dan T. Carter, the Milwaukee campaign stop was "an epiphany." It turned out that Wallace "had been right all along: these chunky Serbs and Hungarians and Poles, these hardworking Catholics, these Yankees, had embraced him with the same adoration that marked his passage among the masses of white Alabamians."[17]

As Wallace's midwestern popularity rose, the governor of Wisconsin blundered into a prediction he would come to regret: if Wallace managed to get 100,000 votes in his longshot run, then the 1964 state primary would be a "catastrophe." Wallace shocked everyone with 264,100 votes—30 percent of the primary vote. Wisconsin proved that he was viable even in the land of the progressive hero Fighting Bob LaFollette as well as Madison liberals and organized labor (and, obviously, Joe McCarthy as well). "We won without winning!" he jubilantly claimed as he danced in his hotel room in a Native American headdress he received. "It looks like a catastrophe has befallen some of my opponents," he deadpanned to the press.[18]

The Black newspaper the *Chicago Defender* explained that the Wisconsin vote meant that "racism was not an evil flower that bloomed only below the Mason and Dixon Line." The Wisconsin victory foretold an even more troubling problem. It may have been difficult to see in the middle of the Great Society, the Civil Rights Act, and the brewing war in Southeast Asia, but the Wisconsin primary showed that a new coalition could be built to exploit racial politics as a path to less government and more white freedom. Many antigovernment activists who had embraced states' rights conservativism, free markets, limited government, and a strict read of the Constitution suddenly found populist traction for their otherwise unpopular ideas. Their political vehicle would be blazoned with banners of American freedom, but the jet fuel that propelled it was racism. As one paper's headline blared after Wisconsin, "Notwithstanding the Bigots, It's Freedom!"[19]

Wallace had undoubtedly tapped into an important segment of angry blue-collar voters. But he also won middlebrow Rotarians as well as rich antitax and antigovernment activists, some of whom bristled at the racial politics of their new ally but marched forth with him nonetheless. His message in Wisconsin, warning of the "destruction of property rights" and the "unnatural and unhealthy accumulation of power in the hands of an all-powerful central bureaucracy," connected with his affluent backers. In fact, the governor's Wisconsin campaign was organized by an advertising executive who chaired the Wisconsin Economic Freedom Committee. His supporters in Wisconsin also included a smattering of kooks from the extreme radical right and plenty of limited government advocates lining up behind him in favor of the Liberty Amendment, a proposal pushed by conservative Californians to starve the welfare state by eliminating the federal income tax. Other supporters were Republican crossover voters prepared to embrace this new kind of right-wing populism. Wallace's populism created a strange and contradictory pile of bedfellows, uniting working-class and rich whites against Black people and the federal government.[20]

The Indiana and Maryland primaries came next. Just like in Wisconsin, Wallace won a 30 percent share of the votes in Indiana, with a remarkably strong showing in the unionized steel-producing region up in the northwestern part of the state. In Maryland, despite a tense campaign, he won a whopping 42.7 percent of the vote. "This is a victory for states' rights, local government and individual liberty in this country," Wallace declared. The press was flabbergasted. "If any responsible official had suggested six months ago that a segregationist from the Deep South could poll such a vote in Indiana," explained the *Indianapolis Star*, "he would have been hooted into silence and shuffled quietly into obscurity."[21]

After his big three primary "wins," however, the Wallace craze began to fizzle. Media attention turned to the inevitability of Johnson's nomination and, after exhaustive and heated congressional debate (including a fourteen-hour filibuster by Senator Robert C. Byrd), the final passage of the Civil Rights Act on July 2, 1964. Directed by

Lyndon Johnson's aggressive parliamentary skills, championed by leading Northern liberal Democrats, supported broadly by liberal Republicans, and buoyed by a "martyr-besotted electorate" after the Kennedy assassination, the act shattered a near century-old logjam on big and meaningful civil rights bills. It prohibited discrimination and segregation in public places and facilities, and it made employment discrimination illegal—essentially making the controversial FEPC from World War II into a permanent national body in the form of the Equal Employment Opportunity Commission. It was the Second Reconstruction, and Lyndon Johnson from Nowhere, Texas, was suddenly acting a lot like General U. S. Grant—and at times even sounding like Radical Republican Thaddeus Stevens.[22]

Two days after the passage of the Civil Rights Act, Wallace appeared at a rabid segregationist demonstration called "American Patriots Day" in Atlanta, Georgia. The bleachers of a stock car track were crammed, shoulder to shoulder, with people sweating in the bright sun, clothed in white shirts and blouses, forming a sea of bleached-white humanity densely peppered with white "George Wallace" signs. In addition to Wallace's appearance, there was a pantheon of other segregationists, including the head of the Georgia Klan, Mississippi governor Ross Barnett, and future Georgia governor Lester Maddox. Barnett began by asking, "Are you with us in the fight for freedom?"[23]

As Wallace was about to be introduced, cheers dissolved into screams of "Kill 'em!" as white men began beating a small number of African American members of the Student Nonviolent Coordinating Committee (SNCC) with metal folding chairs. Others rushed to assist by kicking, hitting, and smashing chairs down upon the activists. The police stopped the white men from pummeling the protestors, possibly to death. When Wallace finally appeared, he ignored the violence, raising both his hands in "V for Victory" signs before launching into one of his more vitriolic speeches.[24]

Wallace declared the Civil Rights Act to be "the assassin's knife stuck in the back of liberty" and "the most monstrous piece of legislation ever enacted," forcing "us back into bondage." He then turned to one of his growing analogies of convenience: that liberals were basically communists—the black hole of freedom in postwar America. "I do not call the members of the United States Supreme Court Communists. But I do say, and I submit for your judgement, the fact that every single decision of the Court in the past ten years... has been decided against freedom and in favor of tyranny." The broad brush of Communism had nothing to do with Marx and Lenin, it was merely shorthand for antifreedom, anything that challenged the "American way of life."[25]

Few leaders in the United States in 1964 loved "freedom" and hated communists more than Arizona Republican senator Barry Goldwater. Most "modern" Republicans had accommodated themselves to the New Deal; Barry Goldwater wanted to destroy it. While Goldwater regarded Wallace as a racist brute, his positions paralleled Wallace's even if he liked to believe his were cloaked in higher principles. Goldwater opposed the Supreme Court's *Brown v. Board* decision as an unwarranted intrusion into states' rights and individual liberties. He also voted against the Civil Rights Act on constitutional grounds. At the 1964 Republican Convention, he outmaneuvered liberal Republican Nelson Rockefeller to gain the nomination as a true conservative, one ready to slice down the government, repeal the income tax, and shutter programs and departments. "Extremism in the defense of liberty is no vice," he famously proclaimed at the convention, and "moderation in the pursuit of justice is no virtue." His campaign slogan was: "In your heart, you know he's right." The Democrats' response was, "In your guts, you know he's nuts."

Like Wallace, Goldwater argued that the Civil Rights Act would lead to "the loss of our God-given liberties." He saw it not as part of a hundred-year struggle for post-emancipation citizenship for African Americans, but as the seeds of authoritarianism. The act, Goldwater argued, would "require the creation of a federal police force of mammoth proportions. It also bids fair to result in the development of an 'informer' psychology in great areas of our national life—neighbors spying on neighbors, workers spying on workers, businessmen spying on businessmen, where those who would harass their fellow citizens for selfish and narrow purposes will have ample inducement to do so.

These, the federal police force and an 'informer' psychology, are the hallmarks of the police state and landmarks in the destruction of a free society."[26]

His racially anodyne vision said nothing of the actual police state that already beat and bombed Black people. While Goldwater couched his fears of creeping totalitarianism in the high principles and virtues of small government, many of his supporters heard the cruder but parallel message that George Wallace had been sending. As King argued, Goldwater may not have been a racist but his policies bred racism. Goldwater believed "civil rights must be left, by and large to the states." No matter what the alleged higher principle at stake was, "states' rights" always meant surrendering the protection of American citizenship to the likes of George Wallace.[27]

The racial conscience of the Republican Party—the segment that connected to Lincoln, to Radical Reconstruction, to dining with Booker T. Washington, to opposing lynching—all but died at the San Francisco convention. A certain bloodthirstiness surfaced, as the 1964 convention became less about genteel country club values and grew more vicious, conspiratorial, and overtly racist. *Newsweek* called Goldwater's nomination "an authentic party revolution, born of deep-seated frustration with the existing order." Others saw something even darker, as rank-and-file Republicans were making racial connections on their own. The Associated Press wire was headlined "Negro Delegates at GOP Convention Suffer Week of Humiliation." African American delegates reported being harassed, spurned, threatened, and physically accosted. Brooklyn Dodgers baseball hero Jackie Robinson found the situation "unbelievable." From his position on the convention floor, he said, "I now believe I know how it felt to be a Jew in Hitler's Germany."[28]

Perhaps a natural alliance was in the offing. Seymore Trammell, a Barbour County native and political brawler who served as one of Wallace's top aides throughout the sixties, recalled Wallace's blunt words on the topic of a possible Goldwater-Wallace ticket. With "all my big victories of the past two years," Trammell recalled Wallace saying, "it must be apparent to a one-eyed nigguh who can't see good outa his other eye, that me and Goldwater would be a winning ticket. We'd have the South locked up, then him and me could concentrate on the industrial states of the North and win." Leading up to the Republican convention, it did seem that Goldwater had been sending seductive praise the governor's way. As a result, Wallace sent an Alabama Goldwater supporter out to the San Francisco Republican Convention to float the idea of putting Wallace on the ticket with Goldwater.[29]

The idea barely got a hearing. Goldwater rejected the possibility of an anti-statist, freedom-loving, racist rapprochement with the Alabama governor. Goldwater's kind words had been designed to lull Wallace into giving up on any ideas of a third-party bid—not to create an alliance with his racist demagoguery. If Wallace stayed in the race, he would divide the Southern vote and weaken Goldwater's growing power in the historically Democratic region. The reality was that in the fall of 1964, Wallace's insurgent political fortunes were fizzling as Johnson took control of his party's fortunes. Besides, Goldwater hated him anyway.

Goldwater, who hoped to avoid the scenario of having his campaign hinging on civil rights, ended up winning only Arizona and the five Deep South states where white voters hated the Civil Rights Act as much as he did. The unionized Polish workmen of Serb Hall were not Barry Goldwater's guys. Lyndon Johnson defeated Goldwater in one of the biggest landslides in American history, with 62 percent of the vote. The *Eufaula Tribune*, in contrast, believed that Goldwater had 98 percent of the Barbour County vote locked up. As an Alabama auto dealer explained, "I have always been a Democrat. I always pulled just one lever—for the Democrats—and I never thought I'd do anything else. But not this year. I'll be pulling a different lever—the one marked Goldwater." He attributed the switch to his belief that the "Republican Party has the South more at heart," he explained. "It seems to me like the Republican Party now is almost like the old Democratic Party."[30]

The long-festering cracks in the Solid South could be heard splitting asunder across southeastern Alabama in 1964. George M. Grant had been elected to Congress in 1938 and won eleven subsequent consecutive victories with impeccable credentials as a white Southern Democrat: he signed the "Southern Manifesto" opposing *Brown v. Board*, he voted against the Civil Rights Act of 1957, and he was on the board of trustees of Bob Jones University. In the 1964 primary, he nonetheless fended off a challenge from a retired rear admiral from the extreme right wing who snarled viciously racist and anti-Semitic terms in the campaign. Then, the unimaginable happened. In the fall 1964 regular election, in what was supposed to be a one-party state, a recent convert to the Republican Party named Bill Dickinson beat George M. Grant by a stunning 25 points. Alabama's Second US Congressional District, including Barbour County and much of the rest of the southeast corner of the state, had not seen a viable Republican candidate, let alone one they would vote for, in multiple generations. By voting for Dickinson, the white people of southeast Alabama rejected the passage of the Civil Rights Act in astonishing numbers. Dickinson remained a Republican and went on to be the longest-serving representative in Alabama history.

Congressman Dickinson's positions on questions of the civil rights movement were beyond clear. When it came to the fight over the schools, he claimed that the federal schools bill would allow the government to "control the minds and channel the thinking of our children in a totalitarian manner that could well have been devised by the inmates of the Kremlin." When President Johnson made his voting rights speech, Dickinson claimed it had "something for everyone except the most discriminated minority of all—The Southern white." The pending Voting Rights Act was designed "to further usurp the powers of the states under the guise of the helping hand of Big Brother." While many of his colleagues in the House debated serious issues of state, Congressman Dickinson took to the House floor to explain that the Selma March was marked by "human flotsam: adventurers, beatniks, prostitutes, and similar rabble" all enjoying free love and drunken interracial "sex orgies." Echoing the preposterous findings of J. Edgar Hoover's FBI, which had been spying on and wiretapping Martin Luther King, he claimed the movement was part of a "systematic" plot by the Communist Party to seed sectional divisions between the Deep South and the rest of the nation. King had personally, Dickinson claimed, amassed more than sixty communist-front affiliations since 1955.[31]

The word "backlash" became "the word of the year in American politics" in 1964, and Wallace was its central figure. Racism, the politics of resentment, the fight against federal intrusion, and the defense of a dominating sense of freedom seemed to be everywhere that year. White people, too, were oppressed, forgotten, and left out, the argument went, their freedoms trammeled by an out-of-control federal government supporting solely the interests of Black people. Political writer Theodore White described the backlash as a "midsummer political thunderhead . . . dangerous as it approached, but then over very quickly." This was hardly the case. The backlash tapped into a highly resonant political myth of victimization, but also seemed to describe the rise of something atavistic, uneducated, unresolved, or the product of an "authoritarian personality." Anyone who knew history, however, could see these ideas were as old as the republic. Martin Luther King Jr. said "backlash" was "a new name for an old phenomenon" that "had always existed underneath and sometimes on the surface of American life." From whites' resistance to federal oversight of Creek Indian removal to Reconstruction to laws against lynching to the civil rights struggle, it was clear that whatever the backlash was, it was not just about 1964. It was about a continuous strand in American history itself.[32]

On March 7, 1965, the Alabama police unleashed their infamous, merciless riot on peaceful protestors as they attempted to cross the Edmund Pettus Bridge in Selma. The police—some mounted on horses, all armed with nightsticks and gas masks—descended upon the band of protestors, who quickly fell or scattered under the force of the rampage, the massive clouds of tear gas, and the swinging batons. The entire nation watched events on their television sets that Sunday night—as the horrific footage from earlier that day interrupted the television debut of Spencer Tracy struggling to make sense of Nazis in *Judgment at Nuremberg*. Among many serious injuries, a policeman cracked the skull of the young SNCC leader, later congressman, John Lewis, in what became known in the movement as "Bloody Sunday." The nation took notice, and Selma forced a tug-of-war over the federal government.

Governor Wallace knew in his heart that if he could just talk to President Johnson that he could convince him that the agitators and radicals were out of control—on the verge of taking over his state. Wallace wanted federal troops called in to control the protestors—not the locals. What should have shocked and concerned Wallace was the fact that President Johnson all but leapt at the chance to meet. Lyndon Johnson liked nothing more than a head-to-head chance to convince someone of what be believed to be the "right" thing to do. Wallace got his audience with the president and flew up to Washington to have a sit-down with a fellow Southerner.

On the day Wallace arrived, the president was unprepared for the hastily organized meeting. "What should I ask him to do?" he asked Attorney General Nick Katzenbach, who had already faced Wallace down at the schoolhouse door two years prior. "I don't know," the attorney general replied, "What do you want him to do?" Johnson scrambled. "Write down six things for me," the president replied. "I don't give a damn how outrageous they are." Katzenbach supposedly had thirty-three lawyers working out the legal questions involved in deploying federal troops in Alabama. None of them were in favor of federal deployment of force no matter who they were protecting. All the legal calculations were dissolving into one ad hoc meeting.[33]

When Wallace arrived, Johnson ushered him onto the couch. The governor sank in low, which exaggerated the already sizable height difference between him and the towering president. Then Johnson pulled up his rocking chair, grabbed Wallace's knee, and locked eyes on his prey. It was time to stop "looking back to 1865 and start planning for 2065," Johnson told him. Seymore Trammell, who had been with Wallace since the Barbour County days, feared the conversation was already off course. "The problem we've come to discuss," Trammell interjected, was "the racial agitators and the growing menace of the Communist demonstrators in Alabama." Johnson shifted his attention toward Wallace's assistant. The president, Trammell recalled, "looked at me like I was some kind of dog mess." Johnson handed Trammell a tiny stub of a pencil and ordered him to take notes.[34]

Johnson fixed his glare on Wallace. Like some lanky Texas soothsayer, he seemed to see both Wallace's New Deal past, his current racist posturing, and a future of repentance for his racist manipulations. "George, why are you doing this? You ought not. You came into office a liberal—you spent all your life wanting to do things for the poor. Now why are you working on this? Why are you off on this black thing? You ought to be down there calling for help for Aunt Susie in the nursing home." The governor needed to think about his legacy, the president argued. "What do you want left when you die?" he asked. "Do you want a great big marble monument that reads, 'George Wallace—He Built,' or do you want a little piece of scrawny pine board that reads, 'George Wallace—He Hated'?" Johnson moved through Katzenbach's last-minute list of things they wanted done. You should comply with federal courts, he told the governor, stop the brutal suppression of the protestors, and declare for freedom of assembly. Most of all, the president demanded that the governor should back universal suffrage—a point on the list that just happened to correspond with the president's current political project, the Voting Rights Act.[35]

If Wallace wanted to end the demonstrations as he claimed, Johnson argued, he had the power in his hands for a quick solution. "Why don't you let the niggers vote?" The answer was simple, Wallace responded. County registrars made the voting registration decisions, not him. Wallace shouldn't have gone there. "Don't you shit me, George Wallace." He had hit a sore spot, since white Alabama had a long history of making sure anyone they did not like would not get on the ballot—a list that included Lincoln, Truman, and Lyndon Johnson. "You had the power to keep the President of the United States off the ballot," he said, referencing Wallace's machinations to have LBJ's name purged from the Alabama state ballot. "Surely you have the power to tell a few poor county registrars what to do." The meeting went on for over three hours, as Trammell remained silent with stubby pencil in hand, and Lyndon Johnson owned George Wallace. The two Southern politicians emerged from their meeting with a confident Johnson and a "cowed and pliable" George Wallace. "When the President works on you," he told his aides on the flight home, "there's not a lot you can do." At a press conference that night, Johnson said he "urged that the Governor publicly declare his support of universal suffrage." LBJ would, he announced, be submitting the Voting Rights Act to Congress the following week.[36]

Two days later, Lyndon Johnson called upon Congress to pass the Voting Rights Act in what was probably the best speech he ever delivered. He combined a secular faith in the nation, the religious motifs of the movement, the honorable acts of the protestors, and appeals to the history and conscience of the nation to make a case that the exercise of federal authority in defense of voting rights was an urgent, moral necessity. If the South wanted to avoid a confrontation, then the answer was just as he told Wallace: "Open your polling places to all of your people. Allow men and women to register and vote whatever the color of their skin. Extend the rights of citizenship to every citizen of this land." Invoking the unbearable delay since the end of Reconstruction, he said, "The time for waiting is gone." And then he did the unthinkable—he connected the moral plight of African Americans to an ongoing struggle for the heart of the nation: "But even if we pass this bill, the battle will not be over. What happened in Selma is part of a far larger movement which reaches into every section and State of America. It is the effort of American Negroes to secure for themselves the full blessings of American life. Their cause must be our cause too. Because it is not just Negroes, but really it is all of us, who must overcome the crippling legacy of bigotry and injustice."

Then Johnson stretched out every single word into what seemed its own sentence: "And—we—shall—overcome." With this single utterance, he, a Southern Democrat, aligned his party with the refrain of the freedom struggle in no uncertain terms. Martin Luther King Jr., his chair drawn up close to the television set to watch the speech, sat in stunned disbelief. People in the room said a tear trailed down his cheek.[37]

A few days after Johnson's voting rights speech, Judge Frank Johnson gave civil rights protestors permission to complete their fifty-four-mile march from Selma to Montgomery. With the Justice Department, the FBI, the federal marshals, nineteen jeeps, four military trucks, and two helicopters watching over the situation, the third attempt to march from Selma to Montgomery began. By the time they hit the narrow part of the highway, they culled their ranks to just over the limit of three hundred marchers set by Judge Johnson. They faced only petty resistance this time, largely because Wallace had capitulated. He appeared before the state legislature just prior to the march and declared, "I do not ask you for cowardice, but I ask you for restraint in the same tradition that our outnumbered forefathers followed." Even "though it be galling," he asked white Alabamians to "stay home." He would refuse to protect the marchers, shifting the blame to Washington for whatever might become of them. "The federal courts have created this matter," and it would be up to the feds to "provide for the safety and welfare of the so-called demonstrators." He washed his hands of the situation, and the state house erupted in applause for what was basically Wallace's bitter retreat. "I have kept faith with you," he declared. Wallace again affirmed his unique political skill set: losing the fight but winning the politics.[38]

When the marchers made it to Montgomery four days later, some twenty-five thousand people gathered at the same spot on the capitol steps where, just a couple of years earlier, white Alabama stood to applaud Wallace's "Segregation Forever" speech. Although more bombs had been planted in Birmingham, and Viola Liuzzo, who had driven down from Detroit to assist the march, had been murdered by Klansmen, the tables had turned. The governor and his aides peered at the enormous African American crowd from behind the curtain in an office in the capitol building, one jesting that the assembled throngs might one day be the voting constituency of Alabama's future. "Don't say that," Wallace replied.[39]

Five months later, the Voting Rights Act became the law of the land.

CHAPTER NINETEEN

The SCOPE of Freedom

CIVIL RIGHTS ACTIVISTS WERE coming around to the realization that there was just so very much work left to do. After the momentous decade between the Montgomery Bus Boycott in 1955 and Selma in 1965, "it wasn't glamourous anymore," remarked Virginia Durr, the white activist and matron of the Montgomery civil rights scene. The breakthrough laws had been passed, but so much work remained on the local level. "There was no romance" left in what lay ahead, she wrote; "It was just grinding head-on work." As the Reverend Ed King noted in 1966, "We don't have anything left to sing about. There isn't enough to praise."[1]

New federal laws may had been passed, but the tenant farmers and domestic workers were still there, the same county voting registrar was still there, the sheriff and the governor were still there, and the segregated schools were still there. The civil rights movement had become a national public mural of heroism and triumph, but what remained was an ongoing pointillist project to be made up of countless unknown dramas, internal conflicts, and attempts to draw federal power into the fight on behalf of local people. The untold, dirt-level fights that never became part of history—in unfamous, unfilmed, unknown places like Barbour County—are where the majority of people experienced, or failed to experience, the Black freedom struggle.

The fight against the white version of freedom—one that said if you cannot be a master then you are not free, that if federal authority is not on your side it should not exist—neither started nor ended with those heroic stories. As it was in the first Reconstruction, so whites hoped it would be with the Second Reconstruction: the defeat of local-level organizing despite the promise of federal law. The last Reconstruction in Barbour County ended in a hail of bullets from local rifles as federal troops turned a blind eye. Whether it could be different a century later remained the key question after the Civil Rights and Voting Rights Acts.

A young divinity student named Larry Butler believed that this time it would be different. In the spring of 1965, Butler was walking across the campus at Dickinson College in Pennsylvania when one of his professors stopped him. Some recruiters from King's Southern Christian Leadership Conference (SCLC) had been looking for him. Butler was the chairman of the campus chapter of the Congress of Racial Equality, more commonly known as CORE, and the recruiters were hoping he could help to organize a meeting of some students who might be interested in going down South to work on civil rights. One of the recruiters was a gangly, smooth-faced young African American man named Leroy Moton. Anyone paying attention to the movement that spring might have recognized him. He had been in the car when the white volunteer Viola Liuzzo was gunned down and murdered by the Klan—and an FBI informant—after the final Selma march. Since it was Moton standing right in front of him, Larry Butler had no illusions about what he might be getting into if he joined the new wave of volunteers heading south. In Alabama, allies were few, and enemies were everywhere. Butler signed up.[2]

The stakes were high. The year before, in the summer of 1964, the Mississippi Freedom Summer Project had barely begun when three young activists were killed. While nobody invited death, such horrible events helped bring federal attention and power to bear on the South. In January 1964, Bob Moses, the Student Nonviolent Coordinating Committee (SNCC) leader and architect of Freedom Summer, made the stakes clear. "The Federal Government must take action even if it means the imposition of federal troops or the occupation of a town or particular locality." If a young Black person got killed in Mississippi or Alabama, it was of no urgent concern to the nation. Asking the children of the elite to place their minds, skills, dedication, and bodies on the line could change the national equation. "These students," Moses said, "bring the rest of the country with them. They're from good schools and their parents are influential. The interest of the country is awakened, and when that happens, the Government responds to that interest." Unfortunately, when the Freedom Summer Project brought its message to the Democratic Convention in Atlantic City in the form of the Mississippi Freedom Democratic Party, they were refused seating in the name of maintaining a stable liberal order under Lyndon Johnson. The segregated Southern delegations remained a crucial, if tenuous, part of the Democratic coalition.[3]

When SCLC launched their summer project in 1965, the year after Freedom Summer, they had the same tactics in mind but with a slightly different strategic vision. King announced the SCLC plan, called the Summer Community Organization and Political Education Project, almost always referred to as SCOPE, in April at UCLA just a month after the Selma to Montgomery march. To the extent that Freedom Summer confronted the liberal establishment, SCOPE danced intimately and directly with SCLC's legislative priorities, of which there was exactly *one* in the summer of 1965: the passage and especially implementation of the Voting Rights Act. Unfortunately, the timing was tricky. Launched in late spring, the plan depended upon the swift passage of the voting rights bill, otherwise there would be a flood of volunteers ready to register and mobilize voters for the 1966 elections who would be exposed to the potential white violence with no federal protection. To run SCOPE, King selected Hosea Williams, whom he liked to call his "Castro" for his militant capacity to make things happen. He quickly sent recruiters like Moton out to find volunteers like Butler.[4]

Bayard Rustin, the strategic visionary for SCLC, encapsulated the organization's thinking about where to go next in his famous essay "From Protest to Politics," which came out the February before the recruiters found Larry Butler. Rejecting the civil rights movement's drift toward greater autonomy, he sought to embed them in a broader social democratic coalition. "No social movement has ever been successful in this country which did not involve as an ally the hard-core white middle class," Rustin argued to the SCLC board in a summary of his thinking. Yet SNCC could counter Rustin with the liberals' betrayal in the seating crisis in Atlantic City, the FBI's vicious harassment of the movement, and, soon, the escalation of the Vietnam War, all of which compromised just about any claim to justice that midsixties liberals could make. Many SNCC workers saw the federal government as an enemy, not an ally. As the SNCC research director put it, the federal voting rights bill was "completely fraudulent," embedded and complicit in "the whole racist structure of the enormously complex U.S. government," which "provides those who govern with too many 'outs.'" The Great Society, he claimed, was little more than a "confidence game."[5]

Others saw hope in the new federal stance on civil rights. Larry Butler, a practicing Quaker, needed little convincing about SCLC's plans for SCOPE. He and other white students from Dickinson and nearby Gettysburg College poured into a green Plymouth Valiant and a VW bus and headed south. With coffee-stained road maps plotting their course, they navigated their way to Morris Brown College in Atlanta on June 14 to begin training. Given the violence in the news, and the fact King had just announced the program in late April, only five hundred volunteers showed up, a quarter of the number they had hoped for. Yet they received formal preparation like few others ever had or ever would. Led by Bayard Rustin, the training program included sessions with Martin Luther King Jr., the Reverend Ralph Abernathy, and Hosea Williams. Other sessions included a staggering array of talent: Vernon Jordan of the Urban League; John Doar, assistant attorney general for civil rights; Ralph Helstein of the racially progressive meatpackers union; Michael Harrington, author of *The Other America*; and SCLC's Andrew Young, among many other members of the organization's staff. The historians John

Hope Franklin and C. Vann Woodward spoke about the deep history of oppression the kids were going to confront. As Woodward told the volunteers, "You will be living intimately with a lot of history. The past will be part your daily environment." As part of the training, the Reverend James Bevel, an SCLC leader raised as a Mississippi sharecropper but who later appeared like a North African mystic in his workers' clothes, bald head, and yarmulke, read the moment like an oracle. "Negroes have seen what white America has done with its freedom," he declared, and they "are worried."[6]

Their training complete, the workers fanned out to 120 different counties in the South. Butler and his group were crestfallen to learn from leadership that the people of Henry County, Alabama, were not ready for freedom workers yet. They were redirected to a new location, a place called Barbour County, where they were told the NAACP had been laying solid groundwork on voter registration

In anticipation of the passage of the Voting Rights Act, SCLC's master organizer Hosea Williams trained northern SCOPE volunteers at the Freedom House in Atlanta. After instruction in everything from history to organizing to nonviolent tactics, the volunteers headed out to their assigned counties to work on voter registration in the summer of 1965.

in the 1950s. None of them had ever heard of Barbour County. The whole idea "left us unimpressed," Butler noted, "until we learned that George Wallace had come from Barbour County." With that fact, he recalled, "there was no more discussion; we were on our way."[7]

"The poverty is beyond belief," Butler noted in his journal as he entered Barbour County. "Mules beside shacks on stilts and scrubby fields. 'Sticks' is too urban of a word for these places." The SCOPE workers immediately made their presence known to the mayor of Eufaula, who had a picture of himself with local hero George Wallace on his desk. The mayor was so shocked that civil rights workers had deployed to his remote corner of the state, Butler recalled, that "his mouth dropped enough for me to catch a doctor's view of his throat and his face burned the color that milk does when it begins to sour. And sour is what the mayor did."[8]

The volunteers sensed the city leaders were genuinely nervous about the presence of nine young white people who had come to town to stir up trouble. Yet the freedom workers also felt vulnerable. "Here were two girls and seven boys against the white structure of a county with all its money, police and power, and they were nervous," Butler noted. "We thought about it and decided that they knew their time had come, they knew what organized negro citizens could do, they knew that once a slave [senses] freedom, that the old ways are gone forever."[9]

As rumors swirled that the "freedom riders" had arrived, Black locals flocked to see the exotics: young white people prepared to stand up for voting rights. The first mass meeting at Eufaula's Baptist Academy was packed with over two hundred people. The cops were there, too, taking down every license plate number of every car in the vicinity of the church. Butler's religious faith quickly revealed itself as a point of connection to the local community. An SCLC volunteer remembered him as extroverted and flamboyant, "shaking his long hair away from his forehead" at the pulpit as he "energized this audience." After a bit of preaching, Butler reflected, "It never fails to delight me to see the expression on people[']s faces to see holiness or Baptist preaching from a Northern boy. I've got to admit that I enjoy preaching. Once I get started it seems that I'm not doing the speaking. It[']s amazing." The people started calling him Reverend Larry.[10]

Following two weeks of canvassing, registration classes, flyer distribution, and what the movement called "mass meetings" no matter how many showed up, the civil rights workers were ready. Despite threats and intimidation—some of it armed—the Barbour SCOPE volunteers had their first voter registration day on July 5 in Clayton. The number of county registration opportunities was strictly limited by state constitutional design. Even prior to the passage of the Voting Rights Act, the Clayton drive proved successful. Besides a lot of verbal harassment, the only trouble they had was a man who tried to run them over with his truck. Well over 200 people showed up. Given the intentionally slow, grinding nature of the county registrar's process, of those, only 90 actually got to take the required literacy exam. Of those, 21 new voters were registered. The registration drive in Eufaula delivered similar success: a pool of 150 applicants waiting in line, 92 processed, and 16 registered. Clearly, it was going to be a long haul to get a critical mass of Barbour County African Americans added to the rolls even when interest was high.[11]

While helping to get voters registered in Clayton, the field workers noticed a car parked in a body shop across the street from the Barbour County courthouse. Inside the car, they saw a short, intensely focused white man watching their moves. It was none other than Clayton's favorite son, Governor George Wallace, who had come to size up the registration of African Americans in his hometown. The gears must have already been turning in his head, calculating how some day he might be able to win these new voters to his side, too. In fact, Wallace remained tight-lipped on the Voting Rights Act itself, merely encouraging as much countervailing white voter turnout as he possibly could. The SCOPE workers were "aglow" at the idea that the most vocal segregationist in America was concerned enough to stake out their registration process. The governor only made one comment the entire afternoon. On the campaign trail he was known to reflexively impugn all "beatniks" and their sartorial standards. At Clayton, however, he changed his tune: "That's the best dressed group of civil rights workers I've ever seen."[12]

After the excitement of the first registration, the doldrums took hold. For the rest of July, there were more mass meetings, organizing, classes, and canvassing, but not a lot more movement and no more registration days. Under SCLC's direction, SCOPE workers had pledged to stick to voter registration and not build a broader social movement, which limited their abilities. Events in Bogalusa, Louisiana, transformed the Barbour County SCOPE operation's position on the social movement question. Word had gone out that any volunteers who were able to do so should make their way to Bogalusa since things were heating up. Several volunteers, including Larry Butler, piled into the car and drove across Alabama to Louisiana. There, they were impressed with what they found. Local people "were running their own movement, they were men and women, who appreciated help, but let it be known they were the leaders." Butler could see how the movement had transformed the community. "The folks over there were whole persons," he wrote to his parents. "They ran the demonstrations and negotiations and they knew it. It was great working with people (negroes) who weren't afraid of whites, of militancy, of the governor or ashamed of being Negro. We hope to do the same here."[13]

The SCOPE workers now had something to aspire to. Bogalusa gave them their first lesson in "creative conflict," that is, generating resistance among the populace through the inventive use of disputes. They realized that their policy of not having demonstrations and working narrowly on voter registration might have worked after the Voting Rights Act passed, but it was inadequate to the task before it passed. Rather than avoid friction and conflict, they could use them, even make them, to generate unity, clarity, and confrontation. "It was a new SCOPE group that came back" from Louisiana. Butler declared that SCOPE needed to be more than a "ladies aid society to register voters."[14]

With permission granted from SCLC, confrontations ensued—demonstrations, integrated takeovers of restaurants, public meetings on the courthouse steps. As designed, confrontation generated further confrontation. Harassment by officials and people on the street became common. On July 29 three volunteers were arrested in Clayton for "operating in Alabama too long without a permit." Volunteers were run off the road, assaulted in their cars and on the streets; local clergy had near fatal shotgun blasts through their windows; and arrests were taking place for everything from muffler "violations" to "disorderly conduct" to having insufficient funds in checking accounts.[15]

While the community organized, politicians in Washington debated the Voting Rights Act. After "Bloody Sunday" on the Edmund Pettus Bridge, President Johnson declared, "Many of the issues of civil rights are very complex and most difficult. But about this there can and should be no argument. Every American citizen must have an equal right to vote." Introduced in March, the act still didn't pass in April, May, June, or July—despite Johnson's demand that Congress pursue the bill with a sense of urgency and priority. The reconciled bill was finally signed into law on August 6, 1965. The entire Alabama delegation, both senators and eight representatives, voted against it.[16]

On the day the voting rights bill was to be signed in Washington, DC, Barbour County local Black activists were determined to express their voices from their tiny dot in southeastern Alabama. On August 6, the Voters' League, as the new community-based group was called, took to those famous broad tree-lined boulevards of Eufaula. They began their march with gloomy clouds and light showers already underway. Forecasters predicted worse weather to come. The local march for the bill ended in a complete Southern downpour, walls of water rushing from the sky. "Everyone was soaked to the skin," Butler recalled, "but on the way back you could hear the freedom songs for three blocks." Then the sun burst through, and the steam rose from the streets. "The sight of lines of now sunlit marchers dancing to the rhythm of freedom songs in wet clothes glued to swaying bodies is one that cannot fail to strike a chord in the most ironclad throat." They gathered at the church, singing freedom songs and dancing—still hoping for good news from Washington.[17]

Then came the word: President Lyndon Baines Johnson had signed the Voting Rights Act. The raucous sense of expectation in the church turned solemn. Everyone stopped, drew quiet, and prayed. The world's oldest democracy had, for the first time, committed itself to becoming an actual democracy. It came late, but the work could now begin. The civil rights workers had managed to register 611 people in Barbour County before the act. The next county registration day, August 16, there were an estimated four or five hundred potential new voters lined up at the Eufaula Courthouse ready to take advantage of the new law. Unfortunately, the local authorities were still not ready to change their heel-dragging ways.[18]

Meantime, there was a new face in town. The man locals came to call "Daddy Bone" showed up in Eufaula that August. Scott B. Smith Jr., a Black man born and raised in the South Side of Chicago, with the reputation of a bit of a "street hustler," became active in the Congress of Racial Equality, rose to vice chair of CORE's Chicago branch, and participated in the Chicago Board of Education sit-ins. He cut his teeth in the South working for Freedom Summer in Canton, Mississippi. Prior to showing up in Eufaula, he spent the previous year organizing alongside Stokely Carmichael in Lowndes County, Alabama, the center of the civil rights struggle—and the center of rising militancy among activists—in the southern United States. The freedom workers there were growing restless with the mainstream of the movement. Some in SNCC began to call King "da lawd" and derided SCLC's top-down tactics.[19]

Smith brought a different sensibility to Barbour County, one that did not always jibe well with the SCOPE volunteers. He had come from a different place, seen the beast, and struggled with it for too long. "I did not agree with being nonviolent," he said, looking back. "I did not, and I do not agree, even today, to be nonviolent. You lay your motherfucking hands on me, and you belong to me." Like many SNCC workers in the midsixties, he had grown impatient. "I had a great deal of difficulty with the civil rights leaders as they expounded constantly about nonviolence," Smith recalled, "while we getting shot at, chased, sometimes different ones were beaten. I didn't like that. I didn't like different ones in SNCC—John Lewis, [James] Forman—crying about nonviolence and being nonviolent." He said he got great "personal satisfaction" fighting the White Citizens' Council and the Klan. He was not interested in dreams of integration; he was interested in "revenge to what Black people had suffered in the past and even today." By 1967, after years in the movement, he stood before SNCC and declared, "I have learned how to hate. I know how to hate."[20]

Smith proudly sported a turkey bone—some whispered it might be an actual human bone—hanging on a leather thong around his neck like a talisman. Some thought that Daddy Bone's unusual necklace was part of his nonviolent practice: that whenever his anger at white oppression boiled to the surface, he would suck on that turkey bone to dissipate his rage. Smith attributed that well-worn bone to a completely different, more messianic, idea. In Ezekiel 37, the Lord sent Ezekiel into a valley of dry bones. Upon the Lord's orders, Ezekiel spoke to the bones. The dry scattered bones were brought back to life, bone to bone, tendon to tendon, and the living were then given a place in the Kingdom of Israel.[21]

In Daddy Bone's report back to SNCC offices, he made the stakes clear about how he saw the struggle in Wallace's Barbour County. "This county will receive the roughest amount of pressure, threats, intimidation because of Gov. Wallace['s] political ambitions for the senate seat in the US Congress and to save face and gather support from the racist element of the State, he will therefore, be forced—because of the position of the Black people are now uniting concern over their rights—to crush this Movement. He will obviously need the help of the Klan and that this move is on has been observed in the city of Eufaula and in the county." With the Voting Rights Act a reality, they could now run African Americans for local and state office. Yet Wallace, he believed, could not afford this in his home county. "Gov. Wallace has caused the seeds of racial hatred to grow to the heights of murders, beating, etc.... a height never known by one man holding the office of governor." As a result, he believed SNCC's job was to "keep the power structure off-balance while the people try and organize for themselves—their own credit union, anti-poverty program, loan improvement for new businesses—small business loans and newspapers."[22]

Despite suspicions about federal authority, Daddy Bone, like SNCC more broadly, still saw the clear need for the transformative power of the federal government. The Voting Rights Act provided for federal observers, often called federal "registrars" in the movement, who could penetrate the local power relations in a given county. Under an agreement with Attorney General Katzenbach (the same person Wallace had stared down in front of the schoolhouse door, now promoted from deputy AG), federal election examiners would be sent to any county where civil rights groups could provide evidence of voter discrimination or repression. Unfortunately, that meant just about every county in the Black Belt. Despite both SNCC and SCLC's pleas to the feds for a strong presence in Barbour County, the stumbling voter registration process had been going well enough that they had a hard time attracting federal attention. Barbour ultimately did not make the list of the seven counties in Alabama in desperate need of federal supervisors. Some believed the feds steered clear because it was Wallace's county and nobody wanted to tweak the segregationist's tail. No matter what the case, the isolated world of Barbour County remained obscured from the sunshine of federal oversight even after passage of the Voting Rights Act. "Without viable federal supervision," explains an Alabama historian, "fair adjudication at the polls regardless of the nature of the political challenge was a structural impossibility."[23]

Mike Bibler, a white volunteer who took over leadership and coordination in Eufaula after Larry Butler left, recalled the impact of federal presence. One day while he was at the Eufaula Freedom House, a white man knocked on the door. He turned out to be an investigator from the United States Department of Justice who had been looking into local complaints filed over the years. "The more we talked, I could tell he was sympathetic to our cause," Bibler recalled. He had visited city hall, where he found local leaders "petrified" that the federal authorities might take over the administration of all of Barbour County. He said that the city officials were trying to avoid federal intervention "at all costs."[24]

Even without federal registrars, the federal Voting Rights Act changed Barbour County, as the enormous courthouse lines suggested.

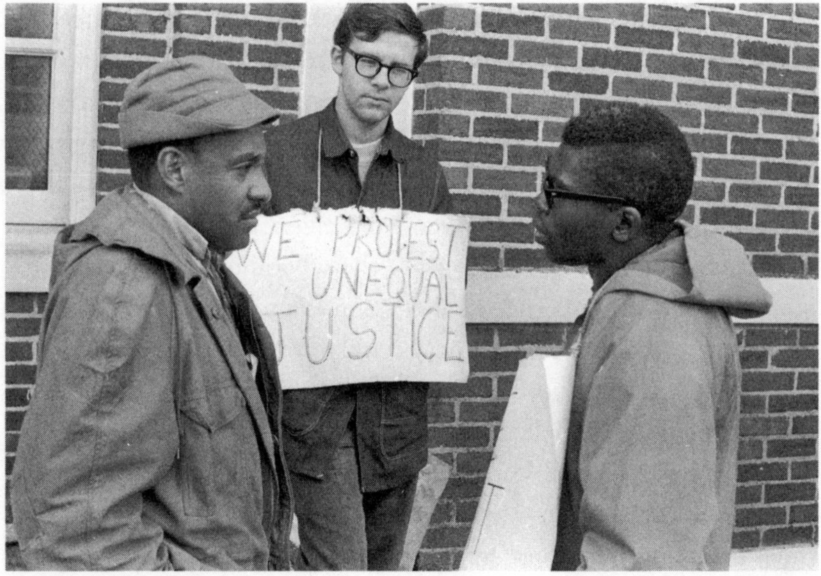

In front of the Barbour County courthouse in Eufaula, SNCC's Scott B. Smith (left) talks with SCOPE volunteers John Davis (right) and Mike Bibler (center) in November 1965. Their signs read "We Want Negro Jurors" and "We Protest Unequal Justice." Philosophical and strategic differences kept the two organizations at odds. Note the turkey bone around Smith's neck, the source of his nickname "Daddy Bone."

The new goal of the Voters' League was to extend and expand the days and hours for registration at the courthouse. They wanted an immediate two-week period of registration followed by an additional two nights every week from then on. The nature of the campaign changed. It became more in the streets, in the restaurants, on the courthouse steps, and, most importantly, in the schools. The residents themselves took over and accepted backup support from the outside volunteers. Permits could not be had, but marches continued without them—and in the presence of the police. Although marked with slow periods and seemingly insurmountable obstacles, the movement in Barbour County began to look exactly like the one Butler and his comrades had seen in Bogalusa.[25]

Then, as if foreordained, came the violence. The local police beat a man named Joseph Daniel Williams without mercy. He was a veteran with epilepsy and steel plates in his head as a result of his service, as well as a known activist from Abbeville. The Eufaula police pulled him over and, after some sort of tussle, wacked him across the head with a nightstick. More police showed up, and they handcuffed him, and the police all took to beating on Mr. Williams. They even continued to hit him in the car on the way to the Eufaula city jail. Upon hearing the news, everyone marched to the courthouse, where speeches were made by Leila Dennis, Lolita Jones, James Key, and Daddy Bone Smith. The mayor ordered everyone to disperse. Nobody did, and the speakers were all arrested. Rolling protests and sporadic arrests continued to give the movement the type of "creative conflicts" the SCOPE activists had been looking for.[26]

By design, however, SCOPE dissolved with the return of the academic semester. Most volunteers returned north, and the organization officially closed down across the South. Some, like Larry Butler, chose to stay on as regular SCLC field workers. The organization by then had its own Freedom House in Eufaula, consisting of a tiny one-story house on a dead-end road with an outhouse in the back and no hot water in the house. When two workers stayed there, recalled one volunteer, they slept at opposite ends of the little house. If they got bombed, hopefully one of them might survive.[27]

The African American women of Barbour County took over the movement and became the heart and soul of the Voters' League. The lists of speakers and office holders overflows with names like Mrs. Leila Dennis, Mrs. Mary Marshall (who would run for school board), Mrs. Jimmie Lou Osborne (affectionately called "Mom"), Mary Smith, Rose Jordan, Lolita Jones, Annie Craddox, Louis Slater, and Elizabeth Hoskey. Mrs. Emma Sheppard, seventy-one years old, marched in both Clayton and Eufaula, swearing to be with the movement "to the end." As so many studies of local civil rights movements show, women were not just "there too"; they staffed the movement, worked the movement, and ran the movement. Women faced jail time, organized mass meetings, and hosted meetings between registration drives. Nights on bare concrete floors in jail—the mattresses having been removed just for the freedom marchers' incarceration—were made bearable by the organizational work and solidarity of the local women activists. Despite the hardships, when the arrested Barbour protestors were freed and returned to the church, "the bus rang with freedom songs when we got to the mass meeting, and then the meeting was like a holiness service. Joy couldn't have been measured."[28]

Football was second only to church as a social institution in Eufaula, and during a football game between two Black high schools, Eufaula's McCoo and the Opelika school, eight young pickets of the local movement's "Youth Squad" appeared. The McCoo principal went onto the field, ripped up the signs, and demanded that the students leave. Eighty more protestors that had been gathering at the church showed up singing freedom songs, which then triggered several hundred more people cascading down from the bleachers to join them. The police showed up, deputized white bystanders, and then started launching tear gas cannisters into the crowd. In compliance with the mayor's orders, Scott Smith and Larry Butler turned to the crowd to calm them down to avoid mass arrests. The police arrested them both anyway, and SCLC and SNCC found common purpose in the Eufaula jail. "This is what happened when we were obeying the mayor," Butler remarked. "I hate to think what would have happened if we disobeyed the mayor."[29]

The Voters' League decided to go on a field trip to where the power was: Washington, DC. They raised the money in dribs and drabs—from churches, teachers, civil organizations, and a boost from Butler's Dickinson College—and scraped together $800 to send a delegation of twenty-three people up to the nation's capital. They stayed with host families and toured the city on the weekend but got down to business on Monday. They met with the League of Women Voters, the Justice Department, and the Small Business Administration—the latter to discuss loans for African American businesses. Members testified to the Civil Rights Division of the Justice Department and the Ad Hoc Subcommittee on Civil Rights of the House Judiciary Committee; they met with the director of the Equal Education Opportunity Program (Eufaula's funding had been recently cut off due to their failure to upgrade their "freedom of choice plan"), and attended hearings of the House Un-American Activities Committee on the

KKK. Assistant Attorney General John Doar met with the group and promised federal investigations of registration procedures. Eufaulans also met with Congressmen Neiman Craley of Pennsylvania and John Conyers Jr., an African American from Michigan. "I was shocked and disturbed by the reports given me by members of the Barbour County Voters' League on continued non-compliance with the Civil Rights Act of 1964, and the Voting Rights Act of 1965," Conyers declared. "I have contacted the Justice Department and other affected agencies to call for immediate investigation."[30]

At the end of the trip, Mrs. Mary Marshall, then the vice president—and soon to be president—of the Barbour County Voters' League, gave a press conference at the church of Walter Fauntroy, the SCLC representative in Washington. "Let me state that Barbour County is the home county of Alabama's racist governor, George C. Wallace," she began. While she outlined her organization's struggles for voting rights and school desegregation, she made a prediction. If registration continued under the Voting Rights Act, she believed, they would be able to elect a Black person to the state legislature from the governor's own district—the first time since Reconstruction, she pointed out. She would end up being part of that electoral fight when she boldly ran for a seat on the school board later that spring. A heady optimism prevailed.[31]

Back in Atlanta, SCLC's adding machines spat out more cautious conclusions about voter registration after the Voting Rights Act. Why had some registration drives worked out so much better than others? No matter how important the Voting Rights Act was, how good the county-level organizing was, who did it, or what tactics were used, there was exactly one variable that explained the rate of SCOPE's success: the presence of federal registrars. By November 1965, Black Belt counties with federal registrars had 84 percent of the "Negro Voting Age Population" registered. The corresponding figure for counties without federal oversight was 41 percent. The data delivered Hosea Williams to "one conclusion." Federal presence in a county is the "only significant variable we can consider responsible" for the different outcomes in different counties. The Department of Justice's selective enforcement was wholly inadequate. The report singled out an illustrative comparison between patterns in a vicious place like Wilcox County, where there was federal oversight, and Barbour County, where there was none. "Barbour County, the home of Governor George Wallace and one of the best movement counties in the Black Belt, has a voting age population roughly similar to that of Wilcox County; yet the registration in Barbour since the VRA is only a little more than 1/3 of that in Wilcox County." Black political rights depended upon federal enforcement. "To expect a Black Belt Negro to face up to the hometown court house of George Corley Wallace," concluded SCLC's report, "is asking just a little bit too much."[32]

By January 1966, Larry Butler returned to Pennsylvania. He was proud of his work. "We have a movement going in this county. The people are formed in to voting leagues. We have marched, picketed and boycotted stores. A lot of people have been threatened, have lost their jobs, in other words they have given up everything for the movement. People have spent up to a week in jail and enduring their children sleeping in a prison camp for a week on concrete floors, eating food with roaches in it and suffering abuse from the guards. Yet they have endured."

Six months of registration drives increased the number of African American voters from about 450 to close to 2,700. As Hosea Williams's analysis pointed out, it would have been more than twice that with a federal registrar. But what Butler was most proud of as he headed back to Atlanta, and then Pennsylvania, was that in Barbour County, "the local organization now directs its own fight for freedom."[33]

Even though the local movement had gone from just registering voters to using creative movement tactics, even though both SCLC and SNCC had organizers on the ground, even though locals took on the leadership of the movement, the core factor in voter registration was the one thing local whites feared the most: federal power. Significant registration had taken place over the summer and fall of 1965, but it was clear to SCLC that for want of a federal registrar, blood was being spilled in a frustrating struggle to get people registered. Hosea Williams summed up the history of the United States: "In short states' rights and civil rights (human rights) don't mix." Without federal aggressive enforcement of citizenship rights, even the Voting Rights Act combined with a vibrant social movement was not going to get the job done.[34]

In the new year, the Barbour County Voters' League organized a boycott of downtown merchants for their discriminatory hiring practices. They ran ongoing supporting demonstrations among the merchants neatly lined along the commercial boulevard of Broad Street. The all-white city council hit its breaking point. They passed an anti-picketing ordinance, which criminalized demonstrations without a permit. The ordinance also gave the mayor sole power to issue a permit, which had to be issued six days in advance of an event and limited the number and spacing of participants. The ordinance had the opposite effect of its intentions, however, as it generated more civil disobedience. Eufaula police arrested anyone protesting without a permit or outside of the tight strictures of the permit's guidelines. The jails filled in no time. Daddy Bone called Solomon Seay, the local movement lawyer, a member of Fred Gray's legal team.

Seay only had seven days to get bonds and appeals set for every one of the mass arrests. That left him so busy with Eufaula protestors that he found himself in an exhausting commute back and forth from Montgomery, a two-hour drive, every day. He ended up chartering a small plane to get the job done. When Seay arrived, he found the sheriff dragging his feet to the point that he had not filled out the official jail identification cards. So, attorney Seay had to do it for him. He filled in all of the necessary information—date of birth, occupation, address, race, etc. But by "race" he put a big "C" on each card. The sheriff looked at a card noting that Seay had marked a "C" for a young white woman. The lawyer clarified that "C" stood for Caucasian. Nodding, the sheriff continued through the deck and came to Scott Smith's card. He gruffly pointed out, "Daddy Bone is a nigra. How come you got 'C' on his card?" "Sheriff," Seay explained, "that stands for Colored."[35]

The lawyer managed to process all of the arrests in the allotted week and filed to have all the people arrested removed to federal court. All cases were consolidated and heard before the sympathetic federal court of Judge Frank M. Johnson, who, once again, was bedeviling the white power structure of Barbour County. The judge ripped through the prosecution's case without mercy. The protestors were not "disorderly," he found, and were engaged in a "constitutionally permissible right." They had also been denied equal protection. The justifications for the arrests were "a guise, nothing more than a subterfuge." The real reason for the arrests was that the boycott was inflicting economic damage, and the city simply did not want to respond to the protestors' demands. He ruled that the whole ordinance was unconstitutional "because it vests too must discretion in the Mayor"; "because it constitutes an undue prior restraint on anyone who desires to exercise their rights that might involve a public assembly"; and it requires a permit "if even two or more persons want to meet together for any of the purposes stated in the Ordinance." The federal gavel dropped and found every element of the Eufaula anti-picketing ordinance unconstitutional.[36]

All winter and spring, the political chatter in Alabama had been about whether Lurleen Wallace would run for governor as a proxy for George Wallace, who was constitutionally prevented from succeeding himself. Despite her secret struggle with cancer, she was reluctantly drawn into the gravitational pull of her husband's astronomically powerful ambitions. Yet the more profound story than the continuation of the Wallaces' power remained below the headlines. On the same day in March 1966 that Lurleen announced her bid to carry on the family fight, four Black candidates from Barbour County also announced their bid for local office. Ten more would shortly follow.[37]

The spring 1966 primaries, the first since the passage of the Voting Rights Act, would be like no other since Reconstruction.

CHAPTER TWENTY

The Vote Is Not Enough

LADIES WORE THEIR BEST dresses, fine shoes, and hats. Shiny pocketbooks swung from their forearms as they walked. Men came in clean overalls with crisp white shirts or suit jackets and short-brimmed fedoras. They piled into pickup trucks, caught rides with friends in crowded automobiles, or simply strode into the long, warm shadows of the early morning sun toward their polling places. Across the Black Belt, they queued up patiently, expectantly, and early—some arriving at 5:00 a.m.—in lines that could wind around for blocks. Waiting in the rising heat, an old man fainted in Birmingham. When an ambulance came for him, he refused it. "I'm not going anywhere till I pull that lever," he said. "This is the first time I'm voting and it might be my last."

By evening there were still one thousand people waiting in line in the capital city of Montgomery. Across the state, over a hundred thousand newly registered African American voters took to the polls like their ancestors had a century prior. Three hundred federal poll watchers fanned out to observe the process, with Assistant Attorney General John Doar directing federal protection of the franchise from headquarters in Selma. They all managed to vote for the very first time. Ninety African American candidates for local office had qualified for the ballot statewide. The US Department of

Justice tabulated it to be the largest turnout in Alabama state election history—by a factor of a third.[1]

Hundreds of people had been jailed in the summer of 1965, many were beaten, others yet lost their livelihoods and even their lives, but the primary elections in May 1966 promised a new day. A preacher over in Wilcox County captured the mood on the eve of election night. "We've been on the outside of the mainstream for America's life," he sang, his melodic voice ringing out at a mass meeting before the vote. "We've been on the outside of society. We've been on the outside of education. We've been on the outside of jobs." The air thick with a reserved hope, he continued: "But we can change that tomorrow. All we got to do is get some black faces there." It was no longer about meeting or singing or protesting. "I don't want you to march tomorrow. But I want you to make some Xs tomorrow, and make it beside those Negro names. Because we are tired of the white man's power. We are tired of being called a 'nigger.' We're tired of being the last hired and first fired. We're tired of all the injustices that the white man been putting on us. So let's do something about it tomorrow. Just put some Xs besides those boys' names."[2]

The spring primaries were what mattered most. African Americans in most counties were seeking voice within the Democratic Party, and the Democratic Party dominated everything in Alabama. In what was still mostly a one-party state, winning the Democratic primary meant winning the election. The *New York Times* predicted that Black voters had achieved large enough registration majorities to send up to eight or nine representatives to the Alabama state legislature. Barbour County, the paper believed, was one of the places that "seem certain to have a Negro representative" sent to Montgomery. If predictions were true, it would be the first time since Reconstruction that an African American had obtained state office anywhere in Alabama. But reality did not match the predictions.[3]

The results were devastating. Despite the Voting Rights Act and scores of Black candidates, not one single African American won any primary race. A few made the runoffs, including attorney Fred Gray, running to represent Barbour, Bullock, and Macon Counties in the

Mary Marshall, president of the Barbour County Voters' League, running for school board in 1966. She poses on her front porch with her husband and six children. The spring primaries were the first elections since the passing of the Voting Rights Act, which generated a strong slate of local Black candidates, often with women in the lead. The primaries came with high hopes for local victories in the Democratic primaries.

state house, and in that there was hope. Those that made the run-offs, however, would face a united white opposition in the next round of voting. Otherwise, the dawn of American democracy resulted in scores of defeats for Black candidates.

Even more demoralizing, the press focused on the fact that white supremacy held strong in the governor's mansion. Lurleen Wallace, standing in as a high-stakes proxy for her term-limited husband, George, bested nine male opponents in the primary, including Richmond Flowers, a white candidate who had the endorsement of SCLC and Martin Luther King Jr. She won sixty-one of sixty-seven counties, getting 52.3 percent of the vote statewide. On the campaign, George Wallace, who did most of the campaigning, had made some adjustments. He began to pronounce the word *negro* correctly, avoided talking directly about segregation, and turned his wrath on the federal establishment as well as the national press and "Communists"—a term that had come to represent everything ready to steal Alabamians' freedom. In the zero-sum battleground Wallace outlined, Mrs. Wallace's clear victory reassured white Alabama that no federally enforced "black rule" was soon in the offing. Since the Democratic Party still ran the state, she had the governorship wrapped up by 10 p.m. on Election Day.[4]

Across the state, people who had fought for civil rights were tired, and many were crestfallen. Some were angry, and rightfully grew cynical about the empty promises of the movement and the federal government. They had expected more, and they had the right to expect more. As is often the case, however, those who were directly involved in the struggle felt a certain joy of having pushed, learned, and seen where persistent problems and future opportunities lay. To the extent there was a victory in May 1966, it was in the voting itself. The first elections after the passage of the Voting Rights Act revealed that the election process remained a convoluted mess, to be slowly untangled through more painstaking effort over the years to come. Democratic representation, it turned out, was only a small part of an immense enfranchisement problem. Voting rights were not enough.[5]

Like African American candidates in the rest of the state, Barbour County's movement faced a complete wipeout on the primary election day: thirteen Black candidates, zero wins. Yet what remained after the election was a great deal of optimism. John Kelly Jr. ran for both the Board of Education and for the Barbour County Democratic Executive Committee. "I feel great," he declared. "We did the important thing. We gave the impression we mean to get into public life." He hadn't expected that one year of concerted activism in the county would change everything, even with the coming of the Voting Rights Act. "Ninety-five per cent of our people haven't given much thought to government until now. They've just begun to get roused up. Our goal will be focused toward keeping them interested in taking an active part in government affairs—local and national."[6]

Many candidates focused on organizing for the future. Mary Marshall, president of the Barbour County Voters' League and one of the sparkplugs in the Eufaula movement, failed to win a seat on the school board. "I didn't really lose," she explained. "I gained knowledge and understanding" of all sorts of new issues, processes, and problems. "I'm not going to give up that easy. I'll win one of these days. If not the next time, the time after that. I got acquainted with some of my white brothers and sisters. Maybe after a while, they'll see I'm a hard worker and vote for me." As she pondered the issue, she said, "It's time we had a Negro mayor." Mrs. Rosie Jordan, also a candidate for the Democratic Executive Committee, understood that many Black people thought voting was futile. "People say, 'They took our votes before. They'll steal 'em again. Our votes is no good.'" She explained it differently. "I tell them, 'Don't feel that. Your votes were some good. We just need more votes.'"[7]

For a nation that had watched a yearlong struggle for voters' rights unfold in Alabama since the conflict on the Edmund Pettus Bridge, the election results were confusing. With a hundred thousand new Black voters registered in Alabama, how did the nation's most vocal segregationist still win the day? The noted political pollster Samuel Lubell explained it as a sense of white unity against federal intervention. "It was at Selma a year ago that Wallace really won Tuesday's election," he noted. The "humiliation of federal intervention," as one of his interviewees put it, was "like a show of force by some foreign occupying power." White Alabama voters were galvanized by the indignity of the national conversation about the backward condition of race relations in their state. It did not help that Attorney General Katzenbach went on the national news just before the 1966 primary to announce the need for hundreds of federal observers to monitor Alabama's elections.[8]

Meantime, wily George Wallace had been working on another strategy to tap the politics of federal and racial resentment and win the day. Unable to stop the increase in registered Black voters since SCOPE, SNCC, and the Voting Rights Act changed the political landscape in the summer of 1965, he simply made sure that there were an additional 110,000 new white voters registered as well. Every student in a white school went home with a red, white, and blue pamphlet, compliments of the governor's office, telling parents to vote to "Stand Up for Alabama." He aimed to drown the Black vote in a sea of white.[9]

Martin Luther King Jr. put the best light on the success of the governor's immovable racism as "a protest vote against the tide of inevitable progress." The election results were not a repudiation of the civil rights movement but something subtly different: a fear of the inevitable transformation to come. By voting for Wallace, King claimed, "white Alabamans are desperately grasping for a way to return to the old days of white supremacy." The governor's overwhelming acclamation by white voters did not outwardly phase King. "Negroes have made more strides in the face of Wallace's stubborn resistance and emotional reactions than under many so-called moderate administrations." At the same time, however, SCLC was packing up and moving out. At times criticized for their lack of long-term commitment to communities, they were already launching projects in Chicago and largely left Alabama after the 1966 midterms.[10]

SNCC launched a radically different political strategy in counties like Dallas, Greene, and Lowndes. In those places, the idea was to build independent political power, separate from the Democratic Party, the party of the bosses. The differences between SCLC, vying for power within the Democratic Party, and SNCC, organizing independent political and economic power outside of the Democrats, came to the fore in 1966. The symbols alone told the story. In regions with limited literacy, political parties often chose symbols to represent their positions on the ballot. The Democrats featured a rooster with the slogan, "White Supremacy, For the Right." The Lowndes County Freedom Organization (LCFO), in contrast, rejected the Democrats and featured a sleek black panther and became known informally as the Black Panther Party (a name and symbol the official Black Panther Party for Self-Defense later adopted in Oakland with permission).

In Lowndes, it had been a brutal year in a brutal place. White landowners had kicked activist African American tenants off their land, many of whom had to live in tents when there was no place left to go. When the general elections arrived in November, the LCFO also failed to win any seats, even in Lowndes, where 80 percent of the county was Black. Like SCLC, SNCC ended up moving on. Yet the Lowndes County message went national: the county leader, Stokely Carmichael, was elected president of SNCC and advocated a struggle that would become known as Black Power. Although the LCFO received a lot of press in Alabama, the Democrats remained the main political story in the state for Blacks—despite still being the party of white supremacy in the South.[11]

With white voters holding a slim voting majority in Barbour County after the exodus of Black people during the Great Migrations to the North, no Black candidate could hope to win a county-wide race in 1966. However, sixteen seats on the Barbour County Democratic Executive Committee were elected on a "beat"-level basis, that is, were offices assigned to local jurisdictions within the county. Given the segregation of the county, that meant that an African American candidate could run for the executive committee, win in their beat, and take a seat on the county committee even if they remained uncompetitive on a county-wide basis. Although an African American candidate had never before run, let alone won a seat on the Democratic executive board, in 1966 chances looked good for African Americans to begin to direct the future of the local Democratic Party. Six Black candidates vied for the executive board in 1966.

At the last minute, the all-white executive committee changed the rules for running for office. A few weeks after the Black candidates had qualified to run, and without debate, public rationale, or official minutes, the committee voted to change all beat-level seats to at-large positions. The effort was so transparent that even though all races would be county-wide, the winning candidates selected would still represent the specific beat from which they came. In sum, *elections* would be at-large, but *representation* would remain on a beat-level basis. As Senator James S. Clark blithely explained, they wanted to "lesson [*sic*] the impact of any block vote." By "block" he meant "Black." The entire resolution was a simplistic, rushed ruse to dilute the African American vote. By submerging beats where Black voting was strong into the larger political waters of the county, they would drown the possibility that any Black candidate might win. The county committee later had the gall to claim that they were keeping up with the times by complying with the "one man, one vote" logic of the civil rights era.[12]

The Voters' League of Barbour County sought a last-minute injunction on the entire election, but their effort was too close to the polling date, and Judge Frank Johnson denied it. All six African American candidates for the Barbour County Democratic Executive Committee lost under the new rules. Two would likely have lost anyway, one was uncertain, but three of those seats had looked very good for Black candidates on the beat level. "I lost in the county," Mrs. Hunter, a Comer resident, said, "but I won in my beat." She intended to contest the results. "I believe the court is going to support us and that I'm going to be able to take my seat. If not, I'll be up again in another four years."[13]

Once again, Fred Gray, the civil rights attorney of Rosa Parks, the Albert Street Club, and the Barbour County Board of Education case, arrived to help. Hardly a fresh face in town, Gray was in and out of Barbour County on civil rights litigation just about every week, and he ran in 1966 as a candidate for state representative. Immediately following the official losses for the executive board, he took the Barbour County Democratic Executive Committee to federal court. *Smith v. Paris*, named after lead plaintiff Mary C. Smith, an active member of the Barbour County Voters' League, came before Judge Frank Johnson's federal bench.

Fred Gray, by then one of the most seasoned civil rights litigants in the state, if not the country, regarded the Barbour County voting case as "one of my most influential civil rights cases," even if it is one of the "least known" as compared with the drama of Rosa Parks back in 1955 or his many school integration cases. All the voting registration and access to the polls imaginable was inadequate if the vote was going to be diluted by the structure of the political process. While *Smith v. Paris* was one of the very first voter dilution cases, Gray had started to fight gerrymandering, illegal reapportionment, and even voter dilution in a case he brought before the Supreme Court in 1960, *Gomillion v. Lightfoot*.[14]

In *Gomillion*, Gray had argued against the radical gerrymandering of the legal boundaries of the City of Tuskegee, Alabama. The plan, propagated by the executive secretary of the White Citizens' Council of Alabama and ratified by the state legislature, reshaped the city in such a way as to include all white residents but eliminate all but a negligible handful of Black people from living within the city limits. The redistricting tactic included gerrymandering Booker T. Washington's famed Tuskegee Institute right out of the city of Tuskegee. Under the scheme, the city boundaries went from being a perfect square, one and a half miles equidistant on each side from the courthouse, to what Gray described accurately as being shaped like a "25-sided sea dragon." As he argued before the United States Supreme Court, the absurd polygon map stood behind him at all times for the justices to see. As in the Barbour County Executive Committee's ploy, the state of Alabama held no public debate and gave no rationale for adopting the changes. The Supreme Court found for the plaintiffs, ruling that the state of Alabama's redrawing of the boundaries was an act of disenfranchisement. By expanding the definition of discriminatory voting practices beyond just registration and voting itself, the decision played a role in both the passage and the structure of the Voting Rights Act.[15]

In Barbour's *Smith v. Paris*, Judge Johnson cited *Gomillion*'s "clear teaching" that "one man, one vote" was not an adequate standard for voting rights. Judge Johnson immediately saw through the Barbour County Democratic Executive Committee's ploy and sided unequivocally with the plaintiffs. The idea that the change to an at-large candidacy supported "one man, one vote" he deemed "nothing more than a sham." This new approach to districting, the federal judge pointed out, was never considered before there was power in the Black vote and probably would not have been considered without it. No other explanation for the adoption of this new strategy was offered, and the fact that elections were held at large while representation was still at the beat level seemed all the more suspicious. His one criticism of the plaintiffs was that they had aggravated their own situation by not jumping on the case sooner in order enjoin the election in a timely way. The only conclusion Judge Johnson could come to was that the Committee's resolution was clearly "born of an effort to frustrate and discriminate against negroes in the exercise of their right to vote, in violation of the Fifteenth Amendment." The judge ordered that the old system be restored. Unfortunately for the candidates, the results of the election did not change. Despite federal intervention, no African American candidates joined the Executive Committee of the Democratic Party of Barbour County in 1966.[16]

As he was arguing *Smith v. Paris*, Fred Gray also had his own race to worry about in 1966, one everyone expected him to win. Given his role in the movement, his growing reputation as one of the most important civil rights attorneys in the South, and the Voting Rights Act, he began to "visualize a political base in Barbour and Bullock counties." He sought a seat as a state representative serving them, plus the third county in that district, Macon. He admitted that he was "not the best campaigner": his voice was a bit reedy, his mindset a bit cautious and legalistic. He was well-known, however, and there were protests and voting drives all over the three counties he would represent. Gray drew the support of many shrewd political minds, including aides to Carl Stokes, who would become one of the first African American mayors of a major American city, Cleveland, in 1967. Gray made up for his plain campaign style with the vibrant support of a group of freedom singers who campaigned hard for him, singing a variety of gospel songs turned civil rights anthems.[17]

On primary election night 1966, Gray's lead in the vote count was a shining star in the otherwise dark night of political defeat. The victory was close, and the *New York Times* hedged its report by stating that he "apparently" won the Democratic nomination. There was little such ambiguity in the campaign as civil rights workers rejoiced at their win. "Victory was sweet. Everyone was jubilant. I was excited," Gray recalled. He celebrated with Martin Luther King and all the other civil rights workers and leaders at SCLC headquarters in Atlanta. "Dr. King was very happy about my winning the primary. . . . I was about to become the first African American to have a seat in the Alabama Legislature since Reconstruction."[18]

Then the tables turned. Absentee ballots, normally counted first, had allegedly not been included in the original count on election night. The official count reversed Gray's lead from a 206 vote majority to a 532 vote deficit. "Something is funny about this thing," Gray remarked about the abrupt dissolution of his historic victory on the arrival of the absentee ballots. He was now in an improbable runoff in which the power structure united against him. Things were not looking good. As a white businessman told him, "Well, Fred, I think you could probably develop into a good legislator, but you're not going to win. We have been stealing elections from each other down here for years and you can imagine what will happen to you." The gentleman knew his Alabama politics. Fred Gray lost the 1966 runoff race.[19]

The race had more than a whiff of corruption. Gray and his team believed they had been victims of "a general pattern of conduct designed to harass, intimidate, and discourage African American voters from going to the polls" in each of the three counties. Their white opponents were doing "everything possible" in order "to make sure that African American candidates did not win the election." Black people may have had the right to vote, but they were still engaged in a guerrilla war for a fair vote, an accurate count, an unobstructed path to the polls, and an equitable and defensible electoral map. Though he shared these suspicions, Gray saw that the allegations would be difficult to prove. He was content to wait for his next chance to run in 1970. His supporters, however, proved less patient and more demanding. So, he headed back to federal court.[20]

Fred Gray's legal partner, Solomon Seay Jr., took up the fight over the 1966 election for state legislature in *Gray v. Main*, a class action suit on behalf of the voters of all three counties. The plaintiffs had a long list of complaints from fraudulent voting to the blocking of legitimate voting, but they were all part of the general charge of depriving Black voters of their rights as laid out in the Fourteenth and Fifteenth Amendments. The sympathetic Judge Frank Johnson submitted an amicus curiae, placing the United States on the plaintiffs' side.

Judge Johnson would not be the one to hear the case, however. Instead, *Gray v. Main* came before Judge Virgil Pittman, newly appointed to the federal bench, who took his seat just after the primary, in June 1966. He had little experience with civil rights cases. Unlike the clear, semi-public conspiracy in the Barbour County Democratic Executive Board case, *Gray v. Main* brought a broad set of accusations. Whites were not using a single large-scale disenfranchisement strategy but rather, so the plaintiffs accused, a ground war of harassment, intimidation, fraud, discrimination, and other voting "irregularities." The plaintiffs' charges included the submission of illegal ballots, deceased voters, manipulated voting lists, false absentee voting, harassment of poll watchers, switching of polling place locations, changing beat assignments for African American voters, and other strategies intended to dilute the Black vote. Bullock County in particular, the plaintiffs argued, was rife with irregularities. Though evidence was clear in some cases—objectively, there were more white people on the voters' lists than actually existed in the general population—Judge Pittman found "insufficient evidence to show that these clerical irregularities were racially motivated, or the product of any fraudulent intent," and found for the defendants.[21]

In his decision, Judge Pittman naively greeted the recent voting registration accomplishments with a "high heart" and looked forward to increased improvement in the defendants' performance in running future elections. His thoughts echoed those of Francis Scott Key during the oncoming Creek War and the waffling federal officers during Reconstruction. All three characters took refuge in compromising proceduralism, preferring to cover their actions in cautious rules rather than bold morality. While not overtly hostile to the civil rights cause, the judge seemed oblivious to the real power dynamics involved in race relations and Alabama politics.

"In the court's judgment, this was a free election," he wrote, "polarized as it was by white and Negro alike." "Nothing," he believed, had been done with "fraudulent intent" against Black voting, and "technical violations" have been in "existence for a long period of time, and the court finds these to have been free from any racial implications." Both sides suffered from history, he believed, his sense of equanimity clouded a bit by the smoldering haze of the Lost Cause. "The Negroes were haunted by slavery and historical discrimination, and the white population was haunted by 19th Century Reconstruction politics." Yet the future was bright, he maintained, and there was good faith on both sides to accept and build a pluralistic society. "It may be from fear that white voted for white and Negro for Negro, but if we would make a reality of the American dream, we should vote for a man on his merit regardless of color, race, or creed. This will include whites voting for meritorious Negroes as well as Negroes voting for meritorious whites." Fred Gray would have to wait until 1970 to take another shot at the Alabama state house.[22]

As for members of the Barbour County Democratic Executive Committee, in 1968 they would return to the same dirty trick they pulled in 1966. Again, they dissolved beats into at-large elections in order to dilute African American voting. "The majority of people in Barbour County," explained Senator Clark, desired "to keep the Democratic committee on an at-large basis and 'freedom from federal intervention.'" For the second time, the executive committee found itself dragged into federal court. Frank Johnson was again on the bench, and he called *United States v. Democratic Executive Committee of Barbour County* the "sequel" to 1966's *Smith v. Paris*. The judge filled his exasperated decision with quotes from the previous case. "Since so little has changed since this Court found that an inference of racial motivation was justified, defendants do not seem to contest seriously plaintiff's contention that the initial inference is again compelling." This time the results of the election were enjoined, but that did not

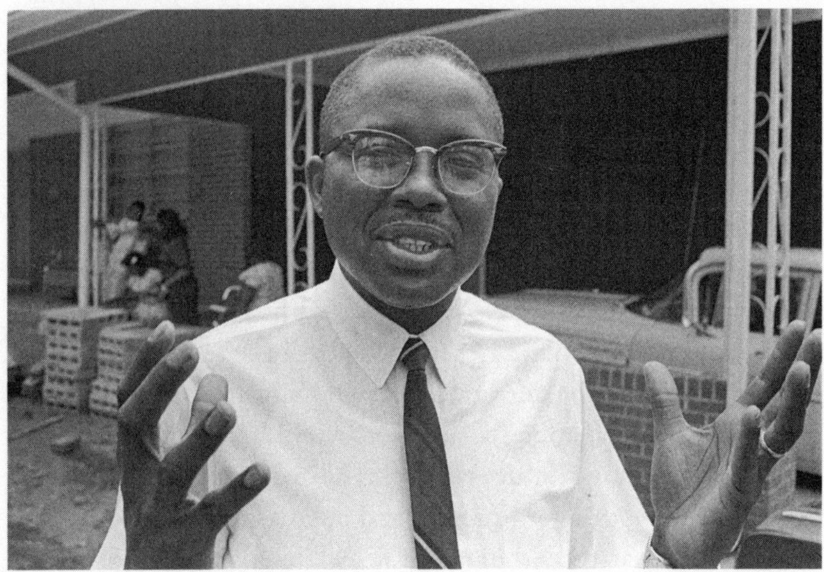

Fred D. Gray, a tireless civil rights lawyer and champion, devoted his life to, as he said, "destroying everything segregated I could find." He argued some of the most important cases in Alabama, the nation, and Barbour County. He finally won a seat in the Alabama state legislature in 1970, representing Barbour, Bullock, and Macon Counties. He and Thomas J. Reed were the first African Americans elected to state government since Reconstruction.

immediately deliver any new victories. It only stopped the current fraud.[23]

While new struggles pulled the center of the freedom movement away from Alabama, Fred D. Gray stayed local. And in 1970, he ran again for the same office denied him in 1966. By then, he was standing on an enormous pyramid of struggles and successes—the Montgomery Bus Boycott, the many court cases, the efforts of SCOPE and SNCC, federal legislation and enforcement, and his own political education in the 1966 race. In the 1970 contest, Tuskegee students served as poll watchers across the three counties, unearthing more dirty tricks in Eufaula. Gray could still not crack Barbour County, but he won handily in Bullock and Macon Counties. That fall, he won a seat in the Alabama state legislature. George Wallace's Barbour County was represented by an African American for the first time since Reconstruction.[24]

In terms of Black political power, Fred Gray was not alone in 1970. It was the year of the great breakthrough in Southern elected office, the year the whiteness barrier that had stood solid since Reconstruction for a century finally shattered. Well over three hundred African American candidates ran across the South, and more than one-third of them won. The political action was almost exclusively local and state, from probate judge to state representative, but 1970 was *the* year of Black political success in the South. Gray won in the Barbour-Bullock-Macon district, and the other seat in the district went to Thomas Reed, the president of the state NAACP, who ran on a third-party ticket. Together, Gray and Reed were the first African Americans to serve in the Alabama state house since Reconstruction. Three Black candidates also won seats in the South Carolina state house. SCLC lieutenant Andrew Young lost his bid for the US Congress in Georgia, only to finally prevail in 1972. In 1970, Arkansas remained the only fully segregated state house in the former Confederacy.[25]

In the fall of 1970, all the elected Democrats in the state of Alabama were invited to come together in Montgomery in order to plan the upcoming legislative session. All, that was, except the sole elected Black Democrat, Fred Gray. It was hardly his first experience of exclusion because of race, but there was a delicious irony to the moment. As Fred Gray climbed the gleaming white marble steps that led up to the state house, for the first time as an elected state legislator, he must have been pleased to consider the fact that he represented all the voters of his district. All the voters, including a constituent named George Corley Wallace. As the 1971 legislative session began, George Wallace was again governor of Alabama, elected after an unusually vitriolic racist campaign even for him, but both of his own state representatives were African American.[26]

Barbour County was ahead of the game, as voter dilutions cases would generally not become central to voting rights until after 1969. By then the courts moved from concerns about barriers to voter registration to an equally important scrutiny of mechanisms for participation and filing of candidacies. After 1969, all proposed changes in state-level voting processes had to be precleared by the Department of Justice prior to implementation. As a result, throughout the 1970s, young and motivated NAACP and ACLU lawyers jumped on the move to at-large voting in communities throughout the state. By 1989, Black elected officials reached proportional representation across the state. As one in-depth analysis of the transformation done by a team of legal scholars figured out, it had a lot less to do with the rise of enlightened racial attitudes and a lot more to do with a massive legal effort and the accumulation of federal case law that provided the "weapons necessary" to enforce federal law and protect minority representation. The lesson was simple: the vigorous enforcement of federal law was what changed voting rights, not the slow drip of racial enlightenment.[27]

The arc from *Smith v. Allwright* (1944) through *Brown* (1954), the creation of SCLC, the Civil Rights and Voting Rights Acts, and, finally, the multiyear ground war just to get votes counted fairly in a fair system took twenty-six years—or one hundred, if we take the story back to Reconstruction—of almost relentless political, social, and legal activity. The limited, embattled, hard-won successes of the freedom movement began to gain momentum and make changes. Those transformations came with political consequences, however, as political alignments began to shift seismically in the late 1960s and 1970s. Rather than share political power, white Southerners began to switch political parties.

By 1968, both SNCC and SCLC had decamped to other struggles. SNCC projected Black Power onto the national and international stages, and King and SCLC moved into the North to take on residential segregation. In Chicago, opening a front in the fight for fair housing, King was greeted with a projectile to the head that knocked him to the ground, and shouts of "Kill the niggers!" and "We want Martin Luther coon!" The animosity he received up North was staggering. "I've been in many demonstrations all across the South, but I can say that I have never seen—even in Mississippi and Alabama—mobs as hostile and as hate-filled as I've seen here in Chicago." That racism was not simply a Southern issue was something George Wallace already knew, and he was shaking up the party establishments with talk of another presidential run in 1968. As King was moving SCLC's struggle toward questions of political economy with his Poor People's Campaign in 1968, he was killed by an assassin's bullet while supporting a sanitation workers' strike in Memphis.[28]

When the Wallaces returned to Clayton for a hometown rally before the 1966 general election, the square was packed with more than half of Barbour County's white population eager to celebrate the state's golden couple. Nine thousand cheering locals heard George promise to renew his fight for the White House in 1968. There he vowed to "get the communists, socialists, beatniks, and atheists out of government." The Barbour County locals devoured every word. It never got old. Yet for George Wallace, this was not just another election, it was the next battle in a century-old campaign to redeem the South.[29]

Thinking about local history early in the morning on Election Day, the day after the rally, Wallace strolled across the empty Clayton town square. He took a long draw on his cigarette and motioned to his friends, "Yeah, this is the exact spot the Republicans were headquartered after the Civil War." He was subtly teasing the Republicans who were with him, thinking about how he might have turned the crowd into any angry Democratic mob by reminding them of the past. But there was something deeper at work. "The Freedman's Bureau was right here during Reconstruction," he emphasized, "all them nigguhs and carpetbaggers and scalawags, right here." Raised on tales of white Southern victimization, Wallace had been haunted by specters of federal intervention on that very spot, in that town, in that county, and in that state, since his boyhood.[30]

In the last ten years of politicking, George Wallace had learned the incendiary power of the very idea of federal intervention with the local racial order. Now they were at it again. Folks both pro and con were calling the 1960s the Second Reconstruction. Wallace felt ready to continue the fight of his ancestors—and to do so on the national level. He would ignite the political power of the idea of the loss of American freedom. Perhaps this was a fight over an ideal, but it was most certainly a fight made from political opportunity. Presidential candidate Richard Nixon was already trying to capitalize on racial anxieties by launching his so-called Southern Strategy to win the white South to the Republican Party. If Nixon could deliver the Southern Democrats to the Republicans, it would be a seismic shift in American coalitional politics.

George Wallace had a different idea for 1968: a Northern Strategy.

CHAPTER TWENTY-ONE

The Northern Strategy

A YEAR BEFORE THE 1968 presidential campaign, George Wallace was on a mission to clarify his political message for the national campaign. Appearing on NBC's *Meet the Press*, he tried to explain that he didn't hate Black people. He did not "recommend" segregation to any region (that was a state-level decision, of course), and he did not even recognize this thing the chattering classes liked to call the "backlash" against the civil rights movement. The Northern press simply misunderstood poor George Wallace, an innocent victim of the petty bias of the liberal press. He was not there to declare war on minorities; he was not a racist, a demagogue, or even, as the student left accused, a fascist. The man who declared "segregation forever," who stood in the schoolhouse door, and who nodded as the state police bludgeoned the marchers in Selma, was trying to explain that his message was, in fact, not about race at all.[1]

Was there a backlash underway in the United States? Of course, Wallace explained, "there's a backlash" brewing. But it wasn't against civil rights, he told viewers, it was "against big government in this country." It was all about federal authority stealing the God-given liberties of the American people.

Wallace's lips tended to twist with anger and impatience when he faced off with the "impudent snobs" of the news business who constantly peppered him with questions about civil rights. He may have looked and sounded different from the men who interviewed him, but he was no less smart and often a whole lot cagier. The governor had one of the smoothest political clutches in the business. He could shift from endearing to belligerent, slip from a joke to a fight, change gears from "awe shucks, fellas" to remorseless attack with smooth precision. He was quick to claim that in Washington or New York—or whatever location fit his purpose—race relations were worse than in Alabama, crime was worse, and the behavior of white liberals who were abandoning the integrated public schools of the North was *the* worst. If everyone could just be left alone, it would all work out fine on the local level. Sounding at times like the anti-establishment protestors he campaigned against, he saw the current uprising against the federal government as "a movement of the people."

Wallace was the master of elision. The defense of the local against the federal allowed race to slip below the surface when needed, though its outline remained just discernable beneath the waterline. The great elision had been at the heart of his politics since he became the "Fightin' Judge" in his stand against the Department of Justice in the 1950s, and it had been at the heart of Barbour County politics since local control meant the federal surrender of the Creek Nation to bands of white intruders.

In 1968, George Wallace took his political formula to the national stage. He had shown his viability in 1964 and proved that his strategy of making room for snarling racists behind a long tradition of populist-style Jeffersonian, antigovernment resistance could work. Now he was ready to win—or at least throw the election into the House of Representatives if he could prevent other candidates from securing a majority in the Electoral College. The vehicle for his message this time would not be the Democratic Party but the newly created American Independent Party. What began in 1967 in a little office outside of Montgomery had by the end of the campaign swelled into an almost $10 million operation with a suite of offices and a warehouse just to process the massive influx of small cash donations.[2]

Approaching the 1968 race, he doubled down on his commitment to freedom. His remarks on the subject during Lurleen Wallace's inaugural in 1967 are worth considering at length:

> There are those who would tell us today that freedom means something different than it meant to our fathers; but when a central government bureaucrat or judge takes from us our right to run our schools, to determine the destiny of our own children, to run our labor unions, our businesses, our hospitals and our very lives, I do not call that freedom, I call that abject slavery to government. I call it slavery of the most degenerate origin, that goes back a thousand years in time and rests its right to rule upon threat and blackmail, upon punishment of the sick and weak and helpless, upon the savage doctrine that might is right, upon the naked ugly power of Tyranny. . . . Alabama is where freedom lives and works, that is why the words Alabama and freedom have come to have the same meaning to many millions of people throughout the world.

Wallace gave national focus to an ongoing, if inchoate, brand of racialized anti-statism that could gather together the most militant white supremacist with the merely suspicious antigovernment activist. He could do so in a way that transcended the state boundaries of Alabama—he had done it in 1964, and he could do it again.[3]

While Wallace fought the feds, the civil rights movement had been trying to trigger them into action. For over a decade, the movement had largely been following a simple, if painful, formula that unfolded in an infinite number of variations: people exercising their constitutional rights would create a confrontation designed to draw federal attention and intervention. They were not local morality plays but pieces of a larger strategy to get the government to enforce—actually, expand—the Constitution and pass supporting legislation. The route forward was to make African Americans federal citizens as much as possible, that is, to release them from the traps of state-level citizenship. The yearlong Montgomery Bus Boycott was won in federal courts. Little Rock forced the tepid President Dwight D.

Eisenhower to call in the troops. In Birmingham, where the movement was called Project C, for "confrontation," SCLC had to place young people's bodies in front of Bull Connor's fire hoses, which managed to win the attention and intervention of the Kennedy administration. The freedom rides drew Robert Kennedy's Department of Justice into action. Freedom Summer in Mississippi was explicitly designed to bring federal action directly to local places and, simultaneously, a social movement into the center of political power at the Democratic Convention in Atlantic City. The Selma March was not aimed at taking a local geographic feature known as the Edmund Pettus Bridge, it was to trigger congressional support for the Voting Rights Act. King's demonstrations in Chicago were not to enlighten brick-throwing Chicagoans but to get fair housing laws. The template was clear: organize confrontation, hope nobody got hurt or killed, and push for federal action.

For Wallace, the system of confrontations created political mechanics of near Newtonian precision. Every increase in federal intervention that civil rights organizers managed to produce also generated an equal and opposite reaction in the form of George Wallace's political prospects. When he said, "The first day they bring federal troops into this state, I'm gonna run for President," he understood exactly the political physics at work. He also intuitively grasped the basic transitive property of politics in the 1960s: to white voters, more federal government meant less freedom and more power to Black people; less freedom meant more fear and rage, and more fear and rage meant more support for George Wallace. As he explained about his stand in the schoolhouse door, his job was to illustrate the "omnipotent march of centralized government that is going to destroy the rights and freedom and liberty of the people of this country." He also seemed to sense the federal government was a paper tiger, but if it did have the courage of its convictions, he could still lose to the feds and advance his political ambitions.[4]

Theodore White, the great chronicler of presidential campaigns in the sixties and seventies, recognized what Wallace was up to. As the exotic emerging from the backwoods of Alabama, Wallace was not just some crazed lyncher of Black people, not a simple cross-burning Klansman—he had a much more resonant message: "If George Wallace hates anything, it is not Negroes—it is the Federal government of the United States and its 'pointy-head' advisers, the 'intellectual morons,' the 'guideline writers' of Washington who try to upset the natural relation of races and force Negroes and whites to live together in unnatural mixing." But even as experienced a journalist as White didn't get it. Deep down, George Wallace didn't hate anything or anyone. He loved power, he disliked those who blocked him from it, and he had an extraordinary knack for pulling the levers that would deliver him more.[5]

The campaign year 1968 was supposed to be the year of the Southern Strategy. With the Democrats established as the party of federal power and civil rights, the theory went, the "solid" South was ready for a partisan realignment away from its historic relationship with the Democrats and toward the Republicans. The political story goes that Richard Nixon built upon Goldwater's victories in the Deep South to transform the South from solidly Democratic into a Republican stronghold. He did so by using coded racial language like "law and order" that appealed not just to the South but to suburbanites from all regions. In local races it might be tricky, but for the presidential race, swaying Southern voters from the Democratic to the Republican column seemed all but inevitable to many political operatives.

Yet the story is incomplete. The South had been in flux for a long time. What might be called the Southern Strategy probably began as early as the 1928 campaign, when a large number of Protestant fundamentalist Southerners (including Donald Comer) voted for Hoover over Al Smith, the New York Catholic wet. As the federal state grew under the New Deal, Southern Democratic leaders began to rethink their relationship to the national party even further, and Franklin Roosevelt tried to shape the transition by pushing the Southern conservatives out of the Democratic Party during the 1938 midterms. Then came the Dixiecrats in 1948. Eisenhower campaigned seriously in the South in 1952 and 1956. Strom Thurmond paved the way for the exodus by joining up with the Goldwater Republicans in 1964. Then, in 1964, Barry Goldwater won both Alabama and Barbour County by an enormous margin. In 1966, as the historian Rick Perlstein put it, Nixon already sounded a lot like Wallace, spending weeks laying campaign preparations by "ventriloquizing a generation of Southern lost-cause speechifying about Yankees dictating to Dixie." Nixon's access to the South went through the front door of segregationist Strom Thurmond. "If Lyndon Johnson's Democrats prevailed," argued Thurmond, "freedom as we have known it in this country is doomed." So Nixon got up and declared to the press, "Strom Thurmond is no racist. Strom is a man of courage and integrity." Thurmond received absolution from the top of the ticket of his new party, and Nixon got inroads into Southern duck hunting.[6]

The white South changed its partisan affiliation slowly, like a lumbering barge twisting its course slowly in the sea, but it reoriented toward the anti-statist party, whichever that happened to be. More than a century after the Civil War, party labels mattered less than consistent voting against federal enforcement of political rights. Alabama has voted either Republican or Wallace's American Independent Party every presidential election cycle since Adlai Stevenson won the state as a Democrat in 1956—with the sole exception of when a regional favorite, Georgian Jimmy Carter, ran in 1976. As more issues piled on in the ensuing decades—women's rights, the evangelical movement, taxation, labor deregulation—the reaction among white voters would be completed. By the 1968 Republican primaries, the move toward the Southern Strategy was in full play. "I know you want to vote for Reagan, the true conservative," Thurmond told his fellow former Southern Democrats who had become Republican, "but if Nixon becomes president, he has promised that he won't enforce either the Civil Rights or the Voting Rights Acts. Stick with him."[7]

What Wallace had in mind was something wholly different, something he had made clear in his 1963 inaugural address: a *Northern* strategy. He had no interest in the South being a political colony to either of the major parties; this time, he wanted to be the colonizer. He was ready to avenge Sherman's March. He knew in his heart, and had affirmed in his 1964 test runs in Wisconsin, Indiana, and Maryland, that his message had national resonance. And in that fight, his allies were everywhere. As he had already explained, "Being a southerner is no longer geographic. It's a philosophy and an attitude."[8]

The locus of the people for whom Wallace spoke moved from the geographic South to a time and place of even fuzzier dimensions, known as "the heartland." There, in the semimythic state of political mind, as the political scientist Paul Taggart writes, "a good life could be found before the corruptions and distortions of the present." Its malleability was its chief asset, as the idea invited the listener to project whatever they wanted onto a blank canvas. The heartland was "felt rather than reasoned, and something that is shrouded in imprecision." The mythical America was locally controlled, far from the bureaucrats and pointy-headed intellectuals that Wallace skewered regularly on the campaign trail, a place of tradition and sovereignty. It was freedom's dominion. This was a place where there were no riots, protests, or Supreme Court interference. Wallace tapped into the inescapable power of the Jeffersonian myth, the yeoman who stood strong and independent in the face of the state. Whether he believed it to be true or not, he knew it was an idea that could always be exploited, and never vanquished, in American politics. What one pundit called Wallace's "whimsical anachronism" and his wielding of "Barbour County's kinds of commonsense solutions" spoke of lost Jeffersonian values and a long ago time when they were relevant. His "essentially village sensibilities," however, were cunning in the extreme.[9]

The great irony of Wallace's message was that his version of freedom required a strong man with the taut fists of an angry pugilist to "Stand Up for America." His belligerence spoke of freedom as domination. He may have wanted to free white people from the federal government, but he was willing to use that same government to crack down on dissent—in very physical ways. Eighty-one percent of the public believed that law enforcement was failing, and that, in the words of *Time* magazine, "a 'strong' President can do something about it." The buzzwords of the 1968 campaign may have been "law and order," but the symptoms were "fear and frustration and anger." Wallace was the strong man who could return America to the heartland it once was. And, to take his own language seriously, he was willing to use physical violence to restore it. His version of freedom revealed itself as a form of latent violence and suppression of not just Creek Indians and African Americans but those with whom one has fundamental political disagreements.[10]

His message won the hearts and minds of many Northern working-class "ethnics"—the children of the immigrants from southern and eastern Europe. He often adopted some class-based sloganeering for such purposes, carving out an effective blue-collar populist message for what would later be called the New Right. "And I think that if the politicians get in the way... a lot of them are going to get run over by this average man in the street—this man in the textile mill, this man in the steel mill, this barber, the beautician, the policeman on the beat... the little businessman." The power roiling up from below, he suggested, was unstoppable. He claimed not to speak against anyone but in favor of "the mass of people" fighting federal incursions into their lives. There was a specter haunting America, and it was the specter of racialized anti-statism.[11]

The 1968 campaign year ended up as one of the most dramatic in American history, with Wallace playing a central role. Lyndon Johnson had won in 1964 in one of the biggest landslides in American political history. A slew of liberalisms—the War on Poverty, the Great Society, the Civil Rights and Voting Rights Acts—all followed. Yet his inability to control the politics or the foreign policy of Vietnam, that "bitch of a war," engulfed every aspect of his presidency. He had inherited a mess that he did not know how to win and could not afford to lose. The war rattled his faith in his own capacity, and he began to see himself as its victim. He had a long history of descending into maudlin bouts of self-pity when things got rough—and things were rough: the kids were protesting outside the White House, the generals wanted more war, his beloved domestic reform agenda was falling apart, and the coalition that delivered him to victory was crumbling at the foundations. At the conclusion of his televised address on March 31, 1968, he declared he would not run again for the presidency. The jaws of politicos dropped everywhere.[12]

Senator Eugene McCarthy had already been nipping at Johnson's heels as the antiwar candidate. Then Bobby Kennedy, the man of gravitas, glamour, and panache, who had done so much to freeze Johnson out of power during his years as vice president, entered the race. Johnson's worst nightmare was coming to pass. "The thing I feared from the first day of my Presidency was actually coming true," Johnson said later. "Robert Kennedy had openly announced his intention to reclaim the throne in the memory of his brother. And the American people, swayed by the magic of the name, were dancing in the streets."[13]

And so, the political dominoes fell. McCarthy sought to fell Johnson, Kennedy sought to take down both, and when Bobby was assassinated while celebrating his California Democratic primary victory—just two months after Martin Luther King Jr. was killed—the only candidate left standing, however weakly, was Vice President Hubert Humphrey. Once the bright shining star of American liberalism, Humphrey suddenly seemed like a tired and out of touch old war hawk saddled with the Johnson legacy. The infamous national convention in Chicago affirmed the suspicions of the student left as well as the worst and most authoritarian tendencies of Democrats like Chicago Mayor Richard Daley. In their disillusionment with escalation in Vietnam, the protestors directed their ire at Humphrey, not the Republicans, for the state of the nation. Yet when they chanted "Dump the Hump," they had nowhere else to go within the mainstream political system. In their impatience and exhaustion with the war, the New Left tore down their nearest potential ally and, inadvertently, strengthened the Republicans. When Richard Nixon looked at the succession of Democrats lined up against him, the person he feared was not a Democrat but George Wallace of the American Independent Party. The liberals would vote for a liberal—even a wounded one—if they voted at all in 1968. But as a third-party conservative wild card, Wallace alone could cripple Nixon's chances in a three-way race.[14]

The basic Wallace rally was the same across the country. It had religion, it had music, it had resentment, it had class, it had race, it had humor, and it had sex. If there were protestors, all the better. It began with a little of that Nashville sound, complete with shiny guitars, flashy sequins, and sappy if heartfelt lyrics, followed by a benediction to ask for God's help in the Wallace cause. Then the Wallace girls in their straw hats would circulate among the crowd as the governor took to championing the cause of the common man. "If they want to call us rednecks, let 'em call us rednecks," Wallace declared from whatever makeshift stage he was on. "If they mean that we have our necks red from a good honest day's toil in the summer sun, let 'em call us rednecks." He continued: "There's two things about them [liberal critics], though. Number one, they won't get out and work in the summer sun. And number two, their hair's so long their necks wouldn't get red anyway!" He loved to attack the "pseudo intellectuals" most of all, those who refused to believe, trust, or respect "the people." He championed local control, common sense, and hard work. The common man ought to be writing the guidelines for the pseudo intellectuals, not the other way around, he proclaimed. Washington was taking over. The federal government was overriding local and state laws, violating local traditions, and defying common sense. They were making society too lenient. The rioters, antiwar protestors, and "militants" were threatening and abusing the people while cowering behind federal authority.[15]

The many hecklers from the left fueled the campaign. They were there to take Wallace down, but they stoked the mood and filled the coffers. He'd give them his patented line about running over protestors or make some crack about having a four-letter word for the kids—S-O-A-P—and the audience would delight in his barbs. If the press were there, they'd also get an us-versus-them earful. He especially enjoyed impugning his hecklers' masculinity. "I love you, too," he was fond of saying to his long-haired protestors. "Oh, my mistake, I thought that he was a she." Or, "Son, if you'll just shut up and take off your sandals, I'll autograph one of them as a souvenir." He'd thank them for all the votes the hecklers drove his way; the crowd ate it up, and they tossed more money into the Wallace girls' buckets.

The show was more or less the same in every town, but to those who came to hear the man it was a political revelation. As Wallace's biographer put it, "A Wallace rally was an act of communion between the speaker and his audience, for he was one of the last grandmasters of the kind of foot-stomping public speaking that characterized American politics, particularly southern politics, in the age before television. A Wallace speech excited the kind of nonanalytical emotional response that media advisers had always sought to evoke."[16]

One of Wallace's not-so-secret secrets was that his campaign workers were employees of the state of Alabama who, if pressed, would claim to be working on the campaign during their "vacations." As had long been the case in Barbour County, graft was the name of the game. The state of Alabama was his instrument, and his anti-statism was directed only at the federals. Campaign bank accounts were filled with kickbacks from state contractors who were expected to give 10 percent of the cost of their contract to the Wallace cause. Jack Wallace, George's brother, said of Gerald, the third brother, who greedily ran the finances of the campaign, that he was so crooked they were going to have to "screw him into the ground" when he died. There were bigwig donors, too, who believed in segregation and limited government and that Wallace was their vessel.[17]

In addition to the rattling buckets of the Wallace girls, the campaign sold everything Wallace: hats, ties, sashes, buttons, bumper stickers, the works. Small donations made up a large amount of the campaign resources, and a lot of that came from showing the dodgy Wallace campaign film on late-night, small-market television. The boiling rage from the glowing tube in the middle of the night touched a nerve. His cheap little film brought in more than five times what Hubert Humphrey's did. Small bills, crumpled up, folded neatly, stuffed in envelopes, were delivered with hand-scrawled addresses to Wallace headquarters in Montgomery. At the enormous warehouse outside of Montgomery, they'd pour the sacks upside down, and the small donations spilled out onto the table, accumulating into mountains of cash.[18]

Through it all, the idea of freedom remained the heartbeat of the campaign. "One of our slogans was 'Stand Up For America,'" said campaign worker Judy Turnipseed. "Of course, we meant white

America. But the way it came across was 'Go away and leave us alone. We don't want the federal government to come in and tell us what to do.'" In his campaign film, Wallace stands before the Alabama State Legislature and declares that they were "obligated to oppose the enemies of freedom wherever we find them." By "enemies of freedom," he explicitly meant the federal government and only the federal government. Wallace laced his thinking and his rhetoric with words like *sovereign*, *freedom*, *free men*, *free peoples*, *freedom-loving*, *freedom-loving blood*, *freedom-loving forefathers*, *freedom of choice*, and *God-given freedoms*. Limits on freedom were the source of American decline and a betrayal of the "system of freedom" that had built the nation.[19]

There were so many lunatic fringe white supremacist groups joining and associating with Wallace's American Independent Party that Wallace occasionally spoofed that they should call it the Squirrel Party—because it collected all the nuts. The Birchers, the White Citizens' Council, and the Klan all showed, as did, in opposition, the student left and Black Power champions of various stripes. There were the usual street fights, demonstrations, counterdemonstrations, throwing of bottles, and injuries, with the left-wing protestors chanting "*Sieg heil!*," the Nazi victory salute, and the Right denouncing filthy communists and hippies. There were also some simply frightening people on the campaign trail that made Wallace seem downright genteel. The campaign saved some Wallace protestors from the maw of a white supremacist mob of blue-collar workers in Milwaukee. In California, a militia group proudly unveiled a truck full of guns, bazookas, and heavy weapons ready to fight. In Massachusetts, where the campaign's director, Tom Turnipseed, was doing advance work to get Wallace's name on the ballot, he went to the local Polish American Club in Webster to see if he could use their hall for a Wallace rally. "Great, we like George Wallace," they exclaimed, and offered to let the governor use their facility free of charge. They went to the hall—the venue was perfect—and then they had a couple of drinks together. As Turnipseed recalled, "Just before I left, the head guy there, the manager and the head bartender looked me right in the eye and he said, 'Now, Mr. Turnipseed,' he says, 'now, when George

Wallace is elected president, he's going to line up all the niggers and kill them, isn't he?'" Turnipseed was shocked when he realized the man was serious. "To know that these people really felt that way, that they wanted to kill Black people, you know, and it got me starting to think in changing my views from that point..."[20]

By the summer of campaign year 1968, the Wallace campaign was doing extraordinarily well. The former governor was back in full swing after the time off to mourn the passing of the long-suffering Lurleen, who succumbed to her struggle with cancer in May. After a relentless schedule of campaign stops across the country, and a Democratic Party in disarray after the chaos of the Chicago convention, he was polling at 21 points, not that far behind heir apparent Hubert Humphrey. It looked like a real possibility that the man from Clio could win enough votes to throw the presidential contest into the House of Representatives, where he could be a major power broker. He owned the Deep South, and he stood a chance in the border states and Florida. If he won every state that he had a chance of winning, still a wild possibility but a possibility nonetheless, Nixon would fail to win the required majority to be president.[21]

The pesky matter of a vice presidential running mate ended up destroying Wallace's slim chance of victory. Some said he needed someone more moderate to soften his image among the mainstream, some said they needed another hard-liner to shore up the base. The moderate of choice was Happy Chandler, a popular Kentucky political figure. But Chandler, as baseball commissioner, had let Jackie Robinson into the Major Leagues. The man who integrated baseball was rejected by the big-money supporters of segregation. Wallace turned to retired General Curtis LeMay, a brilliant if merciless tactician during World War II—he ran the bombing of Japan as well as the Berlin Airlift—but someone who had developed a reputation as a trigger-happy madman with an almost poetic infatuation with the use of nuclear weapons. Stanley Kubrick skewered him in the film *Dr. Strangelove* as the inspiration for the character General Buck Turgidson, played by the surprisingly comical George C. Scott. His caricature turned out to be not too far from the character.

The Wallace campaign prepped LeMay all night before his official naming to the ticket. They specifically trained him not to take any bait on the question of nuclear weapons. Unfortunately for Wallace, LeMay's big jaw continued to make nuclear gaffs like a cigar-chomping, square-shouldered air force general in a china shop. Wallace continued to try to help clarify, catching crashing dishes as they fell. The selection of LeMay was a disaster. Humphrey started calling Wallace and LeMay "The Bombsy Twins." The governor's support melted, especially among women and those north of the Mason-Dixon. If angry white people wanted to vent their spleen in 1968 a bit more rationally, they'd have to go for Nixon.[22]

Despite the debacle of the LeMay nomination, Wallace kept running—and attracting big crowds. In September he arrived in Chicago, where he rode down State Street in an open-air limo with fifty thousand people smashed together in the streets greeting him. The rock-solid support stood in contrast to the violent clashes sponsored by Mayor Daley's police at the Democratic Convention just the previous month. He then went to Cicero, where another eight thousand people rallied for the Alabama governor. His jubilant greeting by white Chicagoans contrasted with Dr. King, who was met with violent white mobs during similar visits. The "government had sold them out," he told aggrieved white people. He hit Boston, where twenty thousand people met him at a rally on the Common—though it was heavily laced with anti-Wallace people and several hundred police to keep the peace. The same happened, with over ten thousand people, in Detroit, Pittsburgh, Portland, San Diego, Phoenix, and Minneapolis. His polling numbers may have been shrinking since his selection of LeMay, but the militancy, energy, and size of his crowds were the envy of the other campaigns.[23]

In October, the exhausted campaign arrived at the center of American liberalism, New York City. Wallace's scowling face, superimposed on the Statue of Liberty, had just appeared on the cover of *New York* magazine. "Red Neck New York: Is This Wallace Country?," queried the cover story. Twenty thousand people packed Madison

Square Garden to shout and stomp their answer. The band played songs of a triumphant America while the governor made his way back and forth across the stage, the crowd chanting his name, "Wallace, Wallace, Wallace!" The audience "prays and hates—in unison," noted an observer. The roar was so loud that anti-Wallace protestors outside the Garden and down the street could hear them. The excitement was explosive. The *New Republic* reported the "menace in the blood shout of the crowd." The parallel was obvious. "Never again will you read about Berlin in the 30s without remembering this wild confrontation." Wallace was "the ablest demagogue of our time" and this was not a campaign, it was a "political revival" for "people who want to save their country."[24]

The size of the rally may have been dramatic, but the audience got the same stage show rhetoric Wallace had been giving in tawdry auditoriums, luncheons, and parking lots across the nation. He had no new ideas, no policies, and no positions to announce. He just revved up the crowd. When the hecklers tried to give him a hard time, he gave them his classic, "Why do the leaders of the two national parties kowtow to these anarchists?" Then he moved to his big applause line: "One of 'em laid down in front of President Johnson's limousine last year. I'll tell you when November comes, the first time they lie down in front my limousine it'll be the last one they'll ever lay down in front; their day is *over*." It never failed. Twenty thousand people were on their feet. His other line worked just as well. "We don't have riots in Alabama," he declared. "They start a riot down there, first one of 'em to pick up a brick gets a bullet in the brain, that's all. And then you walk over to the next one and say, 'All right, pick up a brick. We just want to see you pick up one of them bricks, now!'" This may have been New York City, bastion of liberalism, but it was confirmation of what Wallace knew from the start. As one New Yorker put it, "People are always talking about George Wallace, he just appeals to the rednecks... well, there are a lot of us rednecks in this country, and they don't all live in the South!"[25]

Organized labor began to worry as their own members drifted away from the unions' alliance with the Democrats and toward the

Wallace insurgency. In September, the enormous Flint, Michigan, local of the United Auto Workers endorsed the governor. Internal polling showed that one-third of union members favored Wallace. "Never before has the trade union movement developed so much political muscle and organization sophistication," explained the labor journalist John Herling. "Yet never before has organized labor seemed so ineffectual in combatting an appeal to fear and prejudice." In a last-ditch campaign, organized labor turned its members back toward Humphrey with a campaign of its own that clarified the dismal state of labor and work in Governor Wallace's Alabama. It was, the union leadership made clear, nothing any Northern worker wanted in his future.[26]

Despite the thunderous rallies, Wallace's support was dwindling rapidly from his September highpoint down to his core of diehard supporters. On Election Day, he polled 13.5 percent and won a Deep South victory map similar to Barry Goldwater's in 1964 (Wallace gained Arkansas, lost South Carolina). With Wallace destabilizing the numbers, Nixon defeated Humphrey in the popular vote by a sliver. Thinking of the Nixon victory, Wallace argued, "When you add his vote to our vote," he explained a bit desperately, "there are more of us than there are of them." What sounded like sour grapes was the future of American politics. Nixon's adviser Kevin Phillips famously called it "the emerging Republican majority." Disgruntled Wallace votes—the South, the blue-collar ethnics, the West—added to the traditional but right-moving Republican Party would make up a political juggernaut for the foreseeable future. Banking on the irrefutable political logic that the key to American politics was who hated whom, Phillips predicted that the Wallace vote was the key to the Republican future. "People will ease their way into the Republican Party by way of the American Independents," explained Kevin Phillips. The Nixon team will get "two-thirds to three-fourths of the Wallace vote in nineteen seventy-two."[27]

"What the voice called up from the American spirit in 1968," prophesized campaign journalist Theodore H. White, "may become part of a somber future which Americans prefer to ignore."

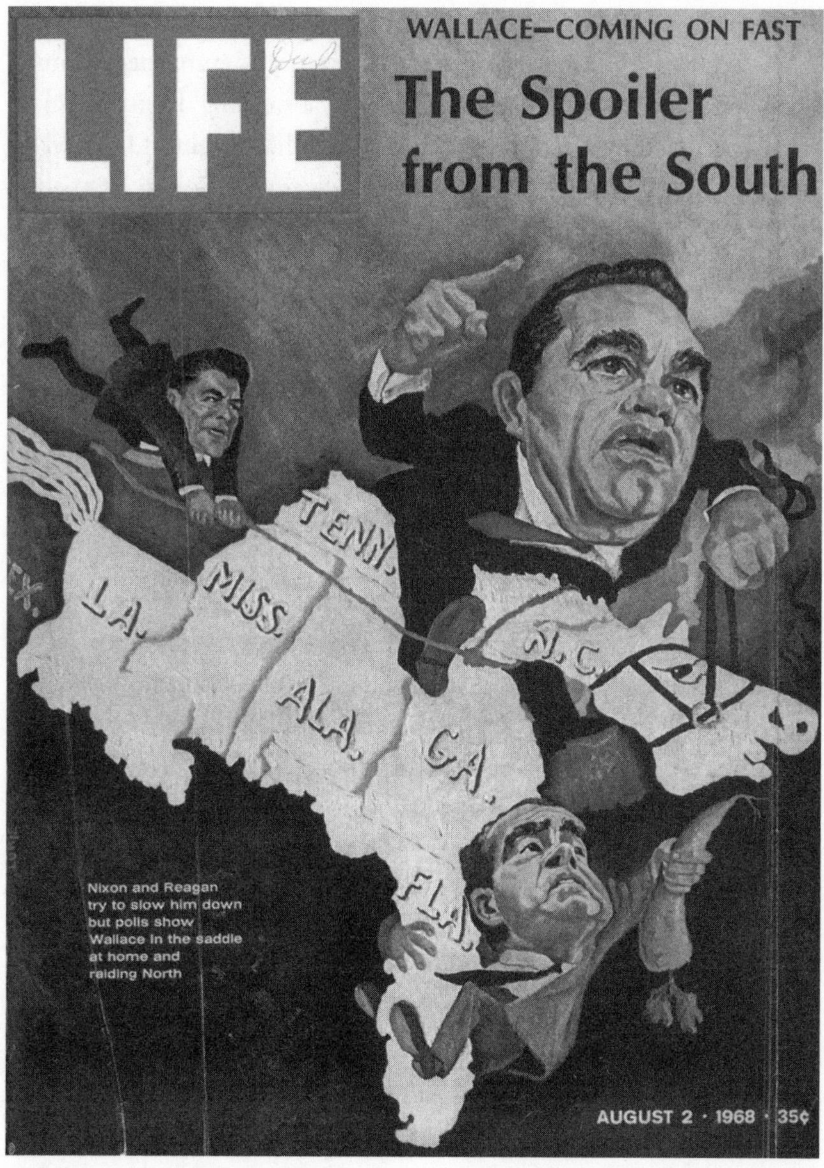

LIFE
WALLACE—COMING ON FAST
The Spoiler from the South
TENN.
MISS.
LA.
ALA.
GA.
N.C.
FLA.
Nixon and Reagan try to slow him down but polls show Wallace in the saddle at home and raiding North
AUGUST 2 · 1968 · 35¢

Wallace rides a runaway horse made up of Southern states. The Alabama Democrat, running for president as an independent in 1968, upset long-stable dynamics between the two major parties in the South and the North. Representing the conservative wing of the Republican Party, California governor Ronald Reagan holds on for dear life while 1968 Republican presidential nominee Richard Nixon tries to coax the Wallace insurgency his way with a carrot. The "Wallace factor" became the key variable for understanding the future of American politics.

To consider White's prediction is to realize that of the major trends of that campaign year, most ended up bruised, embattled, diminished, or gone. The ever-searching, ever-stumbling Republicanism of Richard Nixon ended up settling into the hard right of Goldwater and Reagan. The Black and blue-collar hopes of Bobby Kennedy's campaign did not resurface until Obama. The can-do liberalism of Hubert H. Humphrey and Lyndon Johnson, that which brought the Great Society, War on Poverty, and Civil Rights and Voting Rights Acts, has long passed, subsequently lost in the idea that the "era of big government is over." The liberal Supreme Court, supporting the civil rights struggles of local people on the federal level, is vanquished. The revolutionary fervor of the student left and Black Power movements withered not long after their apex in 1968.

One element of 1968 lived on. Pundits began to see that the future depended upon "the Wallace factor": that which "makes the formation of a Presidential majority impossible without a large portion of the votes of George Wallace supporters." While "the sixties" waned, the anti-statist brand of racialized freedom championed by George C. Wallace grew more powerful and more virulent, deepening and not diminishing in the decades to come. The working assumption of American political development had always been that the South would eventually mature and modernize to look a lot like the North. Yet, as Samuel Lubell put it, "Wallace raised the prospect that the North, as it changes, may become southernized." By 1972, Wallace appeared on America's "most admired person" list, coming in at tenth place just behind Pope Paul VI and Bob Hope. A poll of Democrats selected him third after Humphrey and Maine senator Edmund Muskie as a favored candidate, giving him more than double what George McGovern, who actually won the nomination, received.[28]

A lot of Wallace's racialization of federal intervention worked. His "Northern Strategy" had legs, but other forces were churning as well: a shared suburbanization, a homogenizing commercial culture, and the realignment of the political parties that allowed the Republicans to take over among the once solidly white Democratic South. The "Americanization of Dixie" and the "Southernization of

America" strode forth in the 1970s, hand in hand. Yet North and South did not melt into a bright and hopeful synthesis of the two cultures. As the Southern writer John Egerton put it, each region got busy "exporting vices without importing virtues." The major vice was the freedom to dominate.[29]

In the fall of 1968, *Newsweek*, looking at the Wallace phenomenon in the North, captured the Southernization of America in horror, asking: "Has America caught up to Alabama?" Wallace became a major symbol in the nationalization of Southern culture, but by the time his national campaigns were over, he would not be president. In the words of one of his biographers, however, the gritty politician from Clio, Alabama, had succeeded enormously in one thing. He had become "America's political guru of the final quarter of the twentieth century"—and well beyond.[30]

Conclusion

"THE SOUVENIRS OF THE South flicker past like images in a magic-lantern show," wrote a memoirist upon returning to Barbour County in the 1970s. "Dr. Pepper billboards, a chinaberry tree in every Negro yard yielding its bitter unwanted fruit, peeling white-clapboard churches, each with its own lopsided graveyard, old overalled men sitting on sagging porches, dilapidated barns proclaiming the timeless glories of Prince Albert Tobacco, Garrett Snuff and Spark Plug Chewing Tobacco." The abandoned sharecropper shacks returned slowly to the earth along with the memories of generations of people who inhabited them. A jungle of indiscernible new growth filled the once bountiful plains of cotton and peanuts. Foreign competition slowly killed off the textile mills, while workers with lungs clogged by deadly white fibers sued their once-paternalistic employer to get some of their life back. The town still hung on to its antebellum grandeur, though, which clamored for the attention of tourists as they swiftly motored through town on their way to the Gulf Coast.[1]

In the grand mansions lining Eufaula's tree-lined boulevards, heritage organizations moved in to shore up their crumbling foundations and restore their famed interiors. They also preserved the fantasy of an uncontested antebellum past haunting the rooms within. Tourists, flooding in annually since the first spring heritage festival in

1966, could marvel at "beautiful historic homes built in the days when 'cotton was king'" during their "nostalgic return to the Old South." Here, "grand antebellum and Victorian mansions built by 19th century plantation owners and merchants still house family heirlooms, precious symbols of a bygone era." As visitors come to town during the Eufaula Pilgrimage, promoters promise that "Southern belles in hoops and bustles will grace the area and greet you warmly as you pass." The mighty Chattahoochee had been transformed from mover of cotton to tourist destination when a federal dam transformed it into a massive reservoir stocked with fish. Eufaula declared itself to be the "Big Bass Capital of the World." In a monument to the new era, the city installed a bright twelve-foot-high fiberglass statue of a largemouth bass leaping from the water. Three blocks west, the monument to the Confederate soldier remained unmoved and uncontested.[2]

Fishing and the grandeur of a bygone era brought some money into the county. The Shorter Mansion, once home to the region's most enduring and powerful planter dynasties, became a museum to anchor tours of moonlight, magnolias, hoop skirts, swords, flags, and Southern honor. Always honor. An African American man returned to Eufaula in the early 1980s to make a go of it as part of the reverse migration back to the South of the late twentieth century. "All the surroundings is the resemblance of what the South was before," he noted. And, in the minds of whites, "what it should be like."[3]

Since the 1960s, a slow motion "redemption" undermined the gains of the Second Reconstruction of the civil rights era. Since Fred Gray left office in 1972, no African American Democrat has represented Barbour County. James Rapier's one term in the US Congress during Reconstruction stands out as the lonely interregnum of Black elected leadership to Washington, DC. Over a century after the polling place massacre in 1874, the Eufaula police killed two African American brothers in 1983, inspiring the Southern Christian Leadership Conference to launch a campaign on their behalf. In what amounted to a Black Lives Matter protest long before the videos of police brutality filled America's screens, SCLC organized a boycott of Eufaula and a march from there to Montgomery. Demanding "equal justice," they proclaimed, "Remember the Russaw Brothers!" and "March on Eufaula against police terror and killing of Blacks!" The Klan, donning robes but remaining peaceful, arrived, as they said, "to support the white people." The Black community demanded a federal investigation of the police who, some claimed, "killed in cold blood." The SCLC pinned the expansion of local police brutality in Eufaula and throughout the South on Reagan-era "failure of the Justice Department to vigorously enforce prosecution in cases of police brutality."[4]

Barbour County's greatest export, a race-based anti-statist brand of freedom, remained far more robust than the faded paint on the barn ads, the silence of the shuttered mills, or the vacant fields. The struggle between local freedom, sovereignty, and power continued, still shaped by opposition to the distant powers in Washington. The fetish of localism, while encased in a seductive veneer of democratic intimacy, remained as violent a form of domination as ever.

Conflating the local with the democratic, the United States continued to fail to do what was necessary to make democracy work: protecting—equally, aggressively, unflinchingly, and martially when necessary—the rights of all people. Federal power had always been a dubious ally, sometimes a hostile enemy, of the rights of nonwhite people. In the case, for instance, of Woodrow Wilson's segregation of the federal government or the FBI's spying on King among countless others, the federal government acted aggressively against the rights and interests of African Americans. But, as almost two hundred years of Barbour County's history suggests, federal authority was the key to leveraging the power of local social movements into lasting and enforceable change. Without federal backing, there was little hope of lasting success.

The problem of federal power and local white freedom that shaped Barbour County did not escape the earliest observers of the entire American democratic experiment. About the same time that intruders flooded into Creek lands to fill the rich black soil with cotton seed in the early 1830s, a young and curious French aristocrat was observing the young nation's politics and behavior as he floated down the Ohio River. From his perch on deck, Alexis de Tocqueville could look to the starboard, where he imagined the anxious "desire for wealth" that drove those in the free states to seek fortune at every turn; to the portside, he thought of the "ignorant and lukewarm" torpor of a world shaped by slavery. The Ohio River was the division between North and South, the line between "liberty and servitude," as he noted in the fourteen notebooks he carried on his investigation around the United States. He admitted that he knew little about the South or its slave economy, having what he called "only a superficial acquaintance" with the region. Like generations of commentators on American liberalism, he allowed part of the nation, the North, to be mistaken for the whole.[5]

Tocqueville not only failed to grasp the immense wealth and dynamic productivity of the Southern economy, he showed little interest in its inner workings. Slavery, he determined, "was American but not democratic and it was the portrait of democracy that I wanted to paint." Instead, Tocqueville focused the pages of *Democracy in America* on the free, bustling, and egalitarian world of the North. Here was a new nation, he observed, rooted in the single "basic fact" of "equality of conditions." Moving forward from a Puritan "point of departure," he noted of the supposed roots of the republic in the Massachusetts Bay Colony, the "whole secret of the success of American 'democracy'" lay in the "decentralization" of governmental power. For Tocqueville, a weak federal government was democracy.[6]

As much as Tocqueville appreciated the robust democratic traditions of Jacksonian America—the widespread enfranchisement, urgent speechifying, furious organization building, and dire sense of political consequences on all matters—he nonetheless foretold of a problem. The structure and culture of freedom and democracy that he observed created a near insurmountable obstacle to marshaling the kinds of state power that would one day be necessary to ensure the civil, social, and economic rights of Black people.

Tocqueville was not just skeptical; he was downright fatalistic about American democracy's capacity to deal with racial inequality.

"I do not believe that the white and black races will ever live in any country upon an equal footing," he argued. It would be difficult anywhere, he reasoned, but nearly impossible in America. Even though he hoped for and worked for the end of slavery, he was not naive about the problems that would present for the American democratic experiment. The only hope within the United States might be "a despot," one capable of subjecting "Americans and their former slaves to the same yoke," who would one day prove powerful enough to "succeed in commingling the races." Yet the type of federal power necessary, he believed, was unlikely. "As long as the American democracy remained at the head of affairs," Tocqueville believed, "no one will undertake so difficult a task." White people would have a hard time raising police powers against their own perceived interests. "The freer the white population of the United States becomes," he argued, "the more isolated [segregated] will it remain." As a people, white Americans were not capable of defeating their own interests. As he summarized the political metaphysics at stake: "A whole people cannot rise, as it were, above itself."[7]

Tocqueville tapped into an age-old question, one that Native Americans, African Americans, and European Americans all fought over in Barbour County and much of the rest of the nation. Which people are sovereign? Why not all people? Where is sovereignty located? Whose liberties should be protected from whom? By what mechanisms and whose authority? Even ignoring questions of race, these problems remained the central riddles of the constitutional order. As James Madison explained in 1787, the "great desideratum" of governmental affairs was what would render the state "sufficiently neutral between the different interests and factions, to controul one part of the Society from invading the rights of another, and at the same time sufficiently controuled itself, from setting up an interest adverse to that of the whole Society"? Placing the American racial hierarchy at the center of these questions makes them immensely more complicated than Madison could imagine.[8]

The boundaries of freedom's dominion could not be solved in theory when, in practice, they were deeply grounded in local battles over white freedom, white sovereignty, and white democracy—ideologies orbiting the material realities of red people's land and Black people's labor. It is easy but naive to believe that Madison's "desideratum" was solved with the Civil War, the Reconstruction Acts, and the Thirteenth, Fourteenth, and Fifteenth Amendments. To the contrary, however, the project of "redemption" proved that a militant minority interested in defending their freedoms, with violence as necessary, could defeat blinkered federal commitments to enforcing civil and political rights. Generations of political struggle always remained vulnerable to the bombast of a few.

Substantial and meaningful civil rights victories in the second half of the twentieth century put the lie to the idea that nothing has changed in US race relations. The right to vote has been formally secured, discrimination legally banished, and hate crimes made into federal offenses. Yet the federal project to restrain the freedom to dominate has continued to be an ongoing struggle. While mobs of people may not have directly stormed the voting booths and shot Black voters en masse has they had in 1874, American political power has been aggressively beaten back to the local, more controllable, level of the compound republic since the 1970s.

In the fight against federal power, the resonance of Barbour County's favorite son never ceased. "They all talking like me," George Wallace explained in 1994. Three decades after he stood at the rostrum during his inaugural and declared his campaign to free Barbour County, the state of Alabama, and the entire United States from the yoke of federal oppression, he found that his brand of white freedom had unequivocally gone national. Late in life, straining against his limp and useless legs, his lower body paralyzed by a would-be assassin's bullet, he reminisced about his impact. "Nixon. Reagan. Clinton. Welfare reform. Crime. Big government," he explained, still puffing on his plastic-tipped cigarillos. "They all saying now what I was saying then." After his defeat as an independent presidential candidate in 1968, he coyly declared a sort of victory. "I wish I had copyrighted my speeches," he chided. "I would be drawing immense royalties from Mr. Nixon and especially Mr. Agnew."[9]

Republican political analyst Kevin Phillips put Wallace's logic at the center of his thinking. Compiling reams of data, he located a death rattle in the New Deal coalition of labor, liberals, African Americans, and the white South. The "principal cause of the breakup of the New Deal coalition" was what Wallace already knew: "the Negro problem" (more accurately, the "white problem") which had become "a national rather than a local" issue. The outcome was captured in the revelatory title of his 1969 book: *The Emerging Republican Majority*. The more robustly Black people voted, and the more the Democratic Party accommodated them, the more whites felt their privileged sense of freedom slipping away at the hands of federal authorities. The Voting Rights Act, Phillips argued, was doing a fine job of scaring Democrats into becoming Republicans. On the grounds that voting rights generated anti-statist conservatives, he believed, Black voting should be quietly endorsed—even by the Republicans.[10]

As Phillips recognized, by the end of the 1960s, the political tables had begun to turn. Wallace's Democratic Party, the party of Jefferson, had, from the 1940s to the 1960s, successfully used state power for protecting civil and political rights. Republicans began to capitalize on the very fears of federal power that Wallace had hoped to preserve for the Democrats. The Republicans swooped in to fill the Jeffersonian void left behind. They assembled pieces of anti-statist freedom—from states' rights to economic deregulation to emancipation from meddling social policies—and built them into an enduring coalition. By the 1980s, the party of Lincoln, emancipation, and Reconstruction had become the party of Strom Thurmond, limits on federal power, and the slow redemption of the 1980s. The party of ambivalent Reconstruction in the 1870s had become the party of militant redemption by the 1980s.[11]

In 1972, George Wallace was shot in a Maryland shopping center as he campaigned for the presidential nomination of the Democratic Party. Nixon had gone out of his way to make sure, quite probably through manipulation of an IRS investigation of George's brother, that this time the Wallace cyclone stayed on the Democratic side of the street. If the governor ran as a Democrat, Nixon could happily watch him tear that party asunder, but if he ran as an independent as he had in 1968, he would draw votes away from the Republicans. Once the governor was neutralized as a political threat, Nixon continued to study Wallace as the master of the politics of resentment. He tamed the Alabamian's feral political energies, funneled them into more sterile positions on school integration, affirmative action, and voting rights, and ran on his "silent majority" ideal, cobbling similar sorts of fear, prejudice, and resentment into a winning coalition. As Nixon's domestic policy adviser John Ehrlichman recalled, the president knew the race-and-federalism question needed careful attention. Nixon left much to staff discretion, but when it came to the governor of Alabama, "Nixon *micro-managed* the Wallace threat. That's how important he thought it was."[12]

In the years to come, Republicans recognized that they could build a new party on the carcass of the old Democrats in the South and the West. The locus of anti-statist freedom shifted away from the snarling segregationists and toward the gunfighters, and politicians, of the American West, where the freedom to dominate took on new life. The coalition that was only a whisper when Wallace flirted with Goldwater to select him as his vice presidential nominee became the center of American politics. The politics of resentment found common purpose with the politics of deregulation in the powerful double helix of American conservatism. It was a reminder of the power of Malcom X's succinct explanation of American politics: "'White' means free, boss."[13]

American partisanship reassembled from a cross-hatched political system to a polarized one. Segregationist Democrats were no longer tempered by liberal Democrats; the conservative Goldwater wing of the Republican Party was no longer offset by the liberal Republicans. The liberals all ended up on one side and the conservatives on the other. Intraparty compromise died and interparty competition took over. The regions, the cultures, and the races, once interwoven in their partisan leanings, sorted into distinct and rapidly polarizing camps. The parties seemed to be moving away from each other like celestial bodies with no gravitational center, except the Democrats moved slowly right and the Republicans, pushed by an effective media strategy, moved right at a rapidly accelerated rate. Confederate-era polarization was reborn. Local sources of rage and victimization boiled into a national political rage.[14]

By 1995, a Southern commentator captured it well: "And in the year of the angry white male, the year of the Newt [Gingrich], the year the right took back both houses of Congress, few historical figures of our time seemed both so flamboyantly wrong and so blindingly prophetic as George Corley Wallace—wrong enough to lose the battle [over civil rights], but right enough to serve as a model for how to win the war."[15]

The governor from Clio had since wept and repented, prayed and communed with civil rights leaders about his racist sins. He regretted it all, he openly proclaimed, and asked everyone he could for forgiveness. The moment that had been foretold when he gazed out upon the rally at the end of the Selma March in 1965, fearing the rise of a new constituency, had come to pass. His indomitable political will was never constrained by his wheelchair, and he kept running for the governor's office and winning, completing his final term in 1987 with strong, and forgiving, African American support.

In the meantime, the gains of the civil rights movement and Voting Rights Act were steadily worn down by the aggressive localism Wallace had championed. Starting with Richard Nixon's "New Federalism" and Reagan's notorious calls for "states' rights" through the bipartisan "Devolution Revolution" in federal power in the 1990s, the plans for shifting power to the local level continued apace. In the Supreme Court's monumental decision in 2000, *Bush v. Gore*, the nation learned something long extant but that few people knew. Americans may have been aware that the right to vote was limited through gerrymandering, restrictions to eligibility, barriers to voting, and the antiquated ridiculousness of the Electoral College. Few knew, however, as the court's majority declared, "the individual citizen has no federal constitutional right to vote" short of enforcing what states decide their systems to be.[16]

Voting in the United States remained a bungled, corrupt, power-influenced system, one dependent upon the resources and limited goodwill of the individual states. By 2013, the teeth of the Voting Rights Act were extracted in the Alabama-based Supreme Court case *Shelby County v. Holder.* Under the original Voting Rights Act, jurisdictions with a history of discrimination in voting had to submit any proposed changes to their voting systems and procedures to the US Department of Justice or a federal district court. After *Holder*, they did not. The half-century-long project to redeem power from federal authority was near complete as state after state passed new voting restrictions and rejected proposed federal voting reforms.

Freedom has always been a contested, messy, and ill-defined concept, of course, but it is crucial to recognize that the anti-statist, white power version of it is not an aberration but a virulent part of an American idiom. The writer Ta-Nehisi Coates summarized this "kind of freedom—a white freedom" in brilliant if sprawling terms. It is, he wrote, a "freedom without consequence, freedom without criticism, freedom to be proud and ignorant; freedom to profit off a people in one moment and abandon them in the next; a Stand Your Ground freedom, freedom without responsibility, without hard memory; a Monticello without slavery, a Confederate freedom, the freedom of John C. Calhoun, not the freedom of Harriet Tubman, which calls you to risk your own; not the freedom of Nat Turner, which calls you to give even more." Freedom in the United States, he argued, is a "conqueror's freedom."[17]

In January 2021, Donald Trump's followers, motivated by their ideas of American freedom, stormed the US Capitol building. Willfully embracing the lie that the 2020 election—and their birthright—had been stolen, the rioters imagined themselves the direct descendants of the American Revolution. They sought to restore a specific version of the republic, much the same as those who seceded in 1861 believed themselves to be grounded in first—and endangered—principles of white freedom. The Capitol rioters claimed to defend such values as they pummeled through doors, smashed windows, assaulted police, seized the Capitol rotunda, and ransacked federal offices—all to overturn a fair election count. Even the federal police remained underprepared and unable or unwilling to penetrate the rioters' shield of whiteness. The failed legitimacy of federal authority hung in the air that day, as rioters claimed, "I'm here for freedom," and, "We want our country back." It is too easy to scoff at the rise of a neo-Jacksonian and neo-Confederate discontent without noting that these protestors were, in fact, not wrong to call themselves "freedom fighters" within a deeply flawed American creed.[18]

Spurring them on was Congressman Mo Brooks, who represented Barbour County as part of Alabama's Fifth District. Brooks, secretly wearing body armor for the battle to come, delivered an incendiary speech to the throngs of protestors swathed in camo and combat garb at the "Save America Rally," helping to turn an angry assembly into a violent mob. His graceless political rhetoric made the sneering quips of George Wallace seem like the erudition of Cicero. "Today is the day," Brooks proclaimed, "American patriots start taking down names and kicking ass." He sought the overthrow of a fair and definitive election count because his candidate lost. When criticized for his inflammatory remarks, Brooks declared, "I encourage EVERY citizen to watch my entire rally speech and decide for themselves what kind of America they want: One based on freedom and liberty or one based on Godless dictatorial power."[19]

Although Brooks's surreal phrasing seems detached from the gravitational pull of logic itself, it rests on an epistemology built of long-repeated ideas. Barbour County's story of freedom is, in no small part, the nation's story of freedom. When white people stormed across Creek lands in defiance of federal marshals, when Hardeman Owens tried to blow up federal troops, when white citizens shot Black voters during Reconstruction, when workers and employers railed against the Fair Employment Practices Committee, when Wallace framed his political career in opposition to federal power, when local politicians tried to subvert the Voting Rights Act, all were part of an American tradition that now includes the ransacking of the US Capitol. The fact that politicians of Brooks's sensibilities belong to something called the Congressional "Freedom Caucus" may now seem less ironic and more sickeningly accurate.[20]

Insurrections in the name of white freedom are too often a product of federal appeasement, not overreach. Generations of political actors have balked while carrying out their responsibility to protect a robust vision of citizenship rights. Those willing to use the state for non-democratic ends have invariably rushed in to fill the void. The long and deep irony is that those who proclaim a politics of anti-statism never hesitate to use instruments of state and federal power for their own purposes. The tragedy of this saga of federal power in one small place is that federal force was typically deployed just enough to ignite local resistance in the name of white freedom; rarely was it enough to protect the marginalized, victimized, and disenfranchised. Perhaps it is time to turn Goldwater's infamous 1964 statement about liberty on its head: federal defense of democracy is no vice. Moderation in the face of white freedom is no virtue.

On the eve of Martin Luther King Jr.'s death, while assisting in the defense of the labor rights of the sanitation workers of Memphis, he explained the path forward: "All we say to America is, 'Be true to what you said on paper.'" Yet even those official government documents to which he appealed are flawed and conflicted about the nature of American freedom. Instead, the project needs to be loftier than mere constitutional appeals—as important as they may always remain. After the Selma March, with the protestors assembled at the Alabama state capitol and George Wallace secretly peering out through his office window, King sought what was truly needed: "a society that can live with its conscience."[21]

Can Americans liberate themselves from the burdens of their freedom? Not easily. We continue to struggle with the ways that freedom and subjugation, freedom and white power, freedom and domination work together. Orlando Patterson reminds us, however, freedom is made up of a number of competing parts. The freedom to dominate is only one. The other dimensions, the freedom to engage in civic and political life, and the freedom to enjoy individual rights and liberties, all need to be differentiated and disentangled from the tale of domination. Yet the word is explosive and must be used with caution and precision. As the poet Fred Moten warns, "Freedom is too close to slavery for us to be easy with that jailed imagining."[22]

Stories, like this history of American freedom, are the architecture of our minds, the repository of our most foundational ideas. They are how many Americans consider their heritage, contemplate their ideas of citizenship, imagine their nationhood, and police their identities. That architecture is designed to withstand the challenge of other stories. To confront this saga of freedom is to confront the fundamentals of the American narrative. We ought not embrace the cruelty of the past, but neither should we continue the malignant idea that this story of oppression was never the "real" American story.

The solution is to change the narrative clearly and aggressively, to commit to a bright, sharp, militant defense of the one single, unambiguous thing that federal government should do: defend the civil and political rights on the local level for all people—cries of freedom to the contrary be damned.

mental maps to show me the way through unfamiliar terrain. Dan Usner, John Ellisor, and Claudio Saunt helped make sense of the Indigenous history of the American South; Campbell Scrivner helped out on freedmen's education; Robert "Hobie" Tinkler explained the nature of the Southern Whigs. Larry Glickman and I seem to inhabit parallel research universes, and he helped me with the enduring nature of the American "backlash." Joe Crespino and Jason Morgan Ward pointed the way toward the whole Southern "thing." Tom Sugrue helped with urban policy history. Michael Bibler, who spent his youthful energies organizing with SCOPE in Eufaula, committed a great deal of time explaining Barbour County in the 1960s to me. I regret never getting to speak with Larry Scott Butler before he passed, but I am so grateful that he left such a powerful record of his time in Barbour County. Thanks to Jordan Landes for quick and efficient access to his papers. Peter Coclanis clarified my thinking on resource curses and commodity regimes. Dan Feller assisted at key moments with his mastery of the Andrew Jackson papers. Long-term friend Michael Trotti proved an able, if temperamentally unlikely, expert in the ghastly subject of lynching. Ed Baptist has been a friend and an ongoing inspiration and provocation on race and slavery. Dan T. Carter was very encouraging about this project, and it is almost impossible to imagine having written this book without his incredible work on George Wallace having come before this. Carrie Monahan willingly exchanged ideas about Eufaula as well as her extraordinary elegiac Stanford honors thesis on the town. Needless to say, all mistakes in fact and interpretation remain solely my own.

At Vanderbilt University, my work was boosted by the intellectual power and collegiality of a truly great history department. I presented work in progress at two different Vanderbilt Americanist Seminars, and the sharp and collegial ideas gained there proved invaluable. Particular gratitude to colleagues David Carlton, Paul Kramer, Sarah Igo, Sarah Meyeux, Tom Schwartz, Tiffany Patterson, Dan Sharfstein, and Laura Stark. Two department chairs, Joel Harrington and Eddie Wright-Rios, proved enduring friends and allies. I am grateful to Dean John Geer for his support. The admin team at the Vanderbilt

History Department, particularly Meagan Artus and Mary Lyn Albritton, are people of wonderful skill and wit. My colleagues Kim Welch and Ari Bryen fed my belly as well as my soul. Both my undergraduate and graduate students were a joy to work with on themes like those explored here and they often challenged my thinking. The resources of the Stahlman Chair in American History meant not having to constantly chase down funds to do this research.

Before COVID restrictions, I was able to give some of this research a public workout. The Belle McWilliams Lecture at Memphis University was the first public presentation of these ideas. My host there was Aram Goudsouzian, who also helped with his own work on the election of 1968. Another early outing for this material was as the keynote to the Phil Alpha Theta conference at Belmont University. I presented the conceptual framework at the Department of History at Stanford University, where I received excellent feedback from everyone, but particularly from Gavin Wright and Jennifer Burns. Thanks to the entire Johns Hopkins History Seminar for a vigorous outing that greatly improved the project. I am particularly appreciative of Angus Burgin and Nate Connolly for hosting me. Other people read parts of this manuscript or gave it a boost in some way. Much gratitude to friends like: Joel Dinerstein, who was always ready to field any question from prose to race to Southern cultures; Pete Kuryla, who walked in many large circles with me and listened; Bryant Simon, who talks about books like the skilled craftsman and humane character that he is; the writing voice of Rick Perlstein, one of the great history stylists of our time; and Rob Vanderlan, upon whose sober and empathetic judgment I continue to depend. Gary Gerstle, Stephanie Curry, Kevin Boyle, and Kevin Kruse all advanced this project in very important ways. Graduate student Caroline Johnston read parts of the book and is on her way to being a wonderful scholar. Nick Salvatore taught me much about the race-class conundrum and is an enduring friend. Deep Springs College remains a biannual oasis from mainstream academia. Out in Taos, on the day before I turned this manuscript in, I was concerned about whether my work mattered. I went on a walk with Andy Graybill to the bottom of the Rio Pueblo Gorge. Then we visited a dig of some thirteenth-century Pueblo ruins. The answer to my question was obviously, no. But other things do.

Each of my books has had a soundtrack. I wanted this one to feel like an album by those Alabama boys, the Drive-By Truckers. Listening to another Alabamian and former Trucker, Jason Isbell, showed me how sharp words and metaphors could be if honed long and hard enough on the right whetstone. Far from Southern music, this book was written mostly listening to the haunting violin of Mat Maneri's album *Dust* over and over (and over). I've never met Maneri, but his violin vented the pain of this history in ways that art is supposed to do.

I wrote most of this book while I was a grateful fellow at Stanford University's Center for Advanced Study in Behavioral Sciences. What is there to say about a place that feeds you (too) well, provides a stimulating set of colleagues, wonderful offices, and a beautiful setting overlooking a stunning campus? At least until COVID shut things down, it was a scholar's paradise. Special thanks to Margaret Levy and the entire staff of the center. Particular shout-out to comrades Michael Brownstein, Mike Albertus, Guy Grossman, and Michael Hiscox, who made my stay particularly rich and enjoyable. The presentation of this work at the weekly CASBS research seminar helped frame this book's ideas in a broad and lively interdisciplinary setting.

A number of people read this book in its entirety and made it a lot clearer, more precise, more accurate, and significantly livelier. Greg Downs read it and handed me a sheaf of questions and comments. He is a hell of guy, among our great historians, and the right person to take you to school on issues of Reconstruction. Patricia Sullivan gets the nature of state, race, and social movements like nobody's business, but I am deeply grateful she helped make it my business, too. Nobody knows Alabama like the encyclopedic Mills Thornton. He supported the idea of this book, read the entire manuscript, and saved me from some significant errors of emphasis and fact. As a guide to Alabama, they don't come better than Mills. A comrade in the trenches of local history, William Sturkey, knew the right pressure points to push on issues of local history and state power. Mia Brown's clear thinking on race was invaluable. Jack Metzgar has read so much of my work that it's humbling. He rapidly and sharply critiqued all the early chapter drafts in their crudest and most aggravatingly out-of-order form. It doesn't get any better than the faith, solidarity, and friendship offered by my buddy Jack.

Basic Books did a great job making this publication a reality. It was first acquired by Dan Gerstle and then received into the sharp editorial powers of Brian Distelberg, with a major assist from Kyle Gipson. Brandon Proia, line editor extraordinaire, enriched the prose and rekindled my enthusiasm for what I was doing. Michael Kaler skillfully guided it through production. Bill Warhop miraculously copyedited a messy text into a clean and reliable document.

The Black Lives Matter movement took on particularly inspiring dimensions while I was writing this book about the problems with white freedom. My kids, Aidan and Aliya, continue to surprise, enrich, and delight as they become impressive adults in challenging times. Finally, my true love, Mickey Casad, rebuilt paragraphs, organized chapters, clarified syntax, and improved thinking with a balance of clarity, patience, wit, and love. Few are blessed to receive such rewards—and even fewer are capable of giving them. Mickey is among those rare few.

PHOTO CREDITS

1. George Wallace campaigning in Clayton, Alabama, 1958. Courtesy of Draffus L. Hightower Collection, the Doy Leale McCall Rare Book and Manuscript Library, University of South Alabama.
2. Maps of Alabama and Barbour County, Alabama. Courtesy of Kate Blackmer, Blackmer Maps.
3. Event Map of Eufaula, Alabama. Courtesy of Kate Blackmer, Blackmer Maps.
4. Map of Creek Lands in Georgia and Alabama, Henry Schenck Tanner, cartographer, 1823. Courtesy of the Alabama Department of Archives and History.
5. Andrew Jackson as the Great Father, 1835. Courtesy William L. Clements Library, University of Michigan.
6. Chattahoochee Bridge, Eufaula, Alabama. Alabama Writers' Project, n.d. Courtesy of the Alabama Department of Archives and History.
7. "Let us grasp hands over the bloody chasm," *Harper's Weekly*, 1872. Courtesy of the Collections of the Division of Political History, National Museum of American History, Smithsonian Institution, Washington, DC.
8. "Shall We Call Home Our Troops?" *Harper's Weekly*, 1875. Courtesy of Library of Congress.
9. J.W. Comer, C.S.A., and Burrell. Courtesy of the Alabama Department of Archives and History.
10. Slave cabin in Barbour County, near Eufaula. WPA Slave Narrative Project, 1936–1938. Courtesy of Library of Congress.
11. Shorter Mansion, 1960s. Courtesy of the Alabama Department of Archives and History.
12. Plow mule, Barbour County, n.d. Courtesy of Draffus L. Hightower Collection, the Doy Leale McCall Rare Book and Manuscript Library, University of South Alabama.
13. Alabama cotton harvest, n.d. Courtesy of the Alabama Department of Archives and History.
14. Cotton at the compress at Dean & Moore Warehouse in Eufaula, Alabama, 1930s–1940s. Courtesy of the Alabama Department of Archives and History.

15. Chauncey Sparks and Franklin Roosevelt at Maxwell Field. US Air Force official photograph, 1943. Courtesy of the Alabama Department of Archives and History.
16. Liars' Bench, Clayton, Alabama. Courtesy of Draffus L. Hightower Collection, the Doy Leale McCall Rare Book and Manuscript Library, University of South Alabama.
17. George Wallace campaigning in Clayton, Alabama, 1958. Courtesy of Draffus L. Hightower Collection, the Doy Leale McCall Rare Book and Manuscript Library, University of South Alabama.
18. Wallace inaugural, Montgomery, Alabama, 1963. Courtesy Bettmann Collection, Getty Images.
19. George Wallace and Nicholas Katzenbach, University of Alabama, 1963. Courtesy Bettmann Collection, Getty Images.
20. Hosea Williams, SCOPE training in Atlanta, 1965. Bob Fitch Photography Archive, Department of Special Collections, Stanford University Library.
21. Civil Rights Workers, Eufaula Courthouse, 1965. Jim Peppler, photographer. Courtesy of the Alabama Department of Archives and History.
22. Mary Marshall and family, 1966. Courtesy of Bob Fitch Photography Archive, Department of Special Collections, Stanford University Library.
23. Fred D. Gray. Courtesy of Bob Fitch Photography Archive, Department of Special Collections, Stanford University Library.
24. Wallace riding Southern horse, 1968. Courtesy of the estate of Ranan Lurie and *Life* magazine.

NOTES

Introduction: George Wallace and American Freedom

1 For Wallace and modern conservatism, see Dan Carter, *The Politics of Rage: George Wallace, the Origins of the New Conservatism, and the Transformation of American Politics* (New York: Simon & Schuster, 1995). "The Inaugural Address of Governor George C. Wallace," 14 January 1963, Montgomery, Alabama. An electronic copy of the original document is available at the Alabama Department of Archives and History, http://digital.archives.alabama.gov/cdm/ref/collection/voices/id/2952. All the quotations of this speech used were squared with available video of the actual speech, and the audio selected over the written text in minor cases of discrepancy.

2 Martin Luther King Jr., on NBC's Meet the Press, cited in Carter, *Politics of Rage*, 156; Taylor Branch, *Pillar of Fire: America in the King Years, 1963–1965* (New York: Simon & Schuster, 1998), 708–802, 894–895.

3 See "Speech by George C. Wallace, The Civil Rights Movement Fraud, Sham and Hoax," 4 July 1964, *American History: From Revolution to Reconstruction: Documents*, www.let.rug.nl/usa/documents/1951-/speech-by-george-c-wallace-the-civil-rights-movement-fraud-sham-and-hoax-1964-.php.

4 Eric Foner, *The Story of American Freedom* (New York: Norton, 1998) does an excellent job of exploring the lack of understanding of the idea and the contested nature of it from the right and left. He also shows how it evolves as those contests happen. He only occasionally connects to the idea of freedom to oppression and never makes it actually constitutive. Tyler Stovall, *White Freedom: The Racial History of an Idea* (Princeton, NJ: Princeton University Press, 2021), 5, confirms the argument here by arguing "the relationship between liberty and racism is not necessarily contradictory but rather has its own internal consistency." Annelien de Dijn, *Freedom: An Unruly History* (Cambridge, MA: Harvard University Press, 2020) argues for a historical change from a participatory democratic version of freedom to a modern radical anti-statism that thwarts democracy. George Lakoff claims freedom is "the most important idea" because "it is at the center of all other important

ideas"; see his *Whose Freedom? The Battle over America's Most Important Idea* (New York: Farrar, Straus and Giroux, 2006), 61; and Alex Gourevitch, *From Slavery to the Cooperative Commonwealth: Labor and Republican Liberty in the Nineteenth Century* (New York: Cambridge University Press, 2015), esp. 18–36. Amartya Sen, in *Development as Freedom* (New York: Oxford University Press, 1999), makes the case that the development of a society is not a simple question of economics or income growth but the strength and rigor of political freedom, by which he really means citizenship rights, for all. The difference between "liberty" and "freedom" are largely collapsed in the vernacular; as Isaiah Berlin argues, both words "mean the same." Hannah Arendt, however, posits that the practice of freedom is different than mere liberty, as it is an ongoing positive, political, public project that comes after liberty. See Hanna Fenichel Pitkin, "Are Freedom and Liberty Twins?," *Political Theory* 16, no. 4 (November 1988): 523–552.

5 "fear": J. Mills Thornton III, *Politics and Power in a Slave Society: Alabama, 1800–1860* (Baton Rouge: Louisiana State University Press, 1978), xviii, 213–215; *Montgomery Advertiser* quoted in Thornton, *Politics and Power*, 214.

6 "charm": Federal Writers Project, #2322, "691 Scenic Trips," WPA Files, SG 22717, Box 9, Barbour County Files, Alabama Department of Archives and History (hereafter ADAH).

7 David Brion Davis, *The Problem of Slavery in the Age of Revolution, 1770–1823* (Ithaca, NY: Cornell University Press, 1975), 86; Edmund S. Morgan, *American Slavery, American Freedom: The Ordeal of Colonial Virginia* (New York: W. W. Norton, 1975), 376; Nathan Huggins, *Black Odyssey* (New York: Pantheon, 1977), xliv. As Morgan explains in *American Slavery, American Freedom*, white people could extol the entire republican package of equality, freedom, and democracy more effectively in a slave society than they could in a free one.

8 M. I. Finley, "Was Greek Civilization Based on Slave Labour?," *Historia: Zeitschrift für Alte Geschichte, Bd.* 8, no. 2 (April 1959), 145–164; M. I. Finley, *Economy and Society in Ancient Greece*, ed. B. D. Shaw and R. P. Saller (New York: Penguin, 1983), 12; Orlando Patterson, *Freedom*, vol. 1, *Freedom in the Making of Western Culture* (New York: Basic Books, 1991), 48.

9 Patterson, *Freedom*, 1:4; for a useful summary, see Orlando Patterson, "Freedom, Slavery, and the Modern Construction of Rights," in *The Cultural Values of Europe*, ed. Hans Joas and Klaus Wiegandt (Liverpool: Liverpool University Press, 2008), 115–151.

10 Samuel Johnson, "Taxation No Tyranny: An Answer to the Resolutions and Address of the American Congress," from *The Works of Samuel Johnson*, vol. 14 (Troy, NY: Pafraets & Company, 1913), 93–144, www.samueljohnson.com/tnt.html.

11 Colbert quoted in Claudio Saunt, *Unworthy Republic: The Dispossession of Native Americans and the Road to Indian Territory* (New York: Norton, 2020),

110; Alan Taylor, *American Revolutions: A Continental History, 1750–1804* (New York: Norton, 2016); Woody Holton, *Liberty Is Sweet: The Hidden History of the American Revolution* (New York: Simon & Schuster, 2021).

12 Bernard Bailyn, *The Ideological Origins of the Revolution* (Cambridge, MA: Harvard University Press, 1967); William J. Novak, "The Myth of the 'Weak' American State," *American Historical Review* 113, no. 3 (June 2008): 752–772; Gary Gerstle, *Liberty and Coercion: The Paradox of American Government from the Founding to the Present* (Princeton, NJ: Princeton University Press, 2015).

13 James Madison, *Federalist* no. 51 (1788); Bryce quoted, and the problem discussed, in Kimberley S. Johnson, *Governing the American State: Congress and the New Federalism, 1877–1929* (Princeton, NJ: Princeton University Press, 2007), 1–5; Martha Derthick, *Keeping the Compound Republic: Essays on American Federalism* (Washington, DC: Brookings Institution Press, 2001); and Sara Mayeux and Karen Tani, "Federalism Anew," *American Journal of Legal History* 56 (2016): 128–138.

14 Gregory P. Downs, *After Appomattox: Military Occupation and the Ends of War* (Cambridge, MA: Harvard University Press, 2015), 252.

15 Orlando Patterson, "Unholy Trinity: Freedom, Slavery, and the American Constitution," *Social Research* 54, no. 3 (Autumn 1987): 567.

16 "tree": William W. Winn, *The Triumph of the Ecunnau-Nuxulgee: Land Speculators, George M. Troup, State Rights, and the Removal of the Creek Indians from Georgia and Alabama, 1825–1838* (Macon, GA: Mercer University Press, 2015), 320.

17 "free government": "Platform of the Democratic and Conservative Party, adopted July 30, 1874," reprinted in *Report of the Committees of the Senate of the United States, 1876–1877* (Washington: US Government Printing Office, 1877), 673.

18 "undertakes": Governor Chauncey Sparks, "Speech Before the Alabama Division of the American Legion, July 13, 1943," Gov. Sparks—Speeches, SG 12527, FF 4, ADAH.

Chapter 1. Marshal Crawford's Orders

1 "aid the oppressed": Ebert Herring to Robert L. Crawford, 14 March 1833, Peddy Book: Creek 1833 Jan–Jun, Box 3, Creek Letters, T. J. Peddy Collection, MC 36, Columbus State Archives and Special Collections, Columbus, Georgia (hereafter, Peddy Book).

2 "vigilance and energy" and "white trespassers": Herring to Crawford, 14 March 1833; Claudio Saunt argues the terms "deportation," "expulsion," and "extermination" are more accurate than the popular term of the time, "removal." I have adopted his terminology. See Saunt, *Unworthy Republic: The Dispossession of Native Americans and the Road to Indian Territory* (New York: Norton, 2020), xiii–xiv.

3 "make known": Lewis Cass to Crawford, 5 April 1832, Peddy Book: Creek 1832 Jan–Jun; *Columbus Enquirer*, 21 April 1832; Cass to Crawford, 5 April 1832, M21, Letters Sent by the OIA, Roll #8, 228, National Archives.

4 "left entirely free": Cass to Crawford, 5 April 1832; "facts": Crawford to Cass, 30 August 1832, Peddy Book: Creek Book 1832 Jul–Dec.

5 On Crawford's mission: Cass to Crawford, 5 April 1832; *Columbus Enquirer*, 7 April 1832; on Crawford's public notifications: Crawford to Cass, 27 April 1832, Peddy Book: Creek Book 1832 Jan–Jun.

6 "solemn obligation": Cass to Crawford, 9 May 1832, Peddy Book: Creek 1832 Jan–Jun.

7 "rumors to them": Crawford to Cass, 27 April 1832; Cass to Crawford, 5 April 1832, Peddy Book: Creek 1832 Jan–Jun; *Columbus Enquirer*, 21 April 1832; on Wager, see Michael D. Green, *The Politics of Indian Removal* (Lincoln: University of Nebraska Press, 1985), 109; and *Niles' Weekly Register*, 8 May 1830.

8 Robin Ethridge, *Creek Country: The Creek Indians and Their World* (Chapel Hill: University of North Carolina Press, 2003), 74–75, 92–100.

9 "lawless": Crawford to John Robb, 15 September 1832, Peddy Book: Creek 1832 Jul–Dec. The brewing problem was also being followed nationally: *Niles Register*, vol. 7, 4th series, September 1832–March 1833, 22; "violence to their person": Crawford to Cass, 31 August 1832, in *Correspondence on the Subject of the Emigration of the Indians* (US Senate), vol. 3, *30 November 1831 to 27 December 1833* (Washington, DC: Duff Green, 1835), 439–440; William W. Winn, *The Triumph of the Ecunnau-Nuxulgee: Land Speculators, George M. Troup, and the Removal of the Creek Indians from Alabama and Georgia, 1825–1838* (Macon, GA: Mercer University Press, 2015), 327; John T. Ellisor, *The Second Creek War: Interethnic Conflict and Collusion on a Collapsing Frontier* (Lincoln: University of Nebraska Press, 2010), 59; "absolute expulsion": Crawford to Robb, 30 August 1832, Peddy Book: Creek 1832 Jul–Dec.

10 request to burn, and giving crops to Creeks and "rough men": Crawford to Robb, 15 September 1832, Peddy Book: Creek 1832 Jul–Dec.

11 "brilliant its history": *Columbus Enquirer*, 28 July 1832.

12 "man of Good Reputation": William Irwin to Cass, 30 July 1832, Peddy Book: Creek 1832 Jul–Dec; *Montgomery Gazette*, 31 August 1832; Anne Kendrick Walker, *Backtracking in Barbour County: A Narrative of the Last Alabama Frontier* (Richmond, VA: Dietz Press, 1941), 7; for a sense of the hyperbole, see Green Beauchamp, "Early Chronicles of Barbour County," *Alabama Historical Quarterly* 33, no. 1 (Spring 1971): 70–71.

13 Crowell to Cass, 3 August 1832, in Winn, *Triumph*, 522n32.

14 "armed" and "reenforcement": Crowell to Cass, 3 August 1832.

15 "impossibility": Crawford to Robb, 15 September 1832; "two hundred men": Crawford to Cass, 6 December 1832, Peddy Book: Creek 1832 Jul–Dec.

16 Various Citizens of Irwinton to Cass, 16 November 1832, *Correspondence on the Subject of the Emigration*, 3:528–529.

17 "intrusion part of the whole": Crawford to Cass, 15 September 1832, Peddy Book: Creek 1832 Jul–Dec.

18 See terms of treaty as published in "Indian Treaty," *Columbus Enquirer*, 7 April 1832.
19 Ellisor, *Second Creek War*, 48.
20 "only alterative": Green, *Indian Removal*, 177; Saunt, *Unworthy Republic*, 93.
21 "liberality": Cass to the Chiefs of the Creek Tribe now in Washington, 16 January 1832, Peddy Book: Creek 1832 Jan–Jun.
22 Treaty of Cusseta, 14 April 1832, reproduced in *Niles' National Register*, vol. 41, 1831–1832, 116–117; see Winn, *Triumph*, 301, 305 [full cite in FN 9]; on Crawford's view of the sovereignty problem, see Crawford to Cass, 15 September 1832, *Correspondence on the Subject of the Emigration*, 3:453–454.
23 Mary Elizabeth Young, *Redskins, Ruffleshirts and Rednecks: Indian Allotments in Alabama and Mississippi, 1830–1860* (Norman: University of Oklahoma Press, 1961), 75–76.
24 Green, *Politics of Indian Removal*, 178–179.
25 "distressed": Crowell to Cass, 27 September 1832, Peddy Book: Creek 1832 Jul–Dec; Ellisor, *Second Creek War*, 61; "expulsion," "crowded," "oppressed," and "dissenting voice": Winn, *Triumph*, 328–330; Green, *Politics of Indian Removal*, 177.
26 Major Thomas J. Abbot et al. to John Crowell (forwarded to Cass), 13 October 1832, Peddy Book: Creek 1832 Jul–Dec.
27 Green, *Politics of Indian Removal*, 175; John Brodnax to Cass, 30 July 1832, OIA, LR, CA, RG 75, reel 223: 33–39.
28 "obligatory on the Government": Herring to Crawford, 14 March 1833, Peddy Book: Creek 1833 Jan–Jun; see also Cass to Crawford, 10 May 1833, Peddy Book: Creek 1833 Jan–Jun; Cass to Crawford, 3 June 1833, Peddy Book: Creek 1833 Jan–Jun; "expelling intruders": Herring to Crawford, 14 March 1833, Peddy Book: Creek 1833 Jan–Jun.
29 *Niles Register*, vol. 44, 1833, 222; Winn, *Triumph*, places the phrase "ecunnaunuxulgee" in the title of his book.

Chapter 2. Land, Liberty, and Jackson

1 "violent pain": Robert V. Remini, *Andrew Jackson and His Indian Wars* (New York: Viking, 2001), 206; Remini, *The Life of Andrew Jackson* (New York: Penguin, 1990), 87–89, 54, 70, 137, 223, 355–356; L. M. Deppisc, J. A. Centeno, D. J. Gemmel, N. L. Torres, "Andrew Jackson's Exposure to Mercury and Lead: Poisoned President?," *Journal of the American Medical Association* 283, no. 6 (August 1999): 569–571.
2 All references to the scene at the inaugural in Edwin A. Miles, "The First People's Inaugural—1829," *Tennessee Historical Journal* 37, no. 3 (Fall 1978): 293–307.
3 On voting statistics, see Jill Lepore, *These Truths* (New York: W. W. Norton, 2018), 186; "liberty and equality": J. Mills Thornton III, *Politics and Power in a Slave Society: Alabama, 1800–1860* (Baton Rouge: Louisiana State University

Press, 1978), 221; see Harry Watson, *Liberty and Power: The Politics of Jacksonian America* (New York: Hill and Wang, 1990), 42–72.

4 J. M. Opal, *Avenging the People: Andrew Jackson, the Rule of Law, and the American Nation* (New York: Oxford University Press, 2017), 225; Charles Sellers, *The Market Revolution: Jacksonian America, 1815–1846* (New York: Oxford University Press, 1994).

5 "Old Mad Jackson": Remini, *Andrew Jackson and His Indian Wars*, 81; "signature": Inskeep, *Jacksonland* (New York: Penguin Press, 2015), 186–187.

6 "national honor": Remini, *Andrew Jackson and His Indian Wars*, 232; Inskeep, *Jacksonland*, 193–200. Sean Wilentz, *Rise of American Democracy: Jefferson to Lincoln* (New York: Norton, 2005), 325.

7 "troublemakers" and "prosecution": Remini, *Andrew Jackson and His Indian Wars*, 57.

8 "territorial borders": Robbie Ethridge, *Creek Country: The Creek Indians and Their World* (Chapel Hill: University of North Carolina Press, 2003), 10; "traveling parties": Ethridge, *Creek County*, 147; "shattered zones": Ethridge, *Creek County*, 147.

9 "decentralized": Steven C. Hahn, *The Invention of the Creek Nation, 1670–1763* (Lincoln: University of Nebraska Press, 2004), 233; William W. Winn, *The Triumph of the Ecunnau-Nuxulgee: Land Speculators, George M. Troup, and the Removal of the Creek Indians from Alabama and Georgia, 1825–1838* (Macon, GA: Mercer University Press, 2015), 11.

10 "their black faces": John T. Ellisor, *The Second Creek War: Interethnic Conflict and Collusion on a Collapsing Frontier* (Lincoln: University of Nebraska Press, 2010), 11; "breed may perish": Remini, *Andrew Jackson and His Indian Wars*, 3.

11 Ellisor, *Second Creek War*, 9–32; the religious dimensions are covered in detail in Joel W. Martin, *Sacred Revolt: The Muskogees' Struggle for a New World* (Boston: Beacon Press, 1991).

12 "your frontier": Remini, *Andrew Jackson and His Indian Wars*, 7.

13 "retaliated": Remini, *Andrew Jackson and His Indian Wars*, 64.

14 "conqueror's peace": Michael D. Green, *The Politics of Indian Removal: Creek Government and Society in Crisis* (Lincoln: University of Nebraska Press, 1982), 43; for William McIntosh, see Andrew K. Frank, "The Rise and Fall of William McIntosh: Authority and Identity on the Early Frontier," *Georgia Historical Quarterly* 86 (Spring 2002): 18–48.

15 Inskeep, *Jacksonland*, 49–50.

16 Inskeep, *Jacksonland*, 49–50; Frank, "Rise and Fall of William McIntosh," 18–48.

17 Ellisor, *Second Creek War*, 17–21.

18 "humanity and national honor": Jackson First Annual Message to Congress, 8 December 1829, Presidential Speeches, Miller Center, University of Virginia, https://millercenter.org/the-presidency/presidential-speeches/december-8-1829-first-annual-message-congress.

19 "mercenary influence": Wilentz, *Rise of American Democracy*, 324, 367.
20 Claudio Saunt, *Unworthy Republic: The Dispossession of Native Americans and the Road to Indian Territory* (New York: Norton, 2020), 263; "prevent annihilation": Remini, *Andrew Jackson and His Indian Wars*, 228; on the question of genocide, see the evaluation of the use of the term in Jeffrey Ostler, "Genocide and American Indian History," *Oxford Encyclopedia of American History* (March 2015), https://oxfordre.com/americanhistory/view/10.1093/acrefore/9780199329175.001.0001/acrefore-9780199329175-e-3.
21 "against the aborigines": Wilentz, *Rise of American Democracy*, 236; for Storr's and Crockett's responses to Removal, see Inskeep, *Jacksonland*, 234–235, 238.
22 Eneah Micco et al. to Andrew Jackson, 1 February 1830, *The Papers of Andrew Jackson*, digital edition, ed. Daniel Feller (Charlottesville: University of Virginia Press, Rotunda, 2015) (hereafter, Jackson Papers).
23 The analysis of the Treaty of Cusseta leans on Ellisor, *Second Creek War*, 47–49.
24 "citizens of Alabama": Lewis Cass to Chiefs of the Creek Tribe, 16 January 1832, Peddy Book: Creek 1832 Jan–Jun; Anthony F. C. Wallace, *The Long, Bitter Trail: Andrew Jackson and the Indians* (New York: Hill and Wang, 1993), 75; Jill Norgren, *The Cherokee Cases: The Confrontation of Law and Politics* (New York: McGraw-Hill, 1996); Green, *Politics of Indian Removal*, 172.
25 Wallace, *Long, Bitter Trail*, 75; Green, *Politics of Indian Removal*, 172; Jackson to Senate and House, 15 February 1832, Peddy Book: Creek 1832 Jan–Jun.
26 Wallace, *Long, Bitter Trail*, 75; Green, *Politics of Indian Removal*, 147, 156; see Norgren, *Cherokee Cases*, passim.
27 "bones": G. W. Stiggins to the Senate and House, 24 January 1832, Peddy Book: Creek 1832 Jan–Jun.
28 Green, *Politics of Indian Removal*, 149.

Chapter 3. The Killing of Hardeman Owens

1 "Jeremiah Austill," autobiography, *Alabama Historical Quarterly* 6, no. 1 (Spring 1944): 81–91.
2 "deplorable condition": Jeremiah Austill to Lewis Cass, 26 July 1833, as cited in John T. Ellisor, *The Second Creek War: Interethnic Conflict and Collusion on a Collapsing Frontier* (Lincoln: University of Nebraska Press, 2010), 82.
3 Austill to Cass, 15 November 1832, Peddy Book: Creek 1832 Jul–Dec.
4 On Austill's request for the authority to arrest, see US Congress, Senate Documents, 23rd Cong., 1st sess. (1835), No. 512, "Indian Removal" and "Emigration of the Indians"; Ellisor, *Second Creek War*, 82–84.
5 "blended ignorance": William Winn, *The Triumph of the Ecunnau-Nuxulgee: Land Speculators, George M. Troup, State Rights, and the Removal of the Creek Indians from Georgia and Alabama, 1825–1838* (Macon, GA: Mercer University Press, 2015), 349.
6 On the distribution of land to Creeks, see Winn, *Triumph*, 350.

7 "obnoxious": Winn, *Triumph*, 350; "cruel manner" and "white persons": Jeremiah Austill, "Intruders on the Creek Lands," *Niles' National Register*, vol. 45, 2 November 1833, 160.
8 Austill to Cass, 31 July 1833, in *Niles' National Register*, vol. 45, 160; Winn, *Triumph*, 351.
9 Austill to Cass, 31 July 1833, Peddy Book: Creek Letters 1833 Jul–Dec; Winn, *Triumph*, 351.
10 "politely": Austill to Cass, 31 July 1833, Peddy Book: Creek Letters 1833 Jul–Dec, in Winn, *Triumph*, 351; "shoot him down": Austill to Cass, 31 July 1833, *Niles' National Register*, vol. 45, 160.
11 Austill to Cass, 31 July 1833, *Niles' National Register*, vol. 45, 160.
12 Winn, *Triumph*, 350–352.
13 "wholly unjustifiable" and "malignity": *Columbus Enquirer*, 10 August 1833, as cited in *Charlotte Journal*, 24 August 1833, 3; "peaceable society": Ellisor, *Second Creek War*, 85.
14 "lawful execution" and "decline your invitation": McIntosh [*sic*] to Pickett, 15 October 1883, *Niles' National Register*, vol. 43, 190; Ellisor, *Second Creek War*, 85.
15 "fear of God," "State of Alabama," and "feloniously": Pickett to Circuit Court of State of Alabama, October Term 1833, 13 October 1833, Peddy Book: Creek 1833 Jul–Dec; "legally," "without hesitation," and "slightest obstacle": Cass to Crawford, 19 October 1833, Peddy Book: Creek 1833 Jul–Dec; *Columbus Enquirer*, 14 September 1833, 12 October 1833.
16 The "drunken Indian" stereotype is untrue, but the destruction of an entire culture leads to dependent behaviors. See James K. Cunningham, Teshia A. Solomon, and Myra L. Muramato, "Alcohol Use Among Native Americans Compared to Whites: Examining the Veracity of the 'Native American Elevated Alcohol Consumption' Belief," *Drug and Alcohol Dependence* 160 (March 2016): 65–76.
17 "peace of the country" and "laws of the land": *National Intelligencer*, as quoted in the *Niles' National Register*, vol. 45, 2 November 1833, 160; "dearest rights": *State Rights Expositor*, as quoted in the *Niles' National Register*, vol. 45, 26 October 1833, 144; "expel": *Augusta Chronicle*, as quoted in the *Niles' National Register*, vol. 45, 9 November 1833, 161.
18 "serffs of the system" and "unconstitutional, unequal, and oppressive": Forrest McDonald, *States' Rights and the Union:* Imperium in Imperio, *1776–1876* (Lawrence: University Press of Kansas, 2000), 103–106. At a dinner to honor the late Thomas Jefferson, Jackson made his case clear, toasting "our Federal Union: It must be preserved." Calhoun countered with his own toast, "The Union: next to our Liberty the most dear."
19 On nullification, see Daniel Walker Howe, *What Hath God Wrought: The Transformation of America, 1815–1848* (New York: Oxford University Press, 2007), 395–410; "incompatible" and "league": President Jackson's "Proclamation

Regarding Nullification," 10 December 1832, Avalon Project: Documents in Law, History and Diplomacy, Yale Law School, https://avalon.law.yale.edu/19th_century/jack01.asp; on "government, not a league," see Jill Lepore, *These Truths* (New York: W. W. Norton, 2018), 218.

20 Pauline Maier, "The Road Not Taken: Nullification, John C. Calhoun, and the Revolutionary Tradition in South Carolina," *South Carolina Historical Magazine* 82 (January 1981): 8–17.

21 "great excitement": *Niles' National Register*, vol. 45, 26 October 1833, 129; "desperado": *Charleston Mercury*, 1 November 1833 ;"darling": *State Rights Expositor*, in *Niles' National Register*, vol. 45, 26 October 1833, 143–144; "justifiable homicide": *Charleston Courier*, in *Niles' National Register*, vol. 45, 26 October 1833, 148; "freemen": from the *Charleston Courier*, in *Niles' National Register*, vol. 45, 2 November 1833, 159.

22 "glorious union": *Niles' National Register*, vol. 43, 9 February 1833, 387.

23 "houses of Indians": Cass to Gayle, 5 September 1833, Peddy Book: Creek 1833 Jul–Dec; When Calhoun returned to South Carolina, a state convention had declared the federal tariff "null, void, and no law" in their state. See Howe, *What Hath God Wrought*, 395–410.

24 Gayle to Cass, 12 October 1833, Peddy Book: Creek 1833 Jul–Dec.

25 Gayle to Cass, 12 October 1833, Peddy Book: Creek 1833 Jul–Dec.

26 Cass to Crawford, 26 August 1833, Peddy Book: Creek 1833 Jan–Jun.

27 "necessary facts": Cass to Crawford, 26 August 1833, Peddy Book: Creek 1833 Jan–Jun; Michael R. Rouland and Christian E. Fearer, "Calling Forth the Military: A Brief History of the Insurrection Act," *Joint Force Quarterly* 99 (2020): 124–134.

28 "excite the sympathies": Winn, *Triumph*, 367.

29 "brutal soldiery" and "friends of liberty": Correspondence of the *Augusta Sentinel*, 1 February 1834, Peddy Book: Creek 1834 Jan–Jun.

30 "utterly subversive," "troops or ships," and "lawless white men": Andrew Jackson to the US Congress, November 1833, "Drafts of Andrew Jackson," 786–788; "pure government" and "speculators": Enoch Parsons to Jackson, 21 September 1833, "Drafts of Andrew Jackson," 675–680; all these letters and drafts can be found in *The Papers of Andrew Jackson*, vol. 11, *1833*, ed. Dan Feller (Knoxville: University of Tennessee Press, 2019).

31 For more on Jackson and his policies regarding Native American land rights, see Ellisor, *Second Creek War*, 2; and especially Claudio Saunt, *Unworthy Republic: The Dispossession of Native Americans and the Road to Indian Territory* (New York: Basic Books, 2020).

32 "without hesitation" and "little injury": Cass to John Gayle, 19 October 1833, Peddy Book: Creek 1833 Jul–Dec; "aid the oppressed": Ebert Herring to Robert L. Crawford, 14 March 1833, Peddy Book: Creek 1833 Jan–Jun.

33 "save my life": Austill to Cass, 26 October 1833, Peddy Book: Creek 1833 Jul–Dec.

Chapter 4. The Compromise of Francis Scott Key

1 "rascal": Marc Leepson, *What So Proudly We Hailed: Francis Scott Key, A Life* (New York: Palgrave MacMillan, 2014), 133–135; "heterogenous": see Andrew Jackson to Andrew Jackson Jr., 13 May 1832, Andrew Jackson Papers, vol. 10, 272; *House Journal*, 22nd Cong., 1st sess., 636–638, Serial 215; John Hoyt Williams, *Sam Houston: The Life and Times of the Liberator of Texas, an Authentic American Hero* (New York: Simon & Schuster, 1993), 92–95.

2 For more on Houston's attack on Stanbery and its implications, see Leepson, *What So Proudly We Hailed*, 133–140.

3 "tyranny": Leepson, *What So Proudly We Hailed*, 135.

4 Joanne B. Freeman, *The Field of Blood: Violence in Congress and the Road to Civil War* (New York: Farrar, Straus and Giroux, 2018).

5 "*great* men" and "barbarians": Leepson, *What So Proudly We Hailed*, 139.

6 "proceed to Alabama" and "removal of the intruders": Lewis Cass to Governor John Gayle, 31 October 1833, Peddy Book: Creek Letters 1833 Jul–Dec; "contract" and "feeble" in Cass to Gayle, 5 November 1833, in Senate Document No. 512, 23rd Cong., 1st sess., Vol 111, 50–51; see also, Cass to Gayle, 15 October 1833, Cass to Gayle, 22 October 1833, Peddy Book: Creek Letters 1833 Jul–Dec.

7 "control": Cass to Col. J. J. Abert, 16 November 1833, Peddy Book: Creek 1833 Jul–Dec; though their correspondence suggests Cass, Jackson, and Crawford were interested in protecting the Creeks, author John T. Ellisor questions their sincerity in *The Second Creek War: Interethnic Conflict and Collusion on a Collapsing Frontier* (Lincoln: University of Nebraska Press, 2010).

8 "rank Jackson man": Leepson, *What So Proudly We Hailed*, 133–140.

9 "assemblage of prisons": Leepson, *What So Proudly We Hailed*, 77.

10 "star-spangled banner": Leepson, *What So Proudly We Hailed*, 86.

11 "gloom of the grave" and "land of the free": Leepson, *What So Proudly We Hailed*, 71–73.

12 "marching": *Mobile Commercial Register*, quoted in Thomas Chalmers McCovery, "The Mission of Francis Scott Key to Alabama in 1833," *Alabama Historical Society*, reprint no. 6, Montgomery, Alabama, 1904, 152; "minister of the United States" and "authentic source": *Mobile Commercial Register*, in *Niles' National Register*, 21 December 1833, 267; "faith": Cass to Key, 31 October 1833, Peddy Book: Creek 1833 Jul–Dec.

13 "intruder upon her lands": Key to Cass, 14 November 1833, Peddy Book: Creek 1833 Jul–Dec.

14 "Montg'y Jail" and "intruder": Key to Taney, 14 November 1833, in William Hand Browne and Louis Henry Dielman's *Maryland Historical Magazine*, version 5 (Baltimore: Maryland Historical Society, 1910), 29–31; "fury of the Intruders": William W. Winn, *The Triumph of the Ecunnau-Nuxulgee: Land Speculators, George M. Troup, and the Removal of the Creek Indians from Alabama and Georgia, 1825–1838* (Macon, GA: Mercer University Press, 2015), 363.

15 "indulgence" and "in pursuance": Key to Taney, 14 November 1833, in *Maryland Historical Magazine*, 29–32.

16 "sold their lands" and "for whiskey": Winn, *Triumph*, 363; "send them off": Key to Taney, 6 November 1833, in *Maryland Historical Magazine*, 27; Ellisor, *Second Creek War*, 91.

17 "Nullifiers" and "equal to Nullification": Key to Taney, 6 November 1833, in *Maryland Historical Magazine*, 27–29.

18 "without a title": Winn, *Triumph*, 367.

19 "highest satisfaction," "supremacy," and "become citizens": Gayle, "'Political Message' to the Executive Department," 20 December 1833, Peddy Book: Creek 1834 Jan–Jun.

20 "the Judge": Winn, *Triumph*, 319; "his own conscience": John Hogan to Cass, 29 February 1836, Peddy Book: Creek 1836 Jan–Jun; "land pirates" and "system of villainy": Ellisor, *Second Creek War*, 308; For the fate of Belser's dissent from states' rights orthodoxy, see Ellisor, *Second Creek War*, 463, n11; Christopher D. Haveman, "The Removal of the Creek Indians from the Southeast, 1825–1838" (PhD diss., Auburn University, 2009), 154.

21 Claudio Saunt, "Financing Dispossession: Stocks, Bonds, and the Deportation of Native Peoples in the Antebellum United States," *Journal of American History* (September 2019): 316, 322, 337; Claudio Saunt, *Unworthy Republic: The Dispossession of Native Americans and the Road to Indian Territory* (New York: Norton, 2020), 169–179, 218–219; Ellisor, *Second Creek War*, 308–310.

22 Ellisor, *Second Creek War*, 103–105.

23 "steal all we can": Tarver to M. A. Craven, 1 March 1835; Shorter to Corley and Craven, 1 March 1835; Tarver to Craven, 1 March 1835, in "Hostilities with the Creeks," House Report No. 154, 24th Cong., 2nd sess. (1837), 22–24; "air of urgency" Winn, *Triumph*, 324.

24 "bottom-line figures" and "labor of our hands": Saunt, "Financing Dispossession," 316; "money": Saunt, *Unworthy Republic*, 189; Shorter in Ellisor, *Second Creek War*, 190–191.

25 "tree of Liberty" and "Resolved": Winn, *Triumph*, 319–320; "basely false": Shorter et al. to Secretary of War, 33, House Report No. 154, 33–35; Tim Alan Garrison, *The Legal Ideology of Removal: The Southern Judiciary and the Sovereignty of Native America Nations* (Athens, GA: University of Georgia Press, 2002), 169–197.

26 For the dismissal of existing suits, see Cass to Key, 24 February 1835, Peddy Book: Creek 1835 Jan–Jun; acreage figures from Mary Elizabeth Young, *Redskins, Ruffleshirts and Rednecks: Indian Allotments in Alabama and Mississippi, 1830–1860* (Norman: University of Oklahoma Press, 1961), 105–106.

27 "finding the promises": John S. Scott to Cass, 18 December 1834, Peddy Book: Creek 1834 Jul–Dec; "leave the whole matter": Jackson to Gayle, 11 June 1834, quoted in McCovery, "Mission of Francis Scott Key," 158. the Key compromise went into effect in January 1834; "settled": Crawford to Cass, 25 March 1834, Peddy Book: Creek 1834 Jan–Jun.

Chapter 5. Uprising

1 Hogan to Gibson, 14 May 1835, *American State Papers*, vol. 6, *Military Affairs* (Washington, DC: Gales & Seaton, 1861), 725–726; Report of A. Balch, commissioner on the causes of the Creek hostilities, "Hostilities with the Creek Indians," House Report No. 154, 24th Cong., 2nd sess. (1837), 17.

2 "privileges": Yoholo Micco et al. to Andrew Jackson, 27 August 1835, reprinted in Christopher D. Haveman, *Bending Their Way Onward: Creek Indian Removal in Documents* (Lincoln: University of Nebraska Press, 2018), 153; "grave yard": Christopher D. Haveman, "Removal of the Creeks Indians from the Southeast, 1825–1838," (PhD diss., Auburn University, 2009), 130, 163; "superstitious": Balch, House Report No. 154, 17.

3 "Arkansaw": Opochle Yoholo et al. of the Council Ground to Jackson, 13 June 1835, Peddy Book: 1835 Jan–Jun.

4 "*talk is done*": Yoholo et al. to Jackson, 13 June 1835; Cass to Opothleholo and Creek Council, 20 August 1835, Peddy Book: 1835 Jul–Dec.

5 "*knife*": Haveman, "Removal," 235; John Howard Payne, "The Green-Corn Dance," *Continental Monthly* (January 1862): 17–29; Austill to Cass, 12 July 1835, Peddy Book: 1835 Jul–Dec; connection to Tecumseh's prophecy: John T. Ellisor, *The Second Creek War: Interethnic Conflict and Collusion on a Collapsing Frontier* (Lincoln: University of Nebraska Press, 2010), 245–258.

6 "circumscribed" and "festering": Balch, House Report No. 154, 10; *Columbus Enquirer*, 6 February 1835; "extinction": Journal of R. J. Meigs, 9 August 1834, United States Congress, Senate Doc. 425, *Documents relating to Frauds, &c., in the sale of Indian Reservations of Land*, 2 July 1836, 24th Cong., 1st sess., Serial Set 284, 168–169.

7 Barbour County fears: Abercromie et al. to Governor Clay, 9 April 1836, Peddy Book: Mar–Apr; "meditating": Class to Cass, 25 April 1836, *American State Papers: Documents, Legislative and Executive, of the Congress of the United States* (Washington, DC: 1861), 710.

8 "whip": Claudio Saunt, *Unworthy Republic: The Dispossession of Native Americans and the Road to Indian Territory* (New York: Norton, 2020), 247–250; "plunder": Howard to Cass, 9 May 1836, Peddy Book: 1836 May–Jun.

9 "corn": Christopher Haveman, *Rivers of Sand: Creek Indian Emigration, Relocation, and Ethnic Cleansing in the American South* (Lincoln: University of Nebraska Press, 2020), 182.

10 Shorter to Cass, 13 May 1836, Peddy Book: 1836 May–Jun; Page to Cass [from Fort Mitchell], 16 May 1836, Peddy Book: May–Jun; Ellisor, *Second Creek War*, 190.

11 Cass to Hoban, 21 January 1836, Peddy Book: 1836 Jan–Jul; William W. Winn, *The Triumph of the Ecunnau-Nuxulgee: Land Speculators, George M. Troup, and the Removal of the Creek Indians from Alabama and Georgia, 1825–1838* (Macon, GA: Mercer University Press, 2015), 450–451.

12 Jacob Rhett Motte, *Journey into the Wilderness: An Army Surgeon's Account of Life in Camp and Field During the Creek and Seminole Wars, 1836–1838* (Gainesville: University of Florida Press, 1963), 19–21.

13 Haveman, *Rivers of Sand*, 193, 230–231.

14 Ellisor, *Second Creek War*, 367–370; Anne Kendrick Walker, *Backtracking in Barbour County: A Narrative of the Last Alabama Frontier* (Richmond, VA: Dietz Press, 1941), 36–38. Wellborn already enjoyed cheap land acquired from the Creeks in Irwinton, and after the battle, he was given a seat in the state senate as well.

15 Haveman, *Rivers of Sand*, 258–260.

16 Hogan to Cass, 5 February 1836, *American State Papers*, 6:750–751; Winn, *Triumph*, 461, 463; Ellisor, *Second Creek War*, 191; Balch, House Report No. 154, 10.

17 "damned": Claudio Saunt, "Financing Dispossession: Stocks, Bonds, and the Deportation of Native Peoples in the Antebellum United States," *Journal of American History* (September 2019): 322.

18 Population figures from Lewy Dorman, *A History of Barbour County, Alabama* (Eufaula: Barbour County Genealogy and Local History Society, 2006 [1932]), 175–177; "blood": Adam Rothman, *Slave Country: American Expansion and the Origins of the Deep South* (Cambridge, MA: Harvard University Press, 2005), 219.

19 Aziz Rana, *The Two Faces of American Freedom* (Cambridge, MA: Harvard University Press, 2014): 4, 186.

20 Walter L. Fleming, *Civil War and Reconstruction in Alabama* (New York: Columbia University Press, 1905), 8–9.

21 J. Mills Thornton III, *Politics and Power in a Slave Society: Alabama 1800–1860* (Baton Rouge: Louisiana State University Press, 1981), 221; Ellisor, *Second Creek War*, 227; Winn, *Triumph*, 453–454.

22 Kevin Kokomoor, "Creeks, Federalists, and the Idea of Coexistence in the Early Republic," *Journal of Southern History* 81 (November 2015): 805, 807.

23 The description of the Knox quote as "Hobbesian" belongs to J. M. Opal, *Avenging the People: Andrew Jackson, the Rule of Law, and the American Nation* (New York: Oxford University Press, 2017), 69; Kokomoor, "Creeks, Federalists," 830, 813.

24 Thornton, *Politics and Power*, 29–30.

Chapter 6. Igniting a Wall of Fire

1 Landscape description from Martha Crossley Rumph, quoted in Robert H. Flewellen, *Along Broad Street: A History of Eufaula, Alabama 1823–1984* (Eufaula: City of Eufaula, 1991), 15; various notes on Eufaula by Gertha Couric for the Federal Writers' Project, SG 22717, Box 9, Barbour County Files, ADAH. A moving and elegiac memoir/analysis of Eufaula and its landscape is Carrie Monahan, "'A Dream Remembered': Collective Memory and Ancestral Responsibility in Eufaula, Alabama" (honors thesis, American Studies, Stanford University, 2018).

2 See Gerald R. Webster and Scott A. Samson, "On Defining the Alabama Black Belt: Historical Changes and Variations," *Southeastern Geographer* 32, no. 2 (November 1992): 163–172; "penny coated": Charles Ghigna, "The Alabama Wiregrassers," poem, *Harper's Magazine*, September 1974.

3 "pioneers with means" and general discussion from Gavin Wright, *Slavery and American Economic Development* (Baton Rouge: Louisiana State University Press, 2006), 68, 88–89; James Oakes, *The Ruling Race: A History of American Slaveholders* (New York: W. W. Norton, 1982), 74, 127.

4 On the expansion west, see Adam Rothman, *Slave Country: American Expansion and the Origins of the Deep South* (Cambridge, MA: Harvard University Press, 2005); Tom Blake, transcriber, "Largest Slaveholders from 1860 Census Slave Census Schedules and Surname Matches for African Americans on 1870 Census," Barbour County, Alabama, 1860 Slaveholders and 1870 African Americans (RootsWeb, October 2001), http://freepages.rootsweb.com/~ajac/genealogy/albarbour.htm; "second middle passage": Ira Berlin, *The Making of African America: The Four Great Migrations* (New York: Viking, 2010), 8–9, 100.

5 Richard M. Auty, "Economic Development and the Resource Curse Thesis," in *Economic and Political Reform in Developing Countries*, ed. Oliver Morrissey and Frances Stewart (London: Palgrave Macmillan, 1995): 58–80; the counterintuitive idea about the role of rich factor endowments is developed in Kenneth L. Sokoloff and Stanley L. Engerman, "Institutions, Factor Endowments, and Paths of Development in the New World," *Journal of Economic Perspectives* 14, no. 3 (Summer 2000): 217–232; Gavin Wright, *Slavery and American Economic Development* (Baton Rouge: Louisiana State University Press, 2006), 4–47.

6 The relationship between slavery and capitalism has taken hold in the historical literature, rooted in Eric Williams, *Capitalism and Slavery* (Chapel Hill: University of North Carolina Press, 1994 [1944]); it has recently expanded to include conflicting interpretations, few of which deny the relationship, only contest its nature. See Sven Beckert, *Empire of Cotton: A Global History* (New York: Alfred A. Knopf, 2014); Edward E. Baptist, *The Half Has Never Been Told: Slavery and the Making of American Capitalism* (New York: Basic Books, 2014); and Walter Johnson, *River of Dark Dreams: Slavery and Empire in the Cotton Kingdom* (Cambridge, MA: Harvard University Press, 2013).

7 "derived": Peter A. Coclanis, *The Shadow of a Dream: Economic Life and Death in the South Carolina Low Country, 1670–1920* (New York: Oxford University Press, 1991), 26. Italics mine.

8 Tommy Brown, "'Of All the Hardy Sons of Toil': Class and Race in Antebellum Southcentral and Southeastern Alabama," *Alabama Review* 68 (July 2015): 241–242, 249; Tommy C. Brown, *Deep in the Piney Woods: Southeastern Alabama from Statehood to the Civil War, 1800–1865* (Tuscaloosa: University of Alabama Press, 2018), 22; this idea is complicated by David Williams, *Rich Man's War: Class, Caste, and Confederate Defeat in the Lower Chattahoochee Valley* (Athens: University of Georgia Press, 1999).

9 "business . . . is large": Mike Bunn, *Civil War Eufaula* (Charleston, SC: History Press, 2013), 18–21; Christopher D. Haveman, *Rivers of Sand: Creek Indian Emigration, Relocation, and Ethnic Cleansing in the Southeast* (Lincoln: University of Nebraska Press, 2020).

10 See Ray Mathis, *John Horry Dent: South Carolina Aristocrat on the Alabama Frontier* (Tuscaloosa: University of Alabama Press, 1979); digitized Dent plantation notebooks in John Horry Dent Papers, University of Alabama, Special Collections, http://purl.lib.ua.edu/82799; and Anne Kendrick Walker, *Backtracking in Barbour County: A Narrative of the Last Alabama Frontier* (Richmond, VA: Dietz Press, 1941), 94–107, 137, 144–146.

11 Brown, "'Hardy Sons of Toil,'" 235; "dictates": *Eufaula Democrat*, 23 January 1849; Lewy Dorman Papers, *History of Barbour County*, vol 1, part 2, 375; "waste of the energies": *Eufaula Democrat*, 19 August 1846.

12 for the slave laws in Eufaula, see Bryan Prince, *A Shadow on the Household: One Enslaved Family's Incredible Struggle for Freedom* (Toronto: McClelland & Stewart, 2009), 154–156.

13 J. Mills Thornton III, *Politics and Power in a Slave Society: Alabama, 1800–1860* (Baton Rouge: Louisiana State University Press, 2014), 57, 221; *Montgomery Advertiser*, 25 June 1851. On the Southern Whigs, Jacksonian Democracy, and sectionalism, see Richard E. Ellis, *The Union at Risk: Jacksonian Democracy, States' Rights and the Nullification Crisis* (New York: Oxford University Press, 1989); and Michael Les Benedict, "States' Rights, State Sovereignty, and Nullification," in *Congress and the Emergence of Sectionalism: From the Missouri Compromise to the Age of Jackson*, ed. Paul Finkelman and Donald R. Kennon (Athens, Ohio: Ohio University Press, 2008), 158–187.

14 "patriot": "Captain Elisha Betts," *National Era*, 17 October 1850.

15 "The Slavery of the White Race in the South," *National Era*, 3 October 1850; "Postmaster at Eufaula," *National Era*, 13 November 1851; *Columbus Sentinel* quoted in same article.

16 "savages": "Captain Elisha Betts," 3; "postmaster": "The Southern Press and the Law," *National Era*, October 24, 1850, 2, makes the argument that this is nullification, which if Alabama can do, then Northern states can do too, in the form of protecting fugitive slaves.

17 "Southern Press and the Law"; "The Despotism of Slavery," *National Era*, 17 October 1850.

18 poem: Bunn, *Civil War Eufaula*, 28–29; Eugenia Persons Smartt, *History of Eufaula, Alabama* (Eufaula, AL: J.S. Clark, 1995 [1933]), 61; Thornton, *Politics and Power*, 250–253; "fruits": *Montgomery Advertiser*, 26 February 1851, quoted in Thornton, *Politics and Power*, 253.

19 *Montgomery Advertiser*, 25 June 1851; Henry Mayer, "'A Leaven of Disunion': The Growth of the Secessionist Faction in Alabama, 1847–1851," *Alabama Review* 22 (April 1969): 83–116; Williams, *Rich Man's War*, 35–37.

20 Walter L. Fleming, "The Buford Expedition to Kansas," *Transactions of the Alabama Historical Society* (Tuscaloosa: Alabama Historical Society, 1900), 167–192; Williams, *Rich Man's War*, 33.
21 Fleming, "Buford Expedition."
22 Abraham Lincoln, "Notes for Speeches at Columbus and Cincinnati, Ohio," *Collected Works of Abraham Lincoln*, vol. 3, Roy P. Basler, ed., (New Brunswick, NJ: Rutgers University Press, 1953), 435.
23 "weep": Michael E. Woods, *Emotional and Sectional Conflict in the Antebellum United States* (New York: Cambridge University Press, 2014), 218; the scene is vividly captured in William Barney, *The Road to Secession: A New Perspective on the Old South* (New York: Praeger, 1972), 188–189; lyrics vary widely, and these were taken from "Southern Marseillaise," Lester S. Levey Sheet Music Collection, Johns Hopkins University Library, https://levysheetmusic.mse.jhu.edu/collection/094/119.
24 Williams, *Rich Man's War*, 52.
25 Mike Bunn, *Civil War Eufaula* (Charleston, SC: History Press, 2013), 37, 50; Williams, *Rich Man's War*, 42–44.
26 Walker was citing Coleridge in *Backtracking*, 183; Parthenia Antoinette Hague, *Blockaded Family: Life in Southern Alabama During the War* (Ann Arbor, MI: Charles River Editors, 2018), 1; "outlawry," "maniacs," and "vigilant": Williams, *Rich Man's War*, 42–44.
27 Walter L. Fleming, *Civil War and Reconstruction in Alabama* (New York: Columbia University Press, 1905), 131.
28 Henry M. McKiven, "John Gill Shorter, 1861–1863," in *Alabama Governors: A Political History of the State*, ed. Samuel L. Webb and Margaret E. Armbrester (Tuscaloosa: University of Alabama Press, 2014), 83–86.
29 "perfect": *Columbus Daily Sun*, 13 October 1863; Williams, *Rich Man's War*, 128–132.
30 Abraham Lincoln, "Address at a Sanitary Fair," 18 April 1864, https://teachingamericanhistory.org/library/document/address-at-a-sanitary-fair.
31 Lincoln, "Address at a Sanitary Fair."
32 Bunn, *Civil War Eufaula*, 92–93; Bruce J. Dines and Shirlie A. Leckie, eds., *A Just and Righteous Cause: Benjamin H. Grierson's Civil War Memoir* (Carbondale: Southern Illinois University Press, 2008), 334.
33 Dines and Leckie, *Just and Righteous Cause*, 334–336.
34 "barbarous," "pleased" and "artist": Grierson, *Just and Righteous Cause*, 337, 339; Mattie Thomas Thompson, "Occupation of Eufaula by Union Cavalry was Quiet and Orderly," *Birmingham News*, 10 February 1929, 3; Williams, *Rich Man's War*, 183;
35 "flat-nosed": *Montgomery Advertiser*, 3 March 1865, quoted in Michael W. Fitzgerald, *Reconstruction in Alabama: From Civil War to Redemption in the Cotton South* (Baton Rouge: Louisiana State University Press, 2017), 31.
36 "small," "surging," and "heathens": Williams, *Rich Man's War*, 166; Fitzgerald, *Reconstruction in Alabama*, 112; "home": Hague, *Blockaded Family*, 164.

37 "marauders": *Rich Man's War*, 187.

Chapter 7. "Destroying Freedom and Liberty"

1 Eric Foner, *Reconstruction: America's Unfinished Revolution, 1863–1877* (New York: Harper and Row, 1988), 109; "ambition": Eric Foner, "The Meaning of Freedom in the Age of Emancipation," *Journal of American History* 81, no. 2 (1994): 459.

2 "punishing": Michael W. Fitzgerald, *Reconstruction in Alabama: From Civil War to Redemption in the Cotton South* (Baton Rouge: Louisiana State University Press, 2017), 116.

3 "derangement": *New York Daily Herald*, 23 March 1866; *Chicago Tribune*, 1 February 1866; Ellen B. Have of Columbus, Georgia, letter, published in *National Freedman*, April 4, 1866.

4 "extraconstitutional": Gregory P. Downs, *After Appomattox: Military Occupation and the Ends of War* (Cambridge, MA: Harvard University Press, 2015), 246.

5 "same rights" and Union Leagues in general, see Foner, *Reconstruction*, 283–288; "catechism": Fitzgerald, *Reconstruction in Alabama*, 125.

6 Petition of Colored Citizens, 2 August 1965, Records of the Assistant Commissioner for the State of Alabama, Freedmen's Bureau Records, National Archives, M809 Roll 23, "Miscellaneous Papers."

7 "evil to this country": Report of General John D. Pope, Commanding 3rd Military District, Secretary of War's Report, 1867, quoted in Michael Perlman, *Reunion Without Comprise: The South and Reconstruction: 1865–1968* (New York: Cambridge University Press, 1973), 1.

8 Foner, *Reconstruction*, 77–78; Hans L. Trefousse, *Thaddeus Stevens: Nineteenth-Century Egalitarian* (Chapel Hill: University of North Carolina Press, 1997), 186.

9 "Heaven": *Montgomery Advertiser*, 17 December 1865; "wicked": *Eufaula News*, 1867, article copied in WPA Files, Federal Writers Project, Barbour County, ADAH; "despotism" quotes: Anne Kendrick Walker, *Backtracking in Barbour County: A Narrative of the Last Alabama Frontier* (Richmond, VA: Dietz Press, 1941), 227–228.

10 W. E. Burghardt Du Bois, "The Freedmen's Bureau," *The Atlantic*, March 1901; "Report of Wager Swayne," 31 October 1866, US Congress, Senate Ex. Doc. No. 6, 39th Cong., 2nd sess., 13; see Peter Kolchin, *First Freedom: The Responses of Alabama Blacks to Emancipation and Reconstruction* (Westport, CT: Greenwood Press, 1972), 79–99.

11 Tolerance and opposition for schools in Eufaula: see monthly reports generally, quoted here: "District Superintendent's Monthly School Report," February 1870, Eufaula; "Sub-Assistant Commissioner's Monthly Report," March 1868; "cotton": 31 October 1867; all Bureau of Refugees, Freedmen, and Abandoned Lands, M809, Microfilm Roll 18; "almost every neighborhood" and destroyed schools: Campbell F. Scribner, "Surveying the Destruction of African American Schoolhouses in the South, 1864–1876," *Journal of the Civil War Era* 10, no. 4 (2020): 479, 475; and Sub-District Report (Eufaula, Alabama) March 1868.

12 "sublime": Forrest McDonald, *States' Rights and the Union:* Imperium in Imperio, *1776–1876* (Lawrence; University Press of Kansas, 2000), 193; Eric Foner, *The Second Founding: How the Civil War and Reconstruction Remade the Constitution* (New York: W. W. Norton, 2019); Laura F. Edwards, *A Legal History of the Civil War and Reconstruction: A Nation of Rights* (Princeton, NJ: Princeton University Press, 2015).

13 James M. McPherson, "Who Freed the Slaves?," *Reconstruction* 2, no. 3 (1994): 35–40; Ira Berlin, "Emancipation and Its Meaning in American Life," *Reconstruction* 2, no. 3 (1994): 41–44; James Oakes, *Freedom National: The Destruction of Slavery in the United States, 1861–1865* (New York: W. W. Norton, 2013), 431, 437.

14 "forced:" McDonald, *States' Rights*, 210; *New York Herald* in Foner, *Second Founding*, 36–42; "King's cure": *Collected Works of Abraham Lincoln*, vol. 8 (New Brunswick, NJ: 1953), 255; Timothy S. Huebner, *Liberty and Union: The Civil War Era and the American Constitutionalism* (Lawrence: University of Kansas Press), 330.

15 "Christmas": Michael W. Fitzgerald, *Reconstruction in Alabama: From Civil War to Redemption in the Cotton South* (Baton Rouge: Louisiana State University Press, 2017), 87, 116–117; Foner, *Reconstruction*, 104–105; *Mobile Nationalist*, 16 May 1867.

16 Fitzgerald, *Reconstruction in Alabama*, 69, 77, 87.

17 "manacled": Malcolm Cook McMillan, *Constitutional Development in Alabama, 1798–1901: A Study in Politics, the Negro, and Sectionalism* (Chapel Hill: University of North Carolina Press, 1955), 96.

18 "China" labor: Leon F. Litwack, *Been in the Storm So Long: The Aftermath of Slavery* (New York: Alfred A. Knopf, 1979), 352; "quite as savage": Fitzgerald, *Reconstruction in Alabama*, 127.

19 Eric Burin, *Slavery and the Peculiar Solution: A History of the American Colonization Society* (Gainesville: University of Florida, 2005).

20 *African Repository and Colonial Journal* 44 (March 1868): 72; *African Repository and Colonial Journal* 44 (April 1868): 121.

21 Matthew F. McDaniel, "Emigration to Liberia from the Chattahoochee Valley of Georgia and Alabama, 1853–1903" (MA thesis, Louisiana State University, 2007), 28.

22 David Williams, *Rich Man's War: Class, Caste, and Confederate Defeat in the Lower Chattahoochee Valley* (Athens: University of Georgia Press, 1998), 165–166; see the Goncola manifest in Matthew F. McDaniel, *Emigration to Liberia: From the Chattahoochee Valley of Georgia and Alabama, 1853–1903* (Montgomery: New South Press, 2013).

23 Andrew Johnson's Veto of the Civil Rights bill, 27 March 1866, Miller Center, https://millercenter.org/the-presidency/presidential-speeches/march-27-1866-veto-message-civil-rights-legislation; Fitzgerald, *Reconstruction in Alabama*, 37.

24 Foner, *Reconstruction*, 256–259; Foner, *Second Founding*, 55–92.

25 Gary Gerstle, *Liberty and Coercion: The Paradox of American Government* (Princeton, NJ: Princeton University Press, 2015), 3–7; Foner, *Second Founding*, 85.

26 Fitzgerald, *Reconstruction in Alabama*, 151, 153.

27 "origin": Fitzgerald, *Reconstruction in Alabama*, 54–55, 157–158; Loren Schweninger, *James T. Rapier and Reconstruction* (Chicago: University of Chicago Press, 1978), 54–55.

28 Fitzgerald, *Reconstruction in Alabama*, 166–167.

29 Lewy Dorman, *A History of Barbour County, Alabama* (Eufaula: Barbour County Genealogy and Local History Society, 2006 [1932]), 254; Walker, *Backtracking*, 227; Fitzgerald, *Reconstruction in Alabama*, 168–169.

30 Dorman, *History of Barbour County*, 256; Ronald C. White, *American Ulysses: A Life of Ulysses S. Grant* (New York: Random House, 2016), 468; Ron Chernow, *Grant* (London: Penguin Press, 2017), 623.

31 Downs, *After Appomattox*, 2, 6.

Chapter 8. The Greeley Gamble and the Dueling Dual Legislatures of 1872

1 Speech of Hon. Eli S. Shorter of Alabama on the claims of Georgia and Alabama: delivered in the House of Representatives, 17 December 1858 (Washington: Congressional Global Office, 1858), 4–5, 8.

2 For the range of Greeley's explorations, see Robert C. Williams, *Horace Greeley: Champion of American Freedom* (New York: New York University Press, 2006); "switchboard": Iver Bernstein, *The New York City Draft Riots: Their Significance for American Society and Politics in the Age of the Civil War* (New York: Oxford University Press, 1990), 169.

3 "The Cincinnati Convention," *The Nation*, 21 March 1872 (no. 351), 180.

4 Eric Foner, *Reconstruction: America's Unfinished Revolution, 1863–1877* (New York: Harper and Row, 1988), 500, 502–503; Michael W. Fitzgerald, *Splendid Failure: Postwar Reconstruction in the American South* (Chicago: Ivan R. Dee, 2007), 138; Ron Chernow, *Grant* (New York: Penguin Press, 2017), 741.

5 *Eufaula Daily Times*, 24 July 1872.

6 Michael Fitzgerald, *Reconstruction in Alabama: From Civil War to Redemption in the Cotton South* (Baton Rouge: Louisiana State University Press, 2017), 257.

7 Elaine Frantz Parsons, *Ku-Klux: The Birth of the Klan During Reconstruction* (Chapel Hill: University of North Carolina Press, 2015), 184–185; Charles Lane, *Freedom's Detective: The Secret Service, the Ku Klux Klan, and the Man Who Masterminded America's First War on Terror* (New York: Hanover Square Press, 2019); Ronald C. White, *American Ulysses: A Life of Ulysses S. Grant* (New York: Random House, 2016), 523.

8 "kuklux": Fitzgerald, *Reconstruction in Alabama*, 266; "more national": White, *American Ulysses*, 526.

9 "invader" and "resentment": Mattie Thomas Thompson, *History of Barbour County Alabama* (Eufaula, 1939), 182, 184; Michael Fitzgerald, "The Ku Klux Klan: Property Crime and the Plantation System in Reconstruction

Alabama," *Agricultural History* 71 (Spring 1997): 190; "Godsend": Mary to Brother, April 24, 1868, John R. Buford Correspondence, *Confederados* Papers, Auburn University Digital Library, http://diglib.auburn.edu/collections/confederados.

10 "sleep in the same graveyard": Loren Schweninger, *James T. Rapier and Reconstruction* (Chicago: University of Chicago Press, 1978), 51; J. Mills Thornton, "Class Conflict and Black Enfranchisement in Alabama," *Journal of the Historical Society* 12, no. 3 (September 2012): 238; Alpheus Baker, Address and Diary, 1862–1874, SPR 40, ADAH; Fitzgerald, "Ku Klux Klan," 190, 205–206.

11 Baker, Address and Diary.

12 Report of the Joint Select Committee to Inquire into the Condition of Affairs in the Late Insurrectionary States, made to the two Houses of Congress February 19, 1872, vol. 8, Alabama Testimony, First Volume (Washington: US Government Printing Office, 1872): 404–405, 411; see also vol. 9, Alabama Testimony, Second Volume, 1072–1078.

13 *Eufaula Daily Times*, 11 July 1872; *Eufaula Daily Times*, 5 June 1872; *Eufaula Weekly Times*, 21 November 1872.

14 "penitentiary": Foner, *Reconstruction*, 510–511; Fitzgerald, *Reconstruction in Alabama*, 268; "conceited": Chernow, *Grant*, 741.

15 *Eufaula Weekly Times*, 21 November 1872.

16 Lewy Dorman, *A History of Barbour County, Alabama* (Eufaula: Barbour County Genealogy and Local History Society, 2006), 255–256.

17 Schweninger, *Rapier and Reconstruction*, 36, xiii, 106–116; Loren Schweninger, "James T. Rapier of Alabama and the Noble Cause of Reconstruction," in *Southern Black Leaders of the Reconstruction Era*, ed. Howard N. Rabinowitz (Urbana: University of Illinois Press, 1982), 79–81.

18 Schweninger, "James T. Rapier," 81–82; *Eufaula Daily Times*, 17 August 1872; Schweninger, *Rapier and Reconstruction*, 114.

19 Eric Foner, *Freedom's Lawmakers: A Directory of Black Officeholders During Reconstruction* (New York: Oxford University Press, 1993), 73, 230.

20 See Sarah W. Wiggins, "George E. Spencer: A Carpetbagger in Alabama," *Alabama Review* 19 (January 1966): 41–52; James Lamar Sledge II, "The Alabama Republican Party, 1865–1978" (PhD diss., Auburn University, 1998), 36; Michael Fitzgerald, "Republican Factionalism and Black Empowerment: The Spencer-Warner Controversy and Alabama Reconstruction, 1868–1880," *Journal of Southern History* 64 (August 1998): 491, 474, 491.

21 Richard Nelson Current, *Those Terrible Carpetbaggers: A Reinterpretation* (New York: Oxford University Press, 1989), 424–425, 31; Foner, *Reconstruction*, 137–138

22 Current, *Those Terrible Carpetbaggers*, 434.

23 A parallel drama was also unfolding with a ballot box in Marengo County that supposedly got waterlogged and ruined, but the essence of the issue paralleled that of Barbour County Box One. For the competing stories, see:

Memorial of the General Assembly of Alabama to the President and Congress of the United States, November 1872; and *Report of the Joint Committee of the General Assembly of Alabama in Regard of the Alleged Election of Geo. E. Spencer as U.S. Senator, Together with Memorial and Evidence* (Montgomery, 1875); "Memorial of Francis W. Sykes, of Alabama, Setting forth His claim to a seat in the Senate as a Senator from Alabama," Mis. Doc. 94, 42nd Cong., 3rd sess. (Washington, DC: 28 February 1873); Francis W. Sykes vs. George E. Spencer, Special Session of the Senate, March 1873, 43rd and 44th Cong., 611–613.

24 *Eufaula Weekly Times*, 21 November 1872; *Eufaula Daily Times*, 5 December 1872.

25 Charles M. Crook, "The Barbour County Background to the Election of 1872 and Alabama's Dual Legislatures," *Alabama Review* 56, no. 4 (October 2003): 263. The conclusions of this article are highly suspect.

26 Sarah Van Voorhis Woolfolk, "The Role of the Scalawag in Alabama Reconstruction" (PhD diss., Louisiana State University, 1965), 176–179; *New York Times*, 9 November 1872.

27 "Enforcement Act": "Report of the Joint Committee of the General Assembly of Alabama," (Montgomery: W.W. Screws, 1876), xxxvi; *Montgomery Daily Advertiser*, 19 November 1872; *New York Times*, 18 November 1872; *New York Times*, 19 December 1872.

28 Crook, "Barbour County Background," 270.

29 *New York Times*, 6 December 1872; "reap the fruits": *New York Times*, 9 December 1872; *New York Times*, 14 December 1872; *Eufaula Daily Times*, 5 December 1872.

30 "rascality": *New York Times*, 8 December 1872; Crook, "Barbour County Background," 270–271.

31 "cool impudence": Crook, "Barbour County Background," 271; "revolution": Fitzgerald, *Reconstruction in Alabama*, 271–272.

Chapter 9. The White Line: Afternoon, Election Day 1874

1 Fraser testimony, House of Representatives, *Report on the Alabama Election of 1874*, House Report No. 262, 43rd Cong., 2nd sess. (Washington, DC, 1875), 809.

2 Larkin Brown testimony, House Report No. 262, 813.

3 Steven Hahn, "What Sort of World Did the Civil War Make?," in *The World the Civil War Made*, ed. Gregory P. Downs and Kate Masur (Chapel Hill: University of North Carolina Press, 2015), 345.

4 *New York Times*, 4 November 1874.

5 *New York Times*, 4 November 1874.

6 Fraser testimony, House Report No. 262, 219–220.

7 "embittered": Eric Foner, *Reconstruction: America's Unfinished Revolution, 1863–1877* (New York: Harper and Row, 1988), 552.

8 House Report No. 262, 9–10; Foner, *Reconstruction*, 552; *Eufaula News*, 11 July 1874; Michael Fitzgerald, *Reconstruction in Alabama: From Civil War to*

Redemption in the Cotton South (Baton Rouge: Louisiana State University Press, 2017), 309; see Alan Friedlander and Richard Allan Gerber, *Welcoming Ruin: The Civil Rights Act of 1875* (Boston: Brill, 2018); Jimmy Frank Gross, "Alabama Politics and the Negro, 1874–1902," (PhD diss., University of Georgia, 1970), 31–32; "flagrant": *Denial of Elective Franchise in Alabama at Elections of 1874–1876*, Senate Report No. 704, 3 March 1877 (Washington, DC, 1877), 673.

9 House Report No. 262, 702; Loren Schweninger, *James T. Rapier and Reconstruction* (Chicago: University of Chicago Press, 1978), 133–138; "A White League Crime," *Alabama State Journal*, 8 November 1874; "reign of terror": Richard Bailey, *Neither Carpetbaggers Nor Scalawags: Black Officeholders During the Reconstruction of Alabama, 1867–1878* (Montgomery: NewSouth Books, 2010), 243.

10 "roar": reprinted in *Birmingham Iron Age*, 6 August 1874; *Mobile Register*, 31 July 1874; Fitzgerald, *Reconstruction in Alabama*, 399–302.

11 Testimony of A. S. Daggett, Captain of the Second United States Infantry, House Report No. 262, xxv.

12 Keils letter, 5 October 1874, in Anne Kendrick Walker, *Backtracking in Barbour County: A Narrative of the Last Alabama Frontier* (Richmond, VA: Dietz Press, 1941), 262; on the White Leagues, see Michael W. Fitzgerald, *Splendid Failure: Postwar Reconstruction in the American South* (Chicago: Ivan R. Dee, 2007), 178–179; Foner, *Reconstruction*, 550.

13 J. M. Buford to J. R. Buford, 10 April 1874, *Confederados* Collection, Auburn University Digital Library; Nicolas Barreyre, "The Politics of Economic Crises: The Panic of 1873, the End of Reconstruction, and the Realignment of American Politics," *Journal of the Gilded Age and Progressive Era* 10, no. 4 (October 2011): 416.

14 Description from Henry Fraser, described as "a very intelligent colored man and leader," House Report No. 262, xxvi–xxvii.

15 House Report No. 262, 807, 817; "Fall in Company": *Denial of Elective Franchise in Alabama at Elections of 1874–1876*, Senate Report No. 704, 3 March 1877 (Washington, DC, 1877), 446.

16 Fraser testimony, House Report No. 262, xxvi.

17 "shoot": House Report No. 262, 824.

18 House Report No. 262, xxvii, 433, 221.

19 Steven Hahn, *A Nation Under Our Feet: Black Political Struggles in the Rural South from Slavery to the Great Migration* (Cambridge, MA: Harvard University Press, 2003), 295–297; Foner, *Reconstruction*, 437; Fitzgerald, *Reconstruction in Alabama*, 297; Nicholas Lemann, *Redemption: The Last Battle of the Civil War* (New York: Farrar, Straus & Giroux, 2007), 28–29; Leeanna Keith, *The Colfax Massacre: The Untold Story of Black Power, White Error, and the Death of Reconstruction* (New York: Oxford University Press, 2009).

20 House Report No. 262, 221.

21 House Report No. 262, 428, 823; William Gillette, *Retreat from Reconstruction, 1869–1879* (Baton Rouge: Louisiana State University Press, 1982) points

out how few troops were actually stationed in the South, even though Southerners would have traumatic memories of overwhelming numbers.

22 Melinda M. Hennessey, "Reconstruction Politics and the Military: The Eufaula Riot of 1874," *Alabama Quarterly* 38 (Summer 1976): 120.

23 General Orders No. 75, 54, and 52 are reprinted in House Report No. 262, testimony, 25–26.

24 House Report No. 262, 25–26, 824.

25 General Orders No. 75, 54, and 52 are reprinted in House Report No. 262, 25–26; see also p. 81; Hennessey, "Reconstruction Politics and the Military," 121; House Report No. 262, 328, 427, 1278—Daggett testimony.

26 Thomas Joseph Goss, "A Continuation of Politics by Other Means: Union Generalship During the American Civil War," (PhD diss., Ohio State University, 2001), 137–138, 196; "hard luck": James McPherson, *Battle Cry Freedom: The Civil War Era* (New York: Oxford University, 1988), 335; T. Harry Williams, *Lincoln and His Generals* (New York: Vintage, 2011 [1952]), 93, 113; E. Longacre, "Irvin McDowell (1818–1885)," *Encyclopedia Virginia*, www.EncyclopediaVirginia.org/McDowell_Irvin_1818-1885; Ron Chernow, *Grant* (New York: Penguin, 2017), 141.

27 Directives of the Unites States Marshal's Office, Southern District of Alabama, Mobile, 26 October 1874, House Report No. 262, testimony, 623–624.

28 Baker to Grant, telegram 30 October 1874, *The Papers of Ulysses S. Grant*, vol. 25, *1874*, ed. John Y. Simon (Carbondale: Southern Illinois University Press, 2003), 197.

29 Senate Report No. 704, 4th Cong., 2nd sess., xiii; "riot": House Report No. 262, 1278.

30 Douglas A. Blackmon, *Slavery by Another Name: The Re-enslavement of Black Americans from the Civil War to World War II* (New York: Doubleday, 2008), 41.

31 For instance, in John Dollard, *Caste and Class in a Southern Town* (Garden City, NY: Doubleday, 1957 [1949]), 49.

32 *Montgomery Advertiser*, 31 October 1874; Loren Schweninger, *James T. Rapier and Reconstruction* (Chicago: University of Chicago Press, 1978), 146.

33 *Montgomery Advertiser*, 4 November 1874, 6 November 1874; grand jury "investigation" is reprinted in Eli Shorter's testimony in House Report No. 262, 793; Eli Shorter's testimony in House Report No. 262, 793, 798.

34 Most of this from Shorter testimony, in Walker, *Backtracking*, 270; *Louisville Courier-Journal*, 6 November 1874; "order": House Report No. 262, 795.

35 Shorter testimony, House Report No. 262, 796–797; the Montgomery paper had a slightly different take on federal presence: "United States Marshal Williford acted nobly in the fight. On the first fire he made a precipitate retreat to a house near by, and asked the lady of the house for God's sake to protect him." See *Montgomery Advertiser*, 4 November 1874.

36 Walter L. Fleming, *Civil War and Reconstruction in Alabama* (New York: Columbia University Press, 1905), 793; Anne Kendrick Walker, *Backtracking*

in Barbour County: A Narrative of the Last Alabama Frontier (Richmond, VA: Dietz Press, 1941); J .A. B. Besson, *History of Eufaula: The Bluff City of the Chattahoochee* (Atlanta: Jas. P. Harrison & Co, 1875): 25–26.

Chapter 10. The Fate of the Scalawag: Evening, Election Day 1874

1 "bitterly": Lewy Dorman, *History of Barbour County* (Eufaula: Barbour County Genealogy and Local History Society, 2006), 259; "brilliant": Anne Kendrick Walker, *Backtracking in Barbour County: A Narrative of the Last Alabama Frontier* (Richmond, VA: Dietz Press, 1941), 254, 25.

2 "leper"; Sarah Woolfolk Wiggins, *The Scalawag in Alabama Politics, 1865–1881* (Tuscaloosa: University of Alabama Press, 1977), xxii, 92; *Tuscaloosa Independent Monitor*, 1 September 1868; Walker, *Backtracking*, 254.

3 "bad man": Walker, *Backtracking*, 272; "master of the white": *Montgomery Daily Advertiser*, 19 February 1874, quoted in Sarah Van Voorhis Woolfolk, "The Role of the Scalawag in Alabama Reconstruction" (PhD diss., Louisiana State University, 1965), 192; "The Negro in Politics," *Mobile Register* reprint of *Louisville Jeffersonian Democrat* in "Affairs in Alabama," House Report No. 262, 43rd Cong., 2nd sess., 23 February 1875, v–vi.

4 "The Fifty to Fellow Citizens," 9 April 1874, reprinted in Walker, *Backtracking*, 255–259.

5 "The Fifty to Fellow Citizens"; *Montgomery Advertiser*, 25 February 1874; *Montgomery Advertiser*, 14 April 1874.

6 Walter L. Fleming, *Civil War and Reconstruction in Alabama* (New York: University of Columbia Press, 1905), 791; Sarah Woolfolk Wiggins, "Ostracism of White Republicans in Alabama During Reconstruction," *Alabama Review* 28 (January 1974): 52–64; "Alabama Investigation," 24 December 1874, House Report No. 262, 43rd Cong., 2nd sess., 1–2, 8–9, 1064.

7 The lyrics were sung in 1932 by John W. White to historian Lewy Dorman. Reprinted in Dorman, *History of Barbour County*, 273–275; and Mattie Thompson, *History of Barbour County* (Eufaula, 1939), 337.

8 Keils in "Alabama Investigation," 1–2; Keils in Senate Report No. 704, 4th Cong., 2nd sess., 33 March 1877, 594; Melinda M. Hennessey, "Reconstruction Politics and the Military: The Eufaula Riot of 1874," *Alabama Historical Quarterly* 38 (Summer 1976): 114.

9 Keils-Lewis-Gardner exchange: Gardner to Gov. Lewis, 6 July 1874; Lewis to Gardner, 9 July 1874; Keils to Lewis, 8 August 1874; Keils to Benjamin Gardner, 25 August 1874; Governor Lewis to Gardner, 4 September 1874; in Governor David P. Lewis Papers, General Correspondence, ADAH.

10 Michael W. Fitzgerald, *Reconstruction in Alabama: From Civil War to Redemption in the Cotton South* (Baton Rouge: Louisiana State University Press, 2017), 306–307; *Columbus Enquirer*, 29 August 1874.

11 William Gillette, *Retreat from Reconstruction, 1869–1879* (Baton Rouge: Louisiana State University Press, 1982), 237, 230; Alan Friedlander and Richard

Allan Gerber, *Welcoming Ruin: The Civil Rights Act of 1875* (Boston: Brill, 2018) argues that Reconstruction still had considerable momentum, but the civil rights bill and "threat" of social equality drained the possibility of continued support for Reconstruction.

12 "kill": Williams, Clark, and Laird to Keils, 31 August 1874, "Alabama Investigation," 1227; "troops": Henly to Williams, 7 September 1874, "Alabama Investigation," 122; "carry this county": Dorman, *Barbour County*, 272; Loren Schweninger, *James T. Rapier and Reconstruction* (Chicago: University of Chicago Press, 1978), 142.

13 Keils in "Alabama Investigation," 3; Keils in Senate Report No. 704, 589, 613–616; James D. Williford (US Marshal) in Senate Report No. 704, 445–447.

14 Keils in "Alabama Investigation," 3, 5.

15 Keils in Senate Report No. 704, 599; Keils in "Alabama Investigation," 3, 5.

16 "crowd": Keils in Senate Report No. 704, 599.

17 Comer bribe: Keils in Senate Report No. 704, 589–590, 665.

18 Keils in Senate Report No. 704, 589.

19 Keils in "Alabama Investigation," 3, 4, 8.

20 "Alabama Investigation," 4, 599.

21 "Alabama Investigation," 5; Extract from *Eufaula Times* in Senate Report No. 704, 607.

22 "Alabama Investigation," 3, 5, 599.

23 "Alabama Investigation," 5–6; Senate Report No. 704, 554.

24 *Eufaula News* printed in *Montgomery Advertiser*, 7 November 1874.

25 Senate Report No. 704, 588.

26 *Montgomery Advertiser*, 4 November 1874, 6 November 1874. The *New York Times* accepted the white Democratic story in its totality. See *New York Times*, 4 November 1874.

27 See Keils's letters to Grant in *The Papers of Ulysses S. Grant*, vol. 25, *1874*, ed. John Y. Simon (Carbondale: Southern Illinois University Press, 2003), 198–199.

28 Ron Chernow, *Grant* (New York: Penguin Books, 2017), 784; James S. Pike, *The Prostrate South Carolina Under Negro Government* (New York: D. Appleton and Company, 1874); Eric Foner, *Reconstruction: America's Unfinished Revolution, 1863–1877* (New York: Harper and Row, 1998), 526–528; Gillette, *Retreat from Reconstruction*, 182.

29 Senate Report No. 704, 598; Walker, *Backtracking*, 265–266.

30 Williams in Senate Report No. 704, 602, 617.

31 Senate Report No. 704, 587, 603–610.

32 Senate Report No. 704, 603–607; Senate Report No. 704, 606.

33 Senate Report No. 704, 594, 597, 602–603, 617–618.

34 Albright to James Blaine, forward to Ulysses S. Grant, January 1875, Grant Papers, 199.

35 Foner, *Reconstruction*, 603; for the question of Northern will, see Heather Cox Richardson, *The Death of Reconstruction: Race, Labor, and Politics in the*

Post–Civil War North, 1865–1901 (Cambridge, MA: Harvard University Press, 2004).

36 Keils to Attorney General Edwards Pierrepont, 11 June 1875, Letters Received by the Attorney General, 1871–1884: Southern Law and Order, Middle Alabama, 1875, RG 60, Entry 55 and 56, NARA.

37 Keils to Pierrepont.

Chapter 11. The Prison Mines

1 On balancing the slavery past with the industrial future, see Edward L. Ayers, *Vengeance and Justice: Crime and Punishment in the 19th Century American South* (New York: Oxford University press, 1984), 192.

2 The prison described belonged to Barbour County's J.W. Comer. "damp": *Biennial Report of the Inspectors of the Alabama Penitentiary, 1884* (Montgomery: W.D. Brown, 1885), 199, 216; Robert Louis Cvornyek, "Convict Labor in the Alabama Coal Mines, 1874–1828" (PhD diss., Columbia University, 1993), 161–162; *New York Times*, 17 December 1882; for thorough overviews, see Douglas A. Blackmon, *Slavery by Another Name: The Re-enslavement of Black Americans from the Civil War to World War II* (New York: Doubleday, 2008); Mary Ellen Curtin, *Black Prisoners and Their World, Alabama, 1865–1900* (Charlottesville: University of Virginia Press, 2000).

3 Cvornyek, "Convict Labor," 37–38; Allen Johnston Going, *Bourbon Democracy in Alabama* (Tuscaloosa: University of Alabama Press, 1951), 176; on coal numbers see Alex Lichtenstein, *Twice the Work of Free Labor: The Political Economy of Convict Labor in the New South* (New York: Verso, 1996), 91.

4 Ezekiel Archey to R. H. Dawson, 18 January 1884, ADAH, http://digital.archives.alabama.gov/cdm/singleitem/collection/voices/id/5414/rec/1; *Biennial Report, 1884*, 66–67.

5 "head and front": Senate Report no. 704, 4th Cong., 2nd sess., 30 March 1877, 589–590, 594, 604. For the heroic version of the Comers, see Anne Kendrick Walker, *Braxton Bragg Comer: His Family Tree* (Richmond, VA: Dietz Press, 1947) and Anne Kendrick Walker, *Backtracking in Barbour County: A Narrative of the Last Alabama Frontier* (Richmond, VA: Dietz Press, 1941), 320–325; on J.W. Comer and the mines, see Blackmon, *Slavery by Another Name*, 70–78.

6 Crimes described in: "Tabular Statement Showing the Number of Convicts Employed by Comer & Mccurdy, Residing at Helena, Alabama," *Biennial Report of the Inspector of the Alabama Penitentiary from September 30, 1878, to September 3, 1880* (Montgomery: Barrett & Brown, 1880), 36–37. Talitha L. LeFlouria, *Chained in Silence: Black Women and Convict Labor in the New South* (Chapel Hill: University of North Carolina Press, 2015); *Wall Street Journal*, 16 July 2001.

7 *First Biennial Report of the Inspectors of Convicts to the Governor, 1884–1886* (Montgomery, 1886), 24; "record": Cvornyek, "Convict Labor in the Alabama Coal Mines," 13, 52.

8 "dominant race": Cvornyek, "Convict Labor," 13; "Memorial of Republican Members of Legislature of Alabama to Congress," in *Report of Committees of the Senate of the United States*, 44th Cong., 2nd sess., 1876–1877 (Washington: US Government Printing Office, 1877), 663, hereafter *Committees of the Senate, 1876–1877*.

9 "accused": *Journal of the Senate of the State of Alabama* (Montgomery, 1875), 636.

10 James Gray Pope, "Mass Incarceration, Convict Leasing, and the Thirteenth Amendment: A Revisionist Account," *New York University Law Review* 94 (December 2019): 1467–1554; Patrick Rael, "Demystifying the 13th Amendment and Its Impact on Mass Incarceration," *Black Perspectives*, 9 December 2016, www.aaihs.org/demystifying-the-13th-amendment-and-its-impact-on-mass-incarceration; Eric Foner, *The Second Founding: How the Civil War and Reconstruction Remade the Constitution* (New York: Norton, 2019), 46–47.

11 "charm": Walker, *Braxton Bragg Comer*, 169; Archey letter to Dawson, 20; Blackmon, *Slavery by Another Name*, 78; the historian is Curtin, *Black Prisoners*, 20.

12 "dogs": D. Goode testimony in *Testimony Taken by the Joint Special Committee of the Session of 1880–81 to Enquire into the Condition and Treatment of Convicts of the State* (Montgomery: Allred & Beers, 1881), 5–6; Blackmon, *Slavery by Another Name*, 70–81.

13 Orlando Patterson, *Freedom in the Making of Western Culture* (New York: Basic Books, 1991), 404; the behavior that Orlando Patterson identified, and Comer performed, had Nietzschean dimensions. L. Nathan Oaklander, "Nietzsche on Freedom," *Southern Journal of Philosophy* 22 (2010): 211–222; Martin A. Ruehl, "In Defence of Slavery: Nietzsche's Dangerous Thinking," *Independent*, 2 January 2018.

14 "bateau": Walker, *Braxton Bragg Comer*, 100, 169.

15 "chained": Blackmon, *Slavery by Another Name*, 75, 77; "bad order": Reginald Heber Dawson diaries, ADAH, 22 May 1887.

16 Cvornyek, "Convict Labor," 37–38; Going, *Bourbon Democracy*, 176.

17 "chain gang": Senate Report No. 704, 604, 607.

18 "management": *Annual Report of the Inspectors of the Alabama Penitentiary, for the Year Ending Sept. 30, 1877* (Montgomery: Barrett & Brown, 1878), 8–9; Michael Fitzgerald, *Reconstruction in Alabama: From Civil War to Redemption in the Cotton South* (Baton Rouge: Louisiana State University Press, 2017), 296–297; Going, *Bourbon Democracy*, 91; Curtin, *Black Prisoners*, 65; "mismanagement": Cvornyek, "Convict Labor," 30.

19 Aziz Huq, "Peonage and Contractual Liberty," *Columbia Law Review* 101 (2001): 360–361; Amy Dru Stanley, *From Bondage to Contract: Wage Labor, Marriage, and the Market in the Age of Slave Emancipation* (New York: Cambridge University Press, 1998), 84–86; Foner, *Reconstruction*, 477–79; Pete Daniel, *Shadow of Slavery: Peonage in the South, 1901–1969* (Urbana: University of Illinois Press, 1972), 19; Peter Kolchin, *First Freedom: The Responses of Alabama*

Blacks to Emancipation and Reconstruction (Westport, CT: Greenwood Press, 1972), 35; "denied": Foner, *Reconstruction*, 56, 166.

20 "sword": David M. Oshinsky, *Worse Than Slavery: Parchman Farm and the Ordeal of Jim Crow Justice* (New York: Simon & Schuster, 1997), 81; "combine and strike": *Testimony before the Joint Committee of the [Alabama] General Assembly Appointed to Examine into the Convict System of Alabama, Session of 1888–89* (Montgomery 1889), 39; Curtin, *Black Prisoners*, 203–204; Brian Kelly, *Race, Class, and Power in the Alabama Coalfields, 1908–1921* (Urbana: University of Illinois Press, 2001), 71–72.

21 Curtin, *Black Prisoners*, 71, 75–76; Blackmon, *Slavery by Another Name*, 76; *Biennial Report of the Inspectors of the Alabama Penitentiary, from September 30, 1880, to September 30, 1882* (Montgomery: Allred and Beers, 1882), 5.

22 Brent J. Aucoin, *Thomas Goode Jones: Race, Politics, and Justice in the New South* (Tuscaloosa: University of Alabama Press, 2016), 118; Blackmon, *Slavery by Another Name*, 165; Judith Stein, "'Of Mr. Booker T. Washington and Others': The Political Economy of Racism in the United States," in *Renewing Black Intellectual History: The Ideological and Material Foundations of African American Thought*, ed. Adolph Reed and Kenneth W. Warren (New York: Routledge, 2016 [2010]), 19–43.

23 "delighted": Aucoin, *Jones*, 118–119

24 "scheme": Aucoin, *Jones*, 120–123; Blackmon, *Slavery by Another Name*, 177.

25 Aucoin, *Jones*, 122, 126; Blackmon, *Slavery by Another Name*, 211.

26 "exalted": *Montgomery Advertiser*, 13 June 1903.

27 "God": Aucoin, *Jones*, 128–129.

28 Jones's biographer argues, "Why Jones took this course of action ultimately remains a tragic mystery, however it appears that he had erroneously bought into the popular notion that the convictions and publicity generated by the peonage trials in his courtroom had effectively ended involuntary servitude in central Alabama." "smooth": Aucoin, *Jones*, 135, 61, 62.

29 Aucoin, *Jones*, 139.

30 "impulsive": Huq, "Peonage and Contractual Liberty," 385; Aucoin, *Jones*, 142, 63.

31 "funded": Message of Hon. B.B. Comer, Governor, to the Legislature of Alabama, At the Regular Session, January 10, 1911, 9; Robert David Ward and William Warren Rogers, *Convicts, Coal, and the Banner Mine Tragedy* (Tuscaloosa: University of Alabama Press, 1987).

32 "Swing Low": Blackmon, *Slavery by Another Name*, 369.

Chapter 12. White Oligarchy as Jeffersonian Democracy

1 "reverence": "Confederate Monument at Eufaula, Ala.," *Confederate Veteran* 13, no. 1 (January 1905): 12, www.usgennet.org/usa/al/county/barbour/CSA/confederatemonumen.htm; *Eufaula Times and News*, 1 December 1904; for an overview of the construction and ideology of Confederate monuments, see Karen L. Cox, *Dixie's Daughters: The United Daughters of the Confederacy*

and the Preservation of Confederate Culture (Gainesville: University of Florida Press, 2019), 49–72.

2 "sublime": "Jasper County Confederate Monument (sculpture)," Smithsonian Institution Research Information System, accessed 5 February 2022, https://siris-artinventories.si.edu/ipac20/ipac.jsp?profile=ariall; "weeping": Lucian Lamar Knight, *Georgia's Landmarks, Memorials, and Legends*, vol. 1, pt. 2 (Atlanta: Byrd Printing Company, 1913), 825; "Lest": "Fort Smith Confederate Monument," *Encyclopedia of Arkansas*, accessed 5 February 2022, https://encyclopediaofarkansas.net; "cheerfully": Timothy S. Sedore, *Mississippi Civil War Monuments: An Illustrated Field Guide* (Bloomington: Indiana University Press, 2020); "Conquered": "Alamance County Confederate Monument, Graham," *Documenting the American South*, University of North Carolina at Chapel Hill, https://docsouth.unc.edu/commland/monument/10. A database of monuments is kept at "Whose Heritage? Public Symbols of the Confederacy," Southern Poverty Law Center, www.splcenter.org/20190201/whose-heritage-public-symbols-confederacy.

3 "spirit": Glenn Feldman, *The Disfranchisement Myth: Poor Whites and Suffrage Restriction in Alabama* (Athens: University of Georgia Press, 2010), 39.

4 Jacquelyn Dowd Hall, "'You Must Remember This': Autobiography as Social Critique," *Journal of American History* 85, no. 2 (September 1998): 439–465; "sublimated": V. O. Key, *Southern Politics in State and Nation* (New York: A. A. Knopf, 1949), 15.

5 The racial hierarchy in the United States is consistent but its manifestations and ideologies are not fixed or static. It can be periodized. A Google "ngram" of "white supremacy" reveals an enormous spike starting in the 1880s, followed by one that dwarfs the first in the 1940s and 1950s during the civil rights era; "slave ship": Ira Berlin, *The Making of African America: The Four Great Migrations* (New York: Penguin, 2010), 61.

6 Alex Keyssar, *The Right to Vote: The Contested History of Democracy in the United States* (New York: Basic Books, 2000), 108–109.

7 On more excitement than anything since Reconstruction, see C. Vann Woodward, *Origins of the New South: 1877–1913* (Baton Rouge: Louisiana State University Press, 1951), 254; "existence," "cowardly," and "scheme": Keyssar, *Right to Vote*, 131–134; *Congressional Record*, 51st Cong., 1st sess. (25 June 1890), 6505–6511.

8 "struggle": Richard E. Welch, "The Federal Elections Bill of 1890: Postscripts and Prelude," *Journal of American History* 52 (1965): 519–520; Henry Cabot Lodge, "The Federal Election Bill," *North American Review* 151 (September 1890): 257–273.

9 "dollar" in Heather Cox Richardson, *To Make Men Free: A History of the Republican Party* (New York: Basic Books, 2014), xiv, and the elections bill, 126–127; Michael Perman, *Struggle for Mastery: Disfranchisement in the South, 1888–1908* (Chapel Hill: University of North Carolina Press, 2001), 39–44.

10 "Pandora's": *Eufaula Times and News*, 8 January 1891, 3 November 1892.

11 "feverish": *Eufaula Times and News*, 12 October 1892, 13 October 1892.

12 "jubilee": *Eufaula Daily Times*, April 1, 1892.

13 "handshaker": Charles Grayson Summersell, "Kolb and the Populist Revolt Viewed by Newspapers," *Alabama Historical Quarterly* 19, no. 3 and 4 (Fall and Winter 1957): 380.

14 "cotton idea": Sheldon Hackney, *Populism to Progressivism in Alabama* (Tuscaloosa: University of Alabama Press, 2010), 6; "Gem": William W. Rogers, "Reuben F. Kolb: Agricultural Leader of the New South," *Agricultural History* 32 (April 1958): 109–119.

15 Rogers, "Kolb," n115; "genial": Charles Ellington Porterfield, "A Rhetorical-Historical Analysis of the Third Party Movement in Alabama (PhD diss., Louisiana State University, 1965), 84.

16 William Warren Rogers, *The One-Gallused Rebellion: Agrarianism in Alabama, 1865–1896* (Tuscaloosa: University of Alabama Press, 2001), 121–146; Charles Postel, *Equality: An American Dilemma, 1866–1896* (New York: Farrar, Strauss and Giroux, 2019), 306.

17 Charles Postel, *The Populist Vision* (New York: Oxford University Press, 2009); George Packer, *Blood of the Liberals* (New York: Farrar, Straus and Giroux, 2000), 44; Omar H. Ali, *In the Lion's Mouth: Black Populism in the New South, 1886–1900* (Jackson: University Press of Mississippi, 2013).

18 William Warren Rogers, Robert David Ward, Leah Rawls Atkins, and Wane Flynt, *Alabama: The History of a Deep South State* (Tuscaloosa: University of Alabama Press, 2018), 288–305; Rogers, *One-Gallused Rebellion*, passim; *Montgomery Advertiser*, 10 May 1890;

19 *Montgomery Advertiser*, 10 May 1890; "stove wood": Rogers, *One-Gallused Rebellion*, 180; "plutocrats": Hackney, *Populism to Progressivism in Alabama*, 14.

20 Rogers et al, *Alabama History*, 307; John B. Clark, "Populism in Alabama," PhD diss. (New York University, 1926), 150–157.

21 Porterfield, "Rhetorical-Historical Analysis," 18–20, 35–36; "scurrilous": Hackney, *Populism to Progressivism in Alabama*, 111.

22 "priceless" and "rights": Rogers et al., *Alabama*, 310; "attainment": Hackney, *Populism and Progressivism*, 34–35; Porterfield, "Rhetorical-Historical Analysis," 49; "White Man's": Matthew Hild, *Greenbackers, Knights of Labor, and Populists: Farmer-Labor Insurgency in the Late Nineteenth Century* (Athens: University of Georgia Press, 2007), 166.

23 Rogers et al., *Alabama*, 311–315; Porterfield, "Rhetorical-Historical Analysis," 38; Woodward, *Origins of the New South*, 262; "drowned": *Eufaula Times and News*, 4 August 1892.

24 "plutocracy": Porterfield, "Rhetorical-Historical Analysis," 98–99.

25 "magical": Hackney, *Populism to Progressivism*, 36; Porterfield, "Rhetorical-Historical Analysis," 67; "voted": Charles Grayson Summersell, "A Life of Reuben F. Kolb" (MA thesis, University of Alabama 1930), 77.

26 *Mobile Register*, 13 November 1894 (reprint of Kolb article); "citizens": *Mobile Advertiser*, 20 November 1894 (editorial response); "Revolution": *Daily News* 8 August 1894; Porterfield, "Rhetorical-Historical Analysis," 79, 84.

27 "martyr": Hackney, *Populism to Progressivism*, 69.
28 "Populism": Rogers et al., *Alabama*, 319.
29 "hair": *Proceedings of the Democratic State Convention*, 25 April 1900, 10–11; Feldman, *Disfranchisement Myth*, 46.
30 "ineradicable": William Dorsey Jelks, "The Acuteness of the Negro Question: A Suggested Remedy," *North American Review* 609 (15 February 1907): 389; editorial, *Eufaula Daily Times*, 21 March 1882, cited in David E. Alsobrook, *Southside: Eufaula's Cotton Mill Village and Its People, 1890–1945* (Macon, GA: Mercer University Press, 2017), 29.
31 David E. Alsobrook, "William Dorsey Jelks: Alabama Editor and Legislator" (MA thesis, West Virginia University, 1972); "fighting": R. Volney Riser, "Disfranchisement, the US Constitution, and the Federal Courts: Alabama's 1901 Constitution Convention Debates and the Grandfather Clause," *American Journal of Legal History* 48, no. 3 (2006): 237–279; Michael Perman, *Struggle for Mastery: Disfranchisement in the South, 1888–1908* (Chapel Hill: University of North Carolina Press, 2001). See "Official Proceedings of the Constitutional Convention of the State of Alabama, May 21st, 1901, to September 3rd, 1901" (Wetumpka, AL.: n.p., 1941).
32 Malcolm Cook McMillan, *Constitutional Development in Alabama, 1798–1901: A Study in Politics, the Negro, and Sectionalism* (Chapel Hill: University of North Carolina Press, 1955).
33 "rascality": *Eufaula Time and News*, 31 October 1901.
34 *Eufaula Times and News*, 21 November 1901; Rogers, et al., *Alabama*, 353.
35 Woodward, *Origins of the New South, 1877–1913* (Baton Rouge: Louisiana State University Press, 1951), xii.
36 Feldman, *Disfranchisement Myth*, 71, 136–137.
37 "distinction": Jason Morgan Ward, *Defending White Democracy: The Making of a Segregationist Movement & the Remaking of Racial Politics, 1936–1965* (Chapel Hill: University of North Carolina Press, 2011), 3.
38 Orlando Patterson, "Freedom, Slavery, and the Modern Construction of Rights," in *The Cultural Values of Europe*, ed. Hans Joas and Klaus Wiegandt (Liverpool: Liverpool University Press, 2008), 141, 146, 150; see Barbara J. Fields, "Ideology and Race in American History," in *Region, Race, and Reconstruction: Essays in Honor of C. Vann Woodward*, ed. J. Morgan Kousser and James M. McPherson (New York: Oxford University Press, 1982), 169.

Chapter 13. Lynching as an Act of Freedom

1 David Frost Jr., *Witness to Injustice*, ed. Louise Westling (Oxford: University Press of Mississippi, 1995), 3–8.
2 Richard Wright, *Black Boy* (New York: Harper and Row, 1966 [1945]), 190.
3 *Montgomery Advertiser*, 13 February 1911; David E. Alsobrook, *Southside: Eufaula's Cotton Mill Village and Its People, 1890–1945* (Macon, GA: Mercer University Press, 2017), 38–40.

4 James Baldwin, "Going to Meet the Man," in *Early Novels and Stories*, ed. Toni Morrison (New York: Literary Classics, 1998), 949. The comparison between what Frost imagined, Peterson experienced, and Baldwin wrote comes directly from Carrie Monahan, "'A Dream Remembered': Collective Memory and Ancestral Responsibility in Eufaula, Alabama" (Honors thesis, American Studies Program, Stanford University, 2018). See also Colson Whitehead's novel *The Underground Railroad*, in which his characters come across the aftermath of a phantasmagoria of white violence. He describes how "the corpses hung from trees as rotting ornaments." The setting had a name. "They call this road the Freedom trail now," his character Martin says. Whitehead, *Underground Railroad* (New York: Double Day, 2016), 152–153.

5 *Montgomery Advertiser*, 13 February 1911.

6 Frost, *Witness to Injustice*, 11.

7 Frost, *Witness to Injustice*, 7–8.

8 "terrain": Angela P. Harris, "Race and Essentialism in Feminist Legal Theory," *Stanford Law Review* 42, no. 3 (February 1990): 581–616; for an overview of the vast literature on lynching, see Michael J. Pfeifer, "At the Hands of Parties Unknown? The State of the Field of Lynching Scholarship," *Journal of American History* 101 (December 2014): 832–846; W. Fitzhugh Brundage, "Introduction," *Under Sentence of Death: Lynching in the South* (Chapel Hill: University of North Carolina Press, 1997), 1–20; Jacquelyn Dowd Hall, *Revolt Against Chivalry: Jesse Daniel Ames and the Women's Campaign Against Lynching* (New York: Columbia University Press, 1974), xx–xxi; "pornography": Jacquelyn Dowd Hall, "'The Mind That Burns in Each Body': Women, Rape, and Racial Violence," in *Powers of Desire: The Politics of Sexuality*, ed. Ann Barr Snitow, Christine Stansell, and Sharon Thompson (New York: Monthly Review Press, 1983), 328–349; On the "natural man" see Gail Bederman, *Manliness and Civilization: A Cultural History of Gender and Race in the United States, 1860–1917* (Chicago: University of Chicago Press, 1995), 71–75.

9 "birthright": Ashraf H. A. Rushdy, *American Lynching* (New Haven: Yale University Press, 2012), xi, 145, 149–153; "prerogative": Michael Trotti, "What Counts: Trends in Racial Violence in the Postbellum South," *Journal of American History* (September 2013): 38; Orlando Patterson, "Freedom, Slavery, and the Modern Construction of Rights," in *The Cultural Values of Europe*, ed. Hans Joas and Klaus Wiegandt (Liverpool: Liverpool University Press, 2008), 117.

10 "a world without restraint": Daniel Jonah Goldhagen, *Hitler's Willing Executioners: Ordinary Germans and the Holocaust* (New York: Alfred A. Knopf, 1996), 174–175.

11 Christopher Waldrep argues that lynching was a battle over the nature of the Constitution; see *African Americans Confront Lynching: Strategies of Resistance from the Civil War to the Civil Rights Era* (Lanham: Rowman &

Littlefield Publishers, 2009); "people" and "popular": Larry Kramer, *The People Themselves: Popular Constitutionalism and Judicial Review (*New York: Oxford University Press, 2004), 8; Frederick Douglass, *Three Addresses on the Relations Subsisting Between the White and Colored People of the United States* (Washington, 1886), 60.

12 *Montgomery Weekly Advertiser*, 14 April 1893.

13 Alsobrook, *Southside*, 34–35.

14 "protect": "Eufaula Soldiers Drive Mob from the Jail Doors," *Montgomery Advertiser*, 8 June 1909.

15 Alsobrook, *Southside*, 36–37.

16 "fast drive": "Eufaula Soldiers Drive Mob from the Jail Doors"; Alsobrook, *Southside*, 38, 40.

17 Warren G. Harding, "Address at Birmingham, October 26, 1921," https://archive.org/stream/addressofpresideoohard#page/n3/mode/2up; *New York Times*, 27 October 1921; Patricia Sullivan, *Lift Every Voice: The NAACP and the Making of the Civil Rights Movement* (New York: The New Press, 2009), 105.

18 Sullivan, *Lift Every Voice*, 105, 108.

19 David Bateman, Ira Katznelson, and John S. Lapinski, *Southern Nation: Congress and White Supremacy After Reconstruction* (Princeton, NJ: Princeton University Press, 2020), 353–354.

20 *New York Times*, 3 December 1922; "sea": Sullivan, *Lift Every Voice*, 109–110.

21 "insulting": *Atlanta Constitution*, 12 January 1922; "scratch": Frost, *Witness to Injustice*, 14–17 (Frost recalls the name as "Jenkins"); see Kidada Williams, *They Left Great Marks on Me: African American Testimonies of Racial Violence from Emancipation to World War I* (New York: NYU Press, 2012), 206–207; anonymous letter from Eufaula, Alabama, to James Weldon Johnson, 14 January 1922, Papers of the NAACP, Reel 2, frame 0994.

22 *Clayton Record*, 12 July 1929; *Clayton Record*, 18 July 1929.

23 "detail": *Clayton Record*, 19 July 1929; *Dothan Eagle*, 18 July 1929.

24 Alsobrook, *Southside*, 42; *Chicago Defender*, 3 August 1929.

25 *Clayton Record*, 26 July 1929; *Chicago Defender*, 3 August 1929.

26 *Atlanta Constitution*, 18 July 1929; *New Journal and Guide*, 3 August 1929

27 *New Amsterdam News*, 31 July 1929; *Pittsburgh Courier*, 3 August 1929; "National Guard in Alabama Called to Prevent Lynching of Negro at Murder Trial," *Atlanta Constitution*, 23 July 1929; "Guard Units Are to Protect Negro," *Daily Boston Globe*, 23 July 1929; "500 Troopers Guard Slayer in Alabama," *Chicago Defender*, 3 August 1929; Alsobrook, *Southside*, 43.

28 "National Guard in Alabama Called to Prevent Lynching of Negro at Murder Trial"; "Guard Units Are to Protect Negro"; "500 Troopers Guard Slayer in Alabama"; Alsobrook, *Southside*, 43; *Time* magazine, 5 August 1929.

29 On the structural limits on bills like Costigan-Wagner, see Ira Katznelson et al., "Limiting Liberalism: The Southern Veto in Congress, 1933–1950," *Political Science Quarterly* 108, no. 2 (Summer 1993): 283–306; "Afro-Democratic":

Jason Morgan Ward, "'Negroes, The New Deal, and... Karl Marx,'" in *Nation Within a Nation: The American South and the Federal Government*, ed. Glenn Feldman (Gainesville: University of Florida Press, 2014), 105; "collapsing": Lee D. Baker, *From Savage to Negro: Anthropology and the Construction of Race, 1896–1954* (Berkeley: University of California Press, 1998) 172; "avalanche": Arthur Krock, "In Washington Anti-Lynching Bill Threatens to Tie Up Senate," *New York Times*, April 17, 1935.

30 Hugo Black, *Congressional Record*, 74th Cong., 1st sess., 1935, 79, 6520; "Appomattox": Sullivan, *Lift Every Voice*, 204; "Calhoun": George Rable, "The South and the Politics of Antilynching Legislation, 1920–1940," *Journal of Southern History* 51, no. 2 (May 1985): 204.

31 Worker quote in William E. Leuchtenburg, *The White House Looks South: Franklin D. Roosevelt, Harry S. Truman, Lyndon B. Johnson* (Baton Rouge: Louisiana State University Press, 2007), 89.

32 "afraid": Frost, *Witness to Injustice*, 5–8, 11, 49, 68–69; "Black Lynched by Eufaula Mob," *Atlanta Constitution*, 13 February 1911; "Youth Lynched in Alabama," *Washington Post*, 13 February 1911.

33 Frost, *Witness to Injustice*, 45.

Chapter 14. A New Deal for Southside?

1 "bad": Federal Writer's Project Interview, "Mill Workers," by Gertha Couric, Series 1, Folder 13, Life Histories, the Federal Writers' Project Papers #3709, Southern Historical Collection, Wilson Library, University of North Carolina at Chapel Hill.

2 "snake": David E. Alsobrook, *Southside: Eufaula's Cotton Mill Village and Its People, 1890–1945* (Macon, GA: Mercer University Press, 2017), 68–77.

3 "mule": Wayne Flynt, *Poor but Proud: Alabama's Poor Whites* (Tuscaloosa: University of Alabama, 2001), 60–61.

4 "moneyed cats": Theodore Rosegarten, *All God's Dangers: The Life of Nate Shaw* (New York: Knopf, 1974), 500.

5 "panorama": Charles S. Johnson, Edwin R. Embree, and W. W. Alexander, *The Collapse of Cotton Tenancy: Summary of Field Studies & Statistical Surveys, 1933–1935* (Chapel Hill: University of North Carolina Press, 1935), 14.

6 Alsobrook, *Southside*, 10, 15, 64–65; Robert H. Flewellen, *Along Broad Street: A History of Eufaula, Alabama 1823–1984* (Eufaula: City of Eufaula, 1991), 186; Mary Lether Wingerd, "Rethinking Paternalism: Power and Parochialism in a Southern Mill Village," *Journal of American History* 83, no. 3 (Dec 1996): 877.

7 "fountain": "Mill Workers"; "Fifty-Two Years in the Cotton Mill," by Gertha Couric, FWP Interview, Series 1, Folder 18, 1936–1940, FWP Papers, 1936–1940, Southern Historical Collection, University of North Carolina.

8 "evolved": Bryant Simon, "Choosing Between the Ham and the Union: Paternalism in the Cone Mills of Greensboro, 1925–1930," in *Hanging by a Thread: Social Change in Southern Textiles*, ed. Jeffrey Leiter, Michael Schulman, and

Rhinda Zingraff (Ithaca, NY: ILR Press, 1991), 81–82; Wingerd, "Rethinking Paternalism," 872–902; Jacquelyn Dowd Hall, James Lelouis, Robert Korstad, Mary Murphy, Lu Ann Jones, and Christopher B. Daly, *Like a Family: The Making of a Southern Cotton Mill World* (Chapel Hill: University of North Carolina Press, 1987), 152–172.

9 "contract": B.B. Comer to Dismuke, 3 March 1924, B.B. Comer Papers, Correspondence and Other Papers, 1907–1940, Southern Historical Collection, University of North Carolina.

10 *Atlanta Constitution*, 24 October 1927; Michael Alan Breedlove, "Donald Comer: New Southerner, New Dealer" (PhD diss., American University, 1990), 118–119; Alsobrook, *Southside*, 58.

11 Donald Comer, *Braxton Bragg Comer: An Alabamian Whose Avondale Mills Opened New Paths for Southern Progress* (New York: Newcomen Society of England, American Branch, 1947); Alsobrook, *Southside*, 101; Breedlove, "Comer," 193–194, 97–98; on the Social Gospel, see Heath W. Carter, *Union Made: Working People and the Rise of Social Christianity in Chicago* (New York: Oxford University Press, 2015); Erik S. Gellman and Jarod Roll, *The Gospel of the Working Class: Labor's Southern Prophets in New Deal America* (Urbana: University of Illinois Press, 2011).

12 Breedlove, "Comer," 285.

13 Alsobrook, *Southside*, 162.

14 "Rooseveltian": W.J. Cash, *The Mind of the South* (New York: Alfred A. Knopf, 1941), 364; William E. Leuchtenburg, *The White House Looks South: Franklin D. Roosevelt, Harry S. Truman, Lyndon B. Johnson* (Baton Rouge: Louisiana State University Press, 2007), 119; *Atlanta Constitution*, 6 September 1928.

15 "humane": Frances Perkins, *The Roosevelt I Knew* (New York: Penguin, 2011 [1946]), 315; "obligation": Breedlove, "Comer," 273, 231, 280

16 "far-reaching": Ira Katznelson, *Fear Itself: The New Deal and the Origins of Our Time* (New York: Liveright, 2013), 227–230, 232; Hall et al., *Like a Family*, 290.

17 Katznelson, *Fear Itself*, 127, 229; Lee J. Alston and Joseph P. Ferrie, *Southern Paternalism and the American Welfare State: Economics, Politics, and Institutions in the South, 1865–1965* (New York: Cambridge University Press, 1999), 20.

18 *Atlanta Constitution*, 4 April 1934; Breedlove, "Comer," 283–287, 292; "N.R.A. Reports Textile Wages High as Traffic Will Bear At This Time," *Avondale Sun*, 14 July 1934, 3.

19 Breedlove, "Comer," 288–289.

20 "revolution": Janet Irons, *Testing the New Deal: The General Textile Strike of 1934 in the American South* (Urbana: University of Illinois Press, 2000), 3.

21 Breedlove, "Comer," 314–316; *Birmingham Age-Herald*, 26 July 1934.

22 Alsobrook, *Southside*, 110; Flynt, *Poor but Proud*, 111.

23 "southern industry": Breedlove, "Comer," 316. There was even a celebration in Comer's honor after the strike: "Cowikee Mills Honor Mr. Comer," *Avondale Sun*, 22 September 1934.

24 "velvet": Alsobrook, *Southside*, 110; "invasion": Breedlove, "Comer," 329–330.

25 Irons, *Testing the New Deal*, 176; Kari A. Frederickson, *The Dixiecrat Revolt and the End of the Solid South, 1932–1968* (Chapel Hill: University of North Carolina Press, 2001), 17.

26 Irons, *Testing the New Deal*, 176; "benefited": Frederickson, *Dixiecrat Revolt*, 17; Leuchtenburg, *White House Looks South*, 120.

27 On FLSA, see *Atlanta Constitution*, 11 August 1938; *Christian Science Monitor*, 22 August 1946; "Donald Comer Writes Secretary Roper Concerning Recent Report on Cotton Textile Industry by Cabinet Committee," *Avondale Sun*, 5 October 1935, 1–2; "Donald Comer Writes John Temple Graves," *Avondale Sun*, 1 February 1937, 1, 9, 16; "Mr. Donald Comer Explains Purposes and Accomplishments of Textile Mission to Japan," *Avondale Sun*, 12 April 1937, 1–2; "Address Delivered at Annual Convention in Washington, 13 May 1937, by Donald Comer, Retiring President of the American Cotton Manufacturers Association," *Avondale Sun*, 27 September 1937.

28 Dwight C. Van Meter, "Donald Comer and His 7,000 Partners," *Rotarian* (March 1951): 23, 24; Alsobrook, *Southside*, 112.

29 "tired": *Christian Science Monitor*, 20 August 1946, 21 August 1946; "reinterpret": Bryant Simon, *Fabric of Defeat* (Chapel Hill: University of North Carolina Press, 1998), 80; Barbara S. Griffith, *The Crisis of American Labor: Operation Dixie and the Defeat of the CIO* (Philadelphia: Temple University Press, 1988); Elizabeth Fones-Wolf and Ken Fones-Wolf, *Struggle for the Soul of the Postwar South: White Evangelical Protestants and Operation Dixie* (Urbana: University of Illinois Press, 2015); Robert Korstad, "Rethinking Operation Dixie," *Labor* 14, no. 1 (March 2017): 79–81; Timothy J. Minchin, *Fighting Against the Odds: A History of Southern Labor Since World War II* (Gainesville: University Press of Florida, 2005).

30 "forgetfulness": Katznelson, *Fear Itself*, 168; Robert Mickey, *Paths Out of Dixie: The Democratization of Authoritarian Enclaves in America's Deep South, 1944–1972* (Princeton, NJ: Princeton University Press, 2015), 104, 168; Leuchtenberg, *White House Looks South*, 65-66; *Christian Science Monitor*, 22 August 1956.

31 "semi-autarkic": Maxime Desmarais-Tremblay, "Paternalism and the Public Household: On the Domestic Origins of Public Economics," *History of Political Economy* 53, no. 2 (2021): 179–211; Alston and Ferrie, *Southern Paternalism*; Phillip Scranton, "Varieties of Paternalisms: Industrial Structures and the Social Relations of Production in American Textiles," *American Quarterly* 36, no. 2 (1984): 235–257. See Kant, "On the Proverb: That May Be True in Theory, but Is of No Practical Use," in *Perpetual Peace and Other Essays*, trans. Ted Humphrey (Indianapolis: Hackett Publishing, 1983), 73, 81.

32 "tracks": Van Meter, "Donald Comer and His 7,000 Partners," 23; Griffith, *Crisis of American Labor*, 88–105.

Chapter 15. The Bourbon from Barbour

1 "congested": Bruce Nelson, "Organized Labor and the Struggle for Black Equality in Mobile During World War II," *Journal of American History* 80, no. 3 (1993): 952–957; "trampled": John Dos Passos, *State of the Nation* (Boston: Houghton Mifflin, 1944), 92.

2 Nelson, "Organized Labor and the Struggle for Black Equality," 952–988; James Rawn Jr., *The Double V: How Wars, Protest, and Harry Truman Desegregated America's Military* (New York: Bloomsbury 2013), 114.

3 William P. Jones, *The March on Washington: Jobs, Freedom, and the Forgotten History of Civil Rights* (New York: Norton, 2013), 39; Patricia Sullivan, *Days of Hope: Race and Democracy in the New Deal Era* (Chapel Hill: University of North Carolina Press, 1996), 135–136; Franklin Delano Roosevelt, "Executive Order 8802: Prohibition of Discrimination in the Defense Industry" (1941), www.ourdocuments.gov/doc.php?flash=false&doc=72#.

4 Nelson, "Organized Labor and the Struggle for Black Equality," 974; *New York Times*, 13 July 1943; see also Joseph Abel, "African Americans, Labor Unions, and the Struggle for Fair Employment in the Aircraft Manufacturing Industry of Texas, 1941–1945," *Journal of Southern History* 77, no. 3 (2011): 595–638.

5 See William J. Collins, "Race, Roosevelt, and Wartime Production: Fair Employment in World War II Labor Markets," *American Economic Review* 91, no. 1 (2001): 272–286. For a less sanguine view, see Merl E. Reed, *Seedtime for the Modern Civil Rights Movement: The President's Committee on Fair Employment Practice, 1941–1946* (Baton Rouge: Louisiana State University Press, 1991).

6 Unknown [in DC] to Sparks, 13 August 1943, Gov. Sparks Administrative Files, SG 12409, FF12, ADAH.

7 On the local dimensions of race relations, see J. Mills Thornton III, "Segregation and the City: White Supremacy in Alabama in the Mid-Twentieth Century," in *Fog of War: The Second World War and the Civil Rights Movement*, ed. Kevin Kruse and Stephen Tuck (New York: Oxford University Press, 2012), 51–69; J. Glenn Feldman, *The Great Melding: War, the Dixiecrat Rebellion, and the Southern Model of America's New Conservatism* (Tuscaloosa: University of Alabama Press, 2015), 4–5, 38.

8 "Barbour Bourbon": Harvey H. Jackson III, "Chauncey M. Sparks, 1943–1947," in *Alabama Governors: A Political History of the State*, ed. Samuel L. Webb and Margaret E. Armbrester (Tuscaloosa: University of Alabama Press, 2010), 222–223.

9 Sparks inaugural; Thornton, "Segregation and the City," 60; Webb and Armbrester, *Alabama Governors*, 191.

10 "white Jeffersonian": Jason Morgan Ward, *Defending White Democracy: The Making of a Segregationist Movement & the Remaking of Racial Politics*,

1936–1965 (Chapel Hill: University of North Carolina Press, 2011), 101–103; the entire structure of the New Deal as shaped and delimited by the Southern wing is developed by Sullivan, *Days of Hope*; Ira Katznelson, *Fear Itself: The New Deal and the Origins of Our Time* (New York: Liveright, 2013), 156–194; "backbone" is Senator Robert Byrd's term, see Katznelson, 193; Robert Mickey, *Paths Out of Dixie: The Democratization of Authoritarian Enclaves in America's Deep South, 1944–1972* (Princeton, NJ: Princeton University Press, 2015), 134.

11 "anomalous position": Richard Hofstadter, "Calhoun to Dixiecrats," *Social Research* 16, no. 2 (June 1949): 150.

12 "totalitarian": Jason Morgan Ward, "'Negroes, The New Deal, and...Karl Marx,'" in *Nation Within a Nation: The American South and the Federal Government*, ed. Glenn Feldman (Gainesville: University of Florida Press, 2014), 111; Jason Morgan Ward, "'A War for States' Rights': the White Supremacist Vision of Double Victory," in *Fog of War: The Second World War and the Civil Rights Movement*, ed. Kevin M. Kruse and Stephen Tuck (New York: Oxford University Press, 2012), 126–144.

13 Chauncey Sparks, "Founders Day—Tuskegee Institution, April 4, 1943," Gov. Sparks—Speeches, SG 12527, FF 3, ADAH, 5–6.

14 Chauncey Sparks, "Speech Before General Connectional Board of the Colored Methodist Episcopal Church, Birmingham, Alabama, May 3, 1944," Gov. Spark—Speeches, SG 12527, FF 8, ADAH.

15 See Tuskegee speech; Sparks to Lewis, 24 June 1943; Sparks to Davenport, June 1943, in Sparks Papers 1249; Feldman, *Great Melding*, 38, 41, 95.

16 Richard M. Dalfiume, "The 'Forgotten Years' of the Negro Revolution," in *The Negro in Depression and War: Prelude to Revolution*, ed. Bernard Sternsher (Chicago: Quadrangle Books, 1969), 299; "freedom": Chauncey Sparks, "Speech Before the Alabama Division of the American Legion, July 13, 1943," Gov. Sparks—Speeches, SG 12527, FF 4, ADAH.

17 "intercourse": Chauncey Sparks, "Founders Day—Tuskegee Institution, April 4, 1943," Gov. Sparks—Speeches, SG 12527, FF 3, ADAH; Chauncey Sparks, "Speech Before the State Kiwanis Convention, Auburn, Alabama, October 10, 1944," Gov. Sparks—Speeches, SG 12527, FF 9, ADAH.

18 "master-planners": Feldman, *Melding*, 39–41; Keith M. Finley, *Delaying the Dream: Southern Senators and the Fight Against Civil Rights, 1938–1965* (Baton Rouge: Louisiana State University Press, 2008), 78–96.

19 Sparks to John P. Lewis, 24 June 1943, Gov. Sparks Administrative Files, SG 12409, FF 11, ADAH.

20 Sparks, "Speech Before the State Kiwanis Convention."

21 Sparks to FDR, 24 August 1944, SF 12491, Folder 5, Sparks Papers; Dixon to Sparks, 31 August 1944, Folder 5: Military Order, Maxwell Field, Sparks Administrative Files, SF012491; see coverage in Sparks Scrapbook #24 in Sparks Personal Papers; discussion in Glenn Feldman, *Irony of the Solid*

South: Democrats, Republicans, and Race, 1865–1944 (Tuscaloosa: University of Alabama Press, 2013), 225–228.

22 Darlene Clark Hine, *Black Victory: The Rise and Fall of the White Primary in Texas* (Columbia: University of Missouri Press, 2003 [1979]), 249.

23 Sparks to the United Press, Birmingham, Alabama, 3 April 1944, Gov. Sparks Administrative Files, SG 124990, FF 8, ADAH; Scotty E. Kirkland, "Mobile and the Boswell Amendment," *Alabama Review* 65 (July 2012): 205–249; Hine, *Black Victory*; Feldman, *Melding*, 188, 271, 273.

24 "localism": Thornton, "Segregation and the City," 55; "understand": William D. Barnard, *Dixiecrats and Democrats: Alabama Politics, 1942–1950* (Tuscaloosa: University of Alabama Press, 1974), 67; "intolerance": Feldman, *Melding*, 182.

25 Vera Chandler Foster, "'Boswellianism': A Technique in the Restriction of Negro Voting," *Phylon* 10, no. 1 (1949): 26–37.

26 "serious": *Pittsburgh Courier*, 4 August 1945; "quotidian": Thornton, "Segregation and the City," 56.

27 "confessed": *Chicago Defender*, 14 July 1945; *Atlanta Daily World*, 20 July 1945.

28 "gangs": *Chicago Defender*, 14 July 1945; *Pittsburgh Courier*, 4 August 1945; *Chicago Defender*, 11 August 1945.

29 Sparks memo, Racial Disturbance at Eufaula, Alabama, 10 July 1945, Gov. Sparks Administrative Files, SG 12501, FF 6, ADAH; Lipsett to Sparks, 15 December 1944, Gov. Sparks Administrative Files, SG 12505, FF 2, ADAH; *Dothan Eagle*, 17 July 1945; see Gail Williams O'Brien, *The Color of Law: Race, Violence, and Justice in the Post–World War II South* (Chapel Hill: University of North Carolina Press, 1999); "Eufaula Negro Rape Slayer Is to Die in Chair," *Dothan Eagle*, 17 July 1945.

30 "pottage": Chauncey Sparks address before the Alabama State Bar, *Alabama Lawyer* 3–4 (1942): 417; see also, Ward, *Defending White Democracy*, 103.

31 "hyperindividualism": Feldman, *Irony*, 2; George Packer, *Blood of the Liberals* (New York: Farrar, Straus and Giroux 2000), 116.

32 "Report to Hon. Chauncey Sparks, RE: The alleged ravishing of Recy Taylor," 14 December 1944; "Supplemental Report to Hon. Chauncey Sparks, RE: The alleged ravishing of Recy Taylor," 27 December 1944. The details of the Taylor case are laid out in full in Danielle L. McGuire, *At the Dark End of the Street: Black Women, Rape and Resistance—A New History of the Civil Rights Movement from Rosa Parks to the Rise of Black Power* (New York: Vintage, 2010), xv–17.

Chapter 16. The Fightin' Judge

1 Sandra Baxley Taylor, *Me 'n' George: A Story of George Corley Wallace and His Number One Crony* (Mobile, AL: Greenberry, 1988), 13.

2 "june bug": Wayne Greenhaw, *Fighting the Devil in Dixie: How Civil Rights Activists Took on the Ku Klux Klan in Alabama* (Chicago: Lawrence Hill Books, 2011), 74; "thinking about votes": Jeff Frederick, *Stand Up for*

Alabama: Governor George Wallace (Tuscaloosa: University of Alabama Press, 2007), 18; "Comintern": Dan T. Carter, *The Politics of Rage: George Wallace, the Origins of the New Conservatism, and the Transformation of American Politics* (New York: Simon & Schuster, 1995), 15.

3 "suicide": Stephan Lesher, *George Wallace: American Populist* (Reading, MA: Addison-Wesley Publishing, 1994), 144; Tinsely E. Yarbrough, *Judge Frank Johnson and Human Rights in Alabama* (Tuscaloosa: University of Alabama Press, 2002), 64–65. On the distinction between left- and right-wing populism, see Jan-Werner Muller, *What Is Populism?* (Philadelphia: University of Pennsylvania Press, 2016).

4 "seedy": Theodore White, *The Making of the President 1968* (New York: Atheneum House, 1969), 400.

5 Carter, *Politics of Rage*, 18, 24.

6 Carter, *Politics of Rage*, 26–27.

7 "exciting": Lesher, *George Wallace*, 27; "page": Carter, *Politics of Rage*, 26–31.

8 "lazy": Frederick, *Stand Up for Alabama*, 9; "anxiety": Carter, *Politics of Rage*, 65–67.

9 Carter, *Politics of Rage*, 52–54, 79–80, 104–105; George Wallace Jr. and James Gregory, *The Wallaces of Alabama: My Family* (Chicago: Follette Publishing, 1975), 57–58.

10 Carter, *Politics of Rage*, 74–80.

11 "father": Lesher, *George Wallace*, foreword and p. 12.

12 "To Secure These Rights: The Report of the President's Committee on Civil Rights," www.trumanlibrary.gov/library/to-secure-these-rights#VII.

13 Harry S. Truman, "Address Before the National Association for the Advancement of Colored People," 29 June 1947, National Archives, Harry S. Truman Library, www.trumanlibrary.gov/library/public-papers/130/address-national-association-advancement-colored-people; Thomas J. Sugrue, *Sweet Land of Liberty: The Forgotten Struggle for Civil Rights in the North* (New York: Random House, 2008), 99–102; Joseph Crespino, *Strom Thurmond's America* (New York: Hill and Wang, 2012), 62; Robert Mickey, *Paths Out of Dixie: The Democratization of Authoritarian Enclaves in America's Deep South, 1944–1972* (Princeton, NJ: Princeton University Press, 2015), 132.

14 "sunshine": Kari Frederickson, *The Dixiecrat Revolt and the End of the Solid South, 1932–1968* (Chapel Hill: University of North Carolina Press, 2001), 129; "unalterably": Marshal Frady, *Wallace: The Class Portrait of Alabama Governor George Wallace* (New York: Random House, 1968), 144.

15 "free America": Crespino, *Strom Thurmond's America*, 77; Carter, *Politics of Rage*, 74–77, 87; *Clayton Record*, 30 April 1948; Harvard Sitkoff, "Harry Truman and the Election of 1948: The Coming of Age of Civil Rights in American Politics," *Journal of Southern History* 37 (1971): 597–616; "cast their vote": Frederickson, *Dixiecrat Revolt*, 130.

16 "most promising": Carter, *Politics of Rage*, 78, 88.

17 "Negro vote": Wayne Greenhaw, *Watch Out for George Wallace* (New York: Prentice-Hall, 1976), 18.

18 "most liberal": J. L. Chestnut Jr. and Julia Cass, *Black in Selma: The Uncommon Life of J. L. Chestnut, Jr.* (New York: Farrar, Straus & Giroux, 1990), 117; "professional": Fred D. Gray, *Bus Ride to Justice: Changing the System by the System: The Life and Works of Fred Gray* (Montgomery, AL: NewSouth Books, 1995), 137; Carter, *Politics of Rage*, 236

19 "suds": George E. Sims, *The Little Man's Big Friend: James E. Folsom in Alabama Politics, 1946–1958* (Tuscaloosa: University of Alabama Press, 1985), 23–39; "moonlight": Carter, *Politics of Rage*, 82.

20 William Warren Rogers, Leah Rawls Atkins, Robert David War, and Wayne Flynt, *Alabama: The History of a Deep South State—Bicentennial Edition* (Tuscaloosa: University of Alabama, 2018), 537–538; "plans" and "magic": Carter, *Politics of Rage*, 81.

21 Taylor Branch, *Parting the Waters: America in the King Years, 1954–1963* (New York: Simon & Schuster, 1988), 197–200.

22 "decry": John Kyle Day, *The Southern Manifesto: Massive Resistance and the Fight to Preserve Segregation* (Jackson: University Press of Mississippi, 2014), 3, 106, 104; *Clayton Record*, 16 March 1956.

23 "cussin'": Carter, *Politics of Rage*, 85.

24 "Lucy": *Clayton Record*, 16 March 1956, 2 March 1956.

25 "gestapo": *Birmingham News*, 6 February 1956, 10 March 1956, 9 February 1956; Carter, *Politics of Rage*, 85.

26 Frady argues that "it has not mattered to most Alabamians that in his series of confrontations with the federal government Wallace had met with consistent failure. What matters is that he fought, and continues to fight." See Frady, *Wallace*, 149.

27 Carter, *Politics of Rage*, 237, 239, 297; Lesher, *George Wallace*, 16; "good people": Frye Gaillard, *Cradle of Freedom: Alabama and the Movement That Changed America* (Tuscaloosa: University of Alabama Press, 2006), 57.

28 Dan T. Carter did a valuable close analysis of the many versions of this quote. See Carter, *Politics of Rage*, 96; Frady, *Wallace*, 127.

29 Carter, *Politics of Rage*, 89–90, 96–97.

30 "sift": Report of the United States Commission on Civil Rights, 1959 (Washington, DC: US Government Printing Office, 1959), ix; Robert Caro, *Master of the Senate: The Years of Lyndon Johnson* (New York: Knopf, 2002), Chapter 39; Keith M. Finley, *Delaying the Dream: Southern Senators and the Fight Against Civil Rights, 1938–1965* (Baton Rouge: Louisiana State University Press), Chapter 4; United States Commission on Civil Rights, *One Nation Under God, Indivisible, with Liberty and Justice for All: An Abridgement of the Report of the United States Commission on Civil Rights, 1959* (Washington, DC: US Government Printing Office, 1959), 1.

31 *Montgomery Advertiser*, 25–28 January 1976.
32 Frank Sikora, *The Judge: The Life & Opinions of Alabama's Frank M. Johnson, Jr.* (Montgomery: NewSouth Books, 2007), 92–96; Yarbrough, *Frank Johnson*, 67–68; Carter, *Politics of Rage*, 100.
33 Sikora, *The Judge*, 92-96; Yarbrough, *Frank Johnson*, 67-68; Carter, *Politics of Rage*, 100.
34 Margaret Price, *The Negro and the Ballot in the South* (Atlanta: Southern Regional Council, 1959), 22–24; Carter, *Politics of Rage*, 101; Yarbrough, *Frank Johnson*, 67–68.
35 Wayne Greenhaw, *Fighting the Devil*, 78; Dorman Michael, *The George Wallace Myth* (New York: Bantam Books, 1976), 23–24.
36 "Roman": Greenhaw, *Fighting the Devil*, 77; "fellas": Carter, *Politics of Rage*, 101–102.
37 "guilty" and "refuses": Carter, *Politics of Rage*, 102; "devious methods" and "subterfuge": Dorman, *George Wallace Myth*, 23.
38 Carter, *Politics of Rage*, 103.
39 Price, *Negro and the Ballot*, 24–25.
40 Carter, *Politics of Rage*, 105–106.
41 "scoured": Lesher, *George Wallace*, 141; Greenhaw, *Watch Out for George Wallace*, 122.
42 "The Inaugural Address of Governor George C. Wallace," 14 January 1963, Montgomery, Alabama. An electronic copy of the original document is available at the Alabama Department of Archives and History, downloaded at: http://digital.archives.alabama.gov/cdm/ref/collection/voices/id/2952.

Chapter 17. The Albert Street Club

1 "delirious": Dennis J. Hutchinson, "Introduction: Brown in the Supreme Court," *Journal of Appellate Practice and Process* 11 (2004): 16.
2 "ringing ambiguity": in Hutchinson, "Introduction: Brown in the Supreme Court," 12, 16.
3 "nourish": Richard Kluger, *Simple Justice: The History of* Brown v. Board of Education *and Black America's Struggle for Equality* (New York: Vintage, 2004), xi; Cass R. Sunstein, "Did Brown Matter?," *New Yorker*, 5 April 2004.
4 "convinced": Michael S. Mayer, "With Much Deliberation and Some Speed: Eisenhower and the Brown Decision," *Journal of Southern History* 52 (February 1986): 60 (Italics original).
5 "television" and "tragedy": Howard Ball, *A Defiant Life: Thurgood Marshall and the Persistence of Racism in America* (New York: Crown, 2011), 169.
6 President Dwight D. Eisenhower's 1957 Address on Little Rock, Arkansas, http://historymatters.gmu.edu/d/6335.
7 "injury": *New York Times*, 2 June 1956; Patricia Sullivan, *Life Every Voice: The NAACP and the Making of the Civil Rights Movement* (New York: New Press, 2009), 425.

8 "redevelop": Fred D. Gray, *Bus Ride to Justice: Changing the System by the System: The Life and Works of Fred Gray* (Montgomery, AL: NewSouth Books, 1995), 131–139.

9 "decent": Alexander von Hoffman, "A Study in Contradictions: The Origins and Legacy of the Housing Act of 1949," *Housing Policy Debate* 11, no. 2 (2000): 299–326; Arnold R. Hirsch, "'Containment' on the Home Front: Race and Federal Policy from the New Deal to the Cold War," *Journal of Urban History* 26, no. 2 (January 2000): 158–189.

10 *Clayton Record*, 28 January 1955; *Dothan Eagle*, 3 February 1957; "federally imposed": William Harold Tyler, *Trade Union Sponsorship of Interracial Housing: A Case Study* (Berkeley: University of California Press, 1957), 28; "local wisdom": United States Commission on Civil Rights, *Hearings Before the United States Commission on Civil Rights: Housing: Hearings Held in New York, N.Y., January 2, 1959* (Washington, DC: US Government Printing Office, 1959), 133; see Kevin Kruse, *White Flight, Atlanta and the Making of Modern Conservatism* (Princeton, NJ: Princeton University Press, 2005), 178;

11 "preclude": John F. Bauman, Roger Biles, and Kristin M. Szylvian, *From Tenements to the Taylor Homes: In Search of an Urban Housing Policy in Twentieth-Century America* (University Park, PA: Penn State University Press, 2000) 215.

12 Kruse, *White Flight*, 175, 177.

13 "white park": King to Homes, 15 August 1958, Martin Luther King Jr. Papers, https://kinginstitute.stanford.edu/king-papers/documents/l-h-holmes; David Frost Jr., *Witness to Injustice*, ed. Louise Westling (Oxford: University Press of Mississippi, 1995); Gray, *Bus Ride to Justice*, 132.

14 "destroying": Gray, *Bus Ride to Justice*, 121.

15 "iota": Gray, *Bus Ride to Justice*, 133; "supreme court": Frost, *Witness to Injustice*, 77.

16 "understanding": *Tate v. City of Eufaula, Alabama*, 165 F. Supp. 303 (M.D. Ala. 1958); Gray, *Bus Ride to Justice*, 134; *Clayton Record*, 13 June 1958; Jack Bass, *Taming the Storm: The Life and Times of Judge Frank M. Johnson, Jr. and the South's Fight Over Civil Rights* (New York: Anchor Books, 1993); *Clayton Record*, 21 October 1958.

17 "enforced segregation": United States Commission on Civil Rights, *Report of the United States Commission on Civil Rights* (Washington, DC: US Government Printing Office, The Commission, 1961), 103.

18 *Alabama Journal*, 6 August 1958; *Montgomery Advertiser*, 7 August 1958; "binding covenants" and "enjoin": Gray, *Bus Ride to Justice*, 134–135.

19 "appreciative": Gray, *Bus Ride to Justice*, 135, 137.

20 "wound up": Frost, *Witness to Injustice*, 78; "money": Gray, *Bus Ride to Justice*, 137.

21 "mixed-race": James T. Patterson, *Brown v. Board of Education: A Civil Rights Milestone and Its Troubled Legacy* (New York: Oxford University Press, 2002),

100; "choice": Kruse, *White Flight*, 162–179; *Southern Courier*, 10–11 September 1966.

22 "freedom in reverse": Kruse, *White Flight*, 238–239.

23 *Southern Courier*, 10–11 September 1966; *Southern Courier*, 27–28 November 1965.

24 *Franklin v. Barbour County Bd. of Ed.*, 259 F. Supp. 545 (1966); *Montgomery Advertiser*, 17 September 1966; *Alabama Journal* (state paper), 9 July 1968.

25 Dan T. Carter, *The Politics of Rage: George Wallace, the Origins of the New Conservatism, and the Transformation of American Politics* (New York: Simon & Schuster, 1995), 162–164, 173.

26 "Moses": Gray, *Bus Ride to Justice*, 207.

27 On threatening to join segregation academies in Barbour County, see the *Montgomery Advertiser*, July 1968; on the prom, see AP Report, "Alabama Town's Tradition of Segregated Prom Lives On in the 1990s," 6 May 1990; AP Report, "No Incident at School's First Integrated Prom," 22 May 1991.

Chapter 18. From Clayton to the Nation

1 "Heighdy": Jules Loh, "St. George Wallace vs. Federal Dragon," Associated Press, 13 October 1963, press clipping from *Louisville Courier Journal*, files of Birmingham Public Library, http://bplonline.cdmhost.com/digital/collection/p4017coll2/id/8393/rec/37.

2 "foreign country": Patricia Sullivan, *Justice Rising: Robert Kennedy's America in Black and White* (Cambridge, MA: Harvard University Press, 2020), 151.

3 Martin Luther King Jr., "I Have a Dream," King Papers, Stanford University, https://kinginstitute.stanford.edu/encyclopedia/i-have-dream.

4 "integrate": Loh, "St. George."

5 "bombing": Loh, "St. George."

6 "ruin": Loh, "St. George"; Dan T. Carter, *The Politics of Rage: George Wallace, the Origins of the New Conservatism, and the Transformation of American Politics* (New York: Simon & Schuster, 1995), 157.

7 "schoolhouse": E. Culpepper Clark, *The Schoolhouse Door: Segregation's Last Stand at the University of Alabama* (New York and Oxford: Oxford University Press, 1993), 219; Sullivan, *Justice Rising*, 172–176.

8 "students": Clark, *Schoolhouse Door*, 220; Sullivan, *Justice Rising*, 172–176.

9 "unwelcome": "Statement and Proclamation by Governor George C. Wallace, University of Alabama, June 11, 1963," ADAH, accessed 18 August 2018, www.archives.state.al.us/govs_list/schooldoor.html.

10 "awakening": Clark, *Schoolhouse Door*, 230.

11 John F. Kennedy, "Report to the American People on Civil Rights," 11 June 1963, www.jfklibrary.org/learn/about-jfk/historic-speeches/televised-address-to-the-nation-on-civil-rights; telegrams between John F. Kennedy and George C. Wallace: http://digital.archives.alabama.gov/cdm/ref

/collection/voices/id/2105; "land of the free": *Public Papers of the Presidents of the United States: Containing the Public Messages, Speeches, and Statements of the President* (Washington, DC: US Government Printing Office, 1964).

12 "stir": Loh, "St. George"; Joseph E. Lowndes, *From the New Deal to the New Right: Race and the Southern Origins of Modern Conservatism* (New Haven, CT: Yale University Press, 2008), 80.

13 Robert Caro, *Master of the Senate: The Years of Lyndon Johnson* (New York: Penguin, 2002), introduction.

14 "hookwormy": Carter, *Politics of Rage*, 211.

15 "kick out": Carter, *Politics of Rage*, 197; "They voted": Rick Perlstein, *Before the Storm: Barry Goldwater and the Unmaking of the American Consensus* (New York: Hill and Wang, 2001), 317.

16 "brats": Richard C. Haney, "Wallace in Wisconsin: The Presidential Primary of 1964," *Wisconsin Magazine of History* 61, no. 4 (Summer 1978), 271; "womenfolk": Carter, *Politics of Rage*, 207; Frye Gaillard, *A Hard Rain: America in the 1960s, Our Decade of Hope, Possibility, and Innocence Lost* (NewSouth Books, 2018), 184; George C. Wallace, *Stand Up for America* (New York: Doubleday, 1976), 89; Carter, *Politics of Rage*, 208.

17 "quota," "epiphany": Carter, *Politics of Rage*, 208; Wallace, *Stand Up for America*, 89; Haney, "Wallace in Wisconsin," 271.

18 "catastrophe" and "winning": *Newsweek*, 20 April 1964.

19 *Chicago Defender*, 27 April 1964; *Norfolk New Journal and Guide*, 25 April 1964.

20 "destruction": Carter, *Politics of Rage*, 205; Stephen M. Leahy, "George Wallace and the Myth of the White Ethnic Backlash in Milwaukee, 1958–1964," *Polish American Studies* 75, no. 2 (2018): 31–54; *New York Times*, 9 April 1964; Carter, *Politics of Rage*, 205, 208; Michael Rogin, "Wallace and the Middle Class: The White Backlash in Wisconsin," *Public Opinion Quarterly* 30, no. 1 (1966): 106. On conservative populism, with enemies from above and below, see Jan-Mueller Wenner, *What Is Populism?* (Philadelphia: Penn Press, 2017).

21 "states' rights": *New York Times*, 20 May 1964; "hooted": Carter, *Politics of Rage*, 211.

22 "besotted": Perlstein, *Before the Storm*, 310.

23 "with us": *New York Times*, 5 July 1964; see "Wallace Segregationist Rally," Associated Press video footage, 4 July 1964, www.aparchive.com.

24 *New York Times*, 5 July 1964; AP footage, 4 July 1964.

25 George Wallace, "Civil Rights: Fraud, Sham, and Hoax," 4 July 1964, https://oxfordaasc.com/view/10.1093/acref/9780195301731.001.0001/acref-9780195301731-e-33609; *Washington Post*, 5 July 1964; *Atlanta Journal and Constitution*, 5 July 1964; Carter, *Politics of Rage*, 216–217; *New York Times*, 5 July 1964.

26 "God-given" and "mammoth": Perlstein, *Before the Storm*, 364.
27 "civil rights": Martin Luther King Jr., "The Presidential Nomination," *New York Amsterdam News*, 25 April 1964.
28 "Germany": Taylor Branch, *Pillar of Fire: America in the King Years, 1963–1965* (New York: Simon & Schuster, 1998), 403–405; Perlstein, *Before the Storm*, 371–405.
29 Carter, *Politics of Rage*, 220.
30 "lever" and "heart" and "old": Ross M. Hagen, "LBJ Finding Little Backing in Alabama," *Alabama Journal*, 6 October 1964; *Selma Times-Journal*, 6 October 1964; Lowndes, *From New Deal to New Right*, 82.
31 "discriminated" and "guise": "White Southerner Most Discriminated," *Selma Times-Journal*, 16 March 1965; "minds": *Alabama Journal*, 31 March 1965; "flotsam" and "orgies" and "systematic": *Congressional Record*, House, 89th Cong., 1st sess., vol. 111, pts. 5 and 6 (30 March 1965), 6333–6335.
32 Lawrence Glickman, "How White Backlash Controls American Progress," *The Atlantic*, 21 May 2020, www.theatlantic.com/ideas/archive/2020/05/white-backlash-nothing-new/611914; Theodore H. White, "Backlash," *Life*, 16 October 1964; Carter, *Politics of Rage*, 222; Lowndes, *From New Deal to New Right*, 6.
33 On the Wallace-Johnson meeting narrative, see: Harry Middleton, *LBJ: The White House Years* (New York: Henry N. Abrams, 1990), 86; Howell Raines, *My Soul is Rested: Movement Days in the Deep South Remembered* (New York: Penguin, 1983), 337–340; *New York Times*, 14 May 1965; Carter, *Politics of Rage*, 253–255; Lyndon Johnson, *The Vantage Point: Perspectives of the Presidency, 1963–1969* (New York: Holt, Rinehart and Winston, 1972), 162–165.
34 Middleton, *LBJ*, 86; Raines, *My Soul*, 337-340; *New York Times*, 14 May 1965; Carter, *Politics of Rage*, 253–255; Johnson, *The Vantage Point*, 162-165.
35 Middleton, *LBJ*, 86; Raines, *My Soul*, 337-340; *New York Times*, 14 May 1965; Carter, *Politics of Rage*, 253–255; Johnson, *The Vantage Point*, 162-165.
36 Middleton, *LBJ*, 86; Raines, *My Soul, 337-340; New York Times*, 14 May 1965; Carter, *Politics of Rage*, 253–255; Johnson, *The Vantage Point*, 162-165.
37 Lyndon Johnson, "Speech to Congress on Voting Rights," 15 March 1965, www.archives.gov/legislative/features/voting-rights-1965/johnson.html; Taylor Branch, *At Canaan's Edge: America in the King Years, 1965–1968* (New York: Simon & Schuster, 2006), 114–115.
38 "demonstrators" and "faith": Branch, *Canaan's Edge*, 126–127; Carter, *Politics of Rage*, 256–259.
39 "don't": Carter, *Politics of Rage*, 257; Bill Jones, *The Wallace Story* (Northport, LA: American Southern Publishing, 1966), 432.

Chapter 19. The SCOPE of Freedom

1 Virginia Durr quote from letter to C. Vann Woodward, in Susan Younblood Ashmore, *Carry It On: The War on Poverty and the Civil Rights Movement in*

Alabama, 1964–1972 (Athens: University of Georgia Press, 2008), 11; "praise": *Southern Courier*, 3–4 December 1966.

2 Larry Scott Butler, "A Short History of the Freedom Movement in Barbour County," SFHL-RG5-315, 1, unpublished, Larry Scott Butler Papers, Friends Historical Library of Swarthmore College (hereafter cited as Butler Papers); *Washington Post*, 27 February 2019.

3 Eric Burner, *And Gently He Shall Lead Them: Robert Parris Moses and Civil Rights in Mississippi* (New York: NYU Press, 1994), Chapter 7; John Dittmer, *Local People: The Struggle for Civil Rights in Mississippi* (Urbana: University of Illinois Press, 1995), 209.

4 Taylor Branch, *At Canaan's Edge: America in the King Years, 1965–1968* (New York: Simon & Schuster, 2006), 225; a massive compendium of SCOPE materials, though little on Barbour County, is *The SCOPE of Freedom: The Leadership of Hosea Williams with Dr. King's Summer '65 Student Volunteers*, ed. Willy Siegel Leventhal (Montgomery: Challenge Publishing, 2005).

5 Bayard Rustin, "From Protest to Politics," *Commentary* (February 1965); "stifling enemy" and "racist structure" and "confidence game": Branch, *Canaan's Edge*, 196, 211–212; see Clayborne Carson, *In Struggle: SNCC and the Black Awakening of the 1960s* (Cambridge, MA: Harvard University Press, 1981), 191–211.

6 See Butler, "Short History," 1–2; "SCOPE Project" (recruitment brochure) and "Orientation Session SCLC Summer Community Organization Political Education, Atlanta, 14–19 June 1965," SCLC Records, Box 359, MSS 0183, Emory University Manuscript, Archives, and Rare Book Library, MSS 1083; Leventhal, *SCOPE of Freedom*; "worried": Branch, *Canaan's Edge*, 242.

7 Butler, "Short History," 2–3.

8 Butler, "Short History," 2–3.

9 Larry Butler, "Diary," RG 5/315, Box 1, FF: Diary, Butler Papers.

10 Butler, "Short History," 3–4; Butler, "Diary," 29 June 1965, 1 July 1965; Butler to Parents, Butler Papers, RG5/31523 July 1965, FF: Letters from Butler to his Parents, 1965–1967; "shaking hair": correspondence with SCLC volunteer Mike Bibler, author's possession.

11 Butler, "Short History"; Butler, "Diary."

12 *Southern Courier*, 27–28 November 1965; Butler, "Short History," 5.

13 Butler to Parents, 23 July 1965, RG 5/315, Box 1, FF: Letters from Butler to his Parents, 1965–1967, Butler Papers.

14 Butler Diary, 6; Butler to Parents, 23 July 1965.

15 Telephone Report from Barbour Co., Ala. SCOPE, 7/29/65, 168:16 Field Reports, Folder: 001569-021-0481, Date: January 01, 1954—Dec 31, 1970, Records of the Southern Christian Leadership Conference, 1954–1970, Part 4: Records of the Program Department (hereafter cited as SCLC Records, pt. 4).

16 Lyndon Johnson, "Special Message to the Congress: The American Promise," 15 March 1965, www.presidency.ucsb.edu/documents/special-message-the-congress-the-american-promise.
17 Butler, "Short History," 9.
18 Butler, "Short History," 9; Terry Cowles, "SCLC Moves out of Ala.," *Southern Courier*, 4–5 June 1966.
19 Ashmore, *Carry It On*, 136; Hasan Kwame Jeffries, *Bloody Lowndes: Civil Rights and Black Power in Alabama's Black Belt* (New York: NYU Press, 2010), 60, 100; Scott B. Smith Jr., speech recording, Civil Rights Movement Vets, www.crmvet.org/vet/scot-b.htm.
20 Audio Recordings, SCLC-SCOPE 50th Anniversary Reunion, October 1–4, 2015, Recordings of Alabama activists, Atlanta, Georgia, www.crmvet.org/audio/events/sclc50/151002_AL1.mp3; David Smith, "Report from Selma," vol. 1, no. 8, 13 May 1965, Richard N. Gould Papers, Wisconsin Historical Society, digital identifier: FSGOULD000; on differences, see *Southern Courier*, November 1965; Scott B. Smith Jr., Civil Rights Movement Vets; on Smith see Branch, *Canaan's Edge*, 213–214, 607.
21 For other interpretations, see SNCC papers in Mississippi, and Solomon S. Seay Jr., *Jim Crow and Me: Stories from My Life as a Civil Rights Lawyer* (Montgomery: NewSouth Books, 2008); David Smith, "Report from Selma."
22 Wallace could not run for governor again because of the "succession law" that prevented a governor from serving two consecutive terms. Many thought Wallace would therefore pursue the Senate, but there was not enough executive authority in the job for the ambitious Wallace. He used the trick of running his wife, Lurleen Wallace, in his place for a second term.
23 Fauntroy to King, 9 December 1965; Fauntroy to Doar, Civil Rights Division, US Department of Justice, 25 December 1965, Folder: 001569-008-0933, Records of Randolph T. Blackwell, 1965, SCLC Records, pt. 4; see Scott B. Smith's comments to SNCC, in Smith to SNCC report, https://hv-proquest-com.proxy.library.vanderbilt.edu/pdfs/252253/252253_017_1157/252253_017_1157_From_1_to_147.pdf; Glenn Feldman, *The Disfranchisement Myth: Poor Whites and Suffrage Restriction in Alabama* (Athens: University of Georgia Press, 2010), 170.
24 Correspondence with Mike Bibler (SCLC field worker), author's possession.
25 Butler, "Short History," 10–13, 20–22; Mike Bibler, author's correspondence.
26 "Incident Report," Eufaula, Alabama, 19 August 1965, Civil Rights Movement Letters and Field Reports, SCOPE, www.crmvet.org/lets/scoplets.htm; Butler, "Short History," 10–11.
27 Correspondence with Mike Bibler, author's possession.
28 Butler, "Short History," 13.
29 *Anniston Star*, 11 September 1965; *Alabama Journal*, 11 September 1965. This event was not reported or commented on by the police, mayor, or local press.

30 "Statement from Mrs. Mary Marshall Vice President of the United Barbour County Voters' League," n.d. [24 October 1965], FF 165:12 Field Reports—Ala. Nov–Dec 1965, SCLC Records, pt. 4; Butler, "Short History," 18–19; Several people in SCLC saw the Washington visit as a good way to put pressure on Washington for more federal registrars.

31 "Statement from Mrs. Mary Marshall."

32 "Alabama Registration Statistics," 5 November 1965, FF 165:12 Field Reports—Ala. Nov–Dec 1965, SCLC Records, pt. 4. The report was probably written by Hosea Williams. Adam Fairclough, *To Redeem the Soul of America: The Southern Christian Leadership Conference and Marin Luther King Jr.* (Athens: University of Georgia Press, 1987), 265–266.

33 Butler to Parents, 2 September 1965; Butler, "Short History," 21.

34 "Alabama Registration Statistics," 5 November 1965.

35 Seay, *Jim Crow and Me*, 63–66.

36 Seay, *Jim Crow and Me*, 67–68.

37 Terry Cowles, "SCLC Moves out of Ala.," *Southern Courier*, 4–5 June 1966; the many letters Larry Butler received from SCLC people in Barbour County after he left make up a fascinating record of events after 1966, ranging from the coming elections to the "near dead" feeling of the movement. See FF: Letters from residents of Eufaula, Alabama, RG 5/315, Butler Papers.

Chapter 20. The Vote Is Not Enough

1 SNCC, "Report on Alabama Elections," 6 May 1966, crmvet.org; *Southern Courier*, 7–8 May 1966; Susan Youngblood Ashmore, *Carry It On: The War on Poverty and the Civil Rights Movement in Alabama, 1964–1972* (Athens: University of George Press, 2008), 153–197.

2 *Lay My Burden Down*, produced and directed by Jack Willis (1966), preacher quoted at 45:25, who was identified as LeRoy Randolph in Ashmore, *Carry It On*, 339n49.

3 *New York Times*, 29 January 1966.

4 *New York Times*, 5 May 1966; *Montgomery Advertiser*, 5 May 1966; Dan T. Carter, *The Politics of Rage: George Wallace, the Origins of the New Conservatism, and the Transformation of American Politics* (New York: Simon & Schuster, 1995), 264–293.

5 On the complex terrain beyond voting itself, see Peyton McCrary, Jerome A. Gray, Edward Still, and Huey L. Perry, "Alabama," in *Quiet Revolution in the South: The Impact of the Voting Rights Act, 1965–1990*, ed. Chandler Davidson and Bernard Grofman (Princeton, NJ: Princeton University Press, 1994), 14, 38–39; while the authors of *Quiet Revolution* only cover first- and second-generation voters, the pattern of majority minority districts continues beyond, though not as powerfully; see Susan Welch, "The Impact of At-Large Elections on the Representation of Blacks and Hispanics," *Journal of Politics* 52, no. 4 (1990): 1050–1076.

6 *Southern Courier*, 28–29 May 1966.
7 *Southern Courier*, 28–29 May 1966.
8 "humiliation": Carter, *Politics of Rage*, 287.
9 Carter, *Politics of Rage*, 287.
10 *Montgomery Advertiser*, 5 May 1966; *New York Times*, 5 May 1966; Ashmore, *Carry It On*, 183–185.
11 On the evolution of Lowndes County politics, see Hasan Kwame Jeffries, *Bloody Lowndes: Civil Rights and Black Power in Alabama's Black Belt* (New York: NYU Press, 2010).
12 "block vote": *Clayton Record*, 25 March 1965; *Montgomery Advertiser*, 6 May 1966; *Clayton Record*, 25 March 1965; McCrary et al., "Alabama," 38–39. They got away without federal detection until 1978 in *United States v. Barbour County Commission*, C.A. No. 78-348-N (M.D. Ala.), at which point the county returned to single-member districts.
13 *Southern Courier*, 28–29 May 1966.
14 Fred D. Gray, *Bus Ride to Justice: Changing the System by the System, The Life and Works of Fred Gray* (Montgomery, AL: NewSouth Books, 1995), 250.
15 Gray, *Bus Ride to Justice*, 110–122; *Gomillion v. Lightfoot*, 364 US 339 (1960); see Bernard Taper, *Gomillion versus Lightfoot: Apartheid in Alabama* (New York: McGraw Hill, 1963).
16 *Gomillion v. Lightfoot*, 364 US 339 (1960); *Smith v. Paris*, 257 F. Supp. 901 (1966); see evidence in US Civil Rights Commission, *Participation: A Report of the United States Commission on Civils Rights* (Washington, DC: United States Commission on Civil Rights, May 1968); *Alabama Journal*, 2 May 1968.
17 Gray, *Bus Ride to Justice*, 255.
18 *Southern Courier*, 19–20 February 1966; *New York Times*, 4 May 1966.
19 SNCC, "Report on Alabama Elections," 6 May 1966, www.crmvet.org/docs/660506_sncc_al_elections-rpt.pdf; Binghamton *Evening Press*, 5 May 1966; Gray, *Bus Ride to Justice*, 254–268; *Chicago Defender*, 4 June 1970.
20 Gray, *Bus Ride to Justice*, 259.
21 *Montgomery Advertiser*, 30 March 1968.
22 *Gray v. Main*, C.A. No. 2430-N (M.D. Ala. 1968); Gray, *Bus Ride to Justice*, 260–264.
23 *United States v. Democratic Executive Committee*, 288 F. Supp. 943 (M.D. Ala. 1968); *Eufaula Tribune*, 2 May 1968.
24 *Afro-American*, 13 June 1970.
25 *Oakland Post*, 19 November 1970; *Chicago Daily Defender*, 4 June 1970; Jeffrey Frederick, *Stand Up for Alabama: Governor George Wallace* (Tuscaloosa: University of Alabama Press, 2007), 169; *Montgomery Advertiser*, 27 January, 30 January, 1 February, 24 February, 25 February, and 3 March 1966; *Atlanta Constitution*, 4 October 1970.
26 *New York Times*, 4 May 1966; *New Amsterdam News*, 5 December 1970.

27 McCrary et al., "Alabama," 38–66.

28 Kevin Boyle, *The Shattering: America in the 1960s* (New York: Norton, 2021), 214–220; Taylor Branch, *At Canaan's Edge: America in the King Years, 1965–1968* (New York: Simon & Schuster, 2006), 501–522.

29 "beatniks": Carter, *Politics of Rage*, 291–292.

30 "carpetbaggers": Marshall Frady, *Wallace* (New York: Random House, 1968), 200–202.

Chapter 21. The Northern Strategy

1 Stephan Lesher, *George Wallace: American Populist* (New York: Hachette Books, 1994), 389–393.

2 Dan T. Carter, *The Politics of Rage: George Wallace, the Origins of the New Conservatism, and the Transformation of American Politics* (New York: Simon & Schuster, 1995), 300; *New York Times*, 28 April 1967, 18 June 1967; *Birmingham News*, 17 November 1967.

3 Lurleen Wallace Inaugural 1967, FF: WSFA footage notes, WSFA tape #3, Box 9, Dan T. Carter Papers, Emory University. This was an extended version of a typical argument. See Hearings Before the Committee on Commerce, US Senate 88th Cong., 1st sess. On S. 1732, A Bill to Eliminate Discrimination in Public Accommodations Affecting Interstate Commerce, July 15, 1963, 436; "Wallace Interview," *Playboy*, November 1964, 63.

4 "run for President" and "omnipotent": Joseph E. Lowndes, *From the New Deal to the New Right: Race and the Southern Origins of Modern Conservatism* (New Haven, CT: Yale University Press, 2008), 83; "doorway": "Wallace Interview," 63.

5 Theodore H. White, *The Making of the President 1968* (New York: Atheneum House, 1969), 402.

6 Susan Dunn, *Roosevelt's Purge: How FDR Fought to Change the Democratic Party* (Cambridge, MA: Harvard University Press, 2012); Harry Dent explains how "the old Confederate States of America" went "from the role of prodigal son to favorite son" in *The Prodigal Son Returns to Power* (New York: John Wiley & Sons, 1978); Rick Perlstein, *Nixonland: The Rise of a President and the Fracturing of America* (New York: Simon & Schuster, 2008), 88; *New York Times*, September 1964; Joseph Crespino, *Strom Thurmond's America* (New York: Hill and Wang, 2012), 219–223.

7 "stick": Angie Maxwell and Todd Shields, *The Long Southern Strategy: How Chasing White Voters in the South Changed American Politics* (New York: Oxford University Press, 2019), 18; Carter, *Politics of Rage*, 329; Jeremy D. Mayer, "Nixon Rides the Backlash to Victory: Racial Politics in the 1968 Presidential Campaign," *The Historian* 64, no. 2 (Winter 2002): 363.

8 George C. Wallace, "The Civil Rights Movement: Fraud, Sham and Hoax, 1964," 4 July 1964, www.let.rug.nl/usa/documents/1951-/speech-by-george-c-wallace-the-civil-rights-movement-fraud-sham-and-hoax-1964-.phpallace.

9 Paul Taggart, "Populism and Representative Politics in Contemporary Europe," *Journal of Political Ideologies* 9, no. 3 (2004): 274; Tom Turnipseed, interview conducted for *Eyes on the Prize II*, Washington University Film and Media Archive, http://repository.wustl.edu/concern/videos/mc87pv322; Carter, *Politics of Rage*, 345; "village": Marshal Frady, *Wallace: The Classic Portrait of Alabama Governor George Wallace* (New York: Random House, 1968), 13.

10 "The Fear Campaign," *Time*, 4 October 1968; Maarten Zwiers, "The Whistles of George Wallace: Gender and Emotions in the 1968 Presidential Campaign," *European Journal of American Studies* 14, no. 1 (2019), online.

11 Lesher, *George Wallace*, 390.

12 Aram Goudsouzian, *The Men and the Moment: The Election of 1968 and the Rise of Partisan Politics in America* (Chapel Hill: University of North Carolina Press, 2019) covers the dramatis personae well.

13 Jefferson Cowie, *Stayin' Alive: The 1970s and the Last Days of the Working Class* (New York: The New Press, 2010), 75–84.

14 Goudsouzian, *Men and the Moment*, passim.

15 Joseph Lowndes, "From Founding Violence to Political Hegemony: The Conservative Populism of George Wallace," in *Populism and the Mirror of Democracy*, ed. Francisco Panizza (London and New York: Verso, 2005), 163.

16 Carter, *Politics of Rage*, 345.

17 Carter, *Politics of Rage*, 365.

18 Perlstein, *Nixonland*, 340–341; Carter, *Politics of Rage*, 365. "The thing that makes Wallace so paradoxical is that his great power comes from the billion dollars the state is getting from the Federal Government for interstate highways, and with this much money to spend he is in clover, yet he spend it cuss out the Federal Government": Virginia Durr to Clare Foreman, November 1962, in FF: Virginia Durr Letters, Box 9, Dan T. Carter Papers, Emory University.

19 "Stand Up": *Montgomery Advertiser*, 17 August 2018; Melissa McElroy Smith, "States' Rights, Intellectual Snobs, and Religious Redemption: Three Decades of George C. Wallace and the Media" (PhD diss., University of Alabama, 2003).

20 Interview with Tom Turnipseed, October 22, 1988, Camera Rolls: 4014–4015, Sound Rolls: 404. Interview gathered as part of *Eyes on the Prize II: America at the Racial Crossroads 1965 to* 1985, Housed at the Washington University Film and Media Archive, Henry Hampton Collection, transcript, http://digital.wustl.edu/cgi/t/text/text-idx?c=eop;cc=eop;rgn=main;view=text;idno=tur5427.0990.163.

21 White, *Making of the President 1968*, 412.

22 *New York Times*, 4 October 1968; Lesher, *Wallace*, 425; Carter, *Politics of Rage*, 356–362.

23 Carter, *Politics of Rage*, 293, 364; Kevin Boyle, *The Shattering: America in the 1960s* (New York: Norton, 2021), 266–267; White, *Making of the President 1968*, 349.

24 "T.R.B. from Washington: Wallace," *New Republic*, 9 November 1968; Carter, *Politics of Rage*, 367.

25 "T.R.B. from Washington": Douglas Kiker, "Red Neck New York: Is This Wallace Country?," *New York*, 7 October 1968.

26 *John Herling's Labor Letter*, 12 October 1968; Cowie, *Stayin' Alive*, 83; Carter, *Politics of Rage*, 352.

27 Goudsouzian, *Men and the Moment*, 142; Garry Wills, *Nixon Agonistes: The Crisis of the Self-Made Man* (Boston: Houghton-Mifflin, 1969), 264–269; Carter, *Politics of Rage*, 379.

28 Philip Crass, *The Wallace Factor* (New York: Mason/Charter, 1976), 28; George H. Gallup, *Gallup Poll Public Opinion 1972–1977*, vol. 1 (Wilmington, DE: Scholarly Resources, 1978), 1, 21; Lubell quoted in Carter, *Politics of Rage*, 350.

29 John Egerton, *The Americanization of Dixie: The Southnernization of America* (New York: Harper's Magazine Press, 1974), 19.

30 *Newsweek*, 16 September 1968; Carter, *Politics of Rage*, 300; *New York Times*, 28 April 1967, 18 June 1967; *Birmingham News*, 17 November 1967; "guru": Lesher, *Wallace*, xix.

Conclusion

1 C. Robert Jennings, "Home? Which Way Is That?," *Playboy*, March 1973, 112; for a brilliant elegy to place and memory, see Carrie Monahan, "'A Dream Remembered:' Collective memory and Ancestral Responsibility in Eufaula, Alabama," American Studies Honors Program, Stanford University, 15 May 2018.

2 Promotional quotes from the video at the Eufaula Pilgrimage website, www.eufaulapilgrimage.com; Monahan, "'Dream Remembered,'" 87.

3 Timeri Murari, *Goin' Home: A Black Family Returns South* (New York: G.P. Putnam's Sons, 1980), 51.

4 *New York Times*, 17 May 1983; *Baltimore Afro-American*, 30 July 1983; *Atlanta Constitution*, 17 July 1983; *Atlanta Daily World*, 14 April 1983; Russaw campaign material in SCLC Box 129, Office of the President/Joseph E. Lowery, FF: Selective buying campaign, Eufaula, Alabama, 1983, Emory University.

5 Alexis de Tocqueville, *Democracy in America*, vol. 1 (New York: Vintage Classics, 1990), 367–368.

6 Sally Gershman, "Alexis de Tocqueville and Slavery," *French Historical Studies* 9, no. 3 (Spring 1976): 469; on Puritanism, see Aristide Tessitore, "Tocqueville's American Thesis and the New Science of Politics," *American Political Thought* 4, no. 1 (2015): 72–99.

7 "despot" and "above itself" and "yoke": Tocqueville, *Democracy in America*, 1:373–374; Alison McQueen and Burke A. Hendrix, "Tocqueville in Jacksonian Context: American Expansionism and Discourses of American Indian Nomadism in Democracy in America," *Perspectives on Politics* 15, no. 3 (September 2017): 663–677; Rogers M. Smith, "Beyond Tocqueville, Myrdal, and Hartz: The Multiple Traditions in American," *American Political Science Review* 87, no. 3 (September 1993): 549–566; James L. Crouthamel, "Tocqueville's South," *Journal of the Early Republic* 2, no. 4 (Winter 1982): 382–401.

8 On Madison quote, see Lacy K. Ford Jr., "Inventing the Concurrent Majority: Madison, Calhoun, and the Problem of Majoritarianism in American Political Thought," *Journal of Southern History* 60, no. 1 (February 1994): 22, 57.

9 *New York Times*, 11 February 1994.

10 Kevin P. Phillips, *The Emerging Republican Majority* (New Rochelle, NY: Arlington House, 1969), 33.

11 Rick Perlstein, *Nixonland: The Rise of a President and the Fracturing of America* (New York: Scribner, 2008), 283–285; this process of losing the Jeffersonian, anti-statist core of the old Democratic Party had been well underway since the New Deal; Jefferson Cowie, *The Great Exception: The New Deal and the Limits of American Politics* (Princeton, NJ: Princeton University Press, 2016), 143.

12 Phillips, *Emerging Republican Majority*, 33; Ehrlichman in FF: Ehrlichman Interview, 10-4-93, Box 9, Dan T. Carter Papers, Emory University; on the question of Nixon, Wallace, and bribery, see Dan T. Carter, *The Politics of Rage: George Wallace, the Origins of the New Conservatism, and the Transformation of American Politics* (New York: Simon & Schuster, 1995), 384–386, 408–414.

13 Malcolm X, "Speech at Ford Auditorium," 14 February 1965, www.blackpast.org/african-american-history/speeches-african-american-history/1965-malcolm-x-speech-ford-auditorium/.

14 Ezra Klein, *Why We're Polarized* (New York: Avid Reader Press, 2020); Sam Rosenfeld, *The Polarizers: Postwar Architects of Our Partisan Era* (Chicago: University of Chicago Press, 2018); Nicole Hemmer, *Partisans: The Conservative Revolutionaries Who Remade American Politics in the 1990s* (New York: Basic Books, 2022).

15 Peter Applebome, *Dixie Rising: How the South Is Shaping American Values, Politics, and Culture* (New York: Times Books, 1996), 91.

16 *Bush v. Gore*, 531 US 98 (2000) majority opinion.

17 Ta-Nehisi Coates, "I'm Not Black, I'm Kanye: Kanye West Wants Freedom—White Freedom," *The Atlantic*, 7 May 2018, www.theatlantic.com/entertainment/archive/2018/05/im-not-black-im-kanye/559763.

18 See Elisabeth Ander, "The Exploitation of American Freedom," *New York Times*, 2 February 2022.

19 "Mo Brooks on 'Kick Ass' Speech: 'I Make No Apology' for Inspiring Patriotic Americans," AL.com, 8 January 2021, www.al.com/news/2021/01/mo-brooks-on-kick-ass-speech-i-make-no-apology-for-inspiring-patriotic-americans.html.

20 One might use the term "Orwellian" to describe Brooks's logic, but he already called the Democrats' criticisms of his speech "George Orwellian."

21 Martin Luther King Jr., "Our God Is Marching On!," 25 March 1965, Montgomery, Alabama, https://kinginstitute.stanford.edu/our-god-marching; Martin Luther King Jr., "I've Been to the Mountaintop," Memphis, Tennessee, 3 April 1968, www.afscme.org/about/history/mlk/mountaintop.

22 Orlando Patterson, "The American View of Freedom: What We Say, What We Mean," *Society* 38 (May 2001): 42; Aziz Rana, *The Two Faces of American Freedom* (Cambridge, MA: Harvard University Press, 2010), 3; Fred Moten, Brandon López, and Gerald Cleaver, "The Abolition of Art, the Abolition of Freedom, the Abolition of You and Me," [recording] Reading Group, 2022.

INDEX

Aliya Cowie

Jefferson Cowie holds the James G. Stahlman chair in American history at Vanderbilt University. He is the author of three books, including *Stayin' Alive: The 1970s and the Last Days of the Working Class*, which won a number of awards including the Francis Parkman Prize. His work has appeared in numerous outlets including *Time*, the *New York Times*, *Foreign Affairs*, and *Politico*. He lives in Nashville, Tennessee.